SYMMETRY GROUPS

Theory and Chemical Applications

R. L. FLURRY, JR.
Professor of Chemistry
University of New Orleans

PRENTICE-HALL, INC., Englewood Cliffs, New Jersey 07632

Library of Congress Cataloging in Publication Data

Flurry, Robert L., Jr.
Symmetry groups.

Includes bibliographies and index.
1. Chemistry, Physical and theoretical—Mathematics.
2. Symmetry groups. I. Title.
QD455.3.M3F55 541 79-18729
ISBN 0-13-880013-8

Printed in the United States of America

10 9 8 7 6 5 4 3 2 1

Editorial/production supervision
and interior design by Linda Mihatov
Cover design by Edsal Enterprises
Manufacturing buyer: Edmund W. Leone

PRENTICE-HALL INTERNATIONAL, INC., *London*
PRENTICE-HALL OF AUSTRALIA PTY. LIMITED, *Sydney*
PRENTICE-HALL OF CANADA, LTD., *Toronto*
PRENTICE-HALL OF INDIA PRIVATE LIMITED, *New Delhi*
PRENTICE-HALL OF JAPAN, INC., *Tokyo*
PRENTICE-HALL OF SOUTHEAST ASIA PTE. LTD., *Singapore*
WHITEHALL BOOKS LIMITED, *Wellington, New Zealand*

Contents

Preface

In 1832 the mathematical concept of a group was first outlined by Evarist Galois in a letter to Auguste Chevalier. The next morning Galois was mortally wounded in a duel. I suspect that on the morning after their first encounter with group theory many students feel, with Galois, that they have been "run through" (actually, he was shot). The present book is intended as an attempt to provide a shield from such a feeling.

The whole of group theory encompasses a very large and elegant body of mathematical knowledge. A single volume the size of this one can barely touch upon a few of the concepts. There are groups having an infinite number of elements and groups having a finite number of elements. There are continuous groups and groups with discrete elements. We shall confine our attention to the types of groups most commonly used by workers in the fields of atomic and molecular structure. The basic underlying principles are, however, common to all group theory. It is hoped that this work can provide a working knowledge of the group theory needed for many applications to atomic and molecular structure and provide a bridge to enable the interested student to delve into more advanced works from either the physical or the mathematical point of view.

The choice of the types of groups appropriate for our study is dictated by quantum mechanics. The Hamiltonian operator of a system is invariant under unitary transformations (rotations, inversions, etc.) of the coordinate system and under permutations of identical particles. These are, then, the groups that we will study: the groups of coordinate transformations and the groups of permutations.

It should be emphasized, however, that these are *not* the only groups which are important to quantum mechanics.

We will further restrict our attention primarily to groups of coordinate transformations which leave the system in an arrangement that is indistinguishable from the original arrangement. Such groups are called symmetry groups, since they are a representation of the symmetry possessed by the system. For systems having a finite number of elements in their symmetry groups, the symmetry group can be simply expressed as a group of permutations. Symmetry groups may, however, be either finite or infinite, discrete or continuous. For example, the symmetry groups of nonlinear molecules are discrete and finite. Those of atoms and linear molecules are continuous and infinite. The groups expressing the translational symmetry of atoms in crystals are discrete, but infinite.

The bulk of this book is directed toward a study of symmetry groups having discrete elements: the point groups and space groups. These are the groups most often encountered by most chemists and by many physicists. They are pedagogically attractive because physical operations can be associated with the group elements, making many of the concepts easy to visualize and grasp. The treatment given to continuous groups and to permutation groups draws heavily upon the material previously presented for the discrete symmetry groups.

The material presented here is primarily derived from a one-semester course I taught for several years to advanced undergraduate and graduate students in chemistry. The level is such, however, that it should be comprehensible to anyone whose background includes secondary-school-level algebra and geometry, a minimum knowledge of the ideas of calculus, and introductory chemistry and physics, the latter two being needed as much for the vocabulary as for the content. An effort has been made to keep the level of difficulty as nearly consistent as is feasible. Most of the material is presented by example and by induction. The only rigorous mathematical proofs presented are in connection with Wigner's grand orthogonality theorem. These are presented in Appendix 2.

Since most of the group theory here is presented in terms of geometric operations that we must be able to express precisely, some knowledge of vectors and matrices is required. All that we will use is given in the first chapter. Chapters 2 through 6 present our development of group theory. Since most applications of group theory are based upon quantum mechanics, some knowledge of quantum mechanics is desirable. The most important points for our purposes are summarized in Chapter 7. Since most of our knowledge about atomic and molecular structure arises from observations of the interaction of electromagnetic radiation with matter, Chapter 8 presents a summary of the principles behind such interactions. Neither of these latter two chapters is intended to teach a student the material in it. They are presented in an expository style, and are intended primarily as a bridge between the formal group theory and the detailed applications. Those who wish to do so may skip most of them. The key parts are found in Sections 7.7, 7.11, 8.1, 8.2, 8.6, and 8.7. Those who have been previously exposed to the material should find them a useful review. The brave souls who read them with no previous exposure should accept them as defining the material, rather than developing it.

Many readers will be disappointed by the material in the chapters on applications. Intermittent work on this material held up my submitting the manuscript to the publisher for a considerable time. The problem was one of selectivity rather than difficulty. I felt that many potential readers might judge whether or not the book had anything to offer them by whether or not my choice of applications was parallel to theirs. I hope that this is not the case. In any event, I feel that the material in Chapters 1 through 6 should be of interest to anyone (chemist, physicist, mathematician, or whatever) who wants an introduction to symmetry groups. Most applications of the material in the later chapters are based upon the principles given in Section 5.5 or in Section 7.8. Hopefully, the material in Chapters 9 through 13 will contain enough diverse applications to touch on the interests of most chemists.

Most courses on group theory for chemists could rightfully be called either "*Chemical Applications* of Group Theory" or "*Group Theory* with Chemical Applications." There is enough material here for either approach (I have taught it both ways). To adequately teach all the material would require at least six quarter-hours or four semester-hours. For other course arrangements, I would suggest the following organization:

a. Six quarter-hours or four semester-hours: Everything.
b. Three semester-hours, chemical emphasis: Sections 1.1, 1.2, 1.3, 1.8, 2.1, 2.2, 2.3, 2.9, 2.10, 3.1, 3.2, 3.6, 5.1, 5.4, 5.5, 5.6, 6.2, 6.4, 6.5, 7.8, 7.11, 8.1, 8.2, 8.4, and Chapters 9–13.
c. Three semester-hours; group theory emphasis: Chapters 1–6, Sections 7.8, 7.11, 8.1, 8.2, 8.6, 9.2, 9.3, 9.4, 9.5, 9.8, 9.9, 10.2, 10.3, 10.4, 10.6, 11.2, and 11.3.
d. Three quarter-hours: The material from Chapters 1–6 under outline (b), and the material from Chapters 7–11 under outline (c).

I must express my appreciation to Sharon Baughman for reading the entire manuscript, and to a number of other people for reading and commenting on various portions of it: Drs. Donna L. Breen, Eleanor S. Elder, Thomas H. Siddall, III, and Louis M. Trefonas, and all the students who sat through my Chemistry 198 course. Only I can be blamed for any remaining errors, however. A special debt of gratitude is due my wife, who, in addition to the usual annoyances suffered by one married to someone trying to write a book, typed almost the entire manuscript from my illegible handwriting. Additional typing was done by Elaine Edwards, Lynette Lombas, and Judy Herr. Miss Lombas and J. M. Bopp, Jr. assisted in drawing the figures.

Exercises and Problems

Group theory is one of those fields where you must learn by doing. To this end, there are exercises scattered through each chapter and problems at the end of each chapter. Answers to selected exercises (indicated by an asterisk) are presented in Appendix 3.

University of New Orleans R. L. FLURRY, JR.

1

Vectors and Matrices

1.1 GEOMETRIC INTERPRETATION OF VECTORS

In our discussion of the symmetry properties of physical objects and abstract functions, we will need to precisely define the results of certain symmetry operations. This will require transformations of the coordinates of a point in the system, as defined with reference to some coordinate system (or system of *basis vectors*), to a new set of coordinates. These may be with respect to the same coordinate system or to a rotated coordinate system. Such transformations can most conveniently be accomplished with vector and matrix notation. As a consequence of this, we will start with a brief review of some of the principles of vectors and matrices.

When discussing the properties of a physical system, certain properties, such as mass and other intrinsic properties, have only a magnitude associated with them. Other properties, velocity and momentum, for example, require some variable component (direction in this case) in addition to a magnitude for an adequate description. Still other properties require two, three, or more independent components for their description. The mathematical quantity that can be generalized to represent any property is referred to as a *tensor*. The number of independent components possessed by the property gives the *rank* of the tensor. Tensor properties can be expressed numerically by arrays of numbers. The dimension of the array (i.e., the number of subscripts required) is equal to the rank of the tensor. Thus, scalars, vectors, and matrices are tensors of rank zero, 1, and 2, respectively. Most of our discussions will center around vectors and matrices.

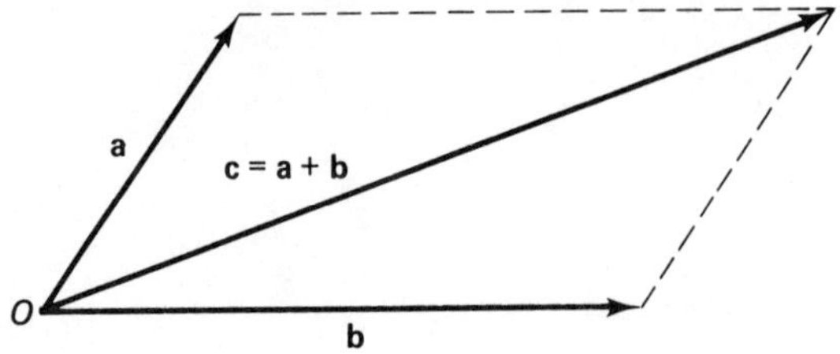

Fig. 1.1. Vector sum using common origin, O.

Vectors may be described from several points of view, which, on the surface, appear to be different. Ultimately, however, the formal mathematical significance of all of these is the same.

The description that is probably most easily grasped on a conceptual basis is the geometric description. In this description a *vector* may be considered as a line (or arrow or ray) having a definite length and a definite direction. Various mathematical operations involving vectors can be defined in terms of geometrical concepts. For example, the sum or resultant of two vectors is defined as the diagonal of the parallelogram that results when the origins of the two vectors are placed in coincidence and the parallelogram is completed from their terminal ends (Fig. 1.1). Similarly, the difference of two vectors is defined as the third side of the triangle formed when the origins of the two vectors are made coincident (Fig. 1.2). Note that the "head of the arrow" for the difference vector points toward that of the first vector (the second vector being subtracted from the first).

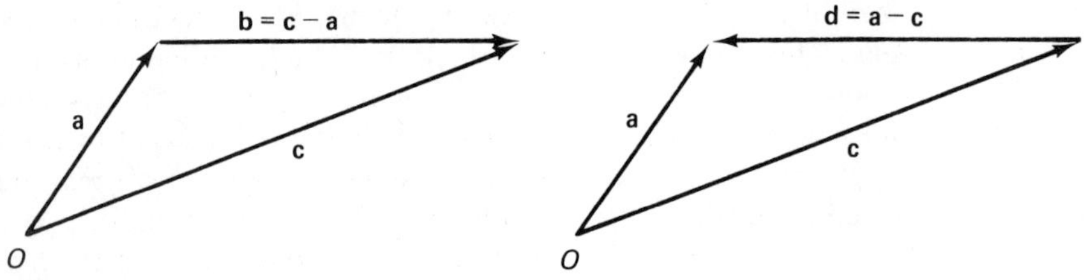

Fig. 1.2. Vector difference using common origin, O.

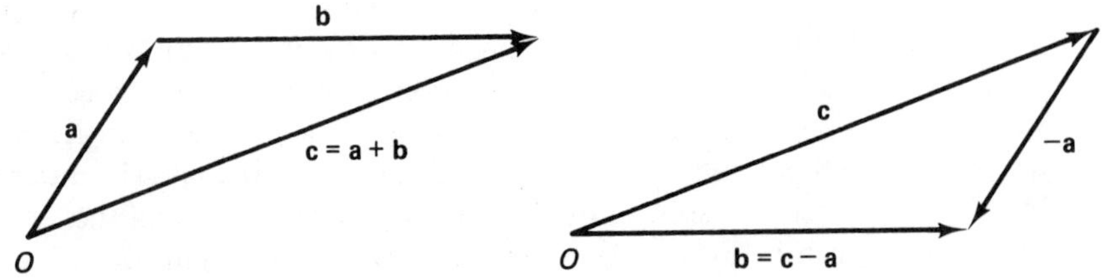

Fig. 1.3. Vector sum and difference using head-to-tail convention.

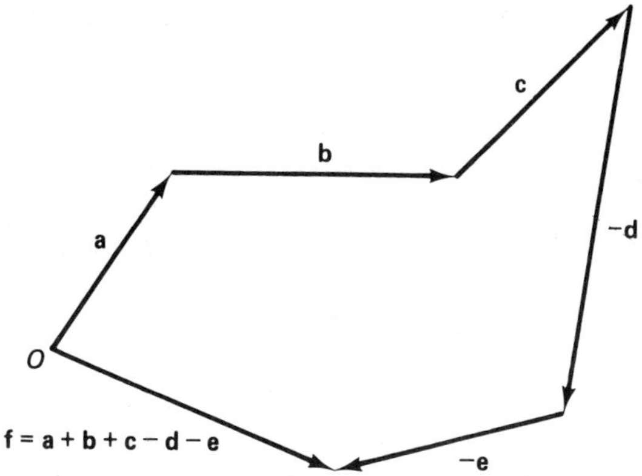

Fig. 1.4. Chain of vector additions and subtractions using head-to-tail convention.

Note also in Fig. 1.2 that $\mathbf{d} = -\mathbf{b}$. Properly speaking, vectors do not have "signs" associated with them. Here we use the minus sign to indicate that the vectors $-\mathbf{a}$ and $-\mathbf{c}$ point in the opposite direction from $\mathbf{a}$ and $\mathbf{c}$.

Another convenient geometric representation is to place the vectors in a head-to-tail arrangement, starting from some convenient origin. The sum or difference is the vector from the origin to the head of the last vector. A minus sign reverses the sense of the vector (Fig. 1.3). This type of representation is very convenient for representing a chain of additions and subtractions (Fig. 1.4).

Vector addition and subtraction obey the *associative* and *commutative laws.* That is, for a chain of operations, the grouping (association) of the individual operations and the order of appearance (commutation) of the various vectors in the chained operation are immaterial.

$$\begin{aligned}\mathbf{a} + \mathbf{b} - \mathbf{c} + \mathbf{d} = \mathbf{b} + \mathbf{a} + \mathbf{d} - \mathbf{c} &= (\mathbf{a} + \mathbf{b}) + (\mathbf{d} - \mathbf{c}) \\ &= \mathbf{a} + (\mathbf{b} - \mathbf{c}) + \mathbf{d}, \text{ etc.}\end{aligned} \tag{1.1}$$

The manipulations of vector addition and subtraction are thus the same as when adding and subtracting normal scalar quantities. Associative and commutative laws are not obeyed for all the operations we will define. We will specifically point out the ones that are obeyed.

Vector multiplication can be defined in three ways. The product of two vectors can be defined as a scalar (or dot) product. The *scalar product* of two vectors is a scalar quantity whose magnitude is the product of the magnitudes of the two vectors multiplied times the cosine of the angle between them:

$$\mathbf{a} \cdot \mathbf{b} = ab \cos \theta \tag{1.2}$$

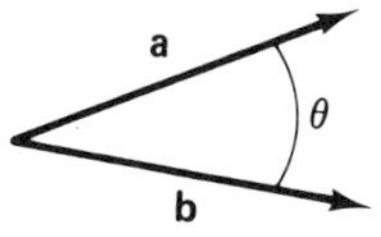

The commutative relationships hold for scalar products:

$$\mathbf{a} \cdot \mathbf{b} = \mathbf{b} \cdot \mathbf{a} \tag{1.3}$$

The second type of product is called the *vector product* (or *cross product*). As the name implies, the vector product of two vectors yields another vector. The product vector is perpendicular (usually, by convention, in a right-hand sense) to the two vectors from which it was formed. In other words, if, in forming the product $\mathbf{a} \times \mathbf{b}$, $\mathbf{a}$ lay along the x axis in a right-handed Cartesian coordinate system and $\mathbf{b}$ along the y axis, the product $\mathbf{c}$ would lie along the z axis (Fig. 1.5). (Sometimes the symbol $\wedge$ is used instead of $\times$; however, we will reserve this for another context.) The product of any two vectors lying in the xy plane would lie along the z axis; however, the sense of the product (whether it lay along the positive or the negative z axis) would depend on the order of the combination:

$$\mathbf{a} \times \mathbf{b} = -(\mathbf{b} \times \mathbf{a}) \tag{1.4}$$

Thus, vector products do not satisfy the commutative law.

Chained products can involve a mixture of multiplication types. For example, $\mathbf{a} \times (\mathbf{b} \times \mathbf{c})$, $(\mathbf{a} \times \mathbf{b}) \times \mathbf{c}$, and $\mathbf{a} \cdot (\mathbf{b} \times \mathbf{c})$ are all valid expressions. The result is different, however, in each case. If the product $(\mathbf{b} \times \mathbf{c})$ yields $\mathbf{d}$, and $(\mathbf{a} \times \mathbf{b})$ yields $\mathbf{e}$, then

$$\mathbf{a} \times (\mathbf{b} \times \mathbf{c}) = \mathbf{a} \times \mathbf{d} \tag{1.5}$$

and

$$(\mathbf{a} \times \mathbf{b}) \times \mathbf{c} = \mathbf{e} \times \mathbf{c} \tag{1.6}$$

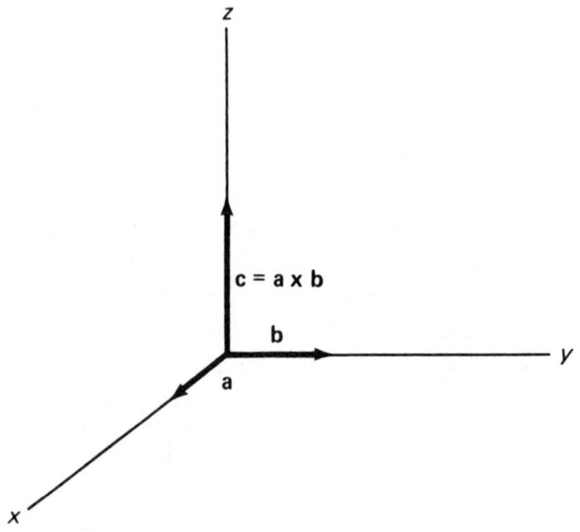

Fig. 1.5. Vector product of vectors **a** and **b** lying along the x and y Cartesian axes.

Similarly,

$$\mathbf{a} \cdot (\mathbf{b} \times \mathbf{c}) = \mathbf{a} \cdot \mathbf{d} \tag{1.7}$$

The magnitude of the vector resulting from a vector product is the product of the magnitudes of the individual vectors times the sine of the angle between them:

$$|\mathbf{a} \times \mathbf{b}| = |ab \sin \theta| \tag{1.8}$$

The vector product of a vector with itself must thus be the *null vector* (a vector whose magnitude is zero) since the sine of zero is zero. Note from Eq. 1.8 that the magnitude of the vector product equals the area of the parallelogram defined by **a** and **b**.

The result of the third type of vector product, the *direct* (or *tensor*) *product*, is a second-rank tensor, or matrix. The notation for the direct product of **a** with **b** is $\mathbf{a}\tilde{\mathbf{b}}$ or $\mathbf{a} \otimes \mathbf{b}$. The significance of the *tilde* will be pointed out later.

1.2 COLUMN AND ROW NOTATION FOR VECTORS

When working with the geometric interpretation of vectors within a three-dimensional Cartesian coordinate system, a vector is frequently represented by an array of three numbers giving the x, y, and z coordinates of the terminus of the vector with reference to a Cartesian coordinate system whose origin is coincident with the origin of the vector:

$$\mathbf{a} = (a^1 a^2 a^3) \tag{1.9}$$

The implication of this is that these are the numbers that would multiply the unit vectors, **i**, **j**, and **k**, in the x, y, and z directions to produce a vector sum equal to **a**:

$$\mathbf{a}^i = a^1\mathbf{i} + a^2\mathbf{j} + a^3\mathbf{k} \tag{1.10}$$

This is illustrated graphically in Fig. 1.6. Notice that in Eq. 1.9 we have indicated our vector by a row of numbers enclosed by parentheses. This is referred to as a *row vector*. (For the present we will indicate row vectors by a suitable superscript.) Vectors can also be represented by a column of numbers and as such are referred to as *column vectors*. For example, the vector

$$\mathbf{e}_i = \begin{pmatrix} e_1 \\ e_2 \\ e_3 \end{pmatrix} \tag{1.11}$$

is a column vector. (For the present, we will indicate column vectors by a subscript.) The row vector having the same elements as $\mathbf{e}_i$ is referred to as its transpose and is denoted $\tilde{\mathbf{e}}_i$. The notations of Eqs. 1.9 and 1.11 can be generalized to give column and row vectors having any desired number of elements. A vector having n elements is said to be an *n-dimensional vector* (by analogy with the three-dimensional vector). These n-dimensional vectors may be considered to be defined

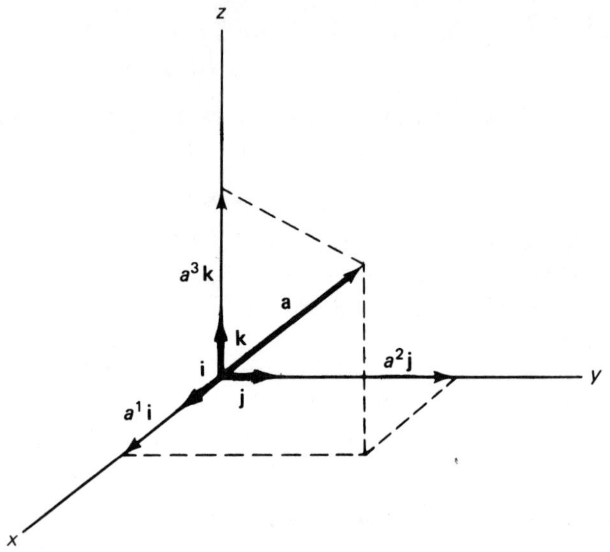

Fig. 1.6. Graphic representation of the vector $\mathbf{a} = a^1\mathbf{i} + a^2\mathbf{j} + a^3\mathbf{k}$.

analogously to Eq. 1.10 (or Eq. 1.12 with the $\mathbf{e}_i$ being designated as the basis vectors in an "n-dimensional space"):

$$\mathbf{r}^i = r^1\mathbf{e}_1 + r^2\mathbf{e}_2 + \ldots + r^n\mathbf{e}_n \tag{1.12}$$

Within the Cartesian coordinate system, the vectors of our basis set, **i**, **j**, and **k**, are *orthogonal* and *normalized* (or *orthonormal*); that is, they are mutually perpendicular and have a magnitude equal to unity. This need not be the case either in three dimensions or n dimensions. Any n noncoplanar vectors can be used as a basis set in n dimensions. For example, in working with solids it is frequently convenient to consider as a basis set the sides of a unit cell of the crystal. In only one of the seven possible crystal systems are the sides all equal and mutually perpendicular.

In dealing with nonorthogonal basis sets, the result of the various forms of vector combinations can be reasoned out from the definition of the vectors in terms of their basis set. (For any of the combinations to have any meaning, the vectors must be represented with respect to the same basis set.) The dot product of two vectors in some nonorthogonal three-dimensional basis set, for example, is as expressed in Eq. 1.13:

$$\begin{aligned}\mathbf{a}^i \cdot \mathbf{b}^i &= (a^1\mathbf{e}_1 + a^2\mathbf{e}_2 + a^3\mathbf{e}_3)\cdot(b^1\mathbf{e}_1 + b^2\mathbf{e}_2 + b^3\mathbf{e}_3)\\ &= a^1b^1\mathbf{e}_1\cdot\mathbf{e}_1 + a^1b^2\mathbf{e}_1\cdot\mathbf{e}_2 + a^1b^3\mathbf{e}_1\cdot\mathbf{e}_3 + a^2b^1\mathbf{e}_2\cdot\mathbf{e}_1\\ &\quad + a^2b^2\mathbf{e}_2\cdot\mathbf{e}_2 + a^2b^3\mathbf{e}_2\cdot\mathbf{e}_3 + a^3b^1\mathbf{e}_3\cdot\mathbf{e}_1 + a^3b^2\mathbf{e}_3\cdot\mathbf{e}_2\\ &\quad + a^3b^3\mathbf{e}_3\cdot\mathbf{e}_3\end{aligned} \tag{1.13}$$

or as generalized for n dimensions:

$$\mathbf{a} \cdot \mathbf{b} = \sum_{i,j=1}^{n} a^i b^j \mathbf{e}_i \cdot \mathbf{e}_j \tag{1.14}$$

Vector products and tensor products can be defined analogously. In an orthonormal basis set, the basis vectors obey the relationship

$$\mathbf{e}_i \cdot \mathbf{e}_j = \delta_{ij} \tag{1.15}$$

where δ_{ij} is the *Kronecker delta function*, which equals unity when i equals j, and zero otherwise.

Exercise 1.1*: Illustrate by the use of graphical procedures the equivalence of the geometrical and column concepts of vectors for vector addition, vector subtraction, and the dot product.

Exercise 1.2*: Find the angles between the following pairs of vectors in three-dimensional space:

$$\begin{pmatrix} 1 \\ 1 \\ 1 \end{pmatrix} \text{ and } \begin{pmatrix} -1 \\ 1 \\ -1 \end{pmatrix}; \quad \begin{pmatrix} 1 \\ -1 \\ 1 \end{pmatrix} \text{ and } \begin{pmatrix} -1 \\ 1 \\ -1 \end{pmatrix}; \quad \begin{pmatrix} -1 \\ 1 \\ 1 \end{pmatrix} \text{ and } \begin{pmatrix} -1 \\ 1 \\ -1 \end{pmatrix};$$

$$\begin{pmatrix} 1/2 \\ 1/\sqrt{2} \\ 1/2 \end{pmatrix} \text{ and } \begin{pmatrix} 1/2 \\ -1/\sqrt{2} \\ 1/2 \end{pmatrix}; \quad \begin{pmatrix} 1 \\ \sqrt{3} \\ 0 \end{pmatrix} \text{ and } \begin{pmatrix} 1 \\ -\sqrt{3} \\ 0 \end{pmatrix}$$

Exercise 1.3: Find the projection of the vector

$$\begin{pmatrix} -1 \\ 1 \\ -1 \end{pmatrix} \text{ on } \begin{pmatrix} 1/2 \\ 1/\sqrt{2} \\ 1/2 \end{pmatrix}$$

Scalar products and tensor products of vectors are easily defined in terms of the column and row notation for vectors. Multiplication of a row vector times a column vector yields a scalar quantity that is equivalent to the dot product:

$$\mathbf{a} \cdot \mathbf{b} = \mathbf{a}^i \mathbf{b}_i \tag{1.16}$$

For an orthonormal basis set (which is usually implied unless otherwise specified), this is

$$\mathbf{a} \cdot \mathbf{b} = (a^1 \quad a^2 \quad \ldots \quad a^n) \begin{pmatrix} b_1 \\ \vdots \\ b_n \end{pmatrix} \tag{1.17}$$

$$= a^1 b_1 + a^2 b_2 + \ldots + a^n b_n \tag{1.17a}$$

$$= \sum_i a^i b_i \tag{1.17b}$$

The tensor product was not defined previously since it can only be defined in terms of the elements of the vector. The direct product must be formulated as in Eq. 1.18. The resulting matrix is as in Eq. 1.18a.

$$\mathbf{a} \otimes \mathbf{b} = \mathbf{C} = \begin{pmatrix} a_1 \\ a_2 \\ \vdots \\ a_n \end{pmatrix} (b^1 \quad b^2 \quad \ldots \quad b^n) \tag{1.18}$$

$$= \begin{bmatrix} a_1 b^1 & a_1 b^2 & \ldots & a_1 b^n \\ a_2 b^1 & a_2 b^2 & \ldots & a_2 b^n \\ \vdots & \vdots & & \vdots \\ a_n b^1 & a_n b^2 & \ldots & a_n b^n \end{bmatrix} \tag{1.18a}$$

In other words, the direct product of two n-dimensional vectors is an $n \times n$ second-rank tensor, or a matrix, $\mathbf{C}$. The individual elements of this are

$$C_{ij} = a_i b^j \tag{1.19}$$

We will encounter the direct product in many contexts; however, there is one specific result involving direct products which is both interesting and useful. Consider the direct product of a unit vector $\mathbf{a}$ with itself, and then consider this product operating on another vector $\mathbf{c}$. The result, written $\mathbf{a\tilde{a}c}$, can be grouped from the right into $\mathbf{a(\tilde{a}c)}$. As we shall see later, however, the grouped expression is another notation for a scalar product. Thus, the relationships of Eq. 1.20 are valid.

$$\mathbf{a\tilde{a}c} = \mathbf{a}(\mathbf{a} \cdot \mathbf{c}) = \mathbf{a}c \cos \theta. \tag{1.20}$$

(Note that a vector times a scalar is a vector of unchanged direction, whose magnitude is the magnitude of the numerical product.) In other words, the result is a vector lying along $\mathbf{a}$ but having the magnitude $c \cos \theta$. This is just the projection of $\mathbf{c}$ on $\mathbf{a}$. The direct square of a unit vector is sometimes referred to as a *projection operator*. The direct squares of other vectors produce similar results; however, the magnitude of the projection will vary with the square of the magnitude of the starting vector:

$$\mathbf{b\tilde{b}c} = \mathbf{b}bc \cos \theta \tag{1.21}$$

The vector product in terms of the column and row vector notation is a bit more complicated. There is no *direct* method of combining column or row vectors to obtain a product that is another vector. The vector product can be constructed, however, by utilizing the expansion in terms of the basis vectors. In three-dimensional Cartesian coordinates the result of a cross product of the vectors $\mathbf{a}$ and $\mathbf{b}$ can be written

$$\begin{aligned} \mathbf{a} \times \mathbf{b} &= (a^1\mathbf{i} + a^2\mathbf{j} + a^3\mathbf{k}) \times (b^1\mathbf{i} + b^2\mathbf{j} + b^3\mathbf{k}) \\ &= a^1b^1\mathbf{i} \times \mathbf{i} + a^1b^2\mathbf{i} \times \mathbf{j} + a^1b^3\mathbf{i} \times \mathbf{k} + a^2b^1\mathbf{j} \times \mathbf{i} + a^2b^2\mathbf{j} \times \mathbf{j} \\ &\quad + a^2b^3\mathbf{j} \times \mathbf{k} + a^3b^1\mathbf{k} \times \mathbf{i} + a^3b^2\mathbf{k} \times \mathbf{j} + a^3b^3\mathbf{k} \times \mathbf{k} \end{aligned} \tag{1.22}$$

But

$$\mathbf{i} \times \mathbf{i} = 0; \qquad \mathbf{i} \times \mathbf{j} = \mathbf{k}; \qquad \mathbf{k} \times \mathbf{i} = \mathbf{j}, \quad \text{etc.} \tag{1.23}$$

Substituting these into Eq. 1.22, we have

$$\mathbf{a} \times \mathbf{b} = (a^2b^3 - a^3b^2)\mathbf{i} + (a^3b^1 - a^1b^3)\mathbf{j} + (a^1b^2 - a^2b^1)\mathbf{k} \tag{1.22a}$$

Equation 1.22a can be conveniently rewritten in the form of a determinant (see Section 1.6):

$$\mathbf{a} \times \mathbf{b} = \begin{vmatrix} \mathbf{i} & \mathbf{j} & \mathbf{k} \\ a^1 & a^2 & a^3 \\ b^1 & b^2 & b^3 \end{vmatrix} \tag{1.22b}$$

Equation 1.22 can be used in any dimensionality as long as the cross product of the basis vectors is defined. The simplification of Eq. 1.22b is possible only in three-dimensional space, however. A more general method involves obtaining a particular kind of matrix or *dyadic* from one of the vectors and taking the product of this with the other vector. In ordinary 3-dimensional space this may be written for column or row vectors as

$$\mathbf{a}_i \times \mathbf{b}_i = \mathbf{A}\mathbf{b}_i = -\mathbf{b}_i \times \mathbf{a}_i \tag{1.24a}$$

$$\mathbf{a}^i \times \mathbf{b}^i = \mathbf{a}^i\mathbf{B} = -\mathbf{b}^i \times \mathbf{a}^i \tag{1.24b}$$

where **A** and **B** are dyadics defined as

$$\mathbf{A} = \begin{bmatrix} 0 & -a^3 & a^2 \\ a^3 & 0 & -a^1 \\ -a^2 & a^1 & 0 \end{bmatrix} \tag{1.25a}$$

$$\mathbf{B} = \begin{bmatrix} 0 & -b^3 & b^2 \\ b^3 & 0 & -b^1 \\ -b^2 & b^1 & 0 \end{bmatrix} \tag{1.25b}$$

These can be derived by expanding the cross products in terms of **i**, **j**, and **k**, then carrying out the matrix-vector multiplication of Eq. 1.24 and comparing the results element by element. This method can be generalized to n dimensions; however, the result of the cross product of each pair of basis vectors must again be defined.

Exercise 1.4: By using as an example the unit vectors **i**, **j**, and **k** in three-dimensional space, verify the relationship of Eq. 1.24a.

$$(\mathbf{a}_i \times \mathbf{b}_i = \mathbf{A}\mathbf{b}_i)$$

1.3 MATRIX MULTIPLICATION

Multiplication relationships for the product of two matrices or the product of a matrix and a vector arise straightforwardly from Eqs. 1.16 and 1.17 by considering the matrix on the left to be a column of row vectors and that on the right to be a row of column vectors. The individual elements of the product matrix can then be determined from Eqs. 1.17. The general relationship for an element is:

$$\text{if} \qquad \mathbf{C} = \mathbf{AB} \tag{1.26a}$$

$$\text{then} \quad C_{ij} = \sum_k A_{ik} B_{kj} \tag{1.26b}$$

A and **B** need not necessarily be square matrices; however, the number of columns in **A** must equal the number of rows in **B**. The product will have the same number of rows as **A** and of columns as **B**. (Note that a row vector can be considered as a $1 \times n$ matrix and a column vector as an $n \times 1$ matrix.)

1.4 RECIPROCALS OF VECTORS

The concept of division is not defined as such for vectors and matrices; however, the concept of a *reciprocal* (or *inverse*) is defined. Thus, $\mathbf{a}/\mathbf{b}$ has no meaning, but $\mathbf{a} \cdot \mathbf{b}^{-1}$ is a perfectly valid expression. The expression

$$\frac{a}{b} = ab^{-1} \tag{1.27}$$

is valid only for scalar quantities. The reciprocal of a vector is defined as a vector that will form a dot product of unity with the original vector. That is, if

$$\mathbf{a}^{-1} = \mathbf{b} \tag{1.28a}$$

then

$$\mathbf{a} \cdot \mathbf{b} = \mathbf{b} \cdot \mathbf{a} = 1 \tag{1.28b}$$

Note that unless a direction is specified, the reciprocal of a vector is not unique. The reciprocal of a matrix is defined such that the product of a matrix and its reciprocal yields the *identity matrix*, a matrix having elements of unity along its diagonal and zero everywhere else.

In ordinary Cartesian three-dimensional space a reciprocal of a vector has a physical significance. It is simply another vector parallel to the original vector whose magnitude is the reciprocal of that of the original vector. A reciprocal of a vector can be found by use of the transformations that convert the original basis set into the reciprocal set. If **u**, **v** and **w** are a set of basis vectors in real space (not necessarily orthonormal), their reciprocals are defined as

$$\mathbf{u}^{-1} = \frac{(\mathbf{v} \times \mathbf{w})}{(\mathbf{u} \times \mathbf{v}) \cdot \mathbf{w}} \tag{1.29a}$$

$$\mathbf{v}^{-1} = \frac{(\mathbf{w} \times \mathbf{u})}{(\mathbf{u} \times \mathbf{v}) \cdot \mathbf{w}} \tag{1.29b}$$

$$\mathbf{w}^{-1} = \frac{(\mathbf{u} \times \mathbf{v})}{(\mathbf{u} \times \mathbf{v}) \cdot \mathbf{w}} \tag{1.29c}$$

The quantity in the denominator of these equations is a scalar quantity referred to as the *triple scalar product* and is frequently written (**uvw**). [The triple scalar product $(\mathbf{a} \times \mathbf{b}) \cdot \mathbf{c}$ represents the volume of the parallelepiped defined by **a**, **b** and **c**. It equals zero if and only if **a**, **b**, and **c** are coplanar.] The numerator in each case is a vector. Note that since this is a cross product, the reciprocal of each of the basis vectors is perpendicular to the conjugate plane of the corresponding real vector. It is not necessarily parallel to the real vector.

If **u**, **v**, and **w** are an orthogonal basis set and **a** is defined as

$$\mathbf{a} = a^1\mathbf{u} + a^2\mathbf{v} + a^3\mathbf{w} \tag{1.30}$$

then the reciprocal of **a** is

$$\mathbf{a}^{-1} = \frac{1}{\mathbf{e} \cdot \mathbf{e}}\left[\frac{\mathbf{u}^{-1}}{a^1} + \frac{\mathbf{v}^{-1}}{a^2} + \frac{\mathbf{w}^{-1}}{a^3}\right] \tag{1.31}$$

The product $\mathbf{e} \cdot \mathbf{e}$ is a normalization constant equal to the scalar product of the basis set with itself. When **u**, **v**, and **w** are not orthogonal, reciprocals can still be constructed by Eq. 1.31. One way of doing this is to refer **a** to an orthonormal coordinate system by the use of projection operators. For example, if **u**, **v**, and **w** are not orthogonal, a set **i**, **j**, and **k**, which are mutually orthogonal can be chosen. The components of **a** with respect to these are

$$a^i\mathbf{i} = \mathbf{i}(\mathbf{i} \cdot \mathbf{a}) = (a^1 u \cos\theta_{iu} + a^2 v \cos\theta_{iv} + a^3 w \cos\theta_{iw})i\mathbf{i} \tag{1.32a}$$

$$a^j\mathbf{j} = \mathbf{j}(\mathbf{j} \cdot \mathbf{a}) = (a^1 u \cos\theta_{ju} + a^2 v \cos\theta_{jv} + a^3 w \cos\theta_{jw})j\mathbf{j} \tag{1.32b}$$

$$a^k\mathbf{k} = \mathbf{k}(\mathbf{k} \cdot \mathbf{a}) = (a^1 u \cos\theta_{ku} + a^2 v \cos\theta_{kv} + a^3 w \cos\theta_{kw})k\mathbf{k} \tag{1.32c}$$

$\mathbf{a}^{-1}$ is then found to be

$$\mathbf{a}^{-1} = \frac{1}{\mathbf{e} \cdot \mathbf{e}}\left[\frac{\mathbf{i}^{-1}}{a^i} + \frac{\mathbf{j}^{-1}}{a^j} + \frac{\mathbf{k}^{-1}}{a^k}\right] \tag{1.33}$$

The original vector can also be constructed with reference to the reciprocal basis set. If we label our real basis set as $\mathbf{e}_1, \mathbf{e}_2, \mathbf{e}_3$ and our reciprocal set as $\mathbf{e}^1, \mathbf{e}^2, \mathbf{e}^3$, then

$$\mathbf{a} = a^1\mathbf{e}_1 + a^2\mathbf{e}_2 + a^3\mathbf{e}_3 = a_1\mathbf{e}^1 + a_2\mathbf{e}^2 + a_3\mathbf{e}^3 \tag{1.34}$$

Notice the convention of the interchange of subscripts. The basis set in real space is labeled by subscripts while the components of an arbitrary vector are labeled with superscripts. Conversely, the basis vectors in reciprocal space are labeled with superscripts while the components of the arbitrary vector are labeled with subscripts. The convention will be used later to describe the transformation properties of vectors. The vectors whose components are labeled with superscripts are said to be *contravariant*, while those with subscript labels are said to be *covariant*.

Exercise 1.5: Find the inverse of each of the vectors of Exercise 1.2, assuming a Cartesian basis set.

1.5 RECIPROCALS OF MATRICES

The reciprocal (or inverse) of a matrix or determinant can be constructed without reference to any specified basis set (although some basis set is usually implied when matrices are under consideration). The relationship is

$$\mathbf{A}^{-1} = \begin{bmatrix} \frac{A_{11}}{D} & \frac{A_{21}}{D} & \cdots & \frac{A_{n1}}{D} \\ \frac{A_{12}}{D} & \frac{A_{22}}{D} & \cdots & \frac{A_{n2}}{D} \\ \vdots & & & \vdots \\ \frac{A_{1n}}{D} & & \cdots & \frac{A_{nn}}{D} \end{bmatrix} \tag{1.35}$$

The D of Eq. 1.35 is the *determinant* of $\mathbf{A}$ (i.e., the quantity obtained when $\mathbf{A}$ is expanded as a polynomial in the elements) and A_{ij} is the *cofactor* of element a_{ij}. [The cofactor of a_{ij} is defined as the determinant remaining when the ith row and the jth column of the determinant of $\mathbf{A}$ are deleted and the result is multiplied by $(-1)^{i+j}$.] For example, if $\mathbf{A}$ is the 3×3 matrix

$$\mathbf{A} = \begin{bmatrix} a_{11} & a_{12} & a_{13} \\ a_{21} & a_{22} & a_{23} \\ a_{31} & a_{32} & a_{33} \end{bmatrix} \tag{1.36}$$

then the expanded form of D is the polynomial

$$\begin{aligned} D = a_{11}a_{22}a_{33} + a_{12}a_{23}a_{31} + a_{13}a_{21}a_{32} - a_{13}a_{22}a_{31} \\ - a_{12}a_{21}a_{33} - a_{11}a_{23}a_{32} \end{aligned} \tag{1.37}$$

The cofactors are

$$A_{11} = \begin{vmatrix} a_{22} & a_{23} \\ a_{32} & a_{33} \end{vmatrix} = a_{22}a_{33} - a_{23}a_{32} \tag{1.38a}$$

$$A_{12} = -\begin{vmatrix} a_{21} & a_{23} \\ a_{31} & a_{33} \end{vmatrix} = a_{23}a_{31} - a_{21}a_{33} \tag{1.38b}$$

$$A_{21} = -\begin{vmatrix} a_{12} & a_{13} \\ a_{32} & a_{33} \end{vmatrix} = a_{13}a_{32} - a_{12}a_{33} \tag{1.38c}$$

and so on. To construct $\mathbf{A}^{-1}$ the values obtained from Eqs. 1.37 and 1.38 would be substituted into Eq. 1.35. No matrix whose determinant equals zero can have an inverse. (Such a matrix is said to be *singular*.) As a consequence of this, inverses exist only for square matrices, because of the fact that nonsquare determinants vanish.

Exercise 1.6*: Find the inverse of the following matrices:

$$\begin{bmatrix} 1 & 2 & 3 \\ 2 & 3 & 1 \\ 3 & 1 & 2 \end{bmatrix}; \quad \begin{bmatrix} 1/2 & 1/\sqrt{2} & 1/2 \\ 1/\sqrt{2} & 0 & -1/\sqrt{2} \\ 1/2 & -1/\sqrt{2} & 1/2 \end{bmatrix}$$

1.6 MATRICES VERSUS DETERMINANTS

At this point a distinction should be made between *matrices* and *determinants*. Both are two dimensional arrays of elements. The operations of matrix algebra can be applied to determinants. However, there is one great difference between the two. If the elements of a determinant are numbers, then the determinant has a definite numerical value. If the elements are functions, the determinant is still equivalent to the expanded form in terms of the functions. A matrix, on the other hand, never has a numerical value or expanded form. Every square matrix does have a determinant associated with it, however. We will adopt a notation convention whereby matrices are enclosed by brackets and determinants are enclosed by straight lines.

The most direct way of expanding a determinant is by the method of cofactors. The expanded determinant has the value

$$D = \sum_{j=1}^{n} (-1)^{(j-1)} a_{ij} A_{ij} \tag{1.39}$$

where n is the rank of the determinant. The process can be repeated until each cofactor is a 2×2 determinant. A 2×2 determinant, A, has the value

$$A = \begin{vmatrix} a & b \\ c & d \end{vmatrix} = ad - bc \tag{1.40}$$

1.7 ASSOCIATED MATRICES

In addition to the inverse, there are a number of other special matrices associated with a given matrix. If **A** contains imaginary numbers, then the matrix $\mathbf{A}^*$ is the *complex conjugate* of **A**. The sign of the imaginary part of each element of **A** is changed. If a matrix is real, then **A** equals $\mathbf{A}^*$.

The *transpose* of **A**, $\tilde{\mathbf{A}}$, is constructed from **A** by an interchange of rows and columns (i.e., $\tilde{a}_{ij} = a_{ji}$). A matrix is said to be symmetric if **A** equals $\tilde{\mathbf{A}}$, or antisymmetric (or skew) if **A** equals $-\tilde{\mathbf{A}}$. If the new matrix is constructed as a transpose and complex conjugate simultaneously, then the new matrix $\mathbf{A}^\dagger$ is said to be the *conjugate transpose* or *Hermitian conjugate* of **A**. (Sometimes workers in quantum mechanics refer to this as the *adjoint*.) If **A** equals $\mathbf{A}^\dagger$, the matrix is said to be *Hermitian*. The transpose, the Hermitian conjugate, and the reciprocal of matrix products are the products of the individual transposes, Hermitian conjugates, and reciprocals in reverse order.

$$(\widetilde{\mathbf{AB}}) = \tilde{\mathbf{B}}\tilde{\mathbf{A}} \tag{1.41a}$$

$$(\mathbf{AB})^\dagger = \mathbf{B}^\dagger\mathbf{A}^\dagger \tag{1.41b}$$

$$(\mathbf{AB})^{-1} = \mathbf{B}^{-1}\mathbf{A}^{-1} \tag{1.41c}$$

There is, in addition to the normal matrix product, an operation referred to as the *matrix direct product*. If **A** is an $n \times n$ matrix and **B** is an $m \times m$ matrix, then the direct product $\mathbf{A} \otimes \mathbf{B}$ is an $(nm) \times (nm)$ matrix defined as follows:

$$\mathbf{A} \otimes \mathbf{B} = \begin{bmatrix} a_{11}\mathbf{B} & a_{12}\mathbf{B} & \dots & a_{1n}\mathbf{B} \\ a_{21}\mathbf{B} & a_{22}\mathbf{B} & \dots & a_{2n}\mathbf{B} \\ \vdots & \vdots & & \vdots \\ a_{n1}\mathbf{B} & a_{n2}\mathbf{B} & \dots & a_{nn}\mathbf{B} \end{bmatrix} \tag{1.42}$$

Transposes, Hermitian conjugates, and inverses of direct products occur in normal order.

$$(\widetilde{\mathbf{A} \otimes \mathbf{B}}) = \tilde{\mathbf{A}} \otimes \tilde{\mathbf{B}}, \quad \text{etc.} \tag{1.43}$$

1.8 UNITARY TRANSFORMATIONS

One additional concept involving matrices needs to be defined. This is the concept of a *unitary transformation.* A unitary transformation is a transformation accomplished by a unitary matrix or operator. It preserves the *magnitude* of the quantity being transformed.

It can be shown that if

$$\mathbf{A}^{-1} = \mathbf{A}^\dagger \tag{1.44}$$

then either the columns or the rows of **A** form an orthonormal set of basis vectors:

$$\mathbf{a}_{*i} \cdot \mathbf{a}_{*j} = \delta_{ij} \tag{1.45a}$$

$$\mathbf{a}_{i*} \cdot \mathbf{a}_{j*} = \delta_{ij} \tag{1.45b}$$

where $\mathbf{a}_{*i}$ represents the ith column vector and $\mathbf{a}_{i*}$ represents the ith row vector. Such a matrix **A** is said to be a *unitary matrix*. The magnitude of the determinant of any unitary matrix equals unity. Consider now what would happen if such a matrix, **A**, in three-dimensional space were multiplied times a unit vector, **i**, along the x axis.

$$\begin{bmatrix} a_{11} & a_{12} & a_{13} \\ a_{21} & a_{22} & a_{23} \\ a_{31} & a_{32} & a_{33} \end{bmatrix} \begin{pmatrix} 1 \\ 0 \\ 0 \end{pmatrix} = \begin{pmatrix} a_{11} \\ a_{21} \\ a_{31} \end{pmatrix} \tag{1.46}$$

The vector is transformed into $\mathbf{a}_{*1}$, one of the **a** set. In a similar fashion **j** is transformed into $\mathbf{a}_{*2}$ and **k** into $\mathbf{a}_{*3}$. In other words, the x, y, and z coordinate system has been rotated into a new coordinate system. Similar transformations can be used to transfer any arbitrary vector from one coordinate system or basis set to another. The magnitude of the vector is not changed; consequently, the transformation is referred to as a unitary transformation.

A unitary transformation, **A**, on a matrix, **B**, requires premultiplication by $\mathbf{A}^\dagger$ and postmultiplication by **A**, or vice versa.

$$\mathbf{B}' = \mathbf{A}^\dagger \mathbf{B} \mathbf{A} \tag{1.47}$$

Any Hermitian matrix can be *diagonalized*, that is, converted into a matrix with nonzero elements only along the diagonal, by the use of a suitable unitary transformation. Physically, this implies a rotation of the basis set of **B** so that all its components lie on the axes of the basis set.

1.9 CHANGE OF BASIS

We have already mentioned a *change of basis* vectors in two connections: the transformation from real to reciprocal space discussed in Section 1.3, and the diagonalization of a Hermitian matrix in Section 1.8. This latter instance was a specialized case of a rotation of the basis set. It will be convenient to have available general methods for rotating a basis set and for rotating a vector relative to its basis set.

Let the vectors $\mathbf{e}_1$, $\mathbf{e}_2$, $\mathbf{e}_3$ be an original basis set and $\bar{\mathbf{e}}_1$, $\bar{\mathbf{e}}_2$, $\bar{\mathbf{e}}_3$ be a rotated basis set, where the two are related by the relations

$$\begin{aligned} \bar{\mathbf{e}}_1 &= t_1^1\mathbf{e}_1 + t_1^2\mathbf{e}_2 + t_1^3\mathbf{e}_3 \\ \bar{\mathbf{e}}_2 &= t_2^1\mathbf{e}_1 + t_2^2\mathbf{e}_2 + t_2^3\mathbf{e}_3 \\ \bar{\mathbf{e}}_3 &= t_3^1\mathbf{e}_1 + t_3^2\mathbf{e}_2 + t_3^3\mathbf{e}_3 \end{aligned} \tag{1.48}$$

involving the transformation coefficients t_i^j. If $\mathbf{a}$ is an arbitrary vector, it can be written with reference to either of the two basis sets

$$\mathbf{a} = a^1\mathbf{e}_1 + a^2\mathbf{e}_2 + a^3\mathbf{e}_3 = \bar{a}^1\bar{\mathbf{e}}_1 + \bar{a}^2\bar{\mathbf{e}}_2 + \bar{a}^3\bar{\mathbf{e}}_3 \tag{1.49}$$

The components of $\mathbf{a}$ in the original basis set are related quite simply to those in the new set by substituting Eqs. 1.48 into 1.49 and equating the coefficients of the $\mathbf{e}_i$:

$$\begin{aligned} a^1 &= t_1^1\bar{a}^1 + t_2^1\bar{a}^2 + t_3^1\bar{a}^3 \\ a^2 &= t_1^2\bar{a}^1 + t_2^2\bar{a}^2 + t_3^2\bar{a}^3 \\ a^3 &= t_1^3\bar{a}^1 + t_2^3\bar{a}^2 + t_3^3\bar{a}^3 \end{aligned} \tag{1.50a}$$

To obtain the converse relation, however, requires a new set of transformation coefficients,

$$\begin{aligned} \bar{a}^1 &= T_1^1 a^1 + T_2^1 a^2 + T_3^1 a^3 \\ \bar{a}^2 &= T_1^2 a^1 + T_2^2 a^2 + T_3^2 a^3 \\ \bar{a}^3 &= T_1^3 a^1 + T_2^3 a^2 + T_3^3 a^3 \end{aligned} \tag{1.50b}$$

where

$$\sum_j T_j^i t_k^j = \delta_k^i \tag{1.50c}$$

and where δ_k^i is a Kronecker delta function equaling unity if i equals k, or zero otherwise. The T_j^i can be obtained by substituting in the t_i^j from Eq. 1.48 and solving the resulting set of simultaneous equations of Eq. 1.50c.

Exercise 1.7*:

(a) Find the unitary transformation matrix which will rotate the vector $\mathbf{a} = \begin{pmatrix} 1 \\ 1 \\ 1 \end{pmatrix}$ so that it lies along the z axis while leaving $\mathbf{b} = \begin{pmatrix} 1 \\ -1 \\ 0 \end{pmatrix}$ unchanged; i.e., find $\mathbf{T}$ such that

$$\mathbf{T}\begin{pmatrix} 1 \\ 1 \\ 1 \end{pmatrix} = \begin{pmatrix} 0 \\ 0 \\ \sqrt{3} \end{pmatrix}; \qquad \mathbf{T}\begin{pmatrix} 1 \\ -1 \\ 0 \end{pmatrix} = \begin{pmatrix} 1 \\ -1 \\ 0 \end{pmatrix}; \qquad \mathbf{T}^\dagger\mathbf{T} = \mathbf{1}$$

(b) Find the result of transforming the following vectors with $\mathbf{T}$:

$$\begin{pmatrix} 1 \\ -1 \\ -1 \end{pmatrix}; \quad \begin{pmatrix} -1 \\ 1 \\ -1 \end{pmatrix}; \quad \begin{pmatrix} -1 \\ -1 \\ 1 \end{pmatrix}$$

(c) Find the angle between each of the vectors in part (b) and the vector in part (a) in the transformed coordinate system.

1.10 ROTATION OF A VECTOR: COVARIANT AND CONTRAVARIANT VECTORS

The rotation of a vector relative to a coordinate system may be accomplished in two ways. Either the coordinate system may be held fixed and the vector rotated or the vector may be held fixed and the coordinate system rotated. These should be defined in terms of matrices and vectors so that the final result is the same in either case.

In Eq. 1.34 of Section 1.4 the vector **a** was written in terms of both contravariant components of real space and covariant components of reciprocal space. This equation can be written in a row and column notation as

$$\mathbf{a} = (a^1 a^2 a^3)\begin{pmatrix} \mathbf{e}_1 \\ \mathbf{e}_2 \\ \mathbf{e}_3 \end{pmatrix} = (\mathbf{e}^1 \mathbf{e}^2 \mathbf{e}^3)\begin{pmatrix} a_1 \\ a_2 \\ a_3 \end{pmatrix} \tag{1.51}$$

If we define an operator R that carries out the rotation of the coordinate system (in real space) presented in Eq. 1.48, we can define the rotated $\bar{\mathbf{e}}$ basis set as

$$\begin{pmatrix} \bar{\mathbf{e}}_1 \\ \bar{\mathbf{e}}_2 \\ \bar{\mathbf{e}}_3 \end{pmatrix} = \bar{\mathbf{e}} = R\mathbf{e} = \begin{bmatrix} t_1^1 & t_1^2 & t_1^3 \\ t_2^1 & t_2^2 & t_2^3 \\ t_3^1 & t_3^2 & t_3^3 \end{bmatrix}\begin{pmatrix} \mathbf{e}_1 \\ \mathbf{e}_2 \\ \mathbf{e}_3 \end{pmatrix} = \mathbf{Re} \tag{1.52}$$

(Note the distinction between the operator R and the matrix $\mathbf{R}$.) If the vector $\mathbf{a}^i$ were held stationary, it could be expressed with reference to the rotated coordinate system as

$$\bar{\mathbf{a}}^i = \mathbf{a}^i R\mathbf{e} = \mathbf{a}^i \mathbf{Re} \tag{1.53}$$

This, however, must be the same as if we rotated the vector and left the coordinate system unchanged:

$$\bar{\mathbf{a}}^i = (R\mathbf{a}^i)\mathbf{e} = \mathbf{a}^i(R\mathbf{e}) = \mathbf{a}^i\mathbf{Re} \tag{1.54}$$

Thus, the matrix equivalent of the operator R operating on $\mathbf{a}^i$ must be

$$R\mathbf{a}^i = \mathbf{a}^i\mathbf{R} \tag{1.55}$$

That is, the rotation operator operating on the vector yields the vector times the matrix representing the rotation (i.e., the order of the matrix representation is the reverse of the order of the operator representation): hence the name *contravariant*. The real *basis* set is, however, *covariant* with respect to the rotation operation. This is, in fact, a general property of operators and vectors. The normal basis set transforms in a covariant manner, while a vector defined in terms of this basis set transforms in a contravariant manner. If, on the other hand, the operation were carried out in reciprocal space, the reciprocal basis vectors would have been contravariant and the components of $\mathbf{a}_i$ covariant. In general, if $\mathbf{u}$ is an arbitrary column vector and $\mathbf{v}$ is an arbitrary row vector, we have the relations

$$\text{covariant:} \qquad R\mathbf{u} = \mathbf{R}\mathbf{u} \tag{1.56a}$$

$$\text{contravariant:} \quad R\mathbf{v} = \mathbf{v}\mathbf{R} \tag{1.56b}$$

For convenience, we will drop the different notations for covariant and contravariant vectors unless it is required to prevent an ambiguity.

When dealing with orthonormal basis vectors, the covariant and contravariant components of any given arbitrary vector are the same. This leads to the common statements that the row and column notations for a given vector are equivalent. When this convention is assumed, it is common to denote an arbitrary vector $\mathbf{a}$ as a column vector. The vector $\tilde{\mathbf{a}}$ would then be a row vector having the same elements as $\mathbf{a}$. This leads to the common notations of $\tilde{\mathbf{a}}\mathbf{b}$ for a dot (or scalar) product and $\mathbf{a}\tilde{\mathbf{b}}$ for a tensor product; notations that we adopted for convenience to describe the projection operator.

Two-dimensional rotations are particularly important. Expressed in two dimensions, a rotation by the angle θ is represented by the matrix

$$\mathbf{R} = \begin{bmatrix} \cos\theta & \sin\theta \\ -\sin\theta & \cos\theta \end{bmatrix} \tag{1.57}$$

The inverse of a rotation by θ is the rotation by $(-\theta)$. Thus, if $\mathbf{R}$ is as in Eq. 1.57, then $\mathbf{R}^{-1}$ is

$$\mathbf{R}^{-1} = \begin{bmatrix} \cos(-\theta) & \sin(-\theta) \\ -\sin(-\theta) & \cos(-\theta) \end{bmatrix} \tag{1.58}$$

But, since

$$\cos(-\theta) = \cos\theta \tag{1.59a}$$

and

$$\sin(-\theta) = -\sin\theta \tag{1.59b}$$

then

$$\mathbf{R}^{-1} = \begin{bmatrix} \cos\theta & -\sin\theta \\ \sin\theta & \cos\theta \end{bmatrix} \tag{1.60}$$

Thus, $\mathbf{R}^{-1}$ equals $\mathbf{R}^{\dagger}$ and $\mathbf{R}$ is, consequently, unitary.

Expressed in three dimensions, the simple rotation matrix becomes

$$R = \begin{bmatrix} \cos\theta & \sin\theta & 0 \\ -\sin\theta & \cos\theta & 0 \\ 0 & 0 & 1 \end{bmatrix}$$

where the third dimension represents the axis about which the rotation occurs.

The treatment of vectors and matrices that we have presented is very brief and incomplete. The topics presented have been chosen for their applicability to the other topics that we will discuss, rather than on the basis of any intrinsic overall value toward the theories of vectors and matrices. A few additional topics will be introduced by example in later chapters.

PROBLEMS

For the following problems, let

$$\mathbf{a} = \begin{pmatrix} 1 \\ 2 \\ 3 \end{pmatrix}; \quad \mathbf{b} = \begin{pmatrix} 2 \\ -5 \\ 7 \end{pmatrix}; \quad \mathbf{c} = \begin{pmatrix} -1/3 \\ i/7 \\ -1/5 \end{pmatrix}; \quad \mathbf{d} = \begin{pmatrix} p \\ q \\ r \end{pmatrix}; \quad \mathbf{e} = \begin{pmatrix} s \\ t \\ u \end{pmatrix}$$

$$\mathbf{A} = \begin{bmatrix} 1 & 2 & 3 \\ 2 & 4 & 5 \\ 3 & 5 & 6 \end{bmatrix}; \quad \mathbf{B} = \begin{bmatrix} 1 & 1 & 1 \\ 1 & 1 & 1 \\ 1 & 1 & 1 \end{bmatrix}; \quad \mathbf{C} = \begin{bmatrix} 1 & 1 & 0 \\ 1 & 1 & 1 \\ 1 & 1 & 1 \end{bmatrix};$$

$$\mathbf{D} = \begin{bmatrix} p & q & r \\ s & t & u \\ v & w & x \end{bmatrix}; \quad \mathbf{E} = \begin{bmatrix} 1 & 2i & 3+i \\ -2i & 4 & 1-5i \\ 3-i & 1+5i & 6 \end{bmatrix}; \quad \mathbf{F} = \begin{bmatrix} 1 & i & 1 \\ i & 1 & i \\ 1 & i & 1 \end{bmatrix}$$

1. Carry out the following operations:

(a)	$\mathbf{a} + \mathbf{b} + \mathbf{c}$	(b)	$\mathbf{a} - \mathbf{b} + \mathbf{c}$
(c)	$\mathbf{a} - \mathbf{b}$	(d)	$\mathbf{b} \times \mathbf{c}$
(e)	$\mathbf{a} \cdot (\mathbf{b} \times \mathbf{c})$	(f)	$\mathbf{a} + \mathbf{d}$
(g)	$\mathbf{b} \cdot \mathbf{d}$	(h)	$\mathbf{d} + \mathbf{e}$
(i)	$\mathbf{d} \cdot \mathbf{e}$	(j)	$\mathbf{d} \times \mathbf{e}$
(k)	$\mathbf{a} \otimes \mathbf{b}$	(l)	$\mathbf{A} + \mathbf{F}$
(m)	$\mathbf{E} - \mathbf{F}$	(n)	$\mathbf{AA}$
(o)	$\mathbf{AB}$	(p)	$\mathbf{AD}$
(q)	$\mathbf{DA}$	(r)	$\mathbf{A} \otimes \mathbf{B}$
(s)	$\mathbf{F}^\dagger\mathbf{F}$	(t)	$(\mathbf{FD})^\dagger$
(u)	$\mathbf{Aa}$	(v)	$\mathbf{c}^\dagger\mathbf{A}$
(w)	$\mathbf{c}^\dagger\mathbf{Ec}$	(x)	$\mathbf{F}^\dagger\mathbf{AF}$

2. Find the transposes and conjugate transposes of **A** through **F**.

3. Evaluate the determinants of **A** through **F**.

4. Assuming an orthonormal basis, find the inverses of **a**, **b**, and **c**.

BIBLIOGRAPHY

AYERS, F., JR., *Matrices*, Schaum Publishing Co., New York, 1963.

HALL, G. G., *Matrices and Tensors*, Macmillan Publishing Co., Inc., New York, 1963. The notation of this chapter comes primarily from Hall.

HOLLINSWORTH, C. A., *Vectors, Matrices, and Group Theory for Scientists and Engineers*, McGraw-Hill Book Company, New York, 1967.

MARTIN, A. D., AND V. J. MIZEL, *Introduction to Linear Algebra*, McGraw-Hill Book Company, New York, 1966.

2

Symmetry and Groups

2.1 IMPORTANCE OF SYMMETRY

Many physical objects have some degree of symmetry associated with them. Consideration of this symmetry can aid in the description of the objects. For example, if a complete quantum mechanical description of a benzene molecule were desired, this could be obtained by completely describing one of the C—H units as it appears in the molecule and then repeating this unit six times to complete a hexagon. If a quantum-mechanical description of a crystalline metal were desired, it could be obtained by completely describing one unit cell of the crystal (or, in this case, usually one atom) and then repeating this many times in all directions.

Frequently, the behavior of an object in certain situations is determined by its symmetry. On the macroscopic level, we realize that a square peg cannot be fitted into a round hole or a right-handed screw into a left-handed nut. On the molecular level, biological organisms are extremely sensitive to symmetry, recognizing the subtle difference in local symmetry between a D- and an L-amino acid in spite of the fact that they are chemically identical.

For our purposes, the symmetry of a molecule or crystal imposes certain restrictions on their interaction with electromagnetic radiation, and hence, on the spectral properties of both and on the diffraction properties of the crystal. A knowledge of the relationships involved can furnish valuable information about the structure of the molecule or crystal. The interrelationships of the symmetry properties of an object define a mathematical *group*. The behavior of groups is well known to mathematicians through *group theory*; thus, the symmetry behavior of an object can be conveniently formalized through group theory.

There are two approaches to the application of group theory to problems of symmetry. The first of these involves the direct use of the generating functions for the symmetry operations under consideration, and the generation of whatever symmetry groups and related group properties are applicable to the problem at hand. Once the groups are generated, the methods of group theory are used to manipulate them in the desired fashion. The second approach is to classify the system under consideration according to previously defined symmetry groups. The appropriate group properties are then those that are associated with the symmetry group chosen. The methods of group theory are then applied as before.

The first method is ultimately the more powerful, but it requires more knowledge and practice than the second method in order to get usable results. We will take a compromise approach in the development and applications of group theory. Enough material on the theory and use of generating functions and related matters will be presented to illustrate the principles that will be required for the second approach.

2.2 DEFINITION OF A GROUP

A mathematical group may be defined operationally as a set of elements that satisfy four general criteria. These are as follows:

1. *Any two elements of the group must combine to give an element that is also a member of the group* (closure property). In other words, if P and Q are members of the group and if their product PQ equals S, then S must also be a member of the group. The term "product" is used for this combination, although this does not have the connotation of multiplication as it does in elementary arithmetic. If the elements were simple numbers, the "product" could be defined in terms of any arithmetical operation: addition, subtraction, multiplication, or division. Once chosen, however, it must retain its definition.

2. *The associative law of combination must be satisfied.* That is,

$$PQRS = P(QR)S = (PQ)(RS) \quad \text{etc.} \tag{2.1}$$

These first two properties taken together are referred to as the *group property*.

3. *The group must contain an element that commutes with all the other elements and also leaves them unchanged.* That is,

$$ER = RE = R \tag{2.2}$$

This element is called the *identity element*, and is usually given the symbol E. It should be noted that only the E element is required to commute. If all the elements should happen to commute among themselves, the group is said to be *Abelian*. Symmetry groups are generally non-Abelian; however, pure rotation and pure translational groups are Abelian.

4. *The reciprocal of every element in the group is also a member of the group.* If P is a member of the group, there must be some element R which equals P^{-1}, so that

$$P^{-1}P = RP = PR = PP^{-1} = E \tag{2.3}$$

In other words, the reciprocal of an element undergoes what the element does.

As an example of a group, the last digit on any digital counter (such as an automobile odometer or a simple adding machine) defines a group when the product is defined as addition. The elements are the set of numbers $\{0, 1, \ldots, 9\}$. The number of elements contained in a group is referred to as its *order*. Thus, this group has an order of 10. The product of any two elements is the algebraic sum. Since only the last digit is being considered, this product must also be a member of the set, thus satisfying the first criterion for a group. Addition satisfies the associative relationship, the second criterion for a group. (It also satisfies the commutative relationship; therefore, this group is Abelian.) The zero corresponds to the identity element in this group. When added to any element, it leaves it unchanged. The reciprocal of each element is the digit that must be added to bring the result to zero. For example, 9 and 1, 8 and 2, 7 and 3, and so on, are all reciprocals of each other. This group is an example of a *cyclic permutation group*. A permutation group is a group in which each operation is defined as an interchange (or permutation) of the members of a set. A cyclic permutation, as the name implies, is one in which the interchange is in a cyclic order, as in going from the set $\{1\,2\,3\,4\}$ to $\{2\,3\,4\,1\}$ to $\{3\,4\,1\,2\}$. Other permutation groups which allow other permutations, such as $\{1\,2\,3\,4\}$ going to $\{2\,1\,3\,4\}$, are possible. In symmetry groups, the pure rotation groups, which we shall discuss later, have the form of cyclic permutation groups. Other symmetry groups can also be defined in terms of other types of permutations. In fact, every finite group can be represented by a permutation group (*Cayley's theorem*).

Exercise 2.1*: Verify that the following sets satisfy the group criteria when the product is as defined. Identify the identity element in each case.

	Group	*Product*
(a)	$\{0, 1\}$	The last digit in binary addition
(b)	$\{1, -1\}$	Multiplication
(c)	$\{1, -1, i, -i\}$ $(i = \sqrt{-1})$	Multiplication
(d)	All positive and negative integers (including zero)	Addition
(e)	All rational numbers greater than zero	Multiplication

Let us now consider the set of *symmetry operations* that can be used to describe a molecule. As a specific example, let us consider methyl chloride (**1**):

$$
\begin{array}{c}
H_1 \\
\diagdown \\
H_3 \diagup C - Cl \\
H_2
\end{array}
$$

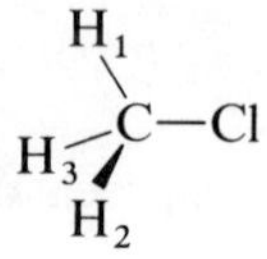

1

(In the drawing, the hydrogens have been numbered so that they may be followed through the symmetry operations.) A symmetry operation is defined as an operation that will leave an object in a configuration indistinguishable from the starting configuration. It need not necessarily be possible to physically carry out the operations; they need only be definitely defined operations with respect to a particular *symmetry element*. (A symmetry element is defined as a geometric entity, such as a plane, a line, or a point, about which a symmetry operation is performed.) Systems can be classified with respect to either symmetry elements or symmetry operations. However, since neither can exist without the other, the classifications are essentially equivalent. There is, however, an unfortunate ambiguity in this terminology. When discussing point symmetry, the symmetry element is the geometric entity about which the symmetry operation is performed. In formal group theory, the elements of the group are the operations that define the group. Thus, symmetry operations are the same as point group elements. Symmetry operations are *not* the same as symmetry elements.

Methyl chloride possesses three types of symmetry elements and can undergo six symmetry operations associated with these. The first of these is the identity operation. This is the operation that either does nothing whatsoever to the system, or returns it to the starting configuration:

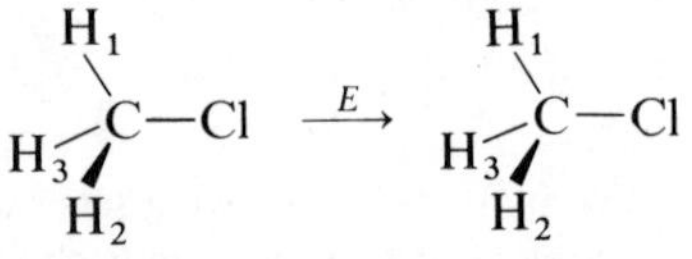

$$
\begin{array}{c}
H_1 \\
\diagdown \\
H_3 \diagup C - Cl \\
H_2
\end{array}
\quad \xrightarrow{E} \quad
\begin{array}{c}
H_1 \\
\diagdown \\
H_3 \diagup C - Cl \\
H_2
\end{array}
\tag{2.4}
$$

Obviously, every system possesses the identity element whether it possesses any others or not. Although it seems trivial to include the identity operation in the operations describing a system, it must be included if the symmetry elements are to define a mathematical group.

Probably the most obvious element, other than the identity element, which is possessed by methyl chloride is the *rotation axis*. If the molecule is rotated by either 120° or 240° about the C—Cl bond, a configuration equivalent to the starting configuration is obtained.

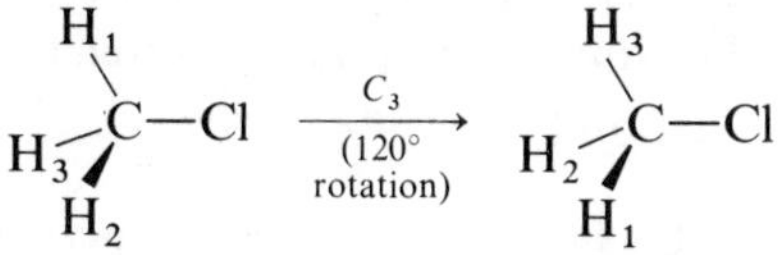

$$\begin{matrix} H_1 \\ \diagdown \\ H_3\diagup C-Cl \\ \diagup \\ H_2 \end{matrix} \quad \xrightarrow[\substack{(120° \\ \text{rotation})}]{C_3} \quad \begin{matrix} H_3 \\ \diagdown \\ H_2\diagup C-Cl \\ \diagup \\ H_1 \end{matrix} \tag{2.5}$$

$$\begin{matrix} H_1 \\ \diagdown \\ H_3\diagup C-Cl \\ \diagup \\ H_2 \end{matrix} \quad \xrightarrow[\substack{(240° \\ \text{rotation})}]{C_3^2} \quad \begin{matrix} H_2 \\ \diagdown \\ H_1\diagup C-Cl \\ \diagup \\ H_3 \end{matrix} \tag{2.6}$$

Note the symbol used for these rotations. If a rotation by $2\pi/n$ reproduces the original configuration, the rotation is said to be a C_n rotation. A rotation by a multiple of some fundamental angle (i.e., $m2\pi/n$) is designated by a superscript C_n^m. When this multiple rotation can be expressed as a nonsuperscripted rotation of a lower order, this takes precedence. For example, C_4^2 is expressed as C_2; C_6^2 as C_3, and so on. A C_n^n (C_3^3 in the present case) would bring the molecule back to its original orientation, and consequently, is equivalent to the identity operation. In Eqs. 2.5 and 2.6 the rotation has been taken in the counterclockwise sense when looking down the Cl—C bond. The rotations could equally well have been defined in the clockwise sense. (In fact, this convention is used by many authors.) The counterclockwise rotation corresponds to the conventions of mathematicians; however, either definition is acceptable from a physical point of view. Once a convention has been chosen, it *must* be rigorously adhered to. The C_n element is called a *proper axis of rotation.*

A third type of symmetry element possessed by methyl chloride is the *plane of symmetry.* There are three of these, each defined by an H—C—Cl plane. These are symbolized by the Greek σ. In this case, a subscript v is added to indicate that the plane of symmetry is a *vertical plane,* one that contains the rotation axis. (We will later find two other types of planes of symmetry, which will be designated σ_h and σ_d.) The σ_v operations for methyl chloride are

$$\begin{matrix} H_1 \\ \diagdown \\ H_3\diagup C-Cl \\ \diagup \\ H_2 \end{matrix} \quad \xrightarrow[(H_1-C-Cl \text{ plane})]{\sigma_v} \quad \begin{matrix} H_1 \\ \diagdown \\ H_2\diagup C-Cl \\ \diagup \\ H_3 \end{matrix} \tag{2.7}$$

$$\begin{matrix} H_1 \\ \diagdown \\ H_3\diagup C-Cl \\ \diagup \\ H_2 \end{matrix} \quad \xrightarrow[(H_3-C-Cl \text{ plane})]{\sigma_v'} \quad \begin{matrix} H_2 \\ \diagdown \\ H_3\diagup C-Cl \\ \diagup \\ H_1 \end{matrix} \tag{2.8}$$

$$\begin{matrix} H_1 \\ \diagdown \\ H_3\diagup C-Cl \\ \diagup \\ H_2 \end{matrix} \quad \xrightarrow[(H_2-C-Cl \text{ plane})]{\sigma_v''} \quad \begin{matrix} H_3 \\ \diagdown \\ H_1\diagup C-Cl \\ \diagup \\ H_2 \end{matrix} \tag{2.9}$$

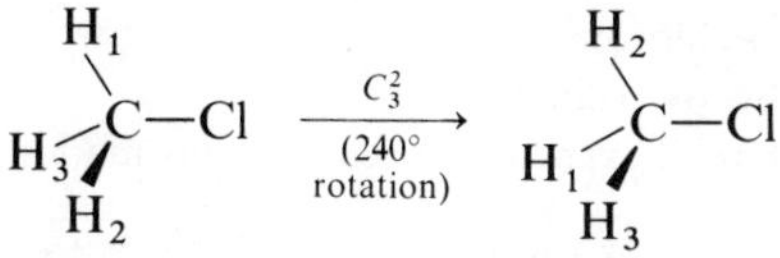

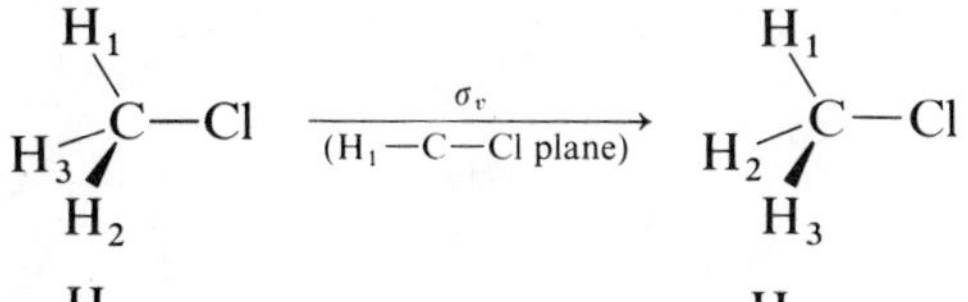

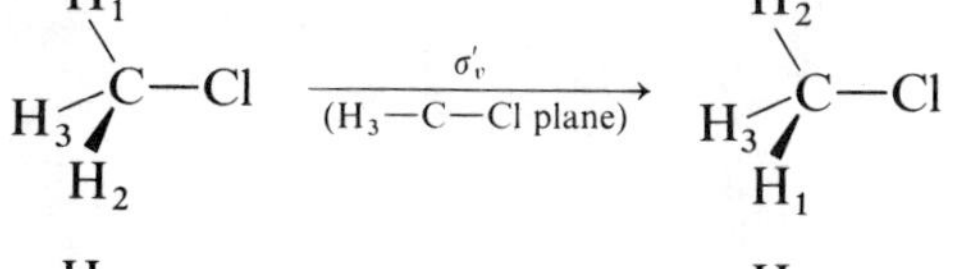

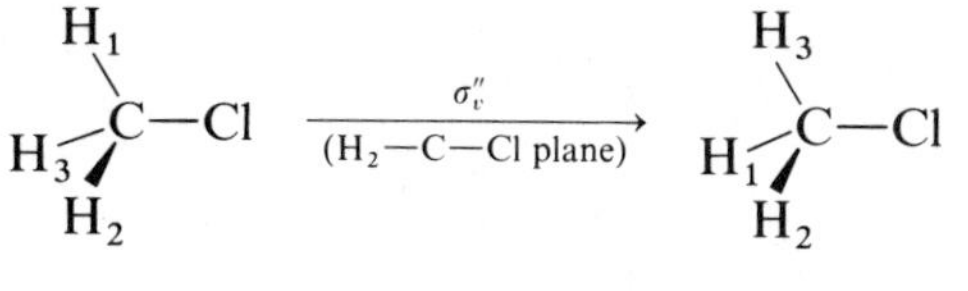

Note that the planes of symmetry for CH_3Cl all intersect on the C_3 axis. All symmetry elements for any physical object will intersect at some point. Consequently, the symmetry is usually referred to as *point symmetry* and the corresponding symmetry groups as *point groups.*

Exercise 2.2*: Find the symmetry elements possessed by the following molecules:

(a) Dichloromethane
(b) Boron trifluoride
(c) Cyclohexane (in the chair conformation)

2.4 GROUP MULTIPLICATION TABLES

The six symmetry operations that we have given, E, C_3, C_3^2, σ_v, σ_v', and σ_v'', describe all the possible symmetry operations for methyl chloride. Its symmetry group has an order of 6. These are summarized in Fig. 2.1. To verify the fact that these satisfy the group criteria, we will define a *group multiplication table.* If we lay out a square

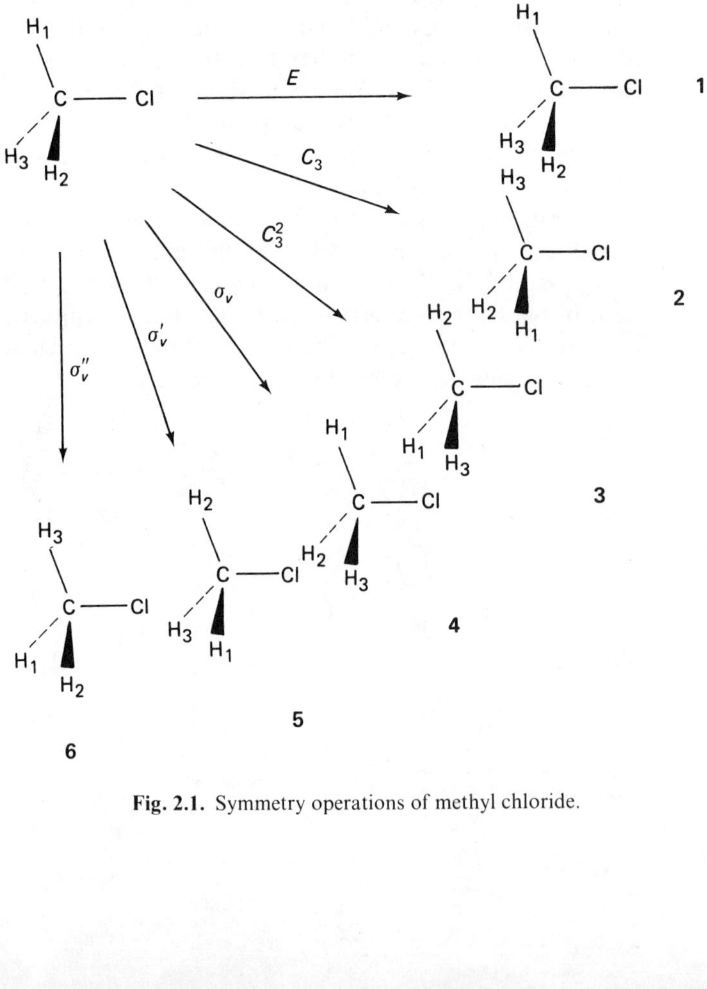

Fig. 2.1. Symmetry operations of methyl chloride.

Table 2.1. Group multiplication table for arbitrary operations

	A	B	C	$\ldots$
A	AA	AB	AC	$\ldots$
B	BA	BB	BC	$\ldots$
C	CA	CB	CC	$\ldots$
$\ldots$	$\ldots$	$\ldots$	$\ldots$	$\ldots$

array, labeling the rows and columns with the operations of the group and allowing the individual entries of the array to be the product of the corresponding operations of the group, we have a group multiplication table. This is illustrated in Table 2.1 for arbitrary operations. The order for the product is column element, row element. The group multiplication table for the symmetry operations of CH_3Cl can be constructed by reference to Fig. 2.1. The product of two operations is to be defined as the successive application of the two operations, the one to the *right* being carried out first. It must be noted that the symmetry elements always retain their original orientation and do not follow the transformations of the molecule. For example, the product $\sigma_v C_3$ involves a C_3 rotation followed by a reflection.

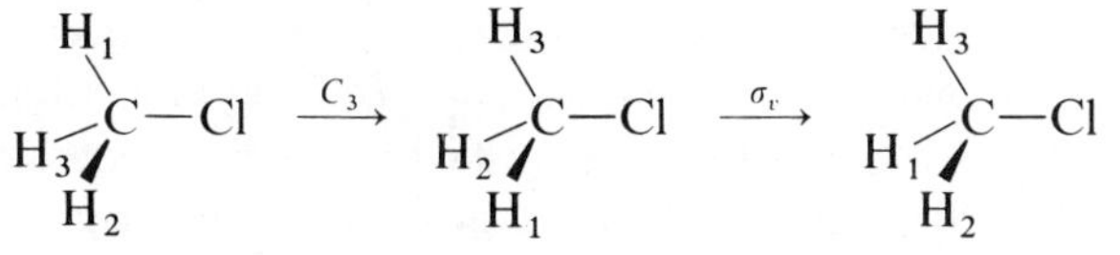

$$
\begin{array}{ccc}
\text{H}_1 & \text{H}_3 & \text{H}_3 \\
\diagdown & \diagdown & \diagdown \\
\text{H}_3 \diagup \text{C—Cl} \xrightarrow{C_3} & \text{H}_2 \diagup \text{C—Cl} \xrightarrow{\sigma_v} & \text{H}_1 \diagup \text{C—Cl} \\
\text{H}_2 & \text{H}_1 & \text{H}_2
\end{array}
\qquad (2.10)
$$

$$
\begin{array}{ccc}
\mathbf{1} & \mathbf{2} & \mathbf{6}
\end{array}
$$

Note that after the C_3, the σ_v involves a reflection in the H_3—C—Cl plane. The final result is configuration **6** of Fig. 2.1. This means that the product $\sigma_v C_3$ is equivalent to σ_v'':

$$
\sigma_v C_3 = \sigma_v'' \qquad (2.11)
$$

All the other binary products can be found similarly. The final result for the multiplication table of the symmetry operations possessed by methyl chloride is shown in Table 2.2. Note that each element of the group appears in each row and each column of the multiplication table once and only once.

Table 2.2. Multiplication table for the symmetry operations of methyl chloride (the C_{3v} point group)

	E	C_3	C_3^2	σ_v	σ_v'	σ_v''
E	E	C_3	C_3^2	σ_v	σ_v'	σ_v''
C_3	C_3	C_3^2	E	σ_v'	σ_v''	σ_v
C_3^2	C_3^2	E	C_3	σ_v''	σ_v	σ_v'
σ_v	σ_v	σ_v''	σ_v'	E	C_3^2	C_3
σ_v'	σ_v'	σ_v	σ_v''	C_3	E	C_3^2
σ_v''	σ_v''	σ_v'	σ_v	C_3^2	C_3	E

Exercise 2.3: Construct the multiplication tables for the symmetry elements of the molecules in the previous problem.

Table 2.2 can be used to verify the fact that the symmetry elements of methyl chloride satisfy the group criteria as follows:

1. *Any two elements of the group must combine to give an element that is also a member of the group.* This is verified by the fact that all the entries in the multiplication table (all the possible binary products of elements) are members of the group.

2. *The associative law of combination must be satisfied.* Consider any arbitrary triple product, say $C_3\sigma_v C_3^2$. This may be grouped in two ways, $(C_3\sigma_v)C_3^2$ or $C_3(\sigma_v C_3^2)$. The results of these products are

$$(C_3\sigma_v)C_3^2 = \sigma_v' C_3^2 = \sigma_v'' \tag{2.12a}$$

$$C_3(\sigma_v C_3^2) = C_3\sigma_v' = \sigma_v'' \tag{2.12b}$$

Similar results are obtained for any multiple product. Note, however, that this group is non-Abelian (the commutative law is not satisfied for all elements). For example, $\sigma_v C_3$ equals σ_v'', while $C_3\sigma_v$ equals σ_v'.

3. *The group must contain an element that commutes with all the other elements and leaves them unchanged.* This element is the identity element. The validity of this criterion is verified by the fact that the first row and first column of the multiplication table are equivalent to the original elements themselves.

$$EA = AE = A \tag{2.13}$$

Crudely put, this says that it does not matter whether you first do nothing to the system and then apply a symmetry operation or whether you first apply a symmetry operation and then do nothing.

4. *The reciprocal of every element in the group is also a member of the group.* This is verified by the fact that every row and every column of the multiplication table contains the identity element. For example, from the table we see that

$$C_3^2 C_3 = C_3 C_3^2 = E \tag{2.14}$$

Thus, C_3 and C_3^2 are the reciprocals of each other. The planes of symmetry are their own reciprocals.

The symmetry elements of methyl chloride are seen to satisfy the group criteria and thus to define a mathematical group. The same type of situation is achieved for the symmetry elements that describe any system. Again, groups, such as this, which define the symmetry of a single object are referred to as *point groups* because all the symmetry elements must intersect at some point. The relationships that apply to the behavior of any mathematical group must apply to symmetry groups.

2.5 GENERATORS AND SUBGROUPS

Let us consider the two elements C_3 and σ_v of the methyl chloride group (this group is referred to as the $\mathbf{C}_{3v}$ *point group*), and consider the results of successive products of these with themselves and with each other. From the multiplication table (Table 2.2) we see that

$$C_3\sigma_v = \sigma_v' \tag{2.15a}$$

$$\sigma_v C_3 = \sigma_v'' \tag{2.15b}$$

$$C_3 C_3 = C_3^2 \tag{2.15c}$$

$$\sigma_v\sigma_v = E \tag{2.15d}$$

In other words, these two elements can be used to generate all the other elements in the point group. These two elements are said to be the *generators* of the group. They are not unique. C_3^2 could have been used instead of C_3, and σ_v' or σ_v'' instead of σ_v. The complete group could not have been generated from only C_3 and C_3^2, however.

Exercise 2.4: The generators for the point groups associated with dichloromethane are C_2 and σ_v; for boron trifluoride they are C_3, a C_2 perpendicular to C_3, and σ_h, a plane of symmetry perpendicular to C_3; for cyclohexane in the chair conformation they are C_3, a C_2 perpendicular to C_3, and σ_d, a plane of symmetry along C_3 but bisecting a pair of C_2's. Verify that all the symmetry elements of these molecules can be generated from these.

The powers of C_3 form what is known as a *cyclic subgroup* of the $\mathbf{C}_{3v}$ point group. A *subgroup* is a collection of elements from a group that satisfy the group criteria within themselves. The elements E, C_3, and C_3^2 form a group (the $\mathbf{C}_3$ point group). This group is contained within the $\mathbf{C}_{3v}$ point group and is thus a subgroup of $\mathbf{C}_{3v}$. There are also three other subgroups contained within the $\mathbf{C}_{3v}$ point group. These are $\{E, \sigma_v\}$, $\{E, \sigma_v'\}$, and $\{E, \sigma_v''\}$, which actually are completely equivalent. A group is said to be *cyclic* if it contains only powers of some single element including the identity element as some power of the element. A group containing only powers of a single element must be cyclic unless it is of infinite order. All cyclic groups are Abelian.

2.6 PRODUCTS OF GROUPS

One of the operations that can be defined for groups is the product of independent groups. If the group **A** contains the n elements $\{A_1, A_2, \ldots, A_n\}$ and the group **B** the m elements $\{B_1, B_2, \ldots, B_m\}$, then the product contains all the $n \times m$ elements of the type A_iB_j. For example, the product of the groups $\{E, C_3, C_3^2\}$ and $\{E, \sigma_v\}$ is

$$\{E, C_3, C_3^2\} \times \{E, \sigma_v\} = \{EE, C_3E, C_3^2E, E\sigma_v, C_3\sigma_v, C_3^2\sigma_v\} \tag{2.16}$$

$$= \{E, C_3, C_3^2, \sigma_v, \sigma_v', \sigma_v''\} \tag{2.16a}$$

In other words, *a group may be generated by products of its independent cyclic subgroups.* All the possible point symmetry groups can be constructed from products of two or three cyclic subgroups, each subgroup arising from a different generator of the group. From the product relationship, it is obvious that *the order of a subgroup must be an integer divisor of the order of the group to which it is a subgroup* (i.e., a group of order 6 may have subgroups of order 2 and 3, or a group of order 8 may have subgroups of order 2 and 4, etc.). Notice, incidentally that the product of the two subgroups $\{E, \sigma_v\}$ and $\{E, \sigma_v'\}$ does not form a group.

$$\{E, \sigma_v\} \times \{E, \sigma_v'\} = \{E, \sigma_v, \sigma_v', C_3^2\} \tag{2.17}$$

It can be verified from Table 2.2 that $\{E, \sigma_v, \sigma_v', C_3^2\}$ does not constitute a group. The reason for this is that $\{E, \sigma_v\}$ and $\{E, \sigma_v'\}$ are not independent groups. The elements σ_v and σ_v' have a distinct meaning only when they are referred to a system that gives them a definite direction.

In Eqs. 2.16 the group $\{E, C_3, C_3^2\}$ was multiplied from the right by the group $\{E, \sigma_v\}$. If the order in the product had been reversed, the result would be

$$\{E, \sigma_v\} \times \{E, C_3, C_3^2\} = \{E, C_3, C_3^2, \sigma_v, \sigma_v'', \sigma_v'\} \tag{2.18}$$

The same elements are obtained, but their ordering is different. This is because the C_3's and the σ_v's do not commute. We shall therefore define two types of products of groups. The products of the type of Eqs. 2.16 and 2.18, where the elements do not individually commute, will be called *semidirect products* (for which we will use $\wedge$ as the product sign). Products in which all the elements of one group commute with all the elements of the other group will be referred to as *direct products* (the symbol $\times$ will be reserved for direct products). Thus, if we label the group $\{E, \sigma_v\}$ as $\mathbf{C}_s$, then we see that

$$\mathbf{C}_{3v} = \mathbf{C}_3 \wedge \mathbf{C}_s \tag{2.19}$$

The ordering in the semidirect product is significant. Consider the products of the $\mathbf{C}_3$ subgroup with σ_v. If the subgroup is multiplied from the right by σ_v, we have

$$\{E, C_3, C_3^2\}\sigma_v = \{\sigma_v, \sigma_v', \sigma_v''\} \tag{2.20a}$$

If the multiplication is from the left, we have

$$\sigma_v\{E, C_3, C_3^2\} = \{\sigma_v, \sigma_v'', \sigma_v'\} \tag{2.20b}$$

That is, the same set of elements results (such sets, which will be discussed later, are called *cosets*). The $\mathbf{C}_3$ subgroup is said to be *invariant* with respect to σ_v. It is obviously invariant with respect to E (since E commutes with all elements and leaves them unchanged). Thus, the $\mathbf{C}_3$ subgroup is invariant with respect to the elements of the $\mathbf{C}_s$ subgroup. Consider the right and left products of $\mathbf{C}_s$ with the C_3 element, however:

$$\{E, \sigma_v\}C_3 = \{C_3, \sigma_v''\} \tag{2.21a}$$

$$C_3\{E, \sigma_v\} = \{C_3, \sigma_v'\} \tag{2.21b}$$

The resulting sets are different. The same situation would result for multiplication by C_3^2. Thus, the $\mathbf{C}_s$ subgroup is not invariant with respect to the elements of the $\mathbf{C}_3$ subgroup. Such a situation always results when semidirect products are involved. One group will be invariant with respect to the elements of the other. By definition, we shall require that in writing semidirect products the invariant subgroup be listed first as in Eq. 2.19. Since in the direct product all elements of one subgroup commute with all elements of the other, the order of listing in the direct product is immaterial. This leads to the commutation relationships

$$\mathbf{A} \times \mathbf{B} = \mathbf{B} \times \mathbf{A} \tag{2.22a}$$

$$\mathbf{A} \wedge \mathbf{B} \neq \mathbf{B} \wedge \mathbf{A} \tag{2.22b}$$

In fact, if the left side of Eq. 2.22b is valid, the right side is undefined.

A third type of product, called the *weak direct product*, also exists. In the weak direct product, neither subgroup commutes with all the elements of the other. This type of product will not be important in our discussions.

Exercise 2.5*:

(a) Find the subgroups of the symmetry groups for the molecules in the previous three problems.

(b) Assign the direct and semidirect product relationships.

2.7 COSETS

Each subgroup has associated with it one or more *cosets*. The coset is defined by taking the product of the subgroup with one of the elements of the group that is not a member of the subgroup. For example, if we take the subgroup $\{E, \sigma_v\}$ from the $\mathbf{C}_{3v}$ point group, we can form cosets of this subgroup with respect to C_3, C_3^2, σ_v', and σ_v''. The results are

$$\{E, \sigma_v\}C_3 = \{C_3, \sigma_v''\} \tag{2.23a}$$

$$\{E, \sigma_v\}C_3^2 = \{C_3^2, \sigma_v'\} \tag{2.23b}$$

$$\{E, \sigma_v\}\sigma_v' = \{\sigma_v', C_3^2\} \tag{2.23c}$$

$$\{E, \sigma_v\}\sigma_v'' = \{\sigma_v'', C_3\} \tag{2.23d}$$

The coset defined here is the *right coset*. Left cosets can also be defined; however, the cosets obtained are the same as the right cosets, only their order of occurrence is changed. For example, if we ignore the ordering within the set,

$$\sigma_v'\{E, \sigma_v\} = \{\sigma_v', C_3\} = \{\sigma_v'', E\}C_3 \tag{2.24}$$

Cosets have four important properties:

1. Every element of a group appears either in the subgroup under consideration or in one of its cosets.
2. No element can be common to both a subgroup and one of its cosets.
3. No element can be common to two different cosets of the same subgroup.
4. No coset can contain the same element more than once.

Just as a group can be constructed as a product of the subgroups formed from its generators, it can also be constructed from a single subgroup and its cosets.

2.8 CONJUGATES AND CLASSES

Two elements, A and B, are said to be *conjugate* if there exists some element R such that

$$A = RBR^{-1} \tag{2.25}$$

Written in this fashion A is said to be conjugate to B with respect to R. The analogous relationship for B is

$$B = R^{-1}AR \tag{2.26}$$

Note that if A is conjugate to B with respect to R, then B is conjugate to A with respect to R^{-1}. Each set of mutually conjugate elements within a group is referred to as a *class*. A class may contain only one element (the identity element is always in a class by itself) or it may contain several elements. The conjugates of the elements of the $\mathbf{C}_{3v}$ point group can be found with the assistance of the group multiplication table (Table 2.2). For example, the conjugate of σ_v with respect to C_3 is

$$C_3\sigma_v(C_3)^{-1} = C_3\sigma_v C_3^2 = \sigma_v' C_3^2 = \sigma_v'' \tag{2.27}$$

A table of conjugates similar to the multiplication table can be constructed. For the $\mathbf{C}_{3v}$ point group this is shown in Table 2.3. The first column within the table

Table 2.3. Table of conjugates of the elements of the $\mathbf{C}_{3v}$ point group.

R \ A	E	C_3	C_3^2	σ_v	σ_v'	σ_v''	A / R^{-1}
E	E	C_3	C_3^2	σ_v	σ_v'	σ_v''	E
C_3	E	C_3	C_3^2	σ_v''	σ_v	σ_v'	C_3^2
C_3^2	E	C_3	C_3^2	σ_v'	σ_v''	σ_v	C_3
σ_v	E	C_3^2	C_3	σ_v	σ_v''	σ_v'	σ_v
σ_v'	E	C_3^2	C_3	σ_v''	σ_v'	σ_v	σ_v'
σ_v''	E	C_3^2	C_3	σ_v'	σ_v	σ_v''	σ_v''

* Each entry in the table is a triple product of the type RAR^{-1}, where the element R comes from the left labeling column, the element A from the labeling row, and the element R^{-1}, the reciprocal of R, from the right labeling column.

contains only E; thus, the single element E forms a class. The C_3 and C_3^2 columns each contain both C_3 and C_3^2, but nothing else. These two elements, then, comprise a class. Each of the three σ_v columns contain all three σ_v's and nothing else; thus, the σ_v elements constitute a class. The elements of the $\mathbf{C}_{3v}$ point group are frequently indicated only by class as $\{E, 2C_3, 3\sigma_v\}$.

Exercise 2.6: Find the classes of each symmetry group found in the previous problems.

Conjugate subgroups can be defined in a manner similar to conjugate elements. If the elements $\{A_1, A_2, \ldots, A_n\}$ form a subgroup of some group, and R is an element of the group, then the set $\{B_1, B_2, \ldots, B_n\}$, defined as

$$\{B_1, B_2, \ldots, B_n\} = R\{A_1, A_2, \ldots, A_n\}R^{-1} \tag{2.28}$$

is the conjugate of the subgroup with respect to R. The conjugate subgroup must also be a subgroup of the group. A special and important case of the conjugate subgroup is the case in which a subgroup is equal to its conjugate with respect to every element in the group:

$$R\{A_1, A_2, \ldots, A_n\}R^{-1} = \{A_1, A_2, \ldots, A_n\} \qquad \text{for all } R \tag{2.29}$$

Such subgroups are referred to as *invariant subgroups.*

2.9 MAPPINGS

It is frequently useful to represent the elements of a group by other quantities that obey the same multiplication table as the group. The original group is said to be *mapped* onto the new group, each element in the original group having an *image* in the new. There is one element in the new group for each element in the original group, although there need not be a different element in the new group for every element in the original one. If there is a different element for every element in the original group, the groups are said to be *isomorphic*; otherwise, they are *homomorphic*. Consider, for example, the mappings of the $\mathbf{C}_4$ cyclic point group shown in Table 2.4. The individual elements in these mappings all have a magnitude of unity. If the product is taken as multiplication, the unique elements of each mapping form a group. The first has an order of 1 (only one unique element), the

Table 2.4. Mappings of the $\mathbf{C}_4$ point group

$\mathbf{C}_4$	E	C_4	C_2	C_4^3
	1	1	1	1
	1	-1	1	-1
	1	i	-1	$-i$
	1	$-i$	-1	i

second an order of 2 (two unique elements) while the last two are of order 4, just as was the original group (four unique elements). Since, in the first case, four elements are mapped onto one the mapping is said to be four-to-one. In the second, the mapping is two-to-one. Both of these are homomorphic mappings. The last two afford one-to-one mappings and groups that are isomorphic to $\mathbf{C}_4$.

2.10 REPRESENTATIONS

Let us consider again the methyl chloride molecule in a three-dimensional Cartesian coordinate system as shown in Fig. 2.2. The three hydrogens are in the xy plane, with H_1 along the positive x axis. The carbon and the chlorine are on the z axis. All the symmetry operations only interchange the hydrogens within the xy plane; consequently, they can be represented by considering only this plane. If normalized vectors are drawn from the origin in the xy plane to each of the hydrogens, we have the situation in Fig. 2.3, the numbers being the x and y components of each of the vectors. Now consider the collection of two-dimensional unitary transformation matrices shown in Eqs. 2.30.

$$\mathbf{T}_1 = \begin{bmatrix} 1 & 0 \\ 0 & 1 \end{bmatrix} \tag{2.30a}$$

$$\mathbf{T}_2 = \begin{bmatrix} -1/2 & \sqrt{3}/2 \\ -\sqrt{3}/2 & -1/2 \end{bmatrix} \tag{2.30b}$$

$$\mathbf{T}_3 = \begin{bmatrix} -1/2 & -\sqrt{3}/2 \\ \sqrt{3}/2 & -1/2 \end{bmatrix} \tag{2.30c}$$

$$\mathbf{T}_4 = \begin{bmatrix} 1 & 0 \\ 0 & -1 \end{bmatrix} \tag{2.30d}$$

$$\mathbf{T}_5 = \begin{bmatrix} -1/2 & \sqrt{3}/2 \\ \sqrt{3}/2 & 1/2 \end{bmatrix} \tag{2.30e}$$

$$\mathbf{T}_6 = \begin{bmatrix} -1/2 & -\sqrt{3}/2 \\ -\sqrt{3}/2 & 1/2 \end{bmatrix} \tag{2.30f}$$

Note that cos 120° and cos 240° equal $-1/2$, while sin 120° equals $\sqrt{3}/2$ and sin 240° equals $-\sqrt{3}/2$. Thus, Eqs. 2.30b and 2.30c are the two-dimensional rotation matrices for 120° and 240° rotations, respectively.

These matrices transform the vectors of Fig. 2.3 exactly as the symmetry operations transform the hydrogen atoms of the methyl chloride molecule. For

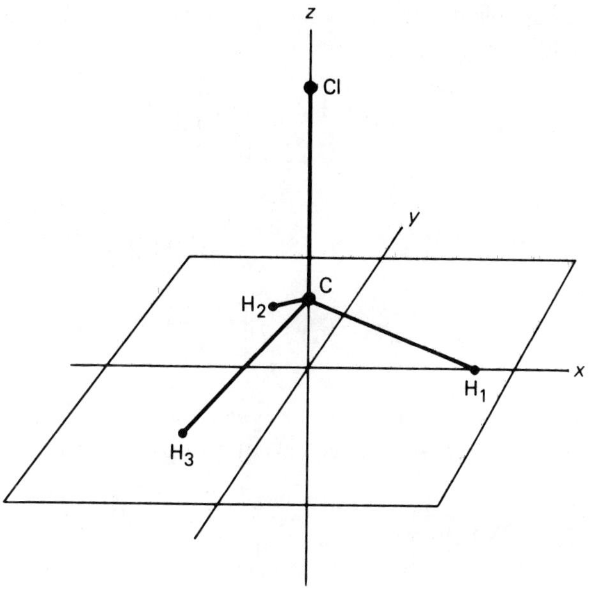

Fig. 2.2. Methyl chloride in a three-dimensional Cartesian coordinate system.

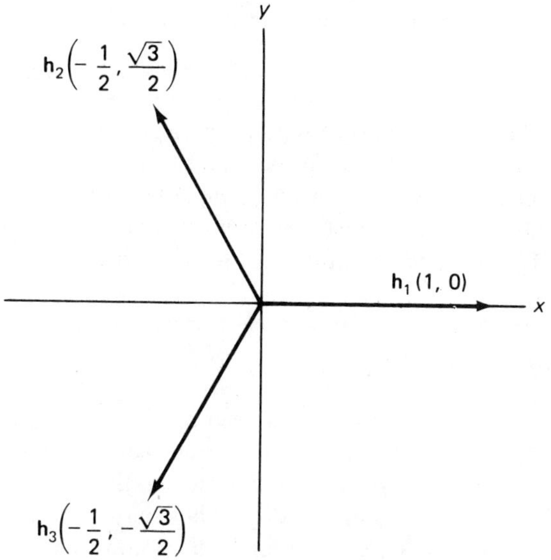

Fig. 2.3. Projection of methyl chloride onto the *xy* plane with normalized vectors from the origin to each hydrogen.

example, consider $\mathbf{T}_5$, which corresponds to σ_v'. Operating on the three vectors yields

$$\mathbf{h}_1\mathbf{T}_5 = (1 \quad 0)\begin{bmatrix} -1/2 & \sqrt{3}/2 \\ \sqrt{3}/2 & 1/2 \end{bmatrix} = (-1/2 \quad \sqrt{3}/2) = \mathbf{h}_2 \tag{2.31a}$$

$$\mathbf{h}_2\mathbf{T}_5 = (-1/2 \quad \sqrt{3}/2)\begin{bmatrix} -1/2 & \sqrt{3}/2 \\ \sqrt{3}/2 & 1/2 \end{bmatrix} = (1 \quad 0) = \mathbf{h}_1 \tag{2.31b}$$

$$\mathbf{h}_3\mathbf{T}_5 = (-1/2 \quad -\sqrt{3}/2)\begin{bmatrix} -1/2 & \sqrt{3}/2 \\ \sqrt{3}/2 & 1/2 \end{bmatrix} = (-1/2 \quad -\sqrt{3}/2) = \mathbf{h}_3 \tag{2.31c}$$

The products of the matrices yield a multiplication table which is exactly like that of the elements of the $\mathbf{C}_{3v}$ point group. For example, the product $\mathbf{T}_2\mathbf{T}_4$ is

$$\mathbf{T}_2\mathbf{T}_4 = \begin{bmatrix} -1/2 & \sqrt{3}/2 \\ -\sqrt{3}/2 & -1/2 \end{bmatrix}\begin{bmatrix} 1 & 0 \\ 0 & -1 \end{bmatrix} = \begin{bmatrix} -1/2 & -\sqrt{3}/2 \\ -\sqrt{3}/2 & 1/2 \end{bmatrix} = \mathbf{T}_6 \tag{2.32}$$

but $\mathbf{T}_2$ corresponds to C_3, $\mathbf{T}_4$ to σ_v, and $\mathbf{T}_6$ to σ_v''; thus, remembering the contravariant behavior of operators and their associated matrices,

$$\mathbf{h}_i\mathbf{T}_2\mathbf{T}_4 = \sigma_v C_3 \mathbf{h}_i \tag{2.33}$$

This is completely analogous to the product

$$\sigma_v C_3 = \sigma_v'' \tag{2.34}$$

The matrices $\mathbf{T}_1$ through $\mathbf{T}_6$ form a group that is isomorphic to the $\mathbf{C}_{3v}$ point group. If a set of matrices can be found which form a group that obeys the group multiplication table for a given group, the matrices are said to form a *matrix representation* (or usually, just *representation*) of that group. The set of matrices $\mathbf{T}_1$ through $\mathbf{T}_6$ form a representation of the $\mathbf{C}_{3v}$ group.

Exercise 2.7*: Find two-dimensional unitary matrices that represent the symmetry operations of dichloromethane.

A group of matrices need not be isomorphic with the group of which it is a representation. Neither must the matrices have a specific dimensionality. They may be one-dimensional (i.e., scalars), two-dimensional, three-dimensional, or of even higher dimensionality. They may be real, complex, or imaginary. The only requirements are that they be homomorphic with the group under consideration and obey the group multiplication table. There are, in fact, an infinite number of possible representations for a given group. We shall return to this question after we consider the symmetry groups and their generators in more detail.

PROBLEMS

1. Find all symmetry operations for the following familiar objects:

(a) Brick

(b) Snowflake

(c) Wooden pencil (neglecting the markings on it)

(d) Book (neglecting all writing)

(e) Human body

(f) Starfish

(g) Fan blade

2. Construct the group multiplication tables for the symmetry operations of the objects in Problem 1.

3. Construct the tables of conjugates for the operations of the objects in Problem 1 and separate the operations into classes.

4. Find all subgroups of the groups from Problem 1. Express each group as a product of the maximum number of independent subgroups.

BIBLIOGRAPHY

ALTMANN, S. L., *Induced Representations in Crystals and Molecules*, Academic Press, Inc., New York, 1977.

CHESTNUT, D. B., *Finite Groups and Quantum Chemistry*, John Wiley & Sons, Inc., New York, 1974.

COTTON, F. A., *Chemical Applications of Group Theory*, 2nd ed., John Wiley & Sons, Inc., New York, 1971.

HALL, L. H., *Group Theory and Symmetry in Chemistry*, McGraw-Hill Book Company, New York, 1969.

JAFFÉ, H. H., AND M. ORCHIN, *Symmetry in Chemistry*, John Wiley & Sons, Inc., New York, 1965.

MCWEENY, R., *Symmetry*, Macmillan Publishing Co., Inc., New York, 1963.

3

Point Symmetry

3.1 THE FIVE TYPES OF POINT-SYMMETRY ELEMENTS

There are five different types of symmetry elements that an isolated object may possess. We have already used three of these: the identity, the rotation axis, C_n (more correctly, the *proper axis of rotation*), and the plane of symmetry, σ. The identity must always be included to complete the requirements for a group. Many systems possess more than one proper axis of symmetry. If this is the case, the one of the highest order is referred to as the *principal axis*. If there is more than one of the same order, one of these must arbitrarily be chosen as the principal axis. This choice is usually made on the basis of a unique direction or property that is to be emphasized.

The planes of symmetry are divided into three types on the basis of their relationship to the principal axis and any subsidiary axes. These are the *vertical plane of symmetry*, σ_v, which contains the principal axis; the *dihedral plane of symmetry*; σ_d, which also contains the principal axis and in addition bisects pairs of twofold axes which are perpendicular to the principal axis or, in certain cases, other symmetry elements; and the *horizontal plane of symmetry*, σ_h, which is perpendicular to the principal axis.

The two symmetry elements that we have not yet discussed are the *improper axis of rotation*, S_n, and the *point of inversion*, *i*. The improper axis can be represented by the product

$$S_n = \sigma_h C_n \tag{3.1}$$

even though the σ_h and C_n need not themselves be present. For example, ethane, in its staggered conformation, possesses an S_6 element:

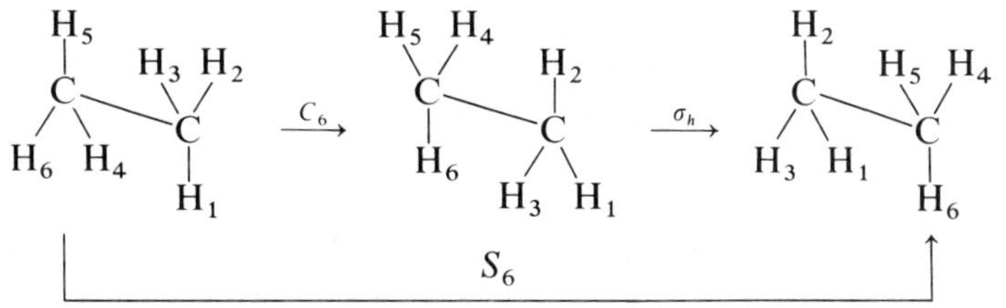

(3.2)

Note that C_6 and σ_h are *not* symmetry elements for staggered ethane.

The point of inversion is just what the name implies. If the origin of a Cartesian coordinate system is placed on the point of inversion, then for every point (x, y, z) in the system there must be a symmetry related point at $(-x, -y, -z)$. The staggered ethane of Eq. 3.2 also possesses this element. Note that the point of inversion is completely equivalent to an S_2 element. Thus, by virtue of Eq. 3.1, all the symmetry operations can be generated from rotation axes and planes of symmetry. Even though five types of symmetry elements are commonly employed in discussions of symmetry, there is actually redundancy in these. The identity is equivalent to a C_1, the plane of symmetry to an S_1, and the point of inversion to an S_2.

3.2 GENERATORS AND POINT GROUPS

As has been mentioned previously, the symmetry elements of any point group can be produced from its generators. Any of the four symmetry elements can be used as generators, either alone or in combination. At most, three of these are sufficient to describe the point symmetry of any system. We have already seen, for example, that C_3 and σ_v are sufficient to describe the $\mathbf{C}_{3v}$ point group. The process of systematically classifying systems into their proper point groups can be carried out by finding the possible generators that are present.

If only one symmetry element, other than the identity, is present, that element defines the point symmetry. The point group that contains only a plane of symmetry is referred to as the $\mathbf{C}_s$ or $\mathbf{S}_1$ point group, and that with only a point of inversion is the $\mathbf{C}_i$ or $\mathbf{S}_2$ point group. All other point groups contain one or more rotation axes. Most of these are frequently grouped together and are referred to as the *axial point groups.* (Actually, the $\mathbf{C}_s$ and $\mathbf{C}_i$ point groups can be considered as special cases of the axial point groups.) The exceptions are systems having the symmetry of a regular polyhedron, such as a tetrahedron, an octahedron, and so on. The point groups that have a single proper rotation axis as the only generating element are labeled by that axis (i.e., $\mathbf{C}_1$, $\mathbf{C}_2$, $\mathbf{C}_3$, etc.). The point group containing only the identity element is considered a special case of this, since C_1 equals E.

The point groups that can be generated by using only an improper axis of rotation are labeled $\mathbf{S}_n$. These are unique only for even values of n. When n assumes an odd value, additional generators are present and the system can be classified in a point group of higher symmetry. Every even-order improper axis of order n has a proper axis of order $n/2$ associated with it. (The S_2 element is equivalent to the point of inversion; consequently, the $\mathbf{C}_i$ point group is frequently designated as the $\mathbf{S}_2$ point group.)

All the point groups other than $\mathbf{C}_i$ (or $\mathbf{S}_2$), $\mathbf{C}_s$, $\mathbf{C}_n$, and $\mathbf{S}_n$ require more than one generating element. For the axial point groups, they are based upon the $\mathbf{C}_n$ groups that appear as subgroups within the point groups. The symmetry elements of these higher symmetry groups may be determined by finding the coset of the subgroup corresponding to the principal axis with respect to the additional generator if only one additional generator is required. If two additional generators are required, the coset of the cyclic subgroup is first taken with respect to one of the additional generators to give an expanded subgroup of the overall point group; then the coset of this expanded subgroup with respect to the final generator is determined to give the entire group. For example, $\mathbf{D}_{3d}$ can be generated by taking the coset of the cyclic subgroup $\mathbf{C}_3$ with respect to a C_2 to obtain the larger subgroup $\mathbf{D}_3$:

$$\{E, C_3, C_3^2\}C_2 = \{C_2, C_2', C_2''\} \tag{3.3a}$$

$$\mathbf{D}_3 = \{E, 2C_3, 3C_2\} \tag{3.3b}$$

and then by taking the coset of $\mathbf{D}_3$ with respect to i:

$$\{E, 2C_3, 3C_2\}i = \{i, 2S_3, 3\sigma_d\} \tag{3.4a}$$

$$\mathbf{D}_{3d} = \{E, 2C_3, 3C_2, i, 2S_3, 3\sigma_d\} \tag{3.4b}$$

Systems that have only one proper axis of rotation can have no more than one additional generator. This can only be a symmetry plane. This plane may either contain the proper axis (σ_v) or it may be perpendicular to it (σ_h). The two resulting types of point groups are designated $\mathbf{C}_{nv}$ or $\mathbf{C}_{nh}$, respectively. (Note that the $\mathbf{C}_s$ group is equivalent to $\mathbf{C}_{1h}$.) The axial point groups having more than one proper axis can have only C_2 axes as the additional axes. These must be perpendicular to the principal axis. One of these C_2 axes may be taken as a second generator to be used along with the principal axis. Axial point groups having a C_n generator and a C_2 generator perpendicular to C_n are designated $\mathbf{D}_n$ groups. The $\mathbf{D}_n$ groups can have a plane of symmetry as an additional generator. These can again either contain the principal axis or be perpendicular to it. The plane of symmetry perpendicular to the principal axis is again a σ_h. Those containing the principal axis must bisect pairs of the C_2's and are designated σ_d. The $\mathbf{D}$ groups containing these are designated $\mathbf{D}_{nh}$ and $\mathbf{D}_{nd}$, respectively.

Tetrahedra and octahedra can conveniently be constructed from cubes, the tetrahedron by drawing a set of planes through face diagonals (Fig. 3.1), and the octahedron by drawing the planes defined by the sets of three points in the center

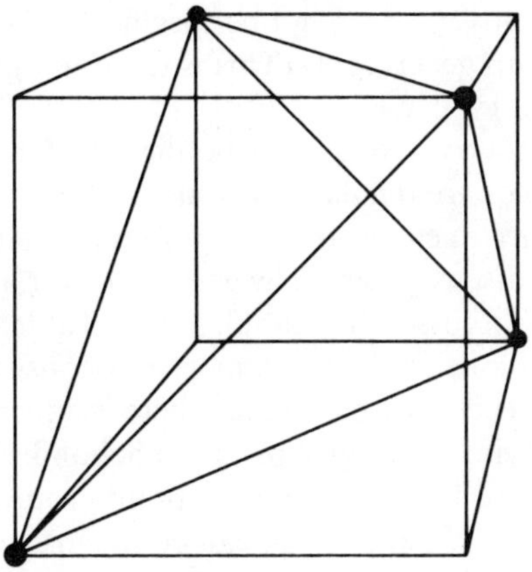

Fig. 3.1. Construction of a tetrahedron within a cube.

of any three faces of the cube (Fig. 3.2). For this reason, these symmetry groups are frequently referred to as the cubic groups.

The basic generators for the cubic point groups are a C_3 axis along a body diagonal and a C_2 axis through the center of one pair of opposed faces of the cube. (Note that these are not mutually perpendicular.) These are the only generators possessed by the basic tetrahedral group, **T**. The $\mathbf{T}_d$ point group adds an S_4 generator coincident with the C_2 axis. (Note that since $S_4^2 = C_2$, the two generators C_3 and S_4 are thus sufficient to describe the $\mathbf{T}_d$ point group.) This is the point group of tetrahedral molecules such as CH_4. The $\mathbf{T}_h$ point group has the generators $\{C_3, C_2, i\}$.

The octahedral point groups are again built up from the basic tetrahedral group. The group **0** adds a C_4 coincident with the C_2 of **T** (again, C_4^2 equals C_2;

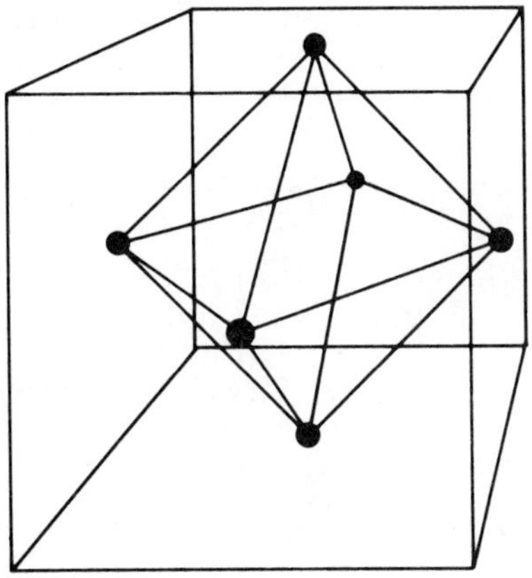

Fig. 3.2. Construction of an octahedron within a cube.

consequently, C_2 need not be specified). The group $\mathbf{O}_h$ adds a point of inversion to the $\mathbf{O}$ group generators. (This is the point group of octahedral complexes such as $[Co(CN)_6]^{3-}$.)

Symmetry groups can be derived for systems based on regular polyhedra whose faces are regular polygons having more than four sides. These are of little importance in chemistry, except for certain polyhedral boranes; consequently, we shall not discuss them. The generators for all of the various types of point groups we have discussed are tabulated in Table 3.1. The procedure for classifying a system according to its point group consists of systematically searching out its possible generating elements. There is a hierarchy in searching out the generators for classifying point groups in the Schönflies notation. This is given in Table 3.2.

The product structure of a point group is basically the same as the generator structure. For example, $\mathbf{O}_h$ can be constructed as the product $\mathbf{C}_3 \wedge \mathbf{C}_4 \times \mathbf{C}_i$. The generator structure, however, does not indicate whether the products are direct or semidirect. Consequently, isomorphisms cannot be determined from the generators alone.

Let us now consider the construction of the symmetry elements of a group from its generators. Let us choose $\mathbf{D}_{3d}$. The first generator is the C_3 element that forms the cyclic $\mathbf{C}_3$ subgroup with elements $\{E, C_3, C_3^2\}$. The second generator is C_2. The coset with respect to this is a set of $3C_2$'s, each rotated 120° from the others. This yields $\mathbf{D}_3$ as the enlarged subgroup $\{E, 2C_3, 3C_2\}$. The final generator is the σ_d. The coset with respect to σ_d contains the product of the $\mathbf{C}_3$ cyclic subgroup with σ_d, leading to three σ_d's at 120° from each other, and the product of the C_2's with σ_d. The three elements arising from this last product are somewhat

Table 3.1. Generators for the various point groups

Group	Generators	Remarks
$\mathbf{C}_n$	$\{C_n\}$	The group of order 1 for systems of no symmetry is $\mathbf{C}_1$
$\mathbf{S}_n$	$\{S_n\}$	The group $\mathbf{C}_i$ is equivalent to, and is sometimes designated, $\mathbf{S}_2$
$\mathbf{C}_{nv}$	$\{C_n, \sigma_v\}$	
$\mathbf{C}_{nh}$	$\{C_n, \sigma_h\}$	The group $\mathbf{C}_s$ is equivalent to, and sometimes designated, $\mathbf{C}_{1h}$
$\mathbf{D}_n$	$\{C_n, C_2\}$	
$\mathbf{D}_{nd}$	$\{C_n, C_2, \sigma_d\}$	
$\mathbf{D}_{nh}$	$\{C_n, C_2, \sigma_h\}$	
$\mathbf{T}$	$\{C_2^z, C_3^{xyz}\}$	This is the basic subgroup appearing in all the cubic groups
$\mathbf{T}_d$	$\{S_4^z, C_3^{xyz}\}$	
$\mathbf{T}_h$	$\{C_2^z, C_3^{xyz}, i\}$	
$\mathbf{O}$	$\{C_4^z, C_3^{xyz}\}$	
$\mathbf{O}_h$	$\{C_4^z, C_3^{xyz}, i\}$	This group contains the full symmetry of the cube

Table 3.2. Hierarchy in generators for assigning finite point groups

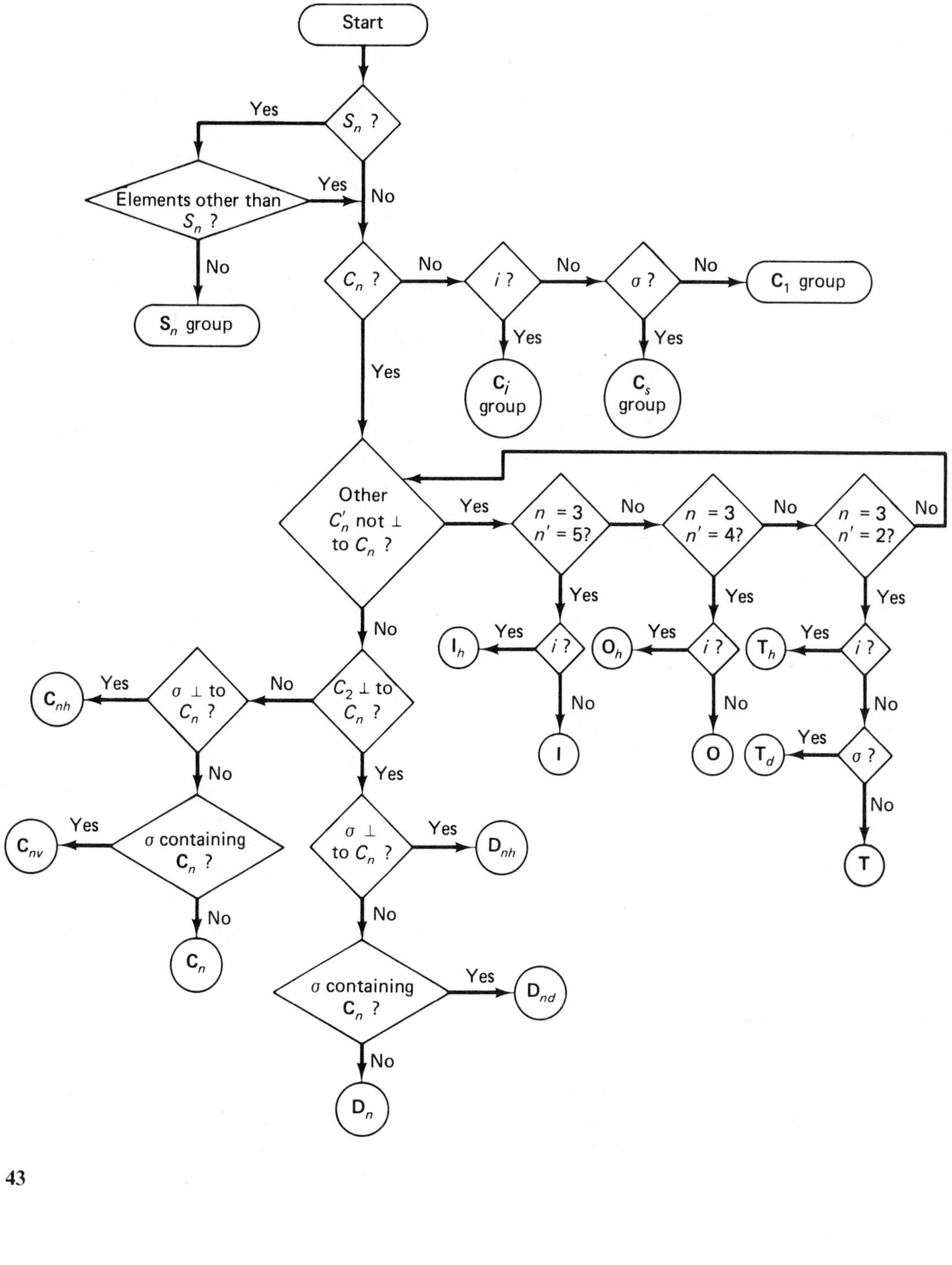

difficult to visualize directly. Consider the following example:

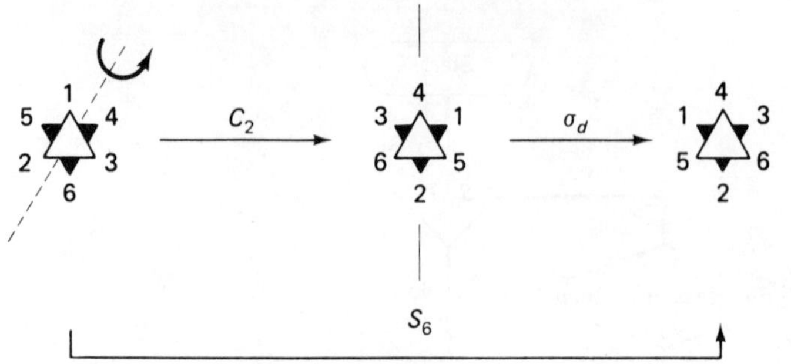

(3.5)

The net result is that the figure is rotated 60° in a counterclockwise fashion and reflected through the horizontal plane, an S_6 operation. Thus, the three elements obtained from the product of the C_2's with σ_d are S_6, S_6^3 (or S_2 or *i*), and S_6^5. This yields for the $\mathbf{D}_{3d}$ group the elements $\{E, 2C_3, 3C_2, 3\sigma_d, \mathrm{i}, 2S_6\}$.

Exercise 3.1: Find all the symmetry elements of the following groups: $\mathbf{C}_{4v}$, $\mathbf{D}_5$, $\mathbf{D}_{4d}$, $\mathbf{D}_{5h}$. Illustrate one element of each class by a suitable drawing.

3.3 PROJECTION DIAGRAMS

In order to visualize the construction of the symmetry elements from the appropriate generators, we will use *projection diagrams* representing the various possible axial point groups for *n* through 6, as shown in Fig. 3.3. The principal axis is indicated by a geometrical figure having the proper rotational symmetry and is assumed to be perpendicular to the plane of the paper. An improper axis, if present, is coincident with the principal axis. The plane of the paper also contains the σ_h if it is present. The other generators are illustrated in the figure: twofold axes by dashed lines and vertical planes by solid lines. If the C_2's and σ's are coincident, half of the line is drawn solid and half dashed. The first cross in a figure represents any arbitrary point in the system. The other crosses and circles are symmetry-related points, the circles representing points below the plane of the paper. The point group and its generators are indicated with each structure.

3.4 SCHÖNFLIES AND INTERNATIONAL NOTATION

The notation we have been using for the symmetry elements and for the point groups is referred to as the *Schönflies notation.* This is the notation used almost exclusively by spectroscopists and theoreticians. There is an alternative system of notation used by crystallographers, referred to as the *Hermann–Mauguin* or

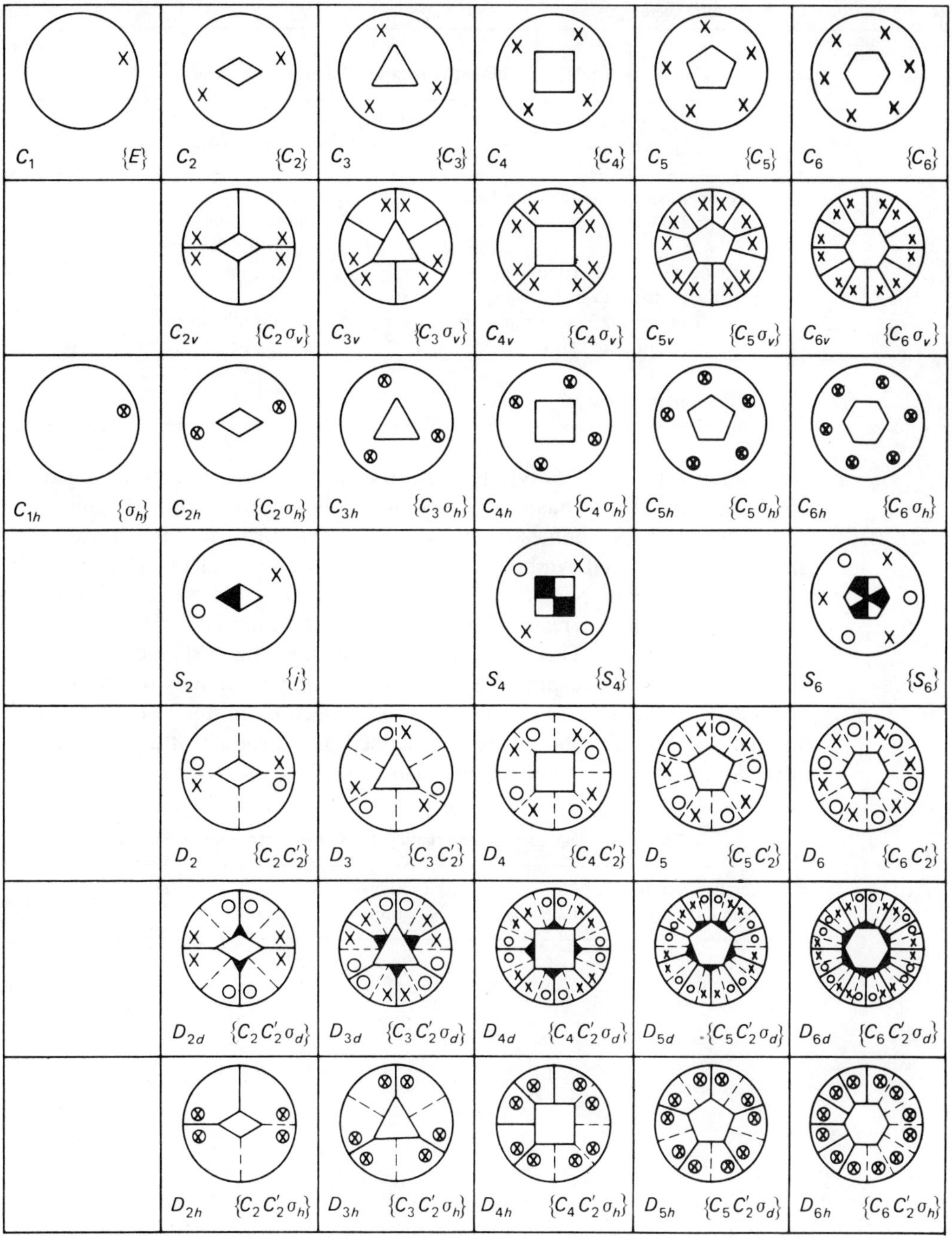

Fig. 3.3. Projection diagrams for the axial groups with principal-axis orders of six or less. All of these except those with a principal-axis order of five, $\mathbf{D}_{4d}$ and $\mathbf{D}_{6d}$, are found in space groups (see Chapter 4). Planes of symmetry are indicated by solid lines; twofold axes in the plane of the paper by dashed lines. Crosses represent points above the plane of the paper; circles, points below the plane.

Table 3.3. Alternative notations for symmetry elements

Element	Schönflies Notation	International Notation
Proper axis of rotation of order n	C_n	n
Improper axis of rotation of order $p = 2n$	S_p	$\bar{n}$ if n is odd, $\bar{p}$ if n is even (called *inversion axis*)
Plane of symmetry containing the principal axis	σ_v or σ_d	m (for mirror)
Plane of symmetry perpendicular to the principal axis	σ_h	$1/m$ (both types of mirror planes can be referred to any proper axis)
Point of inversion	i	$\bar{1}$

international system. This system names a symmetry group by listing the generators for the group. It also has a provision for including translational symmetry elements, which the Schönflies system, in its simplest form, does not have. Table 3.3 lists the international symbols for the various symmetry elements along with the Schönflies notation. Note that the rotation order for an improper axis (Schönflies notation) and the corresponding element in the international notation is not necessarily the same. This is because the elements are defined differently in the two conventions. We have previously defined the improper axis (according to the Schönflies convention) as a rotation and reflection combination. In the international convention, the element is defined as a product of a rotation and an inversion, and is designated an *inversion axis*.

Table 3.4. Schönflies and international notation for the axial point groups

Schönflies Notation and Generators	Example	International Notation	Example	
$\mathbf{C}_n\{C_n\}$	$\mathbf{C}_5$	n	5	
$\mathbf{S}_p\{S_p\}$	$\mathbf{S}_4$	$\bar{n}$ or $\bar{p}$	$\bar{4}$	$\bar{n}$ if n is odd, $\bar{p}$ if n is even ($p = 2n$)
	$\mathbf{S}_6$		$\bar{3}$	$\mathbf{C}_i$ (or $\mathbf{S}_2$) is $\bar{2}$, $\mathbf{C}_s$ is $\bar{1}$ or m
$\mathbf{C}_{nv}\{C_n, \sigma_v\}$	$\mathbf{C}_{3v}$	nm	$3m$	$\mathbf{C}_{2v}$ is more commonly represented as mm or $2mm$
$\mathbf{C}_{nh}\{C_n, \sigma_h\}$	$\mathbf{C}_{5h}$	n/m	5/m	
$\mathbf{D}_n\{C_n, C_2'\}$	$\mathbf{D}_4$	n_2	4_2	
$\mathbf{D}_{nd}\{C_n, C_2', \sigma_d\}$	$\mathbf{D}_{3d}$	$\bar{p}\ 2m$	$\bar{3}\ 2m$	Where $\bar{p}$ is the appropriate improper axis
$\mathbf{D}_{nh}\{C_n, C_2', \sigma_h\}$	$\mathbf{D}_{6h}$	$n/m\ 2/m\ 2/m$ or $(n/m)\ mm$	$6/m\ 2/m\ 2/m$ or $(6/m)\ mm$	$\mathbf{D}_{6h}$ is usually expressed $6/mmm$

Table 3.4 lists the types of axial point groups in Schönflies and international notation. Frequently, listing the generators overdetermines the point group within the conventions of the international notation. In these cases (e.g., $(6/m)mm$ for $\mathbf{D}_{6h}$), an abbreviated notation, giving only the minimum required information ($6/mmm$ for $\mathbf{D}_{6h}$), is used.

3.5 MATRIX REPRESENTATIONS OF THE GENERATORS

We have previously used two-dimensional matrices to represent the symmetry operations in the $\mathbf{C}_{3v}$ point group. Three-dimensional matrices representing the possible generators in a Cartesian coordinate system are relatively easy to construct. If the z axis is chosen as the principal axis for the axial point groups, the matrix representing a proper rotation $\mathbf{R}(C_n)$ is

$$\mathbf{R}(C_n) = \begin{bmatrix} \cos 2\pi/n & +\sin 2\pi/n & 0 \\ -\sin 2\pi/n & \cos 2\pi/n & 0 \\ 0 & 0 & 1 \end{bmatrix} \tag{3.6}$$

while that for an improper rotation is

$$\mathbf{R}(S_n) = \begin{bmatrix} \cos 2\pi/n & +\sin 2\pi/n & 0 \\ -\sin 2\pi/n & \cos 2\pi/n & 0 \\ 0 & 0 & -1 \end{bmatrix} \tag{3.7}$$

The matrix for a σ_h (reflection in the xy plane) is

$$\mathbf{R}(\sigma_h) = \begin{bmatrix} 1 & 0 & 0 \\ 0 & 1 & 0 \\ 0 & 0 & -1 \end{bmatrix} \tag{3.8}$$

If the xz plane is chosen for the σ_v generator, the matrix is

$$\mathbf{R}(\sigma_v) = \begin{bmatrix} 1 & 0 & 0 \\ 0 & -1 & 0 \\ 0 & 0 & 1 \end{bmatrix} \tag{3.9}$$

A twofold axis perpendicular to the principal axis and lying along the x axis would yield

$$\mathbf{R}(C_2^x) = \begin{bmatrix} 1 & 0 & 0 \\ 0 & -1 & 0 \\ 0 & 0 & -1 \end{bmatrix} \tag{3.10}$$

Since σ_d's bisect pairs of twofold axes and since such pairs of twofold axes make angles of $2\pi/n$ with each other, a σ_d generator can be represented as a plane rotated by π/n from the x axis:

$$\mathbf{R}(\sigma_d) = \begin{bmatrix} \cos \pi/n & \sin \pi/n & 0 \\ \sin \pi/n & -\cos \pi/n & 0 \\ 0 & 0 & 1 \end{bmatrix} \tag{3.11}$$

For the point of inversion, the matrix is

$$\mathbf{R}(i) = \begin{bmatrix} -1 & 0 & 0 \\ 0 & -1 & 0 \\ 0 & 0 & -1 \end{bmatrix} \tag{3.12}$$

If the cubic point groups are to be considered, the matrix $\mathbf{R}(C_3^{xyz})$ is needed:

$$\mathbf{R}(C_3^{xyz}) = \begin{bmatrix} 0 & 0 & 1 \\ 1 & 0 & 0 \\ 0 & 1 & 0 \end{bmatrix} \tag{3.13}$$

These matrices are sufficient to generate all the operations of any of the point groups we have discussed. Notice that the *trace* (the sum of the diagonal elements) of each of these matrices can be expressed as $\pm 1 + 2 \cos \theta$, where θ is the angle of rotation. This trace is independent of the choice of the rotation axis.

Exercise 3.2*:

(a) Generate the matrices corresponding to all the symmetry operations of each of the following point groups: $\mathbf{C}_6$, $\mathbf{D}_{2h}$, $\mathbf{T}$.

(b) Find the result of operating on the vector (1 1 1) by each of the symmetry operations from each of these point groups.

3.6 CONTINUOUS POINT GROUPS

Linear molecules have cylindrical symmetry; consequently, a rotation of any arbitrary angle about the molecular axis produces a configuration identical to the starting configuration. There are an infinite number of arbitrary angles; consequently, this rotational element must be C_∞. [This is more commonly denoted $C(\phi)$.] The presence of an infinite-fold rotational axis in a physical object requires the coexistence of an infinite number of σ_v's. This can be visualized from examination of Fig. 3.4. The three arbitrary points A, B, and C would be transformed to A', B', and C' by the indicated σ_v. Point A could also be transformed to A' by rotation by the angle α, point B to B' by β, and C to C' by γ. Since all arbitrary angles are symmetry elements of the C_∞ set, these three particular angles must be members of the set. Consequently, there must be a point equivalent to A at A', one equivalent to B at B', and one equivalent to C at C' (in actual fact, all points on a

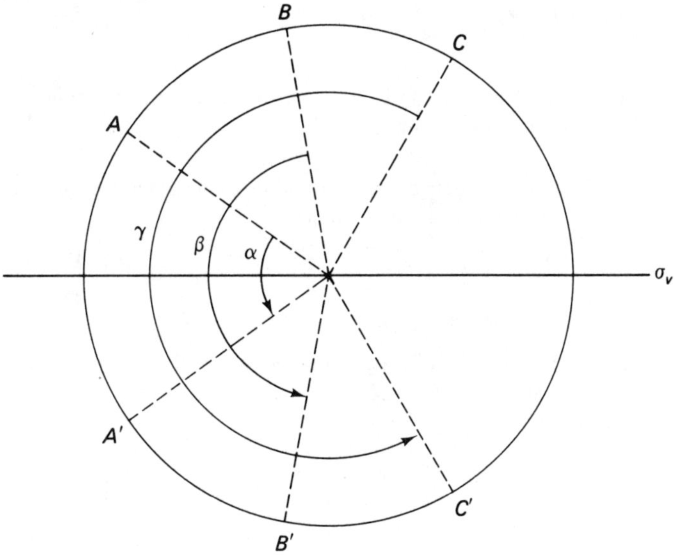

Fig. 3.4. Graphic representation of the fact that a C_∞ must be accompanied by an infinite number of σ_v's (see the text).

circle of a given radius must be equivalent). Consequently, the indicated σ_v must be a symmetry element. Since this particular σ_v is completely arbitrary, there must be an infinite number of σ_v's.

Since an infinite number of σ_v's must coexist with the $C(\phi)$, the minimum symmetry that an object with cylindrical symmetry can have is $\mathbf{C}_{\infty v}$. This is the symmetry possessed by heteronuclear diatomic molecules and other linear molecules without a center of symmetry.

The $\mathbf{C}_{\infty v}$ point group possesses the two generators $C(\phi)$ and σ_v. An additional generator can be added to give a higher symmetry. If a horizontal plane of symmetry (a σ_h) is added, the resulting point group is $\mathbf{D}_{\infty h}$. [The presence of an infinite number of C_2 axes is required by the presence of the $C(\phi)$ and the σ_h.] All homonuclear diatomic molecules and all other linear molecules with a center of symmetry have $\mathbf{D}_{\infty h}$ symmetry.

The highest symmetry that a three-dimensional system can possess is spherical symmetry. Such systems are transformed into equivalent configurations by any arbitrary rotation about any axis passing through the center of the system. There can, of course, be an infinite number of such axes. However, all of these can be resolved into components along three mutually perpendicular axes. These three mutually perpendicular axes can be considered to be the generators for the point group. This point group is referred to as the $\mathbf{R}(3)$ point group. All other point groups are subgroups of the $\mathbf{R}(3)$ point group, or the $\mathbf{R}_h(3)$ point group, the $\mathbf{R}(3)$ group with inversion (see Section 6.2).

PROBLEMS

1. Assign Schönflies and international notation to the point groups of all the objects from Problem 1 in Chapter 2.

2. Generate the matrices corresponding to the generators of the following point groups (within a Cartesian coordinate system):

(a) $\mathbf{C}_{3v}$ (b) $\mathbf{D}_3$

(c) $\mathbf{D}_{3h}$ (d) $\mathbf{D}_{3d}$

3. Use the matrices of the generators from Problem 2 to produce the matrices of all the operations of

(a) $\mathbf{C}_{3v}$ (b) $\mathbf{D}_3$

(c) $\mathbf{D}_{3h}$ (d) $\mathbf{D}_{3d}$

BIBLIOGRAPHY

BERNAL, I., W. C. HAMILTON, AND J. S. RICCI, *Symmetry*, W. H. Freeman and Company, San Francisco, 1972. Contains a set of stereoscopic drawings illustrating the 32 crystallographic point groups.

CHESTNUT, D. B., *Finite Groups and Quantum Chemistry*, John Wiley & Sons, Inc., New York, 1974.

COTTON, F. A., *Chemical Applications of Group Theory*, 2nd ed., John Wiley & Sons, Inc., New York, 1971.

HALL, L. H., *Group Theory and Symmetry in Chemistry*, McGraw-Hill Book Company, New York, 1969.

HEINE, V., *Group Theory in Quantum Mechanics*, Pergamon Press, Inc., New York, 1960.

HOCHSTRASSER, R. M., *Molecular Aspects of Symmetry*, W. A. Benjamin, Inc., Menlo Park, Calif., 1966.

MCWEENY, R., *Symmetry*, Macmillan Publishing Co., Inc., New York, 1963.

4

Space Symmetry

4.1 TRANSLATIONAL SYMMETRY

All the symmetry elements that we have thus far discussed are for point symmetry (i.e., there is at least one point in the system which is not affected by any of the operations). If translational operations are allowed, the system can no longer be described by point symmetry. The symmetry groups that contain translational elements are referred to as *space groups*. These are the groups that are required to describe the symmetry properties of crystals. We shall now turn our attention to a discussion of space groups. In the discussion that follows we shall, for convenience, generalize the term "rotation" to mean *any* of the symmetry elements of the point groups. Thus, a general statement about a rotation and a translation can be taken to include, in the generalization, mirror planes and the point of inversion. When only a particular point symmetry operation is to be considered, this will be explicitly stated.

Let us allow $\mathbf{R}$ to be the matrix corresponding to the (generalized) rotation element R, and $\mathbf{t}$ to be a translation vector. The R operation can be described by the *product* of some given row vector $\mathbf{r}$ and $\mathbf{R}$:

$$R\mathbf{r} = \mathbf{r}\mathbf{R} = \mathbf{r}' \tag{4.1}$$

The translation operation t must be defined by a vector *sum*,

$$t\mathbf{r} = \mathbf{t} + \mathbf{r} = \mathbf{r}'' \tag{4.2}$$

The combination of the two operations, conveniently denoted $\mathbf{r}\{\mathbf{R} \mid \mathbf{t}\}$, is

$$\mathbf{r}\{\mathbf{R} \mid \mathbf{t}\} = \mathbf{rR} + \mathbf{t} \tag{4.3}$$

In this notation, a rotation without a translation would be $\{\mathbf{R} \mid \mathbf{0}\}$, while a translation without a rotation would be $\{\mathbf{E} \mid \mathbf{t}\}$. This notation is also frequently used with only the operators, rather than their matrices, as, for example, $\{R \mid \mathbf{t}\}$. This is the form we shall employ in most cases.

In this convention, the product of two operators, $\{R \mid \mathbf{t}\}$ and $\{S \mid \mathbf{t}'\}$, can be found by the successive application of the matrix operations $\{\mathbf{S} \mid \mathbf{t}'\}$ and $\{\mathbf{R} \mid \mathbf{t}\}$ to some vector $\mathbf{r}$.

$$\{R \mid \mathbf{t}\}\mathbf{r} = \mathbf{r}\{\mathbf{R} \mid \mathbf{t}\} = \mathbf{rR} + \mathbf{t} \tag{4.4a}$$

$$\{S \mid \mathbf{t}'\}\{R \mid \mathbf{t}\}\mathbf{r} = \mathbf{r}\{\mathbf{R} \mid \mathbf{t}\}\{\mathbf{S} \mid \mathbf{t}'\} = (\mathbf{rR} + \mathbf{t})\{\mathbf{S} \mid \mathbf{t}'\} \tag{4.4b}$$

$$= \mathbf{rRS} + \mathbf{tS} + \mathbf{t}' \tag{4.4c}$$

The result in Eq. 4.4c is equivalent to operating on $\mathbf{r}$ by the rotation SR and adding the vector $(\mathbf{t}' + \mathbf{tS})$. This gives the definition, *in terms of operators*,

$$\{S \mid \mathbf{t}'\}\{R \mid \mathbf{t}\} = \{SR \mid \mathbf{t}' + S\mathbf{t}\} \tag{4.5}$$

Equation 4.5 can be used to find the reciprocal of an operation. Let $\{S \mid \mathbf{t}'\}$ be $\{R \mid \mathbf{t}\}^{-1}$. Then SR must be the identity, and $\mathbf{t}' + S\mathbf{t}$ must be a null vector. Thus, S must be R^{-1} and $\mathbf{t}'$ must be $-R^{-1}\mathbf{t}$. We have

$$\{R \mid \mathbf{t}\}^{-1} = \{R^{-1} \mid -R^{-1}\mathbf{t}\} \tag{4.6}$$

If the operations R define a group and if we combine them with all possible arbitrary translations, we form a new group, of which the translations are an invariant subgroup. This may be shown by taking the conjugate of the translation $\{E \mid \mathbf{t}\}$ with respect to an arbitrary translation,

$$\{E \mid \mathbf{t}'\}\{E \mid \mathbf{t}\}\{E \mid \mathbf{t}'\}^{-1} = \{E \mid \mathbf{t}\} \tag{4.7}$$

and with respect to an arbitrary rotation–translation,

$$\{R \mid \mathbf{t}'\}\{E \mid \mathbf{t}\}\{R \mid \mathbf{t}'\}^{-1} = \{E \mid R\mathbf{t}\} \tag{4.8}$$

Since $R\mathbf{t}$ is a member of the set of arbitrary translations, and since Eqs. 4.7 and 4.8 are valid for any $\{E \mid \mathbf{t}\}$, the set of $\{E \mid \mathbf{t}\}$ must form an invariant subgroup of the rotation–translation group. Equation 4.8 is also an algebraic expression of the geometric idea that rotation of a translational symmetry element must give another translational symmetry element, but in the rotated direction.

Although the pure translations form an invariant subgroup of the space group, the pure rotations do not. Consider the conjugate of a pure rotation with respect to some rotation–translation element:

$$\{S \mid \mathbf{t}\}\{R \mid \mathbf{0}\}\{S \mid \mathbf{t}\}^{-1} = \{SRS^{-1} \mid \mathbf{t} - SRS^{-1}\mathbf{t}\} \tag{4.9}$$

$$= \{R' \mid \mathbf{t}'\} \tag{4.9a}$$

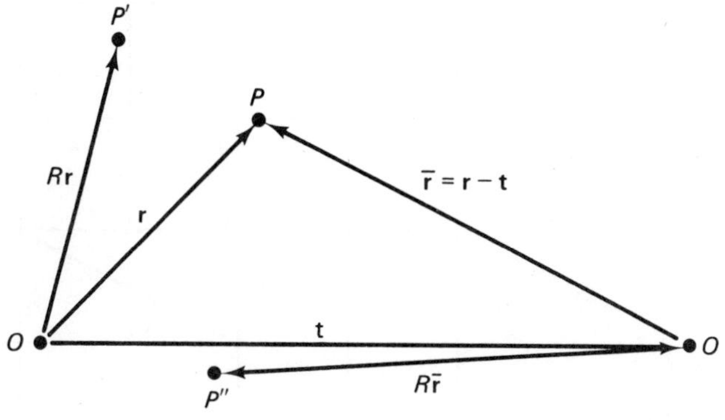

Fig. 4.1. Geometric illustration of the fact that translation of a rotational symmetry operation gives a similar rotation about a new axis which has undergone the translation (see text).

Thus, the conjugate of the pure rotation is a rotation–translation element (i.e., it is no longer a pure rotation). The special case of the conjugate of a pure rotation with respect to a pure translation is useful:

$$\{E \mid \mathbf{t}\}\{R \mid \mathbf{0}\}\{E \mid \mathbf{t}\}^{-1} = \{R \mid \mathbf{t} - R\mathbf{t}\} \tag{4.10}$$

This is an algebraic expression of the idea that translation of a rotational symmetry operation gives a similar rotational operation but about a new axis which has undergone the translation. This is illustrated in two dimensions in Fig. 4.1. The rotation axis is taken as perpendicular to the plane of the paper. The rotation is taken to be a 30° counterclockwise rotation. Before translation, the arbitrary point P is rotated into P' about the axis O. After translation, O is translated to O' and P is rotated (by 30°) into P'' about O'.

4.2 COMPATIBILITY OF TRANSLATIONS AND ROTATIONS

For describing the symmetry of crystals we are interested in the particular **t** vectors

$$\mathbf{t} = m^1\mathbf{t}_1 + m^2\mathbf{t}_2 + m^3\mathbf{t}_3 \tag{4.11}$$

where m^1, m^2, and m^3 are integers and $\mathbf{t}_1$, $\mathbf{t}_2$, and $\mathbf{t}_3$ are the primitive translations [i.e., the smallest repeating translation, of the unit cell (or other suitable repeating units if the system being described is something other than a crystal)]. When limiting our consideration to these translations, the group that is formed from these translations and from the point group that reflects the point symmetry of the system is referred to as a *space group.* The translations and rotations of the space group must be compatible with each other, (i.e., allowable rotations acting on translations must give other allowable translations). This group can be visualized

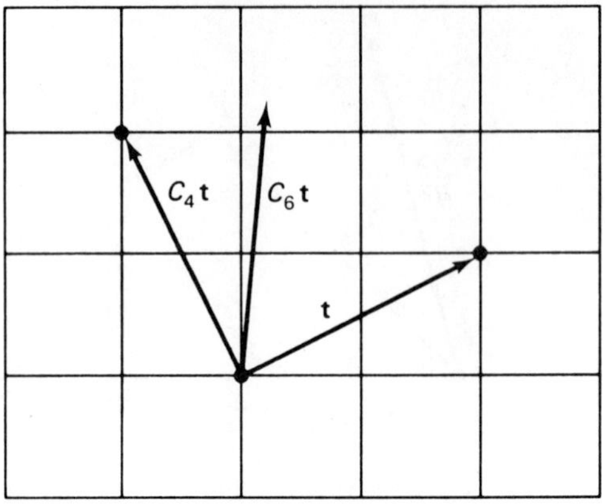

Fig. 4.2. Compatibility of rotations and translations.

from the simple example shown in Fig. 4.2. The vector **t** is a lattice vector, as is the vector $C_4\mathbf{t}$. The vector $C_6\mathbf{t}$ is not a lattice vector, however, and consequently, C_6 is not a compatible rotation within a square (or cubic) lattice.

4.3 CRYSTAL CLASSES

The idea of the compatibility of the symmetry elements to the translational lattice leads directly to a determination of the possible classes of the space groups that describe three-dimensional lattices of points. The defining condition is that if **t** is one of the primitive translation vectors, then every vector **t**′ defined by

$$\mathbf{t}' = \mathbf{tR} \tag{4.12}$$

must be a lattice vector. In order for this to occur, the diagonal form of the matrix **R** must have only integer elements along the diagonal. This can be the case only if the trace of **R** has an integer value (since the trace of a matrix is invariant under a unitary transformation). However, we have already seen that the trace of the rotation matrices obey the relationship

$$\mathrm{tr}\, \mathbf{R} = \pm 1 + 2 \cos \theta \tag{4.13}$$

In order for the trace to have an integer value, $\cos \theta$ can have only the values 0, $\pm\frac{1}{2}$, or ± 1 (i.e., θ can only be an integer multiple of $\pi/2$ or of $\pi/3$). The angle θ equals $k(2\pi/n)$, where k is an integer and n is the order of the (proper or improper) rotation axis. The only allowable values of n satisfying these criteria are 1, 2, 3, 4, or 6. Thus, the axial point groups having these as the order of their principal axis or highest-order improper axis are compatible with translational symmetry. None of the other axial point groups are compatible. In addition to the 27 axial point groups (listed in Table 4.1) that result from these limitations, the five cubic

Table 4.1. The 27 axial point groups that occur in crystal symmetry

Type	Point Groups	Remarks
$\mathbf{C}_n$	$\mathbf{C}_1, \mathbf{C}_2, \mathbf{C}_3, \mathbf{C}_4, \mathbf{C}_6$	
$\mathbf{S}_n$	$\mathbf{S}_2, \mathbf{S}_4, \mathbf{S}_6$	$(\mathbf{S}_2 = \mathbf{C}_i)$
$\mathbf{C}_{nv}$	$\mathbf{C}_{2v}, \mathbf{C}_{3v}, \mathbf{C}_{4v}, \mathbf{C}_{6v}$	
$\mathbf{C}_{nh}$	$\mathbf{C}_{1h}, \mathbf{C}_{2h}, \mathbf{C}_{3h}, \mathbf{C}_{4h}, \mathbf{C}_{6h}$	$(\mathbf{C}_{1h} = \mathbf{C}_s)$
$\mathbf{D}_n$	$\mathbf{D}_2, \mathbf{D}_3, \mathbf{D}_4, \mathbf{D}_6$	
$\mathbf{D}_{nd}$	$\mathbf{D}_{2d}, \mathbf{D}_{3d}$	$\mathbf{D}_{4d}$ is not allowed because it contains an $\mathbf{S}_8$ element; $\mathbf{D}_{6d}$ contains an $\mathbf{S}_{12}$
$\mathbf{D}_{nh}$	$\mathbf{D}_{2h}, \mathbf{D}_{3h}, \mathbf{D}_{4h}, \mathbf{D}_{6h}$	

groups are allowed in repetitive symmetry. This leads to 32 point groups which satisfy the compatibility requirements. These define the 32 *crystal classes.* The point symmetry of a crystal lattice is referred to as its *holohedry*.

4.4 CRYSTAL SYSTEMS

The 32 crystal classes can be distributed among seven *crystal systems*, each system being defined by the relative lengths and inclinations of its primitive translation vectors. In order to see how this is accomplished, we need the concept of a *metrical matrix* (or *metric*). If $\mathbf{a}_1$, $\mathbf{a}_2$, and $\mathbf{a}_3$ are the primitive translation vectors of a unit cell (or any other set of basis vectors, for that matter), then the metric is defined as

$$\mathbf{M} = \begin{bmatrix} \mathbf{a}_1 \cdot \mathbf{a}_1 & \mathbf{a}_1 \cdot \mathbf{a}_2 & \mathbf{a}_1 \cdot \mathbf{a}_3 \\ \mathbf{a}_2 \cdot \mathbf{a}_1 & \mathbf{a}_2 \cdot \mathbf{a}_2 & \mathbf{a}_2 \cdot \mathbf{a}_3 \\ \mathbf{a}_3 \cdot \mathbf{a}_1 & \mathbf{a}_3 \cdot \mathbf{a}_2 & \mathbf{a}_3 \cdot \mathbf{a}_3 \end{bmatrix} \tag{4.14}$$

The individual (scalar) elements of this have the form

$$M_{ij} = a_i a_j \cos \theta_{ij} \tag{4.15}$$

(Note that M_{ij} equals M_{ji}.) The metric may be represented as the direct square of the supervector $\mathbf{a}$, where $\mathbf{a}$ is the column vector of vectors

$$\mathbf{a} = \begin{pmatrix} \mathbf{a}_1 \\ \mathbf{a}_2 \\ \mathbf{a}_3 \end{pmatrix} \tag{4.16}$$

When dealing with a nonorthogonal basis set of vectors, the scalar product of two lattice translations $\mathbf{r} \cdot \mathbf{s}$ can be expressed

$$\mathbf{r} \cdot \mathbf{s} = (r^1 \quad r^2 \quad r^3) \begin{pmatrix} \mathbf{a}_1 \\ \mathbf{a}_2 \\ \mathbf{a}_3 \end{pmatrix} (\mathbf{a}_1 \quad \mathbf{a}_2 \quad \mathbf{a}_3) \begin{pmatrix} s^1 \\ s^2 \\ s^3 \end{pmatrix} = \mathbf{r}\mathbf{M}\tilde{\mathbf{s}} \tag{4.17}$$

This scalar product, being a number, not a vector, must be independent of a rotation of the reference system

$$(R\mathbf{r}) \cdot (R\mathbf{s}) = (\mathbf{rR}) \cdot (\mathbf{sR}) \tag{4.18}$$

This requires that

$$(\mathbf{rR})\mathbf{M}(\widetilde{\mathbf{sR}}) = \mathbf{rRM}\tilde{\mathbf{R}}\tilde{\mathbf{s}} = \mathbf{rMs} \tag{4.19}$$

or that

$$\mathbf{RM}\tilde{\mathbf{R}} = \mathbf{M} \tag{4.20}$$

Relationship 4.20 must be valid for all **R** in the point group, that is, the metric must be invariant under a *congruent transformation* by all the operation matrices of the point group. This imposes severe compatibility restrictions on the mutually acceptable forms of **R** and **M**.

Consider, for example, the $\mathbf{C}_{2v}$ point group. The generators are C_2 and σ_v. The C_2 generator in two dimensions has the representation

$$\mathbf{R}(C_2) = \begin{bmatrix} -1 & 0 \\ 0 & -1 \end{bmatrix} \tag{4.21}$$

There are a number of matrices that can be used to represent σ_v. Reflection in the xz plane yields

$$\mathbf{R}(\sigma_v) = \begin{bmatrix} 1 & 0 \\ 0 & -1 \end{bmatrix} \tag{4.22}$$

while reflection in a plane bisecting the x and y axes gives

$$\mathbf{R}'(\sigma_v) = \begin{bmatrix} 0 & 1 \\ 1 & 0 \end{bmatrix} \tag{4.23}$$

A two-dimensional metric can be written

$$\mathbf{M} = \begin{bmatrix} M_{11} & M_{12} \\ M_{21} & M_{22} \end{bmatrix} \tag{4.24}$$

The C_2 operation imposes no restrictions on this:

$$\mathbf{R}(C_2)\mathbf{M}\tilde{\mathbf{R}}(C_2) = \begin{bmatrix} -1 & 0 \\ 0 & -1 \end{bmatrix}\begin{bmatrix} M_{11} & M_{12} \\ M_{21} & M_{22} \end{bmatrix}\begin{bmatrix} -1 & 0 \\ 0 & -1 \end{bmatrix} = \begin{bmatrix} M_{11} & M_{12} \\ M_{21} & M_{22} \end{bmatrix} \tag{4.25}$$

The σ_v operations do, however, impose restrictions. For example, if Eq. 4.22 is taken for σ_v,

$$\mathbf{R}(\sigma_v)\mathbf{M}\tilde{\mathbf{R}}(\sigma_v) = \begin{bmatrix} 1 & 0 \\ 0 & -1 \end{bmatrix}\begin{bmatrix} M_{11} & M_{12} \\ M_{21} & M_{22} \end{bmatrix}\begin{bmatrix} 1 & 0 \\ 0 & -1 \end{bmatrix} = \begin{bmatrix} M_{11} & -M_{12} \\ -M_{21} & M_{22} \end{bmatrix} \tag{4.26}$$

The requirement that **M** equal $\mathbf{RM}\tilde{\mathbf{R}}$ means that the off-diagonal elements must equal their negative. The only way for this to be satisfied is for them to equal zero.

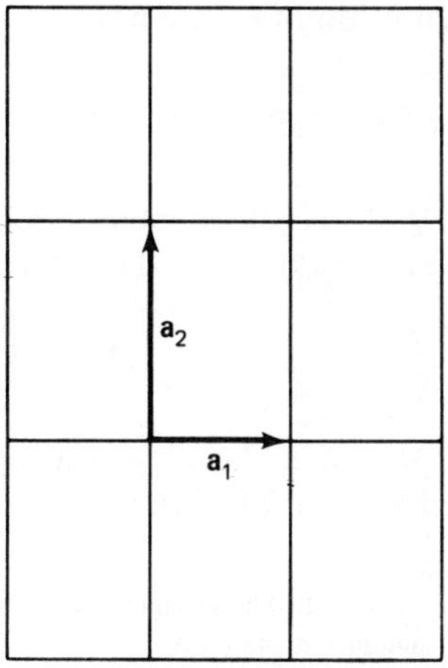

Fig. 4.3. Two-dimensional lattice system having $\mathbf{C}_{2v}$ holohedry where σ_v is the xz plane.

Thus, the metric compatible with this σ_v is

$$\mathbf{M} = \begin{bmatrix} M_{11} & 0 \\ 0 & M_{22} \end{bmatrix} \tag{4.27}$$

Since the off-diagonal elements contain the cosine of the angle, this requires that the vectors $\mathbf{a}_1$ and $\mathbf{a}_2$ be perpendicular to one another. No constraints are placed on the diagonal elements of the metric; consequently, no restraints are placed on the magnitudes of $\mathbf{a}_1$ and $\mathbf{a}_2$. Thus, the metric of Eq. 4.27 defines a rectangular array of lattice points with no restraints on the sides of the rectangles (Fig. 4.3). For

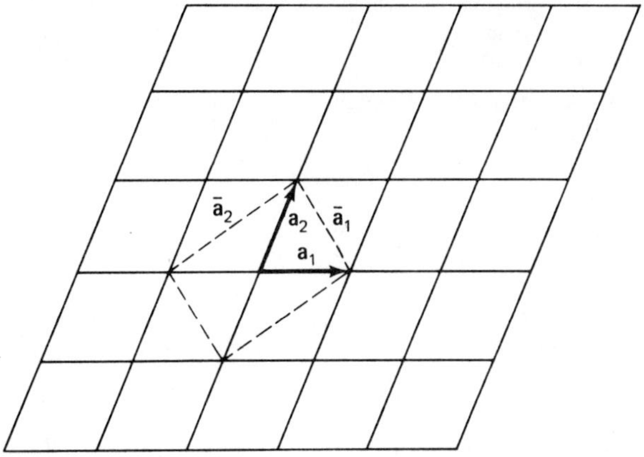

Fig. 4.4. Two-dimensional lattice system having $\mathbf{C}_{2v}$ holohedry where σ_v bisects the x and y axes.

the second definition of σ_v, we have

$$\mathbf{R}'(\sigma_v)\mathbf{M}\tilde{\mathbf{R}}'(\sigma_v) = \begin{bmatrix} 0 & 1 \\ 1 & 0 \end{bmatrix}\begin{bmatrix} M_{11} & M_{12} \\ M_{21} & M_{22} \end{bmatrix}\begin{bmatrix} 0 & 1 \\ 1 & 0 \end{bmatrix} = \begin{bmatrix} M_{22} & M_{21} \\ M_{12} & M_{11} \end{bmatrix} \tag{4.28}$$

This requires that M_{11} must equal M_{22} (and that M_{21} equal M_{12}, which was already the case from Eq. 4.15). The matrix has the form

$$\mathbf{M}' = \begin{bmatrix} M & m \\ m & M \end{bmatrix} \tag{4.29}$$

The fact that M_{11} and M_{22} are equal requires that $\mathbf{a}_1$ equal $\mathbf{a}_2$. No restriction is placed on their inclination with respect to each other, however. The lattice system

Table 4.2. The seven crystal systems and their associated point groups and metric matrices

Point Groups	Crystal System	Metric	Description
$\mathbf{C}_1, \mathbf{S}_2$	Triclinic	$\begin{bmatrix} M_{11} & M_{12} & M_{13} \\ M_{12} & M_{22} & M_{23} \\ M_{13} & M_{23} & M_{33} \end{bmatrix}$	$a_1 \neq a_2 \neq a_3$; $\theta_{12} \neq \theta_{13} \neq \theta_{23}$
$\mathbf{C}_{1h}, \mathbf{C}_2, \mathbf{C}_{2h}$	Monoclinic	$\begin{bmatrix} M_{11} & M_{12} & 0 \\ M_{12} & M_{22} & 0 \\ 0 & 0 & M_{33} \end{bmatrix}$	$a_1 \neq a_2 \neq a_3$; $\theta_{13} = \theta_{23} = 90°; \theta_{12} \neq 90$
$\mathbf{C}_{2v}, \mathbf{D}_2, \mathbf{D}_{2h}$	Orthorhombic	$\begin{bmatrix} M_{11} & 0 & 0 \\ 0 & M_{22} & 0 \\ 0 & 0 & M_{33} \end{bmatrix}$	$a_1 \neq a_2 \neq a_3$; $\theta_{12} = \theta_{13} = \theta_{23} = 90°$
$\mathbf{C}_3, \mathbf{S}_6, \mathbf{C}_{3v}, \mathbf{D}_3, \mathbf{D}_{3d}$ (principal axis is diagonal of unit cell)	Trigonal (or rhombohedral)	$\begin{bmatrix} M & m & m \\ m & M & m \\ m & m & M \end{bmatrix}$	$a_1 = a_2 = a_3$; $\theta_{12} = \theta_{13} = \theta_{23} \neq 90°$
$\mathbf{C}_6, \mathbf{C}_{3h}, \mathbf{C}_{6h}, \mathbf{C}_{6v}, \mathbf{D}_6, \mathbf{D}_{3h}, \mathbf{D}_{6h}$	Hexagonal	$\begin{bmatrix} M_{11} & \frac{-M_{11}}{2} & 0 \\ \frac{-M_{11}}{2} & M_{11} & 0 \\ 0 & 0 & M_{33} \end{bmatrix}$	$a_1 = a_2 \neq a_3; \theta_{12} = 120°$; $\theta_{13} = \theta_{23} = 90°$
$\mathbf{C}_4, \mathbf{C}_{4v}, \mathbf{C}_{4h}, \mathbf{S}_4, \mathbf{D}_4, \mathbf{D}_{2d}, \mathbf{D}_{4h}$	Tetragonal	$\begin{bmatrix} M_{11} & 0 & 0 \\ 0 & M_{11} & 0 \\ 0 & 0 & M_{33} \end{bmatrix}$	$a_1 = a_2 \neq a_3$; $\theta_{12} = \theta_{13} = \theta_{23} = 90°$
$\mathbf{T}, \mathbf{T}_h, \mathbf{T}_d, \mathbf{O}, \mathbf{O}_h$	Cubic	$\begin{bmatrix} M & 0 & 0 \\ 0 & M & 0 \\ 0 & 0 & M \end{bmatrix}$	$a_1 = a_2 = a_3$; $\theta_{12} = \theta_{13} = \theta_{23} = 90°$

is as in Fig. 4.4. These two lattices of Figs. 4.3 and 4.4 are thus both compatible in two dimensions with the $\mathbf{C}_{2v}$ point group. The structure shown in Fig. 4.4 can be represented in a rectangular lattice by defining two new lattice vectors

$$\bar{\mathbf{a}}_1 = \mathbf{a}_1 - \mathbf{a}_2 \tag{4.30a}$$

and

$$\bar{\mathbf{a}}_2 = \mathbf{a}_1 + \mathbf{a}_2 \tag{4.30b}$$

This new lattice has lattice points at the corners of the rectangles and in the center of the rectangle. Thus, whether the planes of symmetry are parallel to the crystal axes or bisect pairs of crystal axes, the $\mathbf{C}_{2v}$ point group fits into rectangular lattice patterns.

By using considerations such as these, the 32 crystal classes can be classified into seven crystal systems or *syngonies*. These are listed in Table 4.2.

Exercise 4.1*: Find the restrictions placed on a three-dimensional metric and the primitive translations by C_2; C_3^{xyz}.

4.5 CENTERING

We have seen from Fig. 4.4 that with a certain choice of the point group generators a two-dimensional rectangular lattice (e.g., a side of an orthorhombic system) can have a lattice point in its center. This may occur in three dimensions, either

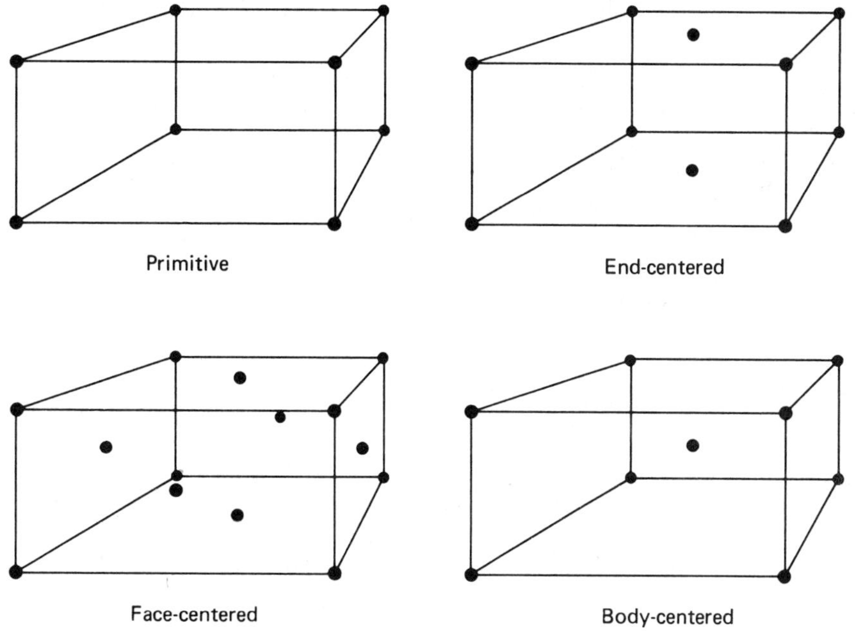

Fig. 4.5. Centering in an orthorhombic lattice system.

Table 4.3. The 14 Bravais lattices

System	Highest Point Symmetry	Cell Type
Triclinic	$\mathbf{S}_2$	Primitive
Monoclinic	$\mathbf{C}_{2h}$	Primitive
		Base-centered
Orthorhombic	$\mathbf{D}_{2h}$	Primitive
		Base (end)-centered
		Face-centered
		Body-centered
Trigonal	$\mathbf{D}_{3d}$	Primitive
Tetragonal	$\mathbf{D}_{4h}$	Primitive
		Body-centered
Hexagonal	$\mathbf{D}_{6h}$	Primitive
Cubic	$\mathbf{O}_h$	Primitive
		Face-centered
		Body-centered

for one pair of parallel faces of an orthorhombic unit cell, in which case it is referred to as an *end-centered* system, or it may occur for all faces, in which case it is referred to as *face-centered*. In addition to these two, there is an orthorhombic lattice which has a lattice point in the center of the unit cell, referred to as *body-centered*. The lattice with no centering is referred to as *primitive*, or *simple*. These lattice types are shown in Fig. 4.5. In many instances, centering in a unit cell can lead to a smaller unit cell. The orthorhombic system is the only system that can exhibit all three types of centering. The triclinic, trigonal, and hexagonal systems can have no centered lattices. The monoclinic system can have an end-centered lattice, the tetragonal system a body-centered lattice, and the cubic system a face-centered or a body-centered lattice. These seven centered lattices, along with the seven primitive lattices, give 14 possible lattice types, known as the 14 *Bravais lattices*. These are listed in Table 4.3.

4.6 SITE SYMMETRY IN CRYSTALS

The point groups listed in Table 4.3 represent the full symmetry of the lattice itself with structureless points occupying the lattice points. In molecular crystals the unit cells are occupied by structured objects, the molecules. If these individually do not have the full symmetry of the lattice points, the point symmetry of the unit cell can be reduced to one of the lower point groups. These systems belonging to classes of reduced symmetry are described as *hemihedral*, since their point groups are subgroups of the holohedry (point symmetry) of the particular lattice system.

To discuss the effects of these, it is useful to define the concept of *site symmetry*. If a point in a lattice is left unmoved by all the operations of a group that is a subgroup of the holohedry of the system, the point is a symmetry point of the system with a site symmetry corresponding to that of the subgroup. These points must lie on symmetry elements of the full point group of the system. Consider, for example, a cubic system (Fig. 4.6). A structureless point at the center would be unmoved by any of the operations of the $\mathbf{O}_h$ point group; consequently, the point exhibits the full holohedry of the system. A cubic object placed at the center would also preserve the symmetry of the system. An object at the center with less than cubic symmetry would cause the point symmetry of the unit cell to be lower. A point on the *xyz* body diagonal, but away from the center, has the hemihedral symmetry $\mathbf{C}_{3v}$. C_3^{xyz} is the axis of symmetry, and the planes of symmetry contain the C_3^{xyz}, and the x, y, and z axes, respectively (Fig. 4.7). For the system to retain full cubic symmetry it would be necessary for there to be eight such points in the system, two on each body diagonal, equally displaced (in opposite directions) from the center (Fig. 4.8).

The symmetry is also preserved if these points are occupied by objects with $\mathbf{C}_{3v}$ symmetry (the site symmetry of the points). The number of such equivalent positions can be found by dividing the order of the point group that expresses the complete holohedry of the lattice by the order of the subgroup that expresses the site symmetry of the position under consideration. For example, the $\mathbf{O}_h$ point group has 48 elements (an order of 48), while the $\mathbf{C}_{3v}$ point group has six elements (an order of six), thus requiring that there be eight equivalent positions for every point of $\mathbf{C}_{3v}$ site symmetry. For a general position (one that is not on any symmetry element), the site symmetry is $\mathbf{C}_1$, and the only symmetry element is the identity element. This means that for every general point in a system with full cubic symmetry, there are 48 equivalent points. The concept of site symmetry and

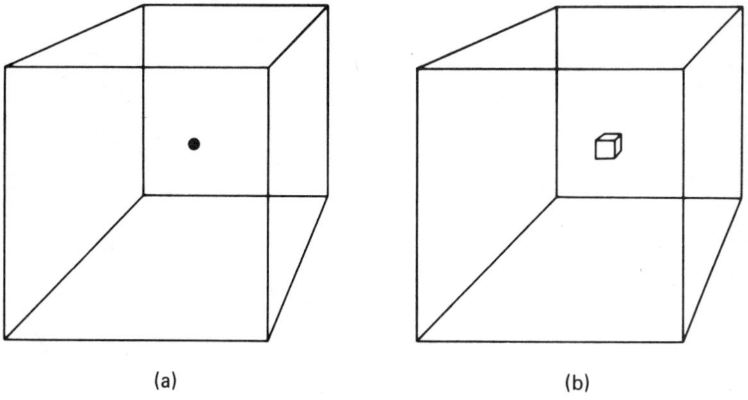

Fig. 4.6. Structureless point (a) and cubic structure (b) at the center of a cubic lattice.

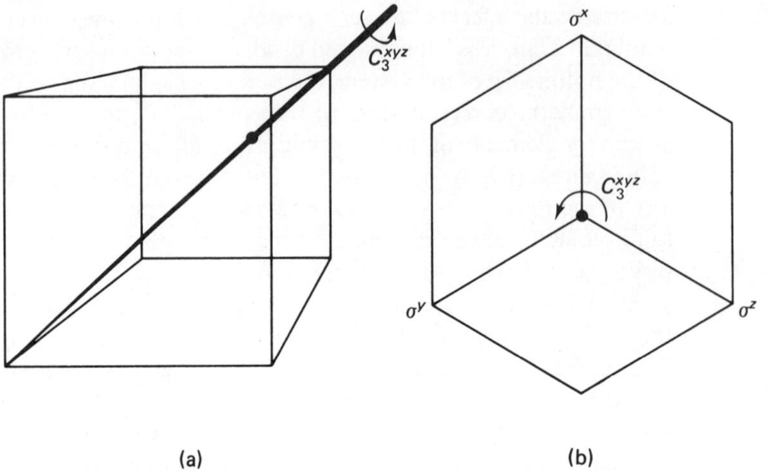

Fig. 4.7. Point on the body diagonal of a cubic lattice having $\mathbf{C}_{3v}$ site symmetry: (a) viewed from the side; (b) viewed along the diagonal.

equivalent positions is very useful to crystallographers. If the number of molecules per unit cell can be determined (from cell dimensions, density, and molecular weight), and if the holohedry of the unit cell is known, the relation of the molecules to the symmetry elements of the unit cell can be determined immediately.

Exercise 4.2*: What is the site symmetry and how many equivalent points are there for each of the following:

(a) Cubic system: a point on a line joining the center of the cube with the center of one face (C_4 axis).
(b) Trigonal system: a point (not the center) on the principal axis.
(c) Trigonal system: a point on the long diagonal of one face.

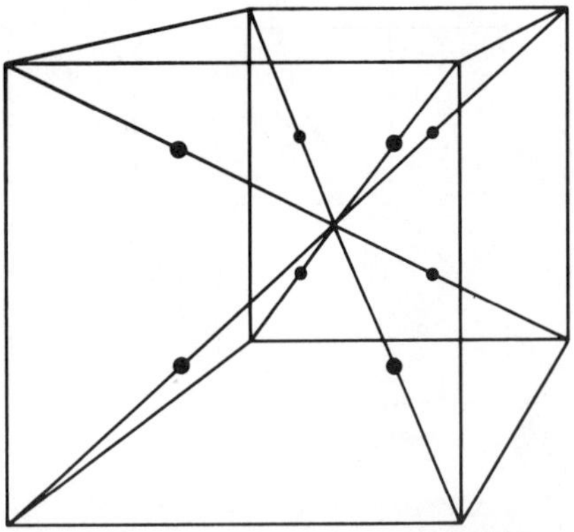

Fig. 4.8. Equivalent points on the body diagonals of a cube.

Let us consider Fig. 4.8 again. If alternating members of the indicated set of equivalent points were missing, the symmetry of the system would be reduced from $\mathbf{O}_h$ to one of the tetrahedral point groups (Fig. 4.9). The number of general points would also be reduced from 48 to either 24 or 12, depending upon which of the tetrahedral groups described the system. Figure 4.10 shows the successive reduction of symmetry from the $\mathbf{O}_h$ point group to the $\mathbf{T}$ point group with respect to equivalent general points on the face of a cube. The reduction of the symmetry of other lattice systems is similar.

Exercise 4.3: By suitable drawings, indicate the equivalent general points on the faces of an orthorhombic system for the three point groups in this system.

If objects of a point symmetry lower than the site symmetry are inserted into special sites, the overall point symmetry of the unit cell will be decreased. This frequently does not effect the overall macroscopic crystal habit (shape); consequently, crystals whose lattice points are occupied by objects that do not have the hemihedral symmetry of the site are still usually classified, in the Schönflies notation, as if they had the maximum symmetry consistent with the holohedry of the lattice. In the Hermann–Mauguin system of notation, this ambiguity does not occur, since only the specific symmetry elements required to define the crystal system are specified.

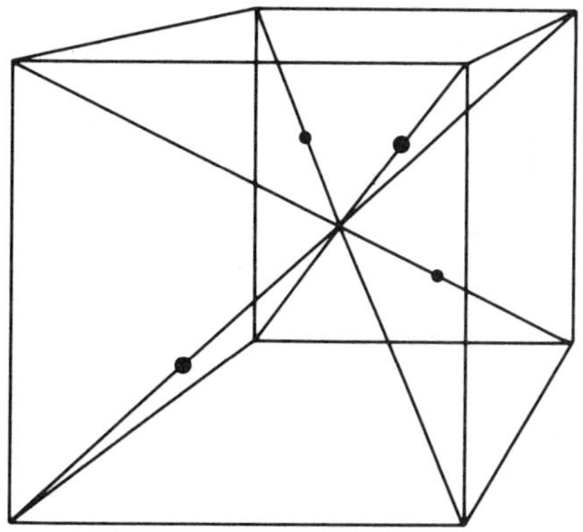

Fig. 4.9. Equivalent points on the body diagonals of a cube within a tetrahedral point group.

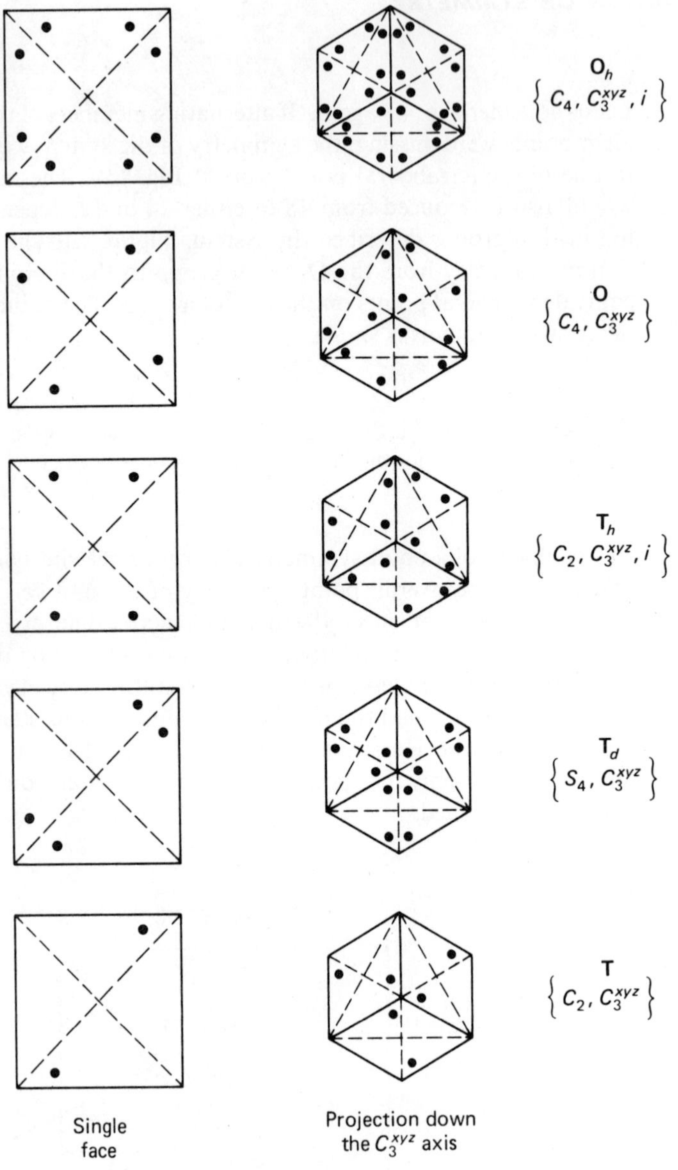

Fig. 4.10. Equivalent general points on the face of a cube for the cubic point groups. (Dashed lines are diagonals of the faces.)

4.8 GLIDE PLANES AND SCREW AXES

Thus far we have considered only pure rotation and pure translation operations in finding allowed crystal lattices. The allowed combinations of the 32 crystal classes (Table 4.2) with the 14 Bravais lattices (Table 4.3) yield 73 different space groups when only $\{R \mid \mathbf{O}\}$ and $\{E \mid \mathbf{t}\}$ are used as the defining operations. There are, however, allowed space-group symmetry operations of the type $\{R \mid \mathbf{v}_R\}$, where $\mathbf{v}_R$ is a specific translation (smaller than a primitive translation) associated with the rotation R. The particular R occurring in this operation must not occur as a member of the point group of the system because if R is a member of the point group, then this introduces nothing new, giving a trivial meaning to $\{R \mid \mathbf{v}_R\}$. We can find these new operations, in an indirect manner, by eliminating the trivial solutions. If $\{R \mid \mathbf{v}_R\}$ is one of these trivial solutions, the conjugate relation in Eq. 4.10 must yield an allowed lattice translation for $\mathbf{v}_R$. That is, there must be some translation $\mathbf{r}$ such that the conjugate of the pure rotation $\{R \mid \mathbf{O}\}$ with respect to the pure translation $\{E \mid \mathbf{r}\}$ yields the operation

$$\{E \mid \mathbf{r}\}\{R \mid \mathbf{O}\}\{E \mid \mathbf{r}\}^{-1} = \{R \mid \mathbf{v}_R\} \tag{4.31}$$

This can be solved by multiplying from the right by $\{E \mid \mathbf{r}\}$ and from the left by $\{E \mid \mathbf{r}\}^{-1}$:

$$\{E \mid \mathbf{r}\}^{-1}\{E \mid \mathbf{r}\}\{R \mid \mathbf{O}\}\{E \mid \mathbf{r}\}^{-1}\{E \mid \mathbf{r}\} = \{E \mid \mathbf{r}\}^{-1}\{R \mid \mathbf{v}_R\}\{E \mid \mathbf{r}\} \tag{4.32}$$

$$\{R \mid \mathbf{O}\} = \{R \mid R\mathbf{r} - \mathbf{r} + \mathbf{v}_R\} \tag{4.32a}$$

$$\mathbf{rR} - \mathbf{r} + \mathbf{v}_R = \mathbf{O} \tag{4.33}$$

$$\mathbf{v}_R = \mathbf{r}(\mathbf{E} - \mathbf{R}) \tag{4.33a}$$

The operation $\{R \mid \mathbf{v}_R\}$ is one of the trivial operations if there can be found some vector $\mathbf{r}$ that is a solution to Eq. 4.33a. There exists a nontrivial operation $\{R \mid \mathbf{v}_R\}$ if R and $\mathbf{v}_R$ can be chosen so that there is *no* solution to Eq. 4.33a. Formally, the solution to this is

$$\mathbf{r} = \mathbf{v}_R(\mathbf{E} - \mathbf{R})^{-1} \tag{4.34}$$

The solution fails to exist if the matrix $(\mathbf{E} - \mathbf{R})$ has any zero eigenvalues [i.e., if a singularity exists in $(\mathbf{E} - \mathbf{R})^{-1}$]. The identity matrix $\mathbf{E}$ has three eigenvalues of $+1$. The matrix $\mathbf{R}$ can have eigenvalues of $+1$ if it represents a reflection or a rotation. If the reflection plane or rotation axis coincides with a corresponding plane or axis in the point group of the lattice, the solution is trivial. There is thus the possibility of new symmetry elements of the type $\{R \mid \mathbf{v}_R\}$ only when R is a reflection or a rotation that is not a member of the point group of the unit cell.

These operations are defined as a *glide plane* when R is a reflection and $\mathbf{v}_R$ is a translation parallel to the reflection plane, and a *screw axis* when R is a rotation and $\mathbf{v}_R$ is a translation along the axis. Applying the glide plane operation twice gives the operation $\{E \mid 2\mathbf{v}_R\}$; thus, the translation $\mathbf{v}_R$ associated with the glide plane must

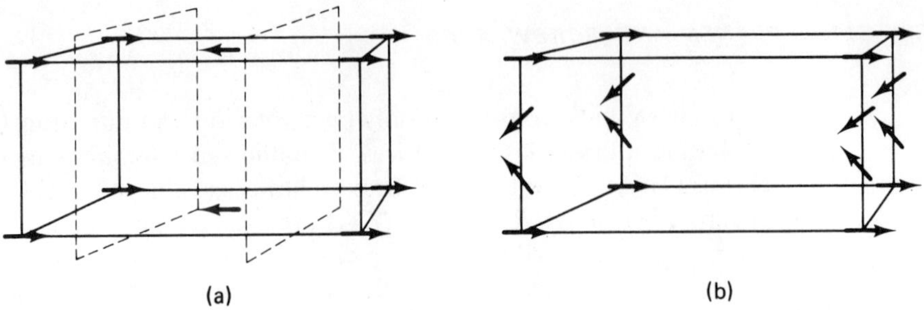

Fig. 4.11. (a) Glide planes; (b) screw axes.

be half of a generalized lattice vector. The basic operation, from which all others can be generated, is that in which $\mathbf{v}_R$ equals half of a primitive translation. Similarly, if R represents a C_n operation, n applications of $\{R \mid \mathbf{v}_R\}$ yield $\{E \mid n\mathbf{v}_R\}$, and the basic operation is one in which $\mathbf{v}_R$ equals a primitive translation divided by n. Examples of these two operations are given in Fig. 4.11. Taking these two rotation–translation operations into account increases the total number of possible space groups to 230. Every possible crystal structure can be classified within one of these 230 possible space groups.

Note that the glide plane and screw axis require structured objects in the unit cell. The glide plane requires that the structured object must occur in a reversed orientation halfway through the unit cell. In the example, the translation is one-half of the short distance of the upper and lower faces, while the reflection is through a plane perpendicular to the faces. The screw axis requires the orientation of the object to be rotated by $2\pi/n$ (120° in the example) every $1/n$ of the distance through the unit cell. The starting points for the objects need not be the vertices of the unit cell, as they are in the examples.

PROBLEMS

1. Let

$$\mathbf{r} = \begin{pmatrix} 1 \\ 1 \\ 1 \end{pmatrix}, \quad \mathbf{t} = \begin{pmatrix} 1 \\ 2 \\ 3 \end{pmatrix}, \quad \mathbf{t}' = \begin{pmatrix} 4 \\ 1 \\ 5 \end{pmatrix}$$

Find the result of the following operations (assume rotation is about the z axis and reflection is in the xz plane):

(a) $\{E \mid \mathbf{t}\}\mathbf{r}$ (b) $\{C_3 \mid \mathbf{O}\}\mathbf{r}$

(c) $\{C_3 \mid \mathbf{t}\}\mathbf{r}$ (d) $\{\sigma_v \mid \mathbf{t}\}\mathbf{r}$

(e) $\{i \mid \mathbf{O}\}\mathbf{r}$ (f) $\{i \mid \mathbf{t}\}\mathbf{r}$

(g) $\{C_5 \mid \mathbf{t}\}\mathbf{r}$ (h) $\{C_3 \mid \mathbf{t}\}\{\sigma_v \mid \mathbf{t}'\}\mathbf{r}$

(i) $\{\sigma_v \mid \mathbf{t}'\}\{C_3 \mid \mathbf{t}\}\mathbf{r}$ (j) $\{C_3 \mid \mathbf{t}'\}\{\sigma_v \mid \mathbf{t}\}\mathbf{r}$

(k) $\{C_3 \mid \mathbf{t}\}\{i \mid \mathbf{t}'\}\mathbf{r}$

2. Construct the operation for a glide plane involving a translation in the y direction.

3. Construct the operation for a threefold screw axis.

BIBLIOGRAPHY

ALTMANN, S. L., *Induced Representations in Crystals and Molecules*, Academic Press, Inc., New York, 1977.

BUERGER, M. J., *Elementary Crystallography*, John Wiley & Sons, Inc., New York, 1956.

JASWON, M. A., *An Introduction to Mathematical Crystallography*, Elsevier North-Holland, Inc., New York, 1965.

KOSTER, G. F., *Space Groups and Their Representations*, Academic Press, Inc., New York, 1957.

LAX, M., *Symmetry Principles in Solid State and Molecular Physics*, John Wiley & Sons, Inc., New York, 1974.

MCWEENY, R., *Symmetry*, Macmillan Publishing Co., Inc., New York, 1963.

SANDS, D. E., *Introduction to Crystallography*, W. A. Benjamin, Inc., Menlo Park, Calif., 1969.

SLATER, J. C., *Quantum Theory of Molecules and Solids*, Vol. II, McGraw-Hill Book Company, New York, 1965.

5

Irreducible Representations of the Symmetry Groups

5.1 IRREDUCIBLE REPRESENTATIONS

Before going on to the applications of group theory we need to consider the concept of representations in more detail. We will not present a formal development of the methods of deriving representations, since an adequate treatment of representation theory would require a large treatise in itself, and since tables of irreducible representations (character tables) are readily available for all the point groups. We shall, rather, present an intuitive development of the significance of representations, irreducible representations, and the other concepts that we will require for making practical use of representation theory. We will have cause to use, without proof, three properties of irreducible representations. These are:

1. If the irreducible representations of a group are one dimensional, they must, in themselves, form a group.
2. The sum of the squares of the dimensions of the irreducible representations is equal to the order of the group.
3. There are as many irreducible representations for a group as there are classes.

Consider the operations of the $\mathbf{C}_2$ point group, E and C_2. The three-dimensional transformation matrices corresponding to these are

$$\mathbf{R}(E) = \begin{bmatrix} 1 & 0 & 0 \\ 0 & 1 & 0 \\ 0 & 0 & 1 \end{bmatrix} \tag{5.1}$$

and

$$\mathbf{R}(C_2) = \begin{bmatrix} -1 & 0 & 0 \\ 0 & -1 & 0 \\ 0 & 0 & 1 \end{bmatrix} \tag{5.2}$$

These matrices form a representation of the $\mathbf{C}_2$ point group. This is not the simplest representation, however. These are diagonal matrices representing transformations in the Cartesian coordinate system. Consequently, the behavior with respect to each axis is independent of the others. If we consider the x, y, and z components of these, we can obtain three independent mappings of our group, $\Gamma(x)$, $\Gamma(y)$, and $\Gamma(z)$:

(5.3)

	E	C_2
$\Gamma(x)$	1	-1
$\Gamma(y)$	1	-1
$\Gamma(z)$	1	1

Because of the orthogonality of our basis vectors in the Cartesian system, these are mutually independent mappings. [Note that $\Gamma(z)$ is homomorphic with the elements of $\mathbf{C}_2$, while $\Gamma(x)$ and $\Gamma(y)$ are isomorphic.] They can be taken individually as representations of the $\mathbf{C}_2$ point group. The individual numbers are called *characters.* (In general, a character is the trace of a representation matrix, representing a given operation in a given group. Here, the independent matrices are one-dimensional.) There is more information here than is required, however, since $\Gamma(x)$ equals $\Gamma(y)$. Thus, $\Gamma(z)$ and either $\Gamma(x)$ or $\Gamma(y)$ form the only two unique independent representations of $\mathbf{C}_2$ within the Cartesian coordinate system. These are referred to as *irreducible representations.* The *character table* for a group lists the characters for the various operations associated with each irreducible representation. The character table for the $\mathbf{C}_2$ group is written

(5.4)

$\mathbf{C}_2$	E	C_2
A	1	1
B	1	-1

Formally, irreducible representations are the simplest possible set of independent representation matrices for a group. A character is the trace of a representation matrix. We shall discuss the significance of the notations A and B for the irreducible representations later.

Consider now the transformation matrices for the $\mathbf{C}_3$ point group:

$$\mathbf{R}(E) = \begin{bmatrix} 1 & 0 & 0 \\ 0 & 1 & 0 \\ 0 & 0 & 1 \end{bmatrix} \tag{5.5}$$

$$\mathbf{R}(C_3) = \begin{bmatrix} \cos 2\pi/3 & \sin 2\pi/3 & 0 \\ -\sin 2\pi/3 & \cos 2\pi/3 & 0 \\ 0 & 0 & 1 \end{bmatrix} = \begin{bmatrix} -1/2 & \sqrt{3}/2 & 0 \\ -\sqrt{3}/2 & -1/2 & 0 \\ 0 & 0 & 1 \end{bmatrix} \tag{5.6}$$

$$\mathbf{R}(C_3^2) = \begin{bmatrix} \cos 4\pi/3 & \sin 4\pi/3 & 0 \\ -\sin 4\pi/3 & \cos 4\pi/3 & 0 \\ 0 & 0 & 1 \end{bmatrix} = \begin{bmatrix} -1/2 & -\sqrt{3}/2 & 0 \\ \sqrt{3}/2 & -1/2 & 0 \\ 0 & 0 & 1 \end{bmatrix} \tag{5.7}$$

The matrices for the C_3 operations are not diagonal; consequently, the x and y components taken separately cannot be used to form irreducible representations of $\mathbf{C}_3$. The z component, however, does still form a unique independent (irreducible) representation. The 2×2 matrices describing the behavior in the xy plane can be used as a two-dimensional representation of the $\mathbf{C}_3$ point group. This is again an irreducible representation. There are two usual ways of expressing this two-dimensional representation. One way is to take the trace of the two-dimensional matrices of this representation as the characters. This leads to

(5.8)

$\mathbf{C}_3$	E	$2C_3$
A	1	1
E	2	-1

as the character table. (Note that the characters in Eq. 5.4 can be considered as the traces of one-dimensional matrices.) The second way of treating the problem is to diagonalize the matrices of Eqs. 5.6 and 5.7 after first expressing the sine and cosine terms as their exponential equivalents. The results are

$$\mathbf{R}'(C_3) = \begin{bmatrix} e^{2\pi i/3} & 0 & 0 \\ 0 & e^{-2\pi i/3} & 0 \\ 0 & 0 & 1 \end{bmatrix} \tag{5.9}$$

$$\mathbf{R}'(C_3^2) = \begin{bmatrix} e^{-2\pi i/3} & 0 & 0 \\ 0 & e^{2\pi i/3} & 0 \\ 0 & 0 & 1 \end{bmatrix} \tag{5.10}$$

The first two diagonal elements of these are still not mutually independent. They are, in fact, the complex conjugates of each other. This, however, does allow us to resolve the two-dimensional representation into two imaginary one-dimensional representations:

(5.11)

$\mathbf{C}_3$	E	C_3	C_3^2
A	1	1	1
E	1	$e^{2\pi i/3}$	$e^{-2\pi i/3}$
	1	$e^{-2\pi i/3}$	$e^{2\pi i/3}$

Either Eq. 5.8 or Eq. 5.11 is an acceptable form of the character table of the $\mathbf{C}_3$ point group. Both show that the group can be represented by one one-dimensional and one two-dimensional irreducible representation. The imaginary form is listed in the character tables of the cyclic groups, while the real form is frequently used when there are additional generators present. The particular choice is made to obtain the proper relationships between the dimensions of the representations and the order of the group.

Let us now consider the $\mathbf{C}_{2v}$ point group. The elements are E, C_2, σ_v, and σ_v'. Their three-dimensional matrices, taking the z axis as the rotation axis, the xz plane for σ_v, and the yz plane for σ_v' are

$$\mathbf{R}(E) = \begin{bmatrix} 1 & 0 & 0 \\ 0 & 1 & 0 \\ 0 & 0 & 1 \end{bmatrix} \tag{5.12}$$

$$\mathbf{R}(C_2) = \begin{bmatrix} -1 & 0 & 0 \\ 0 & -1 & 0 \\ 0 & 0 & 1 \end{bmatrix} \tag{5.13}$$

$$\mathbf{R}(\sigma_v) = \begin{bmatrix} 1 & 0 & 0 \\ 0 & -1 & 0 \\ 0 & 0 & 1 \end{bmatrix} \tag{5.14}$$

$$\mathbf{R}(\sigma_v') = \begin{bmatrix} -1 & 0 & 0 \\ 0 & 1 & 0 \\ 0 & 0 & 1 \end{bmatrix} \tag{5.15}$$

These are again diagonal matrices; therefore, we can immediately write down three one-dimensional representations:

(5.16)

$\mathbf{C}_{2v}$	E	C_2	σ_v	σ_v'
$\Gamma(x)$	1	-1	1	-1
$\Gamma(y)$	1	-1	-1	1
$\Gamma(z)$	1	1	1	1

These, however, are not all the irreducible representations for this point group. The one-dimensional irreducible representations of a group must form a group in themselves when the product is defined as

$$\Gamma(a) \times \Gamma(b) = \Gamma(c) \tag{5.17a}$$

where

$$a_i b_i = c_i \tag{5.17b}$$

and the a_i, b_i, and c_i represent the characters for a given element in the irreducible representations $\Gamma(a)$, $\Gamma(b)$, and $\Gamma(c)$, respectively. Thus, in the case of the three representations for the $\mathbf{C}_{2v}$ point group, we have

$$\begin{aligned} \Gamma(z) \times \Gamma(x) &= 1 \times 1 \quad 1 \times (-1) \quad 1 \times 1 \quad 1 \times (-1) \\ &= \quad 1 \qquad -1 \qquad 1 \qquad -1 \\ &= \Gamma(x) \end{aligned} \tag{5.18}$$

$$\begin{aligned} \Gamma(z) \times \Gamma(y) &= 1 \times 1 \quad 1 \times (-1) \quad 1 \times (-1) \quad 1 \times 1 \\ &= \quad 1 \qquad -1 \qquad -1 \qquad 1 \\ &= \Gamma(y) \end{aligned} \tag{5.19}$$

$$\begin{aligned} \Gamma(x) \times \Gamma(y) &= 1 \times 1 \quad -1 \times (-1) \quad 1 \times (-1) \quad -1 \times 1 \\ &= \quad 1 \qquad 1 \qquad -1 \qquad -1 \end{aligned} \tag{5.20}$$

Equations 5.18 and 5.19 satisfy Eq. 5.17a within the context of the three previously defined representations; however, Eq. 5.20 yields a new representation. These are the only four irreducible representations that can be constructed for the $\mathbf{C}_{2v}$ point group by starting in the fashion that we did. The character table is thus

(5.21)

$\mathbf{C}_{2v}$	E	C_2	σ_v	σ'_v
A_1	1	1	1	1
A_2	1	1	−1	−1
B_1	1	−1	1	−1
B_2	1	−1	−1	1

The $\mathbf{C}_2$ point group has two symmetry elements. It also has two one-dimensional irreducible representations which could be found from the behavior of the elements with respect to a two-dimensional space. The $\mathbf{C}_3$ point group has three symmetry elements. There is one one-dimensional and one two-dimensional representation, derived from a three-dimensional space, in its character table. The $\mathbf{C}_{2v}$ point group has four symmetry elements. Its character table consists of four one-dimensional irreducible representations. If we had a four-dimensional space in which the matrices for the elements of the $\mathbf{C}_{2v}$ point group were

$$\mathbf{R}(E) = \begin{bmatrix} 1 & 0 & 0 & 0 \\ 0 & 1 & 0 & 0 \\ 0 & 0 & 1 & 0 \\ 0 & 0 & 0 & 1 \end{bmatrix} \tag{5.22}$$

$$\mathbf{R}(C_2) = \begin{bmatrix} 1 & 0 & 0 & 0 \\ 0 & 1 & 0 & 0 \\ 0 & 0 & -1 & 0 \\ 0 & 0 & 0 & -1 \end{bmatrix} \tag{5.23}$$

$$\mathbf{R}(\sigma_v) = \begin{bmatrix} 1 & 0 & 0 & 0 \\ 0 & -1 & 0 & 0 \\ 0 & 0 & 1 & 0 \\ 0 & 0 & 0 & -1 \end{bmatrix} \tag{5.24}$$

and

$$\mathbf{R}(\sigma_v') = \begin{bmatrix} 1 & 0 & 0 & 0 \\ 0 & -1 & 0 & 0 \\ 0 & 0 & -1 & 0 \\ 0 & 0 & 0 & 1 \end{bmatrix} \tag{5.25}$$

we would have a situation (analogous to our treatment of $\mathbf{C}_2$) in which we could find the irreducible representations simply by observing the behavior of the elements of the matrix representations of the symmetry elements with respect to each of the basis vectors in our space. We can draw a similar inference for any point group. If there are n symmetry elements, an n-dimensional space can be constructed from which the irreducible representations can be extracted by observing the behavior of the matrix elements of the matrix representations of the symmetry elements within the n-dimensional space.

Within the axial point groups all the irreducible representations will be one- or two-dimensional. The two-dimensional representations will arise for all cyclic groups with a rotational order higher than 2. In addition, in the cubic point groups three-dimensional irreducible representations occur, and in groups based on higher regular polyhedra, higher-dimensional irreducible representations will occur.

5.2 CONSTRUCTION OF CHARACTER TABLES

The character tables for all the axial point groups that can be constructed as direct products of their subgroups can be constructed in a rather simple manner by using the concept of generators. In the diagonal forms of the matrix representations of the symmetry operations that lead to one-dimensional irreducible representations, the diagonal elements are all ± 1, indicating that the operations are either symmetrical or antisymmetrical with respect to the various basis vectors. If the character table for a subgroup of the desired group is known, that for the group can be constructed by taking the characters of the coset of the subgroup with respect to the new generator as ± 1 times the characters of the subgroup. For example, in the $\mathbf{C}_{2v}$ point group, the generators are C_2 and σ_v. The $\mathbf{C}_2$ point group is a subgroup of the $\mathbf{C}_{2v}$ group. The coset of this subgroup is $\{\sigma_v, \sigma_v'\}$. Taking $+1$ for the character of σ_v gives

$$\chi_A(\sigma_v) = +1 \times 1 = 1 \tag{5.26a}$$

$$\chi_A(\sigma_v') = +1 \times 1 = 1 \tag{5.26b}$$

$$\chi_B(\sigma_v) = +1 \times 1 = 1 \tag{5.26c}$$

$$\chi_B(\sigma_v') = +1 \times (-1) = -1 \tag{5.26d}$$

This yields the irreducible representations

(5.27)

	E	C_2	σ_v	σ_v'
A_1	1	1	1	1
B_1	1	-1	1	-1

Taking the antisymmetric behavior (-1) for σ_v gives

$$\chi_A(\sigma_v) = -1 \times 1 = -1 \tag{5.28a}$$

$$\chi_A(\sigma_v') = -1 \times 1 = -1 \tag{5.28b}$$

$$\chi_B(\sigma_v) = -1 \times 1 = -1 \tag{5.28c}$$

$$\chi_B(\sigma_v') = -1 \times (-1) = 1 \tag{5.28d}$$

and for the irreducible representations

(5.29)

	E	C_2	σ_v	σ_v'
A_2	1	1	-1	-1
B_2	1	-1	-1	1

This is exactly the same set of irreducible representations that we obtained previously. The character table for any other axial point group involving only direct products can be obtained in a completely analogous fashion if the characters of the corresponding cyclic subgroups are known. The character tables for axial point groups involving semidirect products can also be constructed in this manner by recognizing the fact that the principal cyclic subgroup must be taken in its real form in these cases. All generators, except rotations of orders higher than 2, form cyclic subgroups of an order of 2, and can thus be represented by representations involving only ± 1 for the characters.

The irreducible representations and characters of the cyclic point groups (or subgroups) can be constructed in a straightforward manner. The basic requirement is that $[\chi(C_n)]^n$ must equal $\chi(E)$, which in turn equals unity. This yields the following results. For the group $\mathbf{C}_n$, if n is even, there will be an A representation, a B representation, and a set of E_k representations with k going from 1 to $n/2 - 1$. If n is odd, there is no B representation, and the values of k for the E_k representations run from 1 to $(n - 1)/2$. The characters of the A representation are all $+1$, while the characters of the B representation, if it exists, alternate between $+1$ and -1. The characters for the pairs of degenerate E_k representations are $[\exp(2\pi i/n)]^{jk}$ and $[\exp(-2\pi i/n)]^{jk}$, where k is the particular one of the E_k under consideration and j comes from the rotational elements C_n^j. (This makes the first element e^0, or unity. Note also that the A and B representations are special cases of this, with k equal to zero and $n/2$, respectively.) If the E representations are desired in real form, they can be obtained by adding the degenerate pairs of imaginary representations, making use of the sine and cosine equivalents of the exponentials. For example, in the $\mathbf{C}_3$ point group we would expect the representations

$\mathbf{C}_3$	E	C_3	C_3^2
A	1	1	1
E_1	1	$e^{2\pi i/3}$	$e^{4\pi i/3}$
	1	$e^{-2\pi i/3}$	$e^{-4\pi i/3}$

(5.30)

This is equivalent to Eq. 5.11 when we realize that a rotation of $+4\pi/3$, or 240°, is completely equivalent to a rotation of $-2\pi/3$, or $-120°$. The real E representation can be obtained as follows:

		E	C_3	C_3^2	
E_{complex}	Γ_1	1	$\cos 2\pi/3 + i \sin 2\pi/3$	$\cos 4\pi/3 + i \sin 4\pi/3$	(5.31a)
	Γ_2	1	$\cos 2\pi/3 - i \sin 2\pi/3$	$\cos 4\pi/3 - i \sin 4\pi/3$	(5.31b)
$\Gamma_1 + \Gamma_2$		2	$2 \cos 2\pi/3$	$2 \cos 4\pi/3$	(5.31c)
E_{real}		2	-1	-1	(5.31d)

As another example, consider the $\mathbf{C}_6$ point group. There will be an A representation, a B representation, and two E representations, E_1 and E_2. If the quantity ε

is defined as exp $(2\pi i/6)$, and ε^* as its complex conjugate, we have

(5.32)

$\mathbf{C}_6$		E	C_6	C_3	C_2	C_3^2	C_6^5
A		1	1	1	1	1	1
B		1	-1	1	-1	1	-1
E_1	{	1	ε	ε^2	ε^3	ε^4	ε^5
		1	ε^*	ε^{*2}	ε^{*3}	ε^{*4}	ε^{*5}
E_2	{	1	ε^2	ε^4	ε^6	ε^8	ε^{10}
		1	ε^{*2}	ε^{*4}	ε^{*6}	ε^{*8}	ε^{*10}

The character table for the $\mathbf{C}_6$ point group is more commonly written as follows:

(5.33)

$\mathbf{C}_6$		E	C_6	C_3	C_2	C_3^2	C_6^5
A		1	1	1	1	1	1
B		1	-1	1	-1	1	-1
E_1	{	1	ε	$-\varepsilon^*$	-1	$-\varepsilon$	ε^*
		1	ε^*	$-\varepsilon$	-1	$-\varepsilon^*$	ε
E_2	{	1	$-\varepsilon^*$	$-\varepsilon$	1	$-\varepsilon^*$	$-\varepsilon$
		1	$-\varepsilon$	$-\varepsilon^*$	1	$-\varepsilon$	$-\varepsilon^*$

The corresponding terms in the E representations in Eqs. 5.32 and 5.33 can be shown to be identical by making use of common trigonometric identities. If the real forms of the E representations are desired, the result is

(5.34)

$\mathbf{C}_6$	E	$2C_6$	$2C_3$	C_2
A	1	1	1	1
B	1	-1	1	-1
E_1	2	1	-1	-2
E_2	2	-1	-1	2

A number of important character tables are given in Appendix 5.

Exercise 5.1: Construct the character tables for the following point groups: $\mathbf{C}_5$; $\mathbf{D}_{2h}$; $\mathbf{C}_{3h}$.

5.3 CONSTRUCTION OF CHARACTER TABLES FROM DIRECT AND SEMIDIRECT PRODUCTS

Character tables can also be constructed from the direct and semidirect product relationships. For the axial point groups this offers no advantage over the method we have outlined using generators. However, when there is more than one cyclic subgroup to the desired group which has an order higher than 2 (as in the groups for regular polyhedra), this method is very important.

The basic procedure is to construct multiplication tables to find the elements, classes, irreducible representations, and characters as products of those of the subgroups. If only direct products are involved, the new classes, the new representations, and the new characters are all direct products of the classes, representations, and characters of the two groups. As an example, for $\mathbf{D}_{3h}$, which equals $(\mathbf{D}_3 \times \mathbf{C}_s)$, we have for the classes and representations

$\mathbf{C}_s$ \ $\mathbf{D}_3$	E	$2C_3$	$3C_2$
E	E	$2C_3$	$3C_2$
σ	σ_h	$2S_3$	$3\sigma_v$

(5.35a)

$\mathbf{C}_s$ \ $\mathbf{D}_3$	A_1	A_2	E
A'	A_1'	A_2'	E'
A''	A_1''	A_2''	E''

(5.35b)

and, for example, for the characters of the E'' representation

$\mathbf{C}_s$	$\chi(A'')$ \ $\mathbf{D}_3$	E	$2C_3$	$3C_2$
	$\chi(E)$	2	-1	0
E	1	2	-1	0
σ	-1	-2	1	0

(5.35c)

The characters for the other irreducible representations can be obtained similarly.

When semidirect products are involved, the process of constructing a character table is a bit more complicated. The class structure usually can be obtained from a multiplication table similar to 5.35a. If the elements of the invariant subgroup are listed vertically, the columns of the table will indicate the classes. Each different type of entry will indicate a class. For example, for $\mathbf{C}_{3v}$, expressed as $(\mathbf{C}_3 \wedge \mathbf{C}_s)$, we have

$\mathbf{C}_3$ \ $\mathbf{C}_s$	E	σ
E	E	σ_v
C_3	C_3	σ_v'
C_3^2	C_3^2	σ_v''

(5.36)

In the first column we have E, C_3, and C_3^2. The two C_3's are elements of the same type, forming one class. The second column contains three σ_v's all belonging to the same class. If it is not obvious from inspection whether or not the elements in a column belong to the same class, conjugate relationships will have to be employed.

We have three classes for $\mathbf{C}_{3v}$. There will also be three irreducible representations. These cannot be obtained directly in the manner that they were in 5.35b. A table similar to 5.35b is, however, useful. Indicating the separable components of the E representation by $E^{(1)}$ and $E^{(2)}$, we have

$\mathbf{C}_3$ \ $\mathbf{C}_s$	A	B
A	AA	AB
$E^{(1)}$	$E^{(1)}A$	$E^{(1)}B$
$E^{(2)}$	$E^{(2)}A$	$E^{(2)}B$

(5.37)

The product of the totally symmetric irreducible representation of the invariant subgroup with the representations of the other subgroup always yields irreducible representations of the new group; thus, the one-dimensional AA and AB lead directly to irreducible representations. These comprise two of the three possible irreducible representations. The other four cannot be independent. From the order of the group, we can find that the remaining representation must be two-dimensional:

$$\begin{aligned} 1^2 + 1^2 + d^2 &= 6 \\ d^2 &= 4 \\ d &= 2 \end{aligned} \tag{5.38}$$

The characters of the representations can be obtained with the help of tables similar to 5.35c. If we construct the tables for $\mathbf{C}_{3v}$, we have [where $\varepsilon = \exp(2\pi i/3)$]

$\chi(AA)$: (5.39a)

$\mathbf{C}_3$ \ $\mathbf{C}_s$		E	σ
		1	1
E	1	1	1
C_3	1	1	1
C_3^2	1	1	1

$\chi(AB)$: (5.39b)

$\mathbf{C}_3$ \ $\mathbf{C}_s$		E	σ
		1	-1
E	1	1	-1
C_3	1	1	-1
C_3^2	1	1	-1

$\chi(E^{(1)}A)$: (5.39c)

C_3 \ C_s		E	σ
		1	1
E	1	1	1
C_3	ε	ε	ε
C_3^2	ε^*	ε^*	ε^*

$\chi(E^{(1)}B)$: (5.39d)

C_3 \ C_s		E	σ
		1	-1
E	1	1	-1
C_3	ε	ε	$-\varepsilon$
C_3^2	ε^*	ε^*	$-\varepsilon^*$

$\chi(E^{(2)}A)$: (5.39e)

C_3 \ C_s		E	σ
		1	1
E	1	1	1
C_3	ε^*	ε^*	ε^*
C_3^2	ε	ε	ε

$\chi(E^{(2)}B)$: (5.39f)

C_3 \ C_s		E	σ
		1	-1
E	1	1	-1
C_3	ε^*	ε^*	$-\varepsilon^*$
C_3^2	ε	ε	$-\varepsilon$

The characters of the A_1 and A_2 representations of $\mathbf{C}_{3v}$ come directly from 5.39a and 5.39b. To obtain the characters of the E representation, we take the weighted average of the characters for the elements in the classes of the various nonindependent representations from the same column of Eq. 5.37, and then combine them in some way to obtain the characters for the independent, irreducible representations. This gives for $E^{(1)}A$ and $E^{(2)}A$ in $\mathbf{C}_{3v}$,

(5.40)

	E	$2C_3$	$3\sigma_v$
$E^{(1)}A$	1	$\frac{1}{2}(\varepsilon + \varepsilon^*)$	$\frac{1}{3}(1 + \varepsilon + \varepsilon^*)$
	(1	$-\frac{1}{2}$	0)
$E^{(2)}A$	1	$\frac{1}{2}(\varepsilon^* + \varepsilon)$	$\frac{1}{3}(1 + \varepsilon^* + \varepsilon)$
	(1	$-\frac{1}{2}$	0)

We know, however, that the two components of the E representation in $\mathbf{C}_3$ are not independent; thus, we might suspect that some combination of them would be required in $\mathbf{C}_{3v}$. If we take the sum of $E^{(1)}A$ and $E^{(2)}A$, we obtain

	E	$2C_3$	σ_v
EA	2	-1	0

(5.41)

This representation satisfies all the criteria for an irreducible representation. It also has the correct dimensionality to be our missing representation. Furthermore, if we hade constructed EB from $E^{(1)}B$ and $E^{(2)}B$, we would have obtained the same representation. Thus, as it should, our semidirect product construction yields the proper character table for $\mathbf{C}_{3v}$.

The same results for $\mathbf{C}_{3v}$ could have been obtained by recognizing at the outset that the semidirect product destroys the separability of the components of an E representation. The E representation of $\mathbf{C}_3$ could be written in real form from the start. This would give, instead of Eq. 5.40, for the representations:

$\mathbf{C}_3$ \ $\mathbf{C}_s$	A	B
A	A	AB
E	E	EB

(5.42)

This yields the three irreducible representations directly, since the product EB equals E.

Let us work through the semidirect product construction for another point group. The group $\mathbf{T}_d$ can be constructed as $(\mathbf{D}_2 \wedge \mathbf{C}_{3v})$. The multiplication table for the elements is

$\mathbf{D}_2$ \ $\mathbf{C}_{3v}$	E	$2C_3$	$3\sigma_v$
E	E	$2C_3$	$3\sigma_v$
$C_2(z)$	$C_2(z)$	$2C_3'$	$3\sigma_v'$
$C_2(y)$	$C_2(y)$	$2C_3''$	$3S_4$
$C_2(x)$	$C_2(x)$	$2C_3'''$	$3S_4'$

(5.43)

Thus, we have the five classes $\{E, 3C_2, 8C_3, 6\sigma_d, 6S_4\}$. (The plane of symmetry is denoted as σ_d to correspond to normal usage.) The multiplication table for the representations is

$\mathbf{D}_2$ \ $\mathbf{C}_{3v}$	A_1	A_2	E
A_1	A_1A_1	A_1A_2	A_1E
B_1	B_1A_1	B_1A_2	B_1E
B_2	B_2A_1	B_2A_2	B_2E
B_3	B_3A_1	B_3A_2	B_3E

(5.44)

We can be assured that the A_1A_1, A_1A_2, and A_1E elements will be irreducible representations (the A_1, A_2, and E of $\mathbf{T}_d$); however, the other nine cannot be independent. Only two more irreducible representations are allowed. Let us consider the characters for these nine nonindependent representations:

$\chi(B_1A_1)$: (5.45a)

$\mathbf{D}_2$ \ $\mathbf{C}_{3v}$		E	$2C_3$	$3\sigma_v$
		1	1	1
E	1	1	1	1
$C_2(z)$	1	1	1	1
$C_2(y)$	-1	-1	-1	-1
$C_2(x)$	-1	-1	-1	-1

$\chi(B_2A_1)$: (5.45b)

$\mathbf{D}_2$ \ $\mathbf{C}_{3v}$		E	$2C_3$	$3\sigma_v$
		1	1	1
E	1	1	1	1
$C_2(z)$	-1	-1	-1	-1
$C_2(y)$	1	1	1	1
$C_2(x)$	-1	-1	-1	-1

$\chi(B_3A_1)$: (5.45c)

$\mathbf{D}_2$ \ $\mathbf{C}_{3v}$		E	$2C_3$	$3\sigma_v$
		1	1	1
E	1	1	1	1
$C_2(z)$	-1	-1	-1	-1
$C_2(y)$	-1	-1	-1	-1
$C_2(x)$	1	1	1	1

$\chi(B_1A_2)$: (5.45d)

$\mathbf{D}_2$ \ $\mathbf{C}_{3v}$		E	$2C_3$	$3\sigma_v$
		1	1	-1
E	1	1	1	-1
$C_2(z)$	1	1	1	-1
$C_2(y)$	-1	-1	-1	1
$C_2(x)$	-1	-1	-1	1

$\chi(B_2A_2)$: (5.45e)

$\mathbf{D}_2$ \ $\mathbf{C}_{3v}$		E	$2C_3$	$3\sigma_v$
		1	1	-1
E	1	1	1	-1
$C_2(z)$	-1	-1	-1	1
$C_2(y)$	1	1	1	-1
$C_2(x)$	-1	-1	-1	1

$\chi(B_3A_2)$: (5.45f)

$\mathbf{D}_2$ \ $\mathbf{C}_{3v}$		E	$2C_3$	$3\sigma_v$
		1	1	-1
E	1	1	1	-1
$C_2(z)$	-1	-1	-1	1
$C_2(y)$	-1	-1	-1	1
$C_2(x)$	1	1	1	-1

$\chi(B_1E)$: (5.45g)

$\mathbf{D}_2$ \ $\mathbf{C}_{3v}$		E	$2C_3$	$3\sigma_v$
		2	-1	0
E	1	2	-1	0
$C_2(z)$	1	2	-1	0
$C_2(y)$	-1	-2	1	0
$C_2(x)$	-1	-2	1	0

$\chi(B_2E)$: (5.45h)

$\mathbf{D}_2$ \ $\mathbf{C}_{3v}$		E	$2C_3$	$3\sigma_v$
		2	-1	0
E	1	2	-1	0
$C_2(z)$	-1	-2	1	0
$C_2(y)$	1	2	-1	0
$C_2(x)$	-1	-2	1	0

$\chi(B_3E)$: (5.45i)

$\mathbf{D}_2$ \ $\mathbf{C}_{3v}$		E	$2C_3$	$3\sigma_v$
		2	-1	0
E	1	2	-1	0
$C_2(z)$	-1	-2	1	0
$C_2(y)$	-1	-2	1	0
$C_2(x)$	1	2	-1	0

If the combination, averaging, and adding process is applied to the nonindependent representations in the various columns of Eq. 5.44, we have

	E	$3C_2$	$8C_3$	$6\sigma_d$	$6S_4$
B_1A_1	(1	$\frac{1}{3}(1-1-1)$	$\frac{1}{4}(1+1-1-1)$	$\frac{1}{2}(1+1)$	$\frac{1}{2}(-1-1)$)
	1	$-\frac{1}{3}$	0	1	-1
B_2A_1	1	$-\frac{1}{3}$	0	0	0
B_3A_1	1	$-\frac{1}{3}$	0	0	0
$B_1A_1 + B_2A_1 + B_3A_1$	3	-1	0	1	-1

(5.46)

	E	$3C_2$	$8C_3$	$6\sigma_d$	$6S_4$
B_1A_2	1	$-\frac{1}{3}$	0	-1	1
B_2A_2	1	$-\frac{1}{3}$	0	0	0
B_3A_2	1	$-\frac{1}{3}$	0	0	0
$B_1A_2 + B_2A_2 + B_3A_2$	3	-1	0	-1	1

(5.47)

	E	$3C_2$	$8C_3$	$6\sigma_d$	$6S_4$
B_3E	2	$-\frac{2}{3}$	0	0	0
B_2E	2	$-\frac{2}{3}$	0	0	0
B_3E	2	$-\frac{2}{3}$	0	0	0
$B_1E + B_2E + B_3E$	6	-2	0	0	0

(5.48)

It is immediately obvious that the representation of 5.48 is the sum of 5.46 and 5.47. Furthermore, 5.46 and 5.47 correspond to the T_1 and T_2 representations of T_d. Thus, in this case, our process gives the two new irreducible representations that were required and a representation that is the sum of the two. This procedure can be applied to construct the character table from any semidirect product relationship. The representations obtained by combining the nonindependent representations from a given column will either correspond to an irreducible representation or to a combination of such representations.

Exercise 5.2: Construct the character table for the group **0** from the relationship

$$\mathbf{0} = (\mathbf{D}_2 \wedge \mathbf{D}_3')$$

5.4 REDUCTION OF REDUCIBLE REPRESENTATIONS

In applications of group theory to molecular and other problems, representations of the various point groups are frequently obtained which are *reducible* (i.e., resolvable into sums of irreducible representations). For example, the product of E_1 and E_2 from $\mathbf{C}_{6v}$ (see Appendix 5),

$$\begin{aligned} E_1 \times E_2 &= 2 \times 2 \quad 1 \times (-1) \quad -1 \times (-1) \quad -2 \times 2 \quad 0 \times 0 \quad 0 \times 0 \\ &= \quad 4 \qquad\quad -1 \qquad\qquad 1 \qquad\qquad -4 \qquad\quad 0 \qquad\quad 0 \end{aligned} \tag{5.49}$$

leads to a representation that equals the sum $B_1 + B_2 + E_1$.

The reduction of reducible representations can frequently be carried out by inspection. There is, however, a more systematic way of doing this. We have previously described irreducible representations as mutually independent mappings of the behavior of the n-dimensional set of orthonormal basis vectors with respect to the operations of the point group. This mutual independence means that the irreducible representations themselves must comprise a set of mutually orthogonal functions. They may be normalized by multiplying through by $g^{-1/2}$, where g is the order of the group. This orthogonality requires that

$$g^{-1}\sum_{i=1}^{g}\chi_i^{*(\mu)}\chi_i^{(\nu)} = \delta_{\mu\nu} \tag{5.50a}$$

where the summation is over *all* elements, or

$$g^{-1}\sum_{i=1}^{k}g_i\chi_i^{*(\mu)}\chi_i^{(\nu)} = \delta_{\mu\nu} \tag{5.50b}$$

where the summation is over the classes and g_i is the order of the ith class. If a reducible representation is used in Eqs. 5.50 instead of the irreducible representation, Γ_ν, the result would be zero if Γ_μ did not appear in the reducible representation, or if Γ_μ did appear, the result would be the number of times it appeared. Thus, the number of times a given irreducible representation μ appears in a reducible representation Γ is

$$a_\mu = g^{-1}\sum_{i=1}^{k}g_i\chi_i^{*(\mu)}\chi_i^{(\Gamma)} \tag{5.51}$$

For example, the reduction of the representation obtained in Eq. 5.49 can be verified with the aid of Eq. 5.51:

$$\begin{aligned} a_{B_1} &= \tfrac{1}{12}[1\times 1\times 4 + 2\times(-1)\times(-1) + 2\times 1\times 1 \\ &\quad + 1\times(-1)\times(-4) + 3\times 1\times 0 + 3\times(-1)\times 0] \\ &= \tfrac{1}{12}[4+2+2+4+0+0] \\ &= 1 \end{aligned} \tag{5.52a}$$

$$\begin{aligned} a_{B_2} &= \tfrac{1}{12}[1\times 1\times 4 + 2\times(-1)\times(-1) + 2\times 1\times 1 \\ &\quad + 1\times(-1)\times(-4) + 3\times(-1)\times 0 + 3\times 1\times 0] \\ &= 1 \end{aligned} \tag{5.52b}$$

$$\begin{aligned} a_{E_1} &= \tfrac{1}{12}[1\times 2\times 4 + 2\times 1\times(-1) + 2\times(-1)\times 1 \\ &\quad + 1\times(-2)\times(-4) + 3\times 0\times 0 + 3\times 0\times 0] \\ &= 1 \end{aligned} \tag{5.52c}$$

That any of the other irreducible representations do not appear can also be verified. For example, for A_1 we have

$$\begin{aligned} a_{A_1} &= \tfrac{1}{12}[1\times 1\times 4 + 2\times 1\times(-1) + 2\times 1\times 1 \\ &\quad + 1\times 1\times(-4) + 3\times 1\times 0 + 3\times 1\times 0] \\ &= 0 \end{aligned} \tag{5.53}$$

The systematic reduction of a reducible representation requires the application of Eq. 5.51 for each irreducible representation of the point group.

Exercise 5.3*: Reduce the indicated representations in the indicated point groups:

(a)

$\mathbf{C}_{3v}$	E	$2C_3$	$3\sigma_v$
Γ	4	1	0

(b)

$\mathbf{D}_{3h}$	E	$2C_3$	$3C_2$	σ_h	$2S_3$	$3\sigma_v$
Γ	5	-1	-1	1	1	-1

(c)

$\mathbf{T}_d$	E	$8C_3$	$3C_2$	$6S_4$	$6\sigma_d$
Γ	6	0	2	0	-2

5.5 PROJECTION OPERATORS

The discussion in the previous section dealt with the projection of irreducible representations out of reducible representations. It is frequently desirable to project functions that transform as a particular irreducible representation from out of a function space. This has applications, for example, in constructing normal modes of vibration, symmetry adapted molecular orbitals, and so on. The most systematic procedure for accomplishing this is to use the technique of *projection operators.* The systematic reduction of reducible representations is, in fact, a special application of projection operators. In this section, we will develop the concept of projection operators.

In Section 5.1 we stated that the irreducible representations of a group of order n could be constructed from the elements of n-dimensional matrices representing the group of transformations within an n-dimensional space. If all the representations are one-dimensional, these matrices may be put in a diagonal form. If any representations have higher dimensionalities, the matrices will be in a block diagonal form (i.e., along the diagonal there will be smaller matrices having the dimensionalities of the irreducible representations). All the other elements will be zero. These smaller matrices correspond to the various irreducible representations of the operations in the various dimensionalities.

There is a theorem (see Appendix 2 for a proof) which states that the elements of the matrices, $\mathbf{D}^{(\mu)}$ and $\mathbf{D}^{(\nu)}$, of any two irreducible representations, Γ_μ and Γ_ν, of a group satisfy the relations

$$\sum_R [\mathbf{D}^{(\mu)}(R)]_{ij}^* [\mathbf{D}^{(\nu)}(R)]_{pq} = \frac{g}{n_\mu} \delta_{\mu\nu} \delta_{ip} \delta_{jq} \tag{5.54}$$

where g is the order of the group, n_μ the dimensionality of the μth irreducible representation, and the summation runs over all the elements of the group. The formal derivation of the equations for reducing reducible representations (Eqs. 5.50) is based upon this theorem.

If we operate on one of the basis vectors, $\mathbf{f}_q^{(\nu)}$, used to define the representation matrices by one of the group operations, the result may be expressed

$$R\mathbf{f}_q^{(\nu)} = \sum_{p=1}^{n_\nu} [\mathbf{D}^{(\nu)}(R)]_{pq}\mathbf{f}_p^{(\nu)} \tag{5.55}$$

That is, the resulting vector is a linear combination of the basis vectors, the combining coefficients being one of the columns of the representation matrix. If Eq. 5.55 is multiplied by $[\mathbf{D}^{(\mu)}(R)]_{ij}^*$, the complex conjugate of some particular element of the matrix of some representation, and the result is summed over all R, we have

$$\sum_R [\mathbf{D}^{(\mu)}(R)]_{ij}^* R\mathbf{f}_q^{(\nu)} = \sum_{p=1}^{n_\nu}\sum_R [\mathbf{D}^{(\mu)}(R)]_{ij}^*[\mathbf{D}^{(\nu)}(R)]_{pq}\mathbf{f}_p^{(\nu)} \tag{5.56}$$

$$= \sum_{p=1}^{n_\nu} \frac{g}{n_\nu}\delta_{\mu\nu}\delta_{ip}\delta_{jq}\mathbf{f}_p^{(\nu)} \tag{5.57}$$

where Eq. 5.57 arises from the use of Eq. 5.54. If only the diagonal elements where i equals j are considered, and these are summed, we have

$$\sum_R\sum_i [\mathbf{D}^{(\mu)}(R)]_{ii}^* R\mathbf{f}_q^{(\nu)} = \sum_R \chi_R^{*(\mu)} R\mathbf{f}_q^{(\nu)} \tag{5.58}$$

$$= \sum_{i=1}^{n_\nu} \frac{g}{n_\nu}\delta_{\mu\nu}\delta_{iq}\mathbf{f}_i^{(\nu)} \tag{5.59}$$

or defining the *projection operator*, $P^{(\mu)}$, as $\sum_R \chi_R^{*(\mu)}R$ and redefining the right-hand side of Eq. 5.59 in terms of μ rather than ν, we have

$$P^{(\mu)}\mathbf{f}_q^{(\nu)} = \sum_R \chi_R^{*(\mu)} R\mathbf{f}_q^{(\nu)} = \sum_{i=1}^{n_\mu} \frac{g}{n_\mu}\delta_{\mu\nu}\delta_{iq}\mathbf{f}_i^{(\mu)} \tag{5.60}$$

Consider now the application of the projection operator to any general vector in the space of Γ_σ:

$$P^{(\mu)}\mathbf{f}^{(\sigma)} = 0 \qquad \text{if} \quad \sigma \not\subset \mu \tag{5.61}$$

$$P^{(\mu)}\mathbf{f}^{(\sigma)} = \frac{g}{n_\mu}\mathbf{f}^{(\mu)} \quad \text{if} \quad \sigma \subset \mu \tag{5.62}$$

or

$$\mathbf{f}^{(\mu)} = \frac{n_\mu}{g} P^{(\mu)}\mathbf{f}^{(\sigma)} \tag{5.63}$$

In other words, $P^{(\mu)}$ annihilates any vector that does not belong to the Γ_μ space, and produces a numerical multiple of $\mathbf{f}^{(\mu)}$ when applied to any vector belonging to the Γ_μ space.

The projection operator can be used with any basis function that contributes to a function belonging to a particular irreducible representation to obtain a properly symmetry-adapted function. All that is needed is the character table and the transformation properties of the basis functions under the various operations of the group.

Let us illustrate the application of projection operators by projecting out functions of x and y that belong to various irreducible representations of the $\mathbf{D}_4$ group when the symmetry elements are aligned such that the z axis is the C_4 axis, and the x and y lie along the C_2''s (Fig. 5.1). Table 5.1 shows the results of operating on x, y, x^2, y^2, and xy with the symmetry operations of $\mathbf{D}_4$. Consider now the projection out of a function of A_1 symmetry from the function x^2. Applying Eq. 5.62, we have

$$\begin{aligned} P^{(A_1)}x^2 &= \chi_E^{*(A_1)}x^2 + \chi_{C_4}^{*(A_1)}(y^2 + y^2) + \chi_{C_2}^{*(A_1)}x^2 + \chi_{C_2'}^{*(A_1)}(x^2 + x^2) \\ &\quad + \chi_{C_2''}^{*(A_1)}(y^2 + y^2) \\ &= 1 \times x^2 + 1 \times (y^2 + y^2) + 1 \times x^2 + 1 \times (x^2 + x^2) \\ &\quad + 1 \times (y^2 + y^2) \\ &= 4(x^2 + y^2) \end{aligned} \tag{5.64}$$

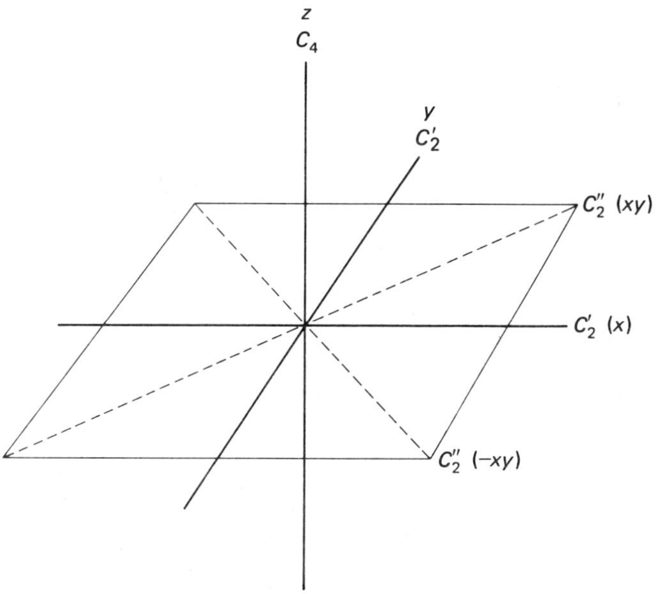

Fig. 5.1. Alignment of symmetry elements of $\mathbf{D}_{4h}$ to illustrate projection operators.

Table 5.1. Effect of operating on x, y, x^2, y^2, and xy with the operations of $\mathbf{D}_4$

		$2C_4$			$2C_2'$		$2C_2''$	
$\mathbf{D}_4$	E	C_4	C_4^3	$C_2(z)$	$C_2'(x)$	$C_2'(y)$	$C_2''(xy)$	$C_2''(-xy)$
x	x	y	$-y$	$-x$	x	$-x$	y	$-y$
y	y	$-x$	x	$-y$	$-y$	y	x	$-x$
x^2	x^2	y^2	y^2	x^2	x^2	x^2	y^2	y^2
y^2	y^2	x^2	x^2	y^2	y^2	y^2	x^2	x^2
xy	xy	$-xy$	$-xy$	xy	$-xy$	$-xy$	xy	xy

Thus, dividing through by the order of the group, we see that the function $\frac{1}{2}(x^2 + y^2)$ has A_1 symmetry. Similarly, for B_1 symmetry, we have

$$\begin{aligned} P^{(B_1)}x^2 &= 1 \times x^2 - 1 \times (y^2 + y^2) + 1 \times x^2 \\ &\quad + 1 \times (x^2 + x^2) - 1 \times (y^2 + y^2) \\ &= 4(x^2 - y^2) \end{aligned} \tag{5.65}$$

Consider now the projection of a B_2 component out of the polynomial $x^2 + 2xy + y^2$. We can in this case simply project out the B_2 component of each term of the polynomial and add the results. This yields

$$\begin{aligned} P^{(B_2)}x^2 &= 1 \times x^2 - 1 \times (y^2 + y^2) + 1 \times x^2 - 1 \\ &\quad \times (x^2 + x^2) + 1 \times (y^2 + y^2) \\ &= 0 \end{aligned} \tag{5.66}$$

$$\begin{aligned} P^{(B_2)}2xy &= 1 \times 2xy - 1 \times (-2xy - 2xy) + 1 \times 2xy - 1 \\ &\quad \times (-2xy - 2xy) + 1 \times (2xy + 2xy) \\ &= 16xy \end{aligned} \tag{5.67}$$

$$\begin{aligned} P^{(B_2)}y^2 &= 1 \times y^2 - 1 \times (x^2 + x^2) + 1 \times y^2 - 1 \\ &\quad \times (y^2 + y^2) + 1 \times (x^2 + x^2) \\ &= 0 \end{aligned} \tag{5.68}$$

Thus, the B_2 component of $x^2 + 2xy + y^2$ is simply $2xy$. Other polynomials and other functions are handled similarly.

Exercise 5.4: Project out the x^2 containing function of the A representation of the group $\mathbf{T}$.

Exercise 5.5: Project out the functions of the bonds in methane that transform as the A and the T representations in the group $\mathbf{T}$.

5.6 NOTATION FOR IRREDUCIBLE REPRESENTATIONS

The notation that we have been using for the irreducible representations (A, B, E) was introduced by Mulliken in 1933, and has since become the standard notation for spectroscopy and for quantum mechanics. In this notation, all one-dimensional representations are referred to as A or B representations, two-dimensional representations as E representations, and three-dimensional representations as T (or sometimes F) representations. If representations of higher dimensionality are encountered, they are labeled successively, G, H, and so on. The distinction between A and B reflects the behavior with respect to the principal axis. Representations that are symmetric with respect to the principal axis are A representations, while those which are antisymmetric are B. If more than one representation of a given type (A, B, E, or T) is present, subscripts or primes are used to distinguish between them. These primes and subscripts depend upon the behavior of the representation with respect to some particular symmetry element. For the A and B representations, the subscripts 1 and 2 represent symmetric and antisymmetric behavior, respectively, with respect to a C_2 perpendicular to the principal axis or to a σ_v or σ_d, the choice being made in the listed order. The $\mathbf{D}_2$ and $\mathbf{D}_{2h}$ point groups, which have three perpendicular C_2's have B_1, B_2, and B_3 representations, indicating which combination of symmetric–antisymmetric behavior with respect to these is appropriate. We have already discussed the subscripts for the E representations. The T_1 representation arises from the basis vector transformation resulting from the transformation matrices we presented in Eqs. 3.6–3.13. The T_2 representation is obtained from the product

$$T_2 = A_2 \times T_1 \tag{5.69}$$

For all irreducible representations, a subscript g (for *gerade*) is added if the system is symmetric with respect to a point of inversion while a subscript u (for *ungerade*) is used if it is antisymmetric. If a σ_h element is present, a single prime indicates symmetric behavior, while a double prime indicates antisymmetric behavior with respect to this element. Only the required number of subscripts and superscripts necessary to eliminate ambiguities are used.

By using the concepts involved in the notation for irreducible representations, multiplication rules can be derived for the products of irreducible representations without going through the effort of a character-by-character multiplication. For one-dimensional representations, this is almost trivial. One only needs to remember that a symmetric character times a symmetric character or an antisymmetric character times an antisymmetric character yields a symmetric character, while an antisymmetric character times a symmetric character yields an antisymmetric character [i.e., $1 \times 1 = (-1) \times (-1) = 1$ and $-1 \times 1 = -1$].

Thus, we have

$$A \times A = B \times B = A \tag{5.70a}$$

$$A \times B = B \times A = B \tag{5.70b}$$

$$X_1 \times X_1 = X_2 \times X_2 = X_1 \tag{5.70c}$$

$$X_1 \times X_2 = X_2 \tag{5.70d}$$

and so on. For products involving two- or three-dimensional representations, the notation alone is not sufficient to determine the rules. The results for all common point groups are shown in Table 5.2.

The notations we have used for irreducible representations is that which is in most common current usage. There are other conventions that are sometimes

Table 5.2. Multiplication properties of irreducible representations*

General rules:
$A \times A = A, B \times B = A, A \times B = B, A \times E = E, B \times E = E, A \times T = T, B \times T = T;$
$g \times g = g, u \times u = g, u \times g = u; ' \times ' = ', ' \times '' = ''; A \times E_1 = E_1, A \times E_2 = E_2,$
$B \times E_1 = E_2, B \times E_2 = E_1$

Subscripts on A or B:
$1 \times 1 = 1, 2 \times 2 = 1, 1 \times 2 = 2$, except for $\mathbf{D}_2$ and $\mathbf{D}_{2h}$, where $1 \times 2 = 3, 2 \times 3 = 1,$
$1 \times 3 = 2$

Doubly degenerate representations:
For $\mathbf{C}_3, \mathbf{C}_{3h}, \mathbf{C}_{3v}, \mathbf{D}_3, \mathbf{D}_{3h}, \mathbf{D}_{3d}, \mathbf{C}_6, \mathbf{C}_{6v}, \mathbf{D}_6, \mathbf{D}_{6h}, \mathbf{S}_6, \mathbf{0}, \mathbf{0}_h, \mathbf{T}, \mathbf{T}_d, \mathbf{T}_h$:

$$E_1 \times E_1 = E_2 \times E_2 = A_1 + A_2 + E_2$$
$$E_1 \times E_2 = B_1 + B_2 + E_1$$

For $\mathbf{C}_4, \mathbf{C}_{4v}, \mathbf{C}_{4h}, \mathbf{D}_{2d}, \mathbf{D}_4, \mathbf{S}_4$: $E \times E = A_1 + A_2 + B_1 + B_2$
For groups in above lists that have symbols A, B, or E without subscripts; $A_1 = A_2 = A$, and so on.

Triply degenerate representations:
For $\mathbf{T}_d, \mathbf{0}, \mathbf{0}_h$: $E \times T_1 = E \times T_2 = T_1 + T_2$

$$T_1 \times T_1 = T_2 \times T_2 = A_1 + E + T_1 + T_2$$
$$T_1 \times T_2 = A_2 + E + T_1 + T_2$$

For $\mathbf{T}, \mathbf{T}_h$: Drop subscripts 1 and 2 from A and T.

Linear molecules ($\mathbf{C}_{\infty v}$ *and* $\mathbf{D}_{\infty h}$):

$$\Sigma^+ \times \Sigma^+ = \Sigma^- \times \Sigma^- = \Sigma^+; \Sigma^+ \times \Sigma^- = \Sigma^-$$
$$\Sigma^+ \times \Pi = \Sigma^- \times \Pi = \Pi; \Sigma^+ \times \Delta = \Sigma^- \times \Delta = \Delta; \quad \text{etc.}$$
$$\Pi \times \Pi = \Sigma^+ + \Sigma^- + \Delta$$
$$\Delta \times \Delta = \Sigma^+ + \Sigma^- + \Gamma$$
$$\Pi \times \Delta = \Pi + \Phi$$

or, in general, $\Gamma^{\lambda} \times \Gamma^{\lambda'} = \Gamma^{|\lambda - \lambda'|} + \Gamma^{(\lambda + \lambda')}$

* E. B. Wilson, Jr., J. C. Decius, and P. C. Cross, *Molecular Vibrations*, McGraw-Hill Book Company, New York, 1955, p. 331, by permission.

used. Several of these notations simply use the symbol Γ for all representations, but with various subscripts and superscripts to distinguish among the representations. Bethe and co-workers introduced a notation that was based on the first few characters of the Greek alphabet (α, β, γ, etc.). We will not go into a discussion of these. They are, however, listed, along with appropriate references, in the work by Slater cited in the bibliography to this chapter.

5.7 IRREDUCIBLE REPRESENTATIONS OF TRANSLATION GROUPS

Cyclic point groups are Abelian. We have seen that the representations of cyclic point groups can be expressed as one-dimensional irreducible representations if we use imaginary numbers. The representations for any Abelian group can be reduced to one-dimensional irreducible representations. The pure translations that we encounter in space groups are Abelian, since $\mathbf{t}_a + \mathbf{t}_b$ obviously equals $\mathbf{t}_b + \mathbf{t}_a$. Thus, the translational subgroup must have one-dimensional irreducible representations. In order to avoid dealing with infinite order groups, we introduce the concept of periodic boundary conditions, that is, assume that for some large value of N,

$$\{E \mid \mathbf{t}\}^N = \{E \mid \mathbf{0}\} \tag{5.71}$$

The translational subgroup $[\{E \mid \mathbf{0}\}, \{E \mid \mathbf{t}\}, \{E \mid \mathbf{t}\}^2, \ldots, \{E \mid \mathbf{t}\}^{(N-1)}]$ now has the form of a cyclic group of order N. We have previously expressed the characters of the irreducible representations of cyclic point groups in the form

$$\chi^{(\Gamma_k)}(C_n^j) = e^{kj2\pi i/n} \tag{5.72}$$

with k having positive or negative values ranging from zero to $\pm n/2$ [or $\pm(n-1)/2$]. The A representation arose from a k value of zero, the B representation from a k value of $n/2$, and the E_k representations from intermediate values. The same set of one-dimensional representations could have been obtained by allowing the k in Eq. 6.72 to have only positive values from zero to $(n-1)$. (The pairs of degenerate E representations would have been E_k and E_{n-k} in this construction.) This alternative form is more convenient for constructing the irreducible representations of the translational groups.

If we have any translation vector $\mathbf{t}$ defined in terms of the primitive translations as

$$\mathbf{t} = m\mathbf{t}_1 + n\mathbf{t}_2 + p\mathbf{t}_3 \tag{5.73}$$

then the operation $\{E \mid \mathbf{t}\}$ is

$$\{E \mid \mathbf{t}\} = \{E \mid m\mathbf{t}_1\}\{E \mid n\mathbf{t}_2\}\{E \mid p\mathbf{t}_3\} \tag{5.74}$$

If we label the representations associated with translation parallel to $\mathbf{t}_1$ with the index l_1, those parallel to $\mathbf{t}_2$ with l_2, and those parallel to $\mathbf{t}_3$ with l_3, the characters will have the following form (assuming that the value of N is the same for each direction):

$$\chi^{(l_1)}(\{E\,|\,\mathbf{0}\}) = 1 \tag{5.75a}$$

$$\chi^{(l_1)}(\{E\,|\,\mathbf{t}_1\}) = e^{2\pi i l_1/N} \tag{5.75b}$$

$$\chi^{(l_1)}(\{E\,|\,m\mathbf{t}_1\}) = \chi^{(l_1)}(\{E\,|\,\mathbf{t}\})^m = e^{2\pi i l_1 m/N} \tag{5.75c}$$

$$\chi^{(l_2)}(\{E\,|\,n\mathbf{t}_2\}) = e^{2\pi i l_2 n/N} \tag{5.76}$$

$$\chi^{(l_3)}(\{E\,|\,p\mathbf{t}_3\}) = e^{2\pi i l_3 p/N} \tag{5.77}$$

For a general three-dimensional translation group with elements $\{E\,|\,\mathbf{t}\}$ (see Eq. 5.74), the characters must be

$$\chi^{(l)}(\{E\,|\,\mathbf{t}\}) = e^{2\pi i l_1 m/N} \cdot e^{2\pi i l_2 n/N} \cdot e^{2\pi i l_3 p/N} \tag{5.78}$$

$$= e^{2\pi i/N(l_1 m + l_2 n + l_3 p)} \tag{5.78a}$$

Notice that Eq. 5.78a can be written in the form

$$\chi^{(l)}(\{E\,|\,\mathbf{t}\}) = e^{i\mathbf{k}\cdot\mathbf{t}} \tag{5.79}$$

where $\mathbf{t}$ is as defined in Eq. 5.73 and

$$\mathbf{k} = \frac{2\pi}{N}(l_1\mathbf{b}^1 + l_2\mathbf{b}^2 + l_3\mathbf{b}^3) \tag{5.80}$$

or

$$\mathbf{k} = k_1\mathbf{b}^1 + k_2\mathbf{b}^2 + k_3\mathbf{b}^3 \tag{5.81}$$

where the $\mathbf{b}^i$ vectors satisfy the relationship

$$\mathbf{b}^i \,.\, \mathbf{t}_j = \delta_{ij} \tag{5.82}$$

and

$$k_i = \frac{2\pi l_i}{N} \tag{5.83}$$

In other words, the $\mathbf{b}^i$ vectors are the previously defined reciprocal-space vectors.

The point symmetry of the unit cell in reciprocal space is the same as that for the unit cell in real space. This can be shown quite simply. The point symmetry requires that the operation of every operator R in the point group on a lattice translation vector yields a vector that is a lattice translation:

$$\{R\,|\,\mathbf{0}\}\mathbf{t} = \mathbf{tR} = \mathbf{t}' \tag{5.84}$$

Consider, now, the effect of operating on $\bar{\mathbf{t}}$, the reciprocal of $\mathbf{t}$, by some arbitrary point symmetry operation S to give $\bar{\mathbf{t}}'$, the reciprocal of $\mathbf{t}'$:

$$\{S\,|\,\mathbf{0}\}\bar{\mathbf{t}} = \mathbf{S}\bar{\mathbf{t}}' \tag{5.85}$$

(Note the covariant behavior of reciprocal vectors.) The scalar product of a vector with its reciprocal yields unity. Thus,

$$\mathbf{t}'\bar{\mathbf{t}}' = \mathbf{tRS}\bar{\mathbf{t}} = 1 \tag{5.86}$$

This can only be satisfied if S is the reciprocal of R. Since the set of all R form a group, the group contains all possible mutual reciprocals; consequently, the set of all S is the same as the set of all R. Thus, the reciprocal lattice belongs to the same point group as the real lattice.

PROBLEMS

1. Construct the character tables for the following point groups:

(a) $\mathbf{D}_{3d}$ (b) $\mathbf{D}_{4h}$

(c) $\mathbf{C}_{6h}$ (d) $\mathbf{T}_d$

(e) $\mathbf{0}_h$

2. The *regular representation* of a group has the order of the group as the character of the identity and zero for all other characters. Reduce the regular representation for the following groups:

(a) $\mathbf{C}_{2v}$ (b) $\mathbf{C}_{3v}$

(c) $\mathbf{D}_5$ (d) $\mathbf{T}_d$

(e) $\mathbf{0}_h$

3. What generalization can be made about the occurrence of the irreducible representations of a group in its regular representation?

4. Construct all binary products of the representations of $\mathbf{D}_{3d}$ and of $\mathbf{D}_{4h}$ from the rules of Table 5.2. Verify the results by multiplying out the representations.

5. Listed below are several groups along with their irreducible representations. On the basis of the rules for labeling irreducible representations, describe the behavior of the representations with respect to as many symmetry elements as possible.

(a) $\mathbf{C}_{2v}$: $\{A_1, B_1, A_2, B_2\}$

(b) $\mathbf{C}_{2h}$: $\{A', B', A'', B''\}$

(c) $\mathbf{D}_{3d}$: $\{A_{1g}, A_{2g}, E_g, A_{1u}, A_{2u}, E_u\}$

BIBLIOGRAPHY

ALTMANN, S. L., *Induced Representations in Crystals and Molecules*, Academic Press, Inc., New York, 1977.

CHESTNUT, D. B., *Finite Groups and Quantum Chemistry*, John Wiley & Sons, Inc., New York, 1974.

HOCHSTRASSER, R. M., *Molecular Aspects of Symmetry*, W. A. Benjamin, Inc., Menlo Park, Calif., 1966.

KOSTER, G. F., *Space Groups and Their Representations*, Academic Press, Inc., New York, 1957.

LAX, M., *Symmetry Principles in Solid State and Molecular Physics*, John Wiley & Sons, Inc., New York, 1974.

MCWEENY, R., *Symmetry*, Macmillan Publishing Co., Inc., New York, 1963.

SCHONLAND, D., *Molecular Symmetry*, Van Nostrand Reinhold Company, New York, 1965.

SLATER, J. C., *Quantum Theory of Molecules and Solids*, Vol. I, McGraw-Hill Book Company, New York, 1963.

6

Some Special Groups

6.1 INTRODUCTION

In this chapter we will briefly discuss four types of special groups. The first of these, the three-dimensional *rotation–reflection group*, $\mathbf{R}_h(3)$, is a true symmetry group that represents spherical symmetry. It has, however, a sufficient number of unique properties to warrant our discussing it separately. One important property is the fact that it contains all other point groups as subgroups. The $\mathbf{R}_h(3)$ point group is a continuous group. The other point groups arise from $\mathbf{R}_h(3)$ by requiring that certain rotations become discrete rather than continuous.

The *double groups*, the second type of special group we will discuss, are important for describing the symmetry properties of systems having half-integer spin moments. They are extensions of the normal point groups we have discussed. We will derive them from a consideration of the rotation group.

The third type of group to be discussed is the *symmetric permutation group* or, more simply, *symmetric group*. This group [denoted $\mathbf{S}(n)$, where n is known as the degree] has as its elements the set of all possible permutations of n objects. This group is, properly speaking, not a symmetry group at all in the point-group sense in which we have been using the term. All point groups are, however, subgroups of some symmetric group; furthermore, permutational symmetry is important in its own right. The symmetric group, in contrast to $\mathbf{R}_h(3)$, is a discrete group. $\mathbf{R}_h(3)$ can be considered as a subgroup of $\mathbf{S}(\infty)$ (the infinite-degree symmetric group).

The fourth type of group consists of the *symmetry groups of nonrigid molecules.* These also are not symmetry groups in the sense in which we have previously used the term. They contain elements that correspond to motions in the molecule; consequently, after certain of the operations of these groups have been carried out, the resulting configuration may not be indistinguishable from the original configuration. (Longuet-Higgins constructs these groups as products of point groups and permutation groups.) These groups are important when two different configurations of a molecule must be connected in a continuous fashion.

6.2 THE THREE-DIMENSIONAL ROTATION-REFLECTION GROUP

The R(3) Group

The maximum point symmetry that any physical object can have is that of a perfect sphere. This is described by the three-dimensional rotation–reflection group, which we shall designate $\mathbf{R}_h(3)$. [This is identical to the three-dimensional orthogonal group, $\mathbf{0}(3)$, of the mathematical literature.] A system having $\mathbf{R}_h(3)$ symmetry is symmetric with respect to rotation about any axis passing through the center, to reflection in any plane containing the center, and to inversion through the center. Groups containing only the rotations, the $\mathbf{R}(3)$ group, are mathematically defined, but have no macroscopic physical counterpart. Certain properties can, however, be derived by considering only the $\mathbf{R}(3)$ subgroup of $\mathbf{R}_h(3)$. The $\mathbf{R}_h(3)$ and $\mathbf{R}(3)$ groups are especially important because they describe the symmetry properties of atomic orbitals. The double group of $\mathbf{R}(3)$ is isomorphic to the unitary–unimodular group of degree 2, $\mathbf{SU}(2)$, the group that describes the intrinsic angular momentum of the electron and other spin-$\frac{1}{2}$ fundamental particles. It is this isomorphism that allows the use of the double groups of point groups to describe the spin properties of atoms and molecules.

The rotations about any arbitrary axis can be resolved into components along three mutually perpendicular axes. For describing systems with spherical symmetry, only the characters of the identity element (E) and a single arbitrary rotation [$C(\phi, x, y, z)$] are required. The diagonal form of the matrix corresponding to an arbitrary rotation $C(\phi)$ in three-dimensional Cartesian space (see Section 3.5) is

$$\mathbf{R}(C(\phi)) = \begin{bmatrix} e^{i\phi} & 0 & 0 \\ 0 & e^{-i\phi} & 0 \\ 0 & 0 & 1 \end{bmatrix} \tag{6.1}$$

The form of the characters for a one-, two-, or three-dimensional irreducible representation can be extracted from this (see Section 5.1). For a one-dimensional representation, the character (the trace of the corresponding matrix) would be 1, for two dimensions, $e^{i\phi} + e^{-i\phi} = 2\cos\phi$, and for three dimensions, $1 + e^{i\phi} + e^{-i\phi} = 1 + 2\cos\phi$. Higher-dimensional rotation matrices can be derived by defining sets of homogeneous, orthogonal polynomials as the set of basis functions to which the matrix is referred. If the polynomials involve x, y, and z to the order x^α, y^β, and z^γ, then the polynomial is of order l, where

$$l = \alpha + \beta + \gamma \tag{6.2}$$

A set of polynomials of order l can be resolved into $2l + 1$ independent (or orthogonal) polynomials. This would lead to a $(2l + 1) \times (2l + 1)$ rotation matrix. In diagonal form, the diagonal elements would be $e^{-il\phi}, e^{-i(l-1)\phi}, \ldots, e^{i(l-1)\phi}, e^{il\phi}$. A formal derivation of these matrices comes from a consideration of the spherical harmonics. The basis functions used to define the rotation matrix are the associated Legendre polynomials (which, for example, describe the angular behavior of a hydrogenic wave function), and the diagonal elements of the matrix are the $(2l + 1)$ possible coefficients of the polynomials of degree l. Elements of the type indicated can be constructed for either integer or half-integer values of l. Either the integer set or the half-integer set is complete in itself. The integer set is useful for describing the properties of physical objects, while the half-integer set is useful for describing electron and nuclear spin properties.

The characters for the rotations in the irreducible representations [denoted $D^{(l)}$] of the various dimensions are, as usual, the trace of the matrix corresponding to the rotation in that dimension. Thus, rearranging the order, they have the form

$$\begin{aligned}\chi(C(\phi)) &= e^0 + e^{i\phi} + e^{-i\phi} + e^{i2\phi} + e^{-i2\phi} + \ldots + e^{il\phi} + e^{-il\phi} \\ &= 1 + 2\cos\phi + 2\cos 2\phi + \ldots + 2\cos l\phi\end{aligned} \tag{6.3}$$

for the integer values of l (odd dimensions), and

$$\begin{aligned}\chi(C(\phi)) &= e^{i\phi/2} + e^{-i\phi/2} + e^{i3\phi/2} + e^{-i3\phi/2} + \ldots + e^{il\phi} + e^{-il\phi} \\ &= 2\cos\phi/2 + 2\cos 3\phi/2 + \ldots + 2\cos l\phi\end{aligned} \tag{6.4}$$

for the half-integer values of l (even dimensions). For many applications (such as atomic spectra and pure rotational spectra of molecules) all that is required of the character table are the characters with respect to the identity and rotation elements [i.e., the **R**(3) group]. This character table is presented in Table 6.1.

Table 6.1. The pure rotation form for the R(3) character table

R(3)	E	$C(\phi, x, y, z)$
$D^{(0)}$	1	1
$D^{(1)}$	3	$1 + 2\cos\phi$
$D^{(2)}$	5	$1 + 2\cos\phi + 2\cos 2\phi$
$D^{(3)}$	7	$1 + 2\cos\phi + 2\cos 2\phi + 2\cos 3\phi$
$D^{(l)}$	$2l + 1$	$1 + 2\cos\phi + \ldots + 2\cos l\phi$
$D^{(1/2)}$	2	$2\cos\phi/2$
$D^{(3/2)}$	4	$2\cos\phi/2 + 2\cos 3\phi/2$
$D^{(5/2)}$	6	$2\cos\phi/2 + 2\cos 3\phi/2 + 2\cos 5\phi/2$
$D^{(l)}$	$2l + 1$	$2\cos\phi/2 + 2\cos 3\phi/2 + \ldots + 2\cos l\phi$

Products of Irreducible Representations

It is instructive to consider the products of some of the irreducible representations of Table 6.1. Quite obviously, $D^{(0)}$ times any representation gives that representation unchanged; therefore, let us consider the product of $D^{(1)}$ with several representations:

$D^{(1)} \times D^{(1)}$:

	E	$C(\phi, x, y, z)$
$D^{(1)}$	3	$1 + 2\cos\phi$
$D^{(1)} \times D^{(1)}$	3×3	$(1 + 2\cos\phi)(1 + 2\cos\phi)$
	9	$1 + 4\cos\phi + 4\cos^2\phi$
	9	$3 + 4\cos\phi + 2\cos 2\phi$

(6.5)

Therefore,

$$D^{(1)} \times D^{(1)} = D^{(0)} + D^{(1)} + D^{(2)} \tag{6.5a}$$

$D^{(1)} \times D^{(2)}$:

	E	$C(\phi, x, y, z)$
$D^{(2)}$	5	$1 + 2\cos\phi + 2\cos 2\phi$
$D^{(1)} \times D^{(2)}$	3×5	$(1 + 2\cos\phi)(1 + 2\cos\phi + 2\cos 2\phi)$
	15	$1 + 4\cos\phi + 4\cos^2\phi + 2\cos 2\phi + 4\cos\phi\cos 2\phi$
	15	$3 + 6\cos\phi + 4\cos 2\phi + 2\cos 3\phi$

(6.6)

$$D^{(1)} \times D^{(2)} = D^{(1)} + D^{(2)} + D^{(3)} \tag{6.6a}$$

$D^{(1)} \times D^{(1/2)}$:

	E	$C(\phi, x, y, z)$
$D^{(1/2)}$	2	$2\cos\phi/2$
$D^{(1)} \times D^{(1/2)}$	6	$2\cos\phi/2 + 4\cos\phi\cos\phi/2$
	6	$4\cos\phi/2 + 2\cos 3\phi/2$

(6.7)

$$D^{(1)} \times D^{(1/2)} = D^{(1/2)} + D^{(3/2)} \tag{6.7a}$$

$D^{(1)} \times D^{(3/2)}$:

	E	$C(\phi, x, y, z)$
$D^{(3/2)}$	4	$2\cos\phi/2 + 2\cos 3\phi/2$
$D^{(1)} \times D^{(3/2)}$	12	$2\cos\phi/2 + 2\cos 3\phi/2 + 4\cos\phi\cos\phi/2$ $+4\cos\phi\cos 3\phi/2$
	12	$6\cos\phi/2 + 4\cos 3\phi/2 + 2\cos 5\phi/2$

(6.8)

$$D^{(1)} \times D^{(3/2)} = D^{(1/2)} + D^{(3/2)} + D^{(5/2)} \tag{6.8a}$$

(The last line in each case involves the use of trigonometric identities.) The pattern that is emerging should be obvious. If the product of $D^{(j)}$ and $D^{(k)}$ is taken, the result is

$$D^{(j)} \times D^{(k)} = D^{|j-k|} + D^{|j-k|+1} + \ldots + D^{(j+k)} \tag{6.9}$$

Equation 6.9 is known as the *Clebsch–Gordan formula.*

To see why the results of the products are as they are, it is necessary to consider in more detail the meaning of a multiplication of two representations. The main point to notice is that the resulting representation has a dimensionality that is the product of the dimensionalities of the starting representations. This means that if one representation was derived from an m-dimensional matrix and the other from an n-dimensional matrix, the resulting representation must arise from an $(m \times n)$-dimensional matrix. In other words, the matrix product involved must have been a *matrix direct product.* Thus, if we denote the diagonal rotation matrix associated with $D^{(j)}$ by $\mathbf{D}^{(j)}$, and that with $D^{(k)}$ by $\mathbf{D}^{(k)}$, we have

$$\mathbf{D}^{(j)} \times \mathbf{D}^{(k)} = \begin{bmatrix} e^{-ij}\mathbf{D}^{(k)} & & & & 0 \\ & e^{-i(j-1)}\mathbf{D}^{(k)} & & & \\ & & \ddots & & \\ & & & e^{i(j-1)}\mathbf{D}^{(k)} & \\ 0 & & & & e^{ij}\mathbf{D}^{(k)} \end{bmatrix} \tag{6.10}$$

In the trace of the supermatrix, $e^{\pm i(j+k)}$ will occur once, $e^{\pm(j+k-1)}$ will occur twice, $e^{\pm i(j+k-2)}$ three times, and so on. Summing these yields Eq. 6.9.

Exercise 6.1: Verify the Clebsch–Gordan results for $D^{(1)} \times D^{(1/2)}$ by constructing the appropriate supermatrix and finding its trace.

The $R_h(3)$ Group

All point groups are subgroups of the full $\mathbf{R}_h(3)$ point group. They can, in fact, be so constructed. We shall not go through the construction of the point groups from $\mathbf{R}_h(3)$; however, we will have occasion to reduce the symmetry of $\mathbf{R}_h(3)$ to that of the finite groups. To do this, the characters of the irreducible representations with respect to symmetry elements other than the rotation are needed. These can be constructed by considering the products of the $C(\phi)$ element with other generators. The inversion is actually sufficient [i.e., $\mathbf{R}_h(3)$ equals $\mathbf{R}(3) \times \mathbf{C}_i$]. The matrix corresponding to the improper axis of rotation may be derived by requiring that for the specific case of ϕ equaling π, the $\mathbf{S}(\phi)$ matrix must equal the $\mathbf{i}$ matrix (i.e., $S_2 = i$). The matrix for a plane of symmetry is obtained by requiring that $\boldsymbol{\sigma}$ equal $\mathbf{S}(\phi)$ for the specific case where ϕ equals zero (i.e., $\sigma = S_1$). When the function under consideration is antisymmetric with respect to i (*ungerade*), the appropriate form of the $\mathbf{i}$ matrix is the negative of the unit matrix (all diagonal elements equal -1). Thus, since $e^{\pm i\pi}$ equals -1, we have for the three-dimensional $\mathbf{S}(\pi)$ matrix,

$$\mathbf{S}(\pi) = \begin{bmatrix} e^{i\pi} & 0 & 0 \\ 0 & e^{-i\pi} & 0 \\ 0 & 0 & -1 \end{bmatrix} \tag{6.11}$$

$$= \begin{bmatrix} -1 & 0 & 0 \\ 0 & -1 & 0 \\ 0 & 0 & -1 \end{bmatrix} \tag{6.11a}$$

or for the general three-dimensional $\mathbf{S}(\phi)$ matrix,

$$\mathbf{S}(\phi) = \begin{bmatrix} e^{i\phi} & 0 & 0 \\ 0 & e^{-i\phi} & 0 \\ 0 & 0 & -1 \end{bmatrix} \tag{6.12}$$

The other dimensionalities can be derived similarly. Taking the trace of these, we have for the character of $S(\phi)$ in $D_u^{(l)}$ (the u is, as usual, for *ungerade*) for integer values of l,

$$\chi(S(\phi)) = -(1 - 2\cos\phi + 2\cos 2\phi + \ldots + (-1)^l 2\cos l\phi) \tag{6.13}$$

If the function under consideration is *gerade*, the appropriate matrix for **i** is the unit matrix and the sign of $\chi(S(\phi))$ is changed. For functions that are polynomials in the Cartesian coordinates, the *gerade–ungerade* alternation is such that the leading term in $\chi(S(\phi))$ equals $(-1)^l$. For functions involving rotations about the coordinates, the sign of the character is reversed. The sign of the character of $S(\phi)$ is always determined by the behavior with respect to inversion, since $S(\phi)$ equals $i \times C(\phi + \pi)$.

Examining Eq. 6.12 for $\phi = 0$, we see that, for an odd dimension, the magnitude of $\chi(\sigma)$ must always be unity. (The diagonal form of the σ matrix has alternating $+1$ and -1 elements.) The sign is determined by the last term in $\chi(S(\phi))$. Since $\pm 2\cos 0$ equals ± 2, the first term of unity coupled with the sign alternation of the succeeding terms causes the final term to determine the sign. [For polynomials in the Cartesian coordinates, $\chi(\sigma)$ always equals $+1$, and for rotations, -1.] Thus, for describing a three-dimensional object in the $\mathbf{R}_h(3)$ point group, our only two independent generators are $C(\phi)$ and i.

The characters for half-integer values of l can be constructed similarly. In this case, the character for $S(\phi)$ for *ungerade* representations turns out to be

$$\chi(S(\phi)) = -\sin\phi/2 + \sin 3\phi/2 + \ldots + (-1)^k \sin l\phi \tag{6.14}$$

where k equals $(l + \frac{1}{2})$. For the gerade representations, the signs are again reversed. The character for σ is zero for all the even-dimensional (half-integer l)

representations (the diagonal form of the $\boldsymbol{\sigma}$ matrix again has alternating $+1$ and -1 elements). The expanded $\mathbf{R}_h(3)$ character table is given in Appendix 5.

The characters for i, $S(\phi)$, and σ in products of irreducible representations can again be found by constructing the appropriate supermatrices. This is not necessary, however. The $g \times u$ rules for multiplication are valid. In a given product, the rule holds for all of the irreducible representations that comprise the product representation. For example,

$$D_g^{(1)} \times D_u^{(1)} = D_u^{(0)} + D_u^{(1)} + D_u^{(2)} \tag{6.15}$$

Exercise 6.2: Construct the following irreducible representations of the $\mathbf{R}_h(3)$ point group:

$$D_u^{(4)};\ D_g^{(1/2)}.$$

Exercise 6.3*: Find the following products:

$$D_g^{(2)} \times D_g^{(2)};\ D_g^{(2)} \times D_u^{(1/2)}.$$

Symmetry Reduction

In order to reduce the symmetry of a representation in $\mathbf{R}_h(3)$ to one of the finite point groups, one simply maps the elements of the finite group onto the elements of a corresponding type in the $\mathbf{R}_h(3)$ group, substituting in the proper numerical values for ϕ. For example, to reduce the symmetry of $D_u^{(1)}$ and $D_g^{(2)}$ to $\mathbf{T}_d$ symmetry, we have

$\mathbf{R}_h(3)$ / $\mathbf{T}_d$	E / E	$C(\phi = 120°)$ / $8C_3$	$C(\phi = 180°)$ / $3C_2$	$S(\phi = 90°)$ / $6S_4$	σ / $6\sigma_d$
$D_u^{(1)}$	3	$1 + 2\cos 120°$	$1 + 2\cos 180°$	$-1 + 2\cos 90°$	1
	3	0	-1	-1	1
$D_g^{(2)}$	5	$1 + 2\cos 120° + 2\cos 240°$	$1 + 2\cos 180° + 2\cos 360°$	$1 - 2\cos 90° + 2\cos 180°$	1
	5	-1	1	-1	1

(6.16)

We see that $D_u^{(1)}$ becomes the irreducible T_2 representation while $D_g^{(2)}$ becomes a reducible representation that equals $E + T_2$ in the $\mathbf{T}_d$ point group. This concept is closely related to the splitting of atomic energy levels in crystal field theory. In fact, the $D_u^{(1)}$ representation is the representation to which atomic p orbitals belong in a free atom. In a field of tetrahedral symmetry, the p orbitals would transform as the T_2 irreducible representation. Atomic d orbitals transform as $D_g^{(2)}$ in a free atom and are split into functions that transform as E and T_2 in a tetrahedral field.

Exercise 6.4:* To what irreducible representation or representations do $D_g^{(1)}$, $D_u^{(2)}$, and $D_u^{(3/2)}$ correspond in $\mathbf{O}_h$, in $\mathbf{D}_{4h}$, and in $\mathbf{C}_{3v}$?

6.3 DOUBLE-VALUED REPRESENTATIONS AND DOUBLE GROUPS

The Even-Dimensional Representations of $R_h(3)$

The even-dimensional irreducible representations of $\mathbf{R}(3)$ and $\mathbf{R}_h(3)$ have some interesting and unusual properties. Consider the character of a rotation by $(\phi + 2\pi)$ for both an integer and a half-integer value of l. For integer l, the character is

$$\begin{aligned}\chi(C(\phi + 2\pi)) &= 1 + 2\cos(\phi + 2\pi) + \ldots + 2\cos l(\phi + 2\pi) \\ &= 1 + 2\cos\phi + \ldots + 2\cos l\phi \\ &= \chi(C(\phi))\end{aligned} \tag{6.17}$$

For half-integer l, the character is

$$\begin{aligned}\chi(C(\phi + 2\pi)) &= 2\cos\tfrac{1}{2}(\phi + 2\pi) + 2\cos 3/2(\phi + 2\pi) + \ldots + 2\cos l(\phi + 2\pi) \\ &= 2\cos(\phi/2 + \pi) + 2\cos(3\phi/2 + 3\pi) + \ldots + 2\cos(l\phi + 2l\pi) \\ &= -2\cos\phi/2 - 2\cos 3\phi/2 - \ldots - 2\cos l\phi \\ &= -\chi(C(\phi))\end{aligned} \tag{6.18}$$

Thus, for the representations corresponding to integer values of l, a rotation by 2π corresponds to the identity operation. For half-integer l values, on the other hand, a rotation by 4π corresponds to the identity operation. Physically, however, a rotation by 2π brings an object back to its original orientation. Thus, for systems in which the even-dimensional representations are required, there are two different elements that transform physically as the identity. This also requires that there be two elements for all the other normal symmetry elements. [If $\bar{E}$ is the new element, then $\bar{E}C(\phi)$, and so on, must also be allowed elements.] The representations are said to be *double-valued*. These double-valued representations are important when considering the spin properties of systems with half-integral spins. The point groups that are utilized in such cases are referred to as *double groups*.

Character Tables for Double Groups

The character table for a double group can be derived from that for the corresponding normal point group. The usual method for doing this is a bit indirect. The procedure is to determine the number of elements (twice that for the normal point group, since $\bar{E}$ acts as a new generator of order 2), the number of classes, and the number of irreducible representations (the same as the number of classes) in the double group. The dimensions of the new irreducible representations are obtained by requiring that the sum of the squares of the irreducible representations equal the order of the double group. Since the dimensions of the representations for the original point group are known, this usually presents no difficulties. Once the dimensions of the new irreducible representations are known, the characters for the other elements can be obtained either from a consideration of the multiplication properties of the elements or from a mapping of the corresponding representations of $\mathbf{R}_h(3)$ onto the elements in question.

The derivation of the double groups corresponding to proper groups (i.e., groups whose only generators are proper axes of rotation) and proper groups with inversion follows straightforward rules. The character tables for improper groups are obtained by equating them to the corresponding tables for the proper groups to which they are isomorphic. In general, if a set of elements R forms a class in an ordinary proper point group, there is a class of R and a class of $\bar{R}$ in the double group. There is only one exception to this. If R corresponds to a C_2, and if there is a C_2' perpendicular to the original C_2, then the $\bar{C}_2$ and the $\bar{C}_2'$ belong to the same classes as the original C_2 and C_2'. This can be obtained by the conjugate relation. For a two-dimensional representation, the equation

$$\bar{C}_2 = SC_2S^{-1} \tag{6.19}$$

is satisfied if S is a rotation by 180° about an axis perpendicular to that of C_2. To verify this, however, requires the construction of a two-dimensional representation of a general rotation. This is done by reference to *Eulerian angles.* The Eulerian angles ϕ, θ, and χ may be described as a rotation about the z axis, a rotation of the z axis about an axis perpendicular to it, and a rotation about the rotated z' axis, respectively (Fig. 6.1). (Note that ϕ and θ correspond to the direction cosines of the z' axis.) In matrix notation, a generalized rotation may be described by a

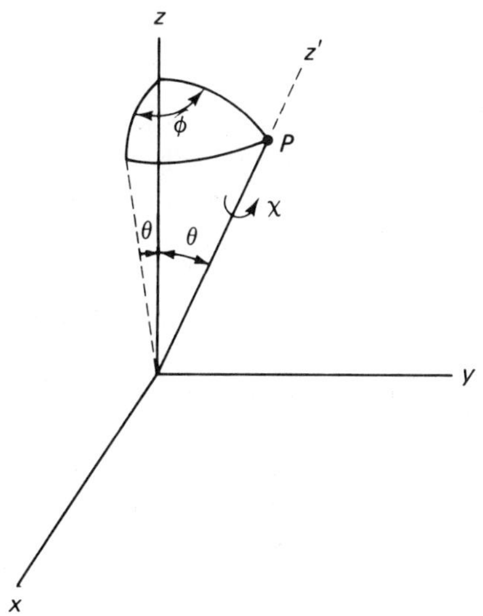

Fig. 6.1. Eulerian angles θ, ϕ, and χ.

product of three two-dimensional matrices, each involving only ϕ, θ, or χ. Using $\mathbf{C}(\alpha)$ to distinguish the arbitrary rotation from the Eulerian angle ϕ, we have

$$\mathbf{C}(\alpha) = \begin{bmatrix} e^{i(1/2)\phi} & 0 \\ 0 & e^{-i(1/2)\phi} \end{bmatrix} \begin{bmatrix} \cos\frac{1}{2}\theta & \sin\frac{1}{2}\theta \\ -\sin\frac{1}{2}\theta & \cos\frac{1}{2}\theta \end{bmatrix} \begin{bmatrix} e^{i(1/2)\chi} & 0 \\ 0 & e^{-i(1/2)\chi} \end{bmatrix} \tag{6.20}$$

Now for the special case of $\phi = \pi$, Eq. 6.19 is satisfied only if θ equals π (i.e., if there is a twofold axis of rotation perpendicular to z). If there are no such perpendicular sets of C_2's, the double group will have twice as many classes (and, hence, twice as many irreducible representations) as the ordinary group. If there are such sets of C_2's, then the double group will have correspondingly fewer classes and irreducible representations. For example, the group $\mathbf{D}_3$ has the classes $\{E, 2C_3, 3C_2\}$, and since there are no C_2''s perpendicular to the C_2's in $\mathbf{D}_3$, the double group has the classes $\{E, 2C_3, 3C_2, \bar{E}, 2\bar{C}_3, 3\bar{C}_2\}$. The $\mathbf{D}_4$ group, on the other hand, has the classes $\{E, 2C_4, C_2(C_4^2), 2C_2', 2C_2''\}$. The class structure for the double group is

$$\left\{ \begin{matrix} & \bar{C}_2, 2\bar{C}_2', 2\bar{C}_2'', \bar{E}, 2\bar{C}_4 \\ E, 2C_4, C_2, 2C_2', 2C_2'' & \end{matrix} \right\}$$

(i.e., only two new classes). The double group for $\mathbf{D}_3$ thus has six irreducible representations, while that for $\mathbf{D}_4$ has seven. For the dimensionalities, we have for $\mathbf{D}_3$

$$\sum_{i=1}^{6} g_i^2 = 12 \tag{6.21}$$

We know that for the ordinary $\mathbf{D}_3$ group we have three irreducible representations and a group order of 6; consequently, for the new representations we have

$$\sum_{i=1}^{3} g_i^2 = 6 \tag{6.22}$$

The only solution of this gives us two one-dimensional representations and one two-dimensional representation. For the ordinary $\mathbf{D}_4$ group we have five irreducible representations and an order of 8. This means that for the new representations, we have

$$\sum_{i=1}^{2} g_i^2 = 8 \tag{6.23}$$

or two two-dimensional representations. All the other proper groups and proper groups with inversion can be treated similarly. For the axial point groups only one- or two-dimensional representations will be found. For the cubic groups, there will be four-dimensional representations and for the icosohedral groups, six-dimensional representations will occur.

The characters for the new elements in the original representation in the double point group will be the same as for the corresponding ordinary elements. The characters for the original elements in the new even-dimensional irreducible representations can be obtained by substituting in the proper angles into the characters for the $C(\phi)$, *etc.*, in the even-dimensional representations for $\mathbf{R}_h(3)$. The characters for the new elements have the opposite sign. If more than one representation of a given dimension occurs, the angle is increased by successive increments of $2\pi/n$ until all the irreducible representations are accounted for. Note that this is equivalent to increasing the multiple of ϕ along the half-integer series $\frac{1}{2}, \frac{3}{2}, \frac{5}{2}, \ldots$. If the number and dimensions of the representations have been properly chosen, an increase in the series beyond what is required will give a representation that has already been obtained. The symbol that we shall use for these irreducible representations follows Herzberg in assigning an E to all two-dimensional representations, a G to four-dimensional representations, and an I to six-dimensional representations. The letters are subscripted by the half-integer that was used in deriving it. Thus, for the new representations of $\mathbf{D}_4$, we have

$\mathbf{D}_4$	E	$2C_4$	$\bar{C}_2$ C_2	$2\bar{C}'_2$ $2C'_2$	$2\bar{C}''_2$ $2C''_2$	$\bar{E}$	$2\bar{C}_4$
$E_{1/2}$	2	$2\cos\frac{90°}{2}$	$2\cos\frac{180°}{2}$	$2\cos\frac{180°}{2}$	$2\cos\frac{180°}{2}$	-2	$-2\cos\frac{90°}{2}$
	(2	$\sqrt{2}$	0	0	0	-2	$-\sqrt{2}$)
$E_{3/2}$	2	$2\cos\frac{3\times 90°}{2}$	$2\cos\frac{3\times 180°}{2}$	$2\cos\frac{3\times 180°}{2}$	$2\cos\frac{3\times 180°}{2}$	-2	$-2\cos\frac{3\times 90°}{2}$
	(2	$-\sqrt{2}$	0	0	0	-2	$\sqrt{2}$)

(6.24)

The new one-dimensional representations that appear in the double groups occur in pairs if there are an even number of them. They represent separable components of a two-dimensional representation (similar to the E_j representations in the $\mathbf{C}_n$ point groups). The characters for the two components can be taken directly from the diagonal forms of the two-dimensional transformation matrices corresponding to the various symmetry elements. Thus, for the two new one-dimensional representations in the double group of $\mathbf{D}_3$, we have for a j value of $\frac{3}{2}$,

$$\mathbf{R}(E) = \begin{bmatrix} 1 & 0 \\ 0 & 1 \end{bmatrix} \tag{6.25a}$$

$$\mathbf{R}(C_3) = \begin{bmatrix} e^{i(3/2)(2\pi/3)} & 0 \\ 0 & e^{-i(3/2)(2\pi/3)} \end{bmatrix} = \begin{bmatrix} -1 & 0 \\ 0 & -1 \end{bmatrix} \tag{6.25b}$$

$$\mathbf{R}(C_2) = \begin{bmatrix} e^{i(3/2)(2\pi/2)} & 0 \\ 0 & e^{-i(3/2)(2\pi/2)} \end{bmatrix} = \begin{bmatrix} -i & 0 \\ 0 & i \end{bmatrix} \tag{6.25c}$$

The treatment of the two-dimensional $E_{1/2}$ representation of $\mathbf{D}_3$ is just as in $\mathbf{D}_4$. This gives us, for our new irreducible representations in $\mathbf{D}_3$,

$\mathbf{D}_3$	E	$2C_3$	$3C_2$	$\bar{E}$	$2\bar{C}_3$	$3\bar{C}_2$
$E_{1/2}$	2	1	0	-2	-1	0
$E_{3/2}$ {	1	-1	$-i$	-1	1	i
	1	-1	i	-1	1	$-i$

(6.26)

One-dimensional representations such as these occur only when the numerical values of the elements of the diagonal form of the transformation matrix that correspond to $e^{il\phi}$ and $e^{-il\phi}$ are different for some element.

The double groups for improper groups are identical to those of the isomorphic proper groups. This isomorphism is found by resolving the groups into the appropriate product of cyclic subgroups. Groups having the same structure are isomorphic. For example, $\mathbf{D}_3$ has the structure $\mathbf{C}_3 \wedge \mathbf{C}_2'$, the semidirect product of a cycle of order 3 and a cycle of order 2. $\mathbf{C}_{3v}$ has the structure $\mathbf{C}_3 \wedge \mathbf{C}_s$, also the semidirect product of a cycle of order 3 and one of order 2. Thus, $\mathbf{D}_3$ and $\mathbf{C}_{3v}$ are isomorphic. Groups having the inversion as a generator are, as usual, constructed directly from the proper subgroup without the inversion by taking the symmetric and antisymmetric behavior with respect to i and its associated elements.

One caveat is in order for the construction of double groups that we have presented here. When a C_n and its inverse belong to the same class, the inverse must be interpreted as C_n^{-1} rather than as $C_n^{(n-1)}$. In the second interpretation (which is used by many authors), the classes for the double groups become $\{C_n, \bar{E}C_n^{(n-1)}\}$ and $\{C_n^{(n-1)}, \bar{E}C\}$.

Exercise 6.5: Construct the double groups corresponding to the following point groups: $\mathbf{C}_5$; $\mathbf{D}_5$; $\mathbf{C}_{5v}$; $\mathbf{D}_{5d}$; $\mathbf{C}_{5h}$.

6.4 THE SYMMETRIC PERMUTATION GROUP

Permutations

An especially important permutation group is the *symmetric permutation group* (or more commonly, the *symmetric group*). The symmetric group of degree n [denoted $S(n)$] is the set of all $n!$ possible permutations of n objects. The symmetric groups of degree 1, 2, 3, and 4 are, however, isomorphic to the point groups $\mathbf{C}_1$, $\mathbf{C}_2$ (or $\mathbf{C}_i$ or $\mathbf{C}_s$), $\mathbf{C}_{3v}$, and $\mathbf{T}_d$. All other point groups are subgroups of some symmetric group, or of some symmetric group with inversion, even though there are no point groups that are isomorphic with the higher-degree symmetric groups. We shall not discuss the symmetric group in sufficient detail to take full advantage of its

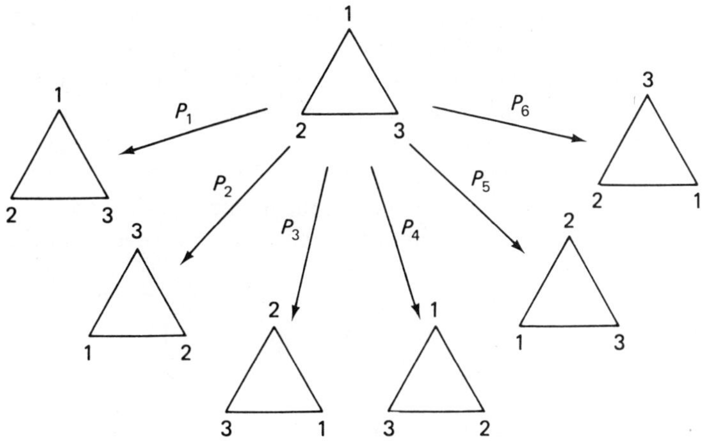

Fig. 6.2. Permutations for the elements of $\mathbf{C}_{3v}$.

relationship to the point groups. Since, however, it is important to chemical problems in its own right (e.g., in finding Pauli allowed states and in applying group theory to NMR problems), we shall present some of its properties.

In order to discuss the symmetric group, let us consider the specific example of $\mathbf{S}(3)$; and to visualize the permutations, let us consider a system belonging to the isomorphic point group, $\mathbf{C}_{3v}$. The elements of $\mathbf{C}_{3v}$ are illustrated, in two dimensions, in Fig. 6.2. We shall call the permutation associated with the E element P_1, that associated with C_3, P_2, and so on. The permutations among the labels can be symbolized by two rows of numbers, the upper signifying the original order of the elements, and the lower, the positions to which these have gone after permutation. (In this notation the ordering in the upper row is immaterial; only the relationship between the rows is important.)

$$P_1 = \begin{pmatrix} 1 & 2 & 3 \\ 1 & 2 & 3 \end{pmatrix} \tag{6.27a}$$

$$P_2 = \begin{pmatrix} 1 & 2 & 3 \\ 2 & 3 & 1 \end{pmatrix} \tag{6.27b}$$

$$P_3 = \begin{pmatrix} 1 & 2 & 3 \\ 3 & 1 & 2 \end{pmatrix} \tag{6.27c}$$

$$P_4 = \begin{pmatrix} 1 & 2 & 3 \\ 1 & 3 & 2 \end{pmatrix} \tag{6.27d}$$

$$P_5 = \begin{pmatrix} 1 & 2 & 3 \\ 2 & 1 & 3 \end{pmatrix} \tag{6.27e}$$

$$P_6 = \begin{pmatrix} 1 & 2 & 3 \\ 3 & 2 & 1 \end{pmatrix} \tag{6.27f}$$

In other words, the description of P_6, for example, is a permutation that takes the element from position 1, puts it in position 3, leaves the element in position 2 where it was, and puts the element from position 3 in position 1. The description of the other permutations is analogous. Note that P_2 and P_3 are cyclic permutations among all three elements, while P_4, P_5, and P_6 can be considered cyclic permutations among two elements, with the third being held constant. P_1 (the identity) represents all three elements in the list being held constant.

Products of permutations can be constructed. For example, consider the product

$$P_2P_4 = \begin{pmatrix} 1 & 2 & 3 \\ \downarrow & \downarrow & \downarrow \\ 2 & 3 & 1 \end{pmatrix}\begin{pmatrix} 1 & 2 & 3 \\ \downarrow & \downarrow & \downarrow \\ 1 & 3 & 2 \end{pmatrix} = \begin{pmatrix} 1 & 2 & 3 \\ 2 & 1 & 3 \end{pmatrix} = P_5 \tag{6.28}$$

(This is equivalent to the product $C_3 \times \sigma_v = \sigma_v'$). The procedure is simply to carry out the permutation indicated among the elements given on the right and follow it with the permutation on the left. (Some authors use the reverse convention.) The arrows have merely been added for clarity. The elements that are left unchanged can be omitted in the notation; thus, P_4 can be written as

$$P_4 = \begin{pmatrix} 2 & 3 \\ 3 & 2 \end{pmatrix} \tag{6.29}$$

and the product of P_2 and P_4 as

$$P_2P_4 = \begin{pmatrix} 1 & 2 & 3 \\ 2 & 3 & 1 \end{pmatrix}\begin{pmatrix} 2 & 3 \\ 3 & 2 \end{pmatrix} \tag{6.30}$$

Exercise 6.6: Find the products P_2P_3, P_3P_4, and P_4P_5. Verify the results from the multiplication table for $\mathbf{C}_{3v}$.

All permutations can be resolved into cyclic permutations. Consider, for example, the permutation of order 8,

$$P_A = \begin{pmatrix} 1 & 2 & 3 & 4 & 5 & 6 & 7 & 8 \\ 4 & 3 & 2 & 7 & 5 & 8 & 6 & 1 \end{pmatrix} \tag{6.31}$$

This can be resolved into cycles as

$$P_A = \begin{pmatrix} 1 & 4 & 6 & 7 & 8 \\ 4 & 7 & 8 & 6 & 1 \end{pmatrix}\begin{pmatrix} 2 & 3 \\ 3 & 2 \end{pmatrix}\begin{pmatrix} 5 \\ 5 \end{pmatrix} \tag{6.32}$$

(i.e., three cycles, one on five elements, one on two elements and one on one). All cyclic permutations, and consequently, all permutations, can be resolved into products of cycles of order 2, or *transpositions*. For example, P_2 can be resolved into a product of two transpositions,

$$P_2 = \begin{pmatrix} 1 & 2 \\ 2 & 1 \end{pmatrix}\begin{pmatrix} 2 & 3 \\ 3 & 2 \end{pmatrix} = \begin{pmatrix} 1 & 2 & 3 \\ 2 & 3 & 1 \end{pmatrix} \tag{6.33}$$

and P_A into a product of five transpositions,

$$P_A = \begin{pmatrix}1 & 4\\ 4 & 1\end{pmatrix}\begin{pmatrix}4 & 6\\ 6 & 4\end{pmatrix}\begin{pmatrix}4 & 7\\ 7 & 4\end{pmatrix}\begin{pmatrix}6 & 8\\ 8 & 6\end{pmatrix}\begin{pmatrix}2 & 3\\ 3 & 2\end{pmatrix}\begin{pmatrix}5\\ 5\end{pmatrix} = \begin{pmatrix}1 & 2 & 3 & 4 & 5 & 6 & 7 & 8\\ 4 & 3 & 2 & 7 & 5 & 8 & 6 & 1\end{pmatrix} \tag{6.34}$$

[the $\begin{pmatrix}5\\ 5\end{pmatrix}$ is redundant in the product notation]. A permutation is classified as *even* or *odd* depending upon whether the number of transpositions it can be resolved into is even or odd. Thus, P_2 is an even permutation while P_A is an odd permutation. This even–odd concept is very important in considering the properties of the symmetric group. It is not, however, necessary to actually resolve the permutation into transpositions. It is sufficient to resolve it into cycles. A cycle of order n can be resolved into $(n - 1)$ transpositions. Thus, if a given permutation can be resolved into a cycles of order p, b cycles of order q, c cycles of order r, and so on, it can be resolved into $a(p - 1) + b(q - 1) + c(r - 1) + \ldots$ transpositions. The subgroup of the symmetric group that contains only the even permutations is known as the *alternating group*, and is given the symbol **A**(n).

Exercise 6.7: Resolve the permutations in **S**(3) into cycles. To which symmetry group is **A**(3) isomorphic?

An abbreviated notation is usually used for cyclic permutations. This is just a list of numbers giving the cyclic order. The first element of the cycle is listed first, followed by the element to which that element is permuted, and so on, until the cycle is completed. For example, P_2, P_3, and P_A would be abbreviated

$$P_2 = \begin{pmatrix}1 & 2 & 3\\ 2 & 3 & 1\end{pmatrix} = (1\ \ 2\ \ 3) \tag{6.35}$$

$$P_3 = \begin{pmatrix}1 & 2 & 3\\ 3 & 1 & 2\end{pmatrix} = (1\ \ 3\ \ 2) \tag{6.36}$$

$$P_A = \begin{pmatrix}1 & 4 & 6 & 7 & 8 & 2 & 3 & 5\\ 4 & 7 & 8 & 6 & 1 & 3 & 2 & 5\end{pmatrix} = (1\ \ 4\ \ 7\ \ 6\ \ 8)(2\ \ 3)(5) \tag{6.37}$$

This is the *active* convention to correspond to the active convention we have used in symmetry groups. [Some authors use a *passive* convention which, after the first element, lists the elements that are permuted to the preceding element. In this convention, P_A would equal (1 8 6 7 4)(2 3)(5); i.e, 8 replaces 1, 6 replaces 8, etc.]. The specification of the elements that are not changed by a permutation is redundant, and these are usually omitted. Thus, P_A would normally be written (in the active convention) as (1 4 7 6 8)(2 3).

Classes of S(n)

The permutations of the symmetric group can be divided into classes by making use of the conjugate relationships. It turns out that all permutations having the same cycle structure belong to the same class. For example, in **S**(3) the six permutations are (1 2 3), (1 3 2), (1 2)(3), (1 3)(2), (2 3)(1), and (1)(2)(3). The first two form one class (corresponding to the $2C_3$ of $\mathbf{C}_{3v}$), the next three form another class (corresponding to the $3\sigma_v$), while the last (the identity) is in a class by itself. In **S**(4) there are classes of the types (1 2 3 4), (1 2 3)(4), (1 2)(3 4), (1 2)(3)(4), and (1)(2)(3)(4). There are, thus, five classes, having six, eight, three, six, and one members, respectively. (These are analogous to the $6S_4$, $8C_3$, $3C_2$, $6\sigma_d$, and E of $\mathbf{T}_d$.)

If a permutation of a given class and degree n can be resolved into a cycles of degree p, b cycles of degree q, c cycles of degree r, and so on, where

$$ap + bq + cr + \ldots = n \tag{6.38}$$

then the number of permutations in that class (the order of the class, g_i) is

$$g_i = \frac{n!}{p^a a! q^b b! r^c c! \ldots} \tag{6.39}$$

For example, for permutations of the type (1 2)(3)(4) in **S**(4), we have

$$g_i = \frac{4!}{2^1 \times 1! \times 1^2 \times 2!} = 6 \tag{6.40}$$

while for permutations of the type (1 2)(3 4), we have

$$g_i = \frac{4!}{2^2 \times 2!} = 3 \tag{6.41}$$

The P_A in **S**(8) would be a member of a class of

$$g_i = \frac{8!}{5^1 \times 1! \times 2^1 \times 1! \times 1^1 \times 1!} = 4032 \tag{6.42}$$

permutations.

Exercise 6.8: Find the classes and the number of elements in each class for S(5).

Irreducible Representations of S(n)

Space will not permit our going into detail on the theory of representations of the symmetric group. We will, however, present a simplified method (due to Coleman) for finding the character for any class of permutations in any given irreducible representation. For most of the uses we will make of the symmetric group, only the degeneracy of the representations (the character of the identity) will be required.

For completeness, however, we will illustrate a method for general classes as well as the identity. The method we shall illustrate is based upon a graphical procedure using what is known as *Young diagrams.* The Young diagram for a class is a group of blocks or dots arranged to illustrate the cyclic structure of the class, the longest cycle being illustrated on the top line, and succeeding shorter cycles on succeeding lines, the lines being aligned to the left. For example, the classes of **S**(4) would be

(1 2 3 4): 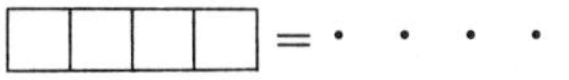 : (4) (6.43a)

(1 2 3)(4): 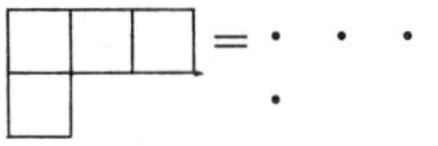 : (3, 1) (6.43b)

(1 2)(3 4): 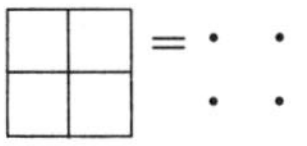 : (2, 2) = (2^2) (6.43c)

(1 2)(3)(4): 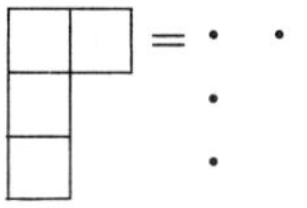 : $(2, 1^2)$ (6.43d)

(1)(2)(3)(4):  : (1^4) (6.43e)

(The symbols to the far right are yet another abbreviated notation for the classes. The numbers are the lengths of the cycles, and the superscripts are the number of times a cycle of a given length appears in the permutation.)

Each class has a *conjugate class* associated with it. The conjugate class represents the class that results when the rows and columns of the Young diagram are interchanged. For example, (1^4) is the conjugate class of (4), $(2, 1^2)$ is the conjugate class of (3, 1), and (2^2) is self-conjugate. For our purposes, the most important significance of the conjugate classes is that they are the labels of the irreducible representations. (When used in this context, we will use square brackets rather than parentheses.) The representations are usually listed in the order of the conjugates of the classes. For example, the structure of the character table of **S**(4) would be (listing the identity first)

S(4)	(1^4)	$6(2, 1^2)$	$3(2^2)$	8(3, 1)	6(4)
[4]					
[3, 1]					
$[2^2]$					
$[2, 1^2]$					
$[1^4]$					

(6.44)

To derive the elements of the character table we will use the *hook diagrams* derived from the Young diagrams. A hook diagram is a series of numbers arranged like the entries in the Young diagram. Each entry in the hook diagram for a given Young diagram is equal to the number of elements (dots or boxes) to the right of its position, plus the number of elements below its position, plus one. For example, the hook diagrams for the representations of S(4) are

[4] → 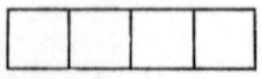 → 4 3 2 1 (6.45a)

[3, 1] → 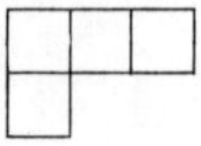 → 4 2 1
1 (6.45b)

[2^2] → 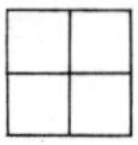 → 3 2
2 1 (6.45c)

[2, 1^2] → 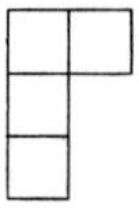 → 4 1
2
1 (6.45d)

[1^4] → 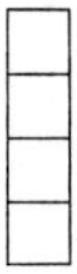 → 4
3
2
1 (6.45e)

The procedure to follow to obtain the characters is to relate the cycles of the class under consideration to the *principal hook lengths* of the hook diagram corresponding to the representation under consideration. (The principal hook lengths are the numbers in the first column of the hook diagram.) The numbers are reduced by successively subtracting out the cycle lengths of the class from the principal hook length, in all possible combinations, until all cycles have been subtracted out. Fewer difficulties are encountered if the cycles are eliminated in descending order. In the procedure, each array of resulting numbers that contains a negative number and each array that contains the same number twice is discarded. Consider, for example, the character of the (2, 1^2) class in the [2^2] representation. The principal hook lengths for [2^2] are 3 and 2. Thus, we have

Cycles of the class: *Principal hook lengths of the representation:*

2, 1^2: $|3 \quad 2|$ (6.46a)

Subtracting out the 2 in all possible ways yields

1^2: $|1 \quad 2| + |3 \quad 0|$ (6.46b)

Subtracting out a 1 yields

1: $|0 \quad 2| + |2 \quad 0|$ (the $|1 \quad 1|$ is discarded) (6.46c)

and subtracting out the final 1 leaves

ϕ: $|0 \quad 1| + |1 \quad 0|$

If there are p principal hook lengths, the final result should contain only the numbers $(p-1)(p-2)\ldots 0$. If these are in descending order, the array contributes $+1$ to the character. If they are not in descending order, the contribution to the character is $+1$ or -1, depending upon whether an even or an odd number of transpositions is required to place them in descending order. Thus, for $\chi(2, 1^2)$ in $[2^2]$, we have

$$\chi(2, 1^2) = -1 + 1 = 0 \tag{6.47}$$

To complete the irreducible representation of $[2^2]$, let us find the characters for the other classes:

$$\begin{aligned}
&\chi(1^4) = \chi(E)\\
&\qquad 1^4:\ |3\quad 2|\\
&\qquad 1^3:\ |3\quad 1| \qquad \text{(the } |2\quad 2| \text{ is discarded)}\\
&\qquad 1^2:\ |2\quad 1| + |3\quad 0|\\
&\qquad 1^1:\ |2\quad 0| + |2\quad 0|\\
&\qquad \phi:\ \ 2|1\quad 0|\\
&\chi(E) = 2
\end{aligned} \tag{6.48a}$$

$$\begin{aligned}
&\chi(2^2)\\
&\qquad 2^2:\ |3\quad 2|\\
&\qquad 2:\ |1\quad 2| + |3\quad 0|\\
&\qquad \phi:\ 2|1\quad 0|\\
&\chi(2^2) = 2
\end{aligned} \tag{6.48b}$$

$$\begin{aligned}
&\chi(3, 1)\\
&\qquad 3, 1:\ |3\quad 2|\\
&\qquad 1:\ |0\quad 2|\\
&\qquad \phi:\ |0\quad 1|\\
&\chi(3, 1) = -1
\end{aligned} \tag{6.48c}$$

$$\begin{aligned}
&\chi(4)\\
&\qquad 4:\ |3\quad 2|\\
&\qquad \phi:\ 0\\
&\chi(4) = 0
\end{aligned} \tag{6.48d}$$

Thus, we have for the irreducible representation

S(4)	(1^4)	$6(2, 1^2)$	$3(2^2)$	$8(3, 1)$	$6(4)$
$[2^2]$	2	0	2	-1	0

(6.49)

When the permutations are mapped on the corresponding symmetry elements of $\mathbf{T}_d$ we see that the representation $[2^2]$ is isomorphic to the E representation. Similarly, [3, 1] is isomorphic to T_1, $[2, 1^2]$ to T_2, [4] to A_1, and $[1^4]$ to A_2.

There is actually an easier way to derive the character of the identity element, which is frequently all that is needed for applications. It turns out that the degeneracy of the representation (the character of the identity) is equal to the order of the group ($n!$) divided by the product of all the numbers in the hook diagram corresponding to the representation.

Exercise 6.9: Complete the character table for **S**(4) and verify the isomorphism with $\mathbf{T}_d$.

Exercise 6.10: Construct the character table for **S**(5).

The Symmetric Permutation-Inversion Group

An inversion can be added to the symmetric permutation group to give the *symmetric permutation-inversion group*. We will adopt the symbol **S***(n) for this group and indicate the permutation-inversion operations by an asterisk after the corresponding permutation operation [thus, the permutation-inversion operator corresponding to (1 2 3) would be (1 2 3)*]. The permutation-inversion group has an order that is twice that of the corresponding permutation group. It will also have twice as many classes and irreducible representations associated with it. The characters for the individual permutation-inversion elements can be ± 1 times those for the permutation elements. The $+1$ corresponds to the original irreducible representations, while the -1 produces the new irreducible representations (which we shall again indicate with an asterisk, as, for example, [3, 1]*).

The permutation-inversion group **S***(n) is a subgroup of the group **S**($2n$). However, the permutation-inversion construction is frequently useful for class and representation structures. For example, the **S***(3) group is isomorphic to the $\mathbf{D}_{3d}$ point group, the point group of staggered ethane. Let us consider the **S***(3) and **S**(6) descriptions of the permutations of the hydrogens. If these are arranged as in **1**, the classes within $\mathbf{D}_{3d}$, **S***(3), and **S**(6) and one example of each from **S**(6) are

$\mathbf{D}_{3d}$:	**S***(3):	**S**(6):	Example:	
E	$= (1^3)$	$= (1^6)$	= (1)(2)(3)(4)(5)(6)	(6.50a)
C_3	= (3)	$= (3^2)$	= (1 2 3)(4 5 6)	(6.50b)
σ_d	= (2, 1)	$= (2^2, 1^2)$	= (1 2)(3)(4)(5 6)	(6.50c)
i	$= (1^3)^*$	$= (2^3)$	= (1 5)(2 6)(3 4)	(6.50d)
S_3	= (3)*	= (6)	= (1 4 2 5 3 6)	(6.50e)
C_2	= (2, 1)*	$= (2^3)$	= (1 6)(2 5)(3 4)	(6.50f)

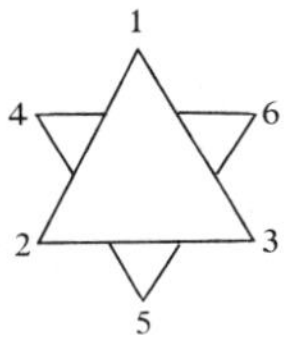

1

We see that in the mapping on **S**(6), the elements $(1^3)^*$ and $(2, 1)^*$ (or i and C_2) belong to the same class. This is not the case in **S***(3) (or $\mathbf{D}_{3d}$).

Exercise 6.11: To which point group is **S***(4) isomorphic?

6.5 THE SYMMETRY GROUPS OF NONRIGID MOLECULES

Introduction

Many real molecules are not rigid. For example, all organic molecules having "single bonds" in them are capable of rotation about these bonds. Thus, ethane in its most stable conformation has $\mathbf{D}_{3d}$ symmetry. The least stable conformation has $\mathbf{D}_{3h}$ symmetry. In between these two extremes the molecule has the lower $\mathbf{D}_3$ symmetry (Fig. 6.3). Although the rotation barrier is small, it is still sufficiently large that, in a collection of ethane molecules at room temperature, the predominant symmetry will be $\mathbf{D}_{3d}$. Dimethylacetylene (**1**) can exist in the same three point

$$CH_3{-}C{\equiv}C{-}CH_3$$

1

groups as ethane. Here, however, the rotational barrier is negligibly small. As a consequence, the most probable instantaneous point symmetry for dimethylacetylene is $\mathbf{D}_3$. A related, but somewhat different, situation occurs in the case of

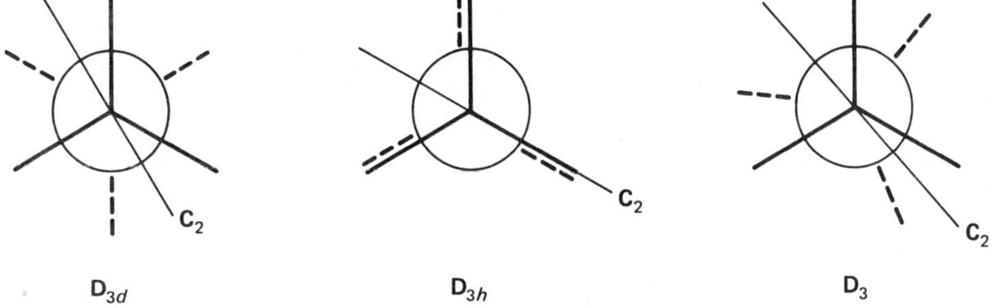

Fig. 6.3. Newman projections representing the three possible point groups for ethane.

ammonia. The ammonia molecule has $\mathbf{C}_{3v}$ point symmetry. It is, however, capable of undergoing molecular inversion:

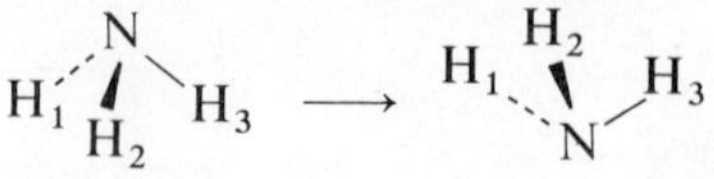

$$
\underset{H_2}{\overset{N}{H_1 \diagup \diagdown H_3}} \longrightarrow \underset{N}{\overset{H_2}{H_1 \diagdown \diagup H_3}} \tag{6.51}
$$

During the course of the inversion process, the molecule must pass through a configuration having $\mathbf{D}_{3h}$ point symmetry.

In all three cases we have mentioned, there are experimental measurements that require the treatment of the molecule to be carried through using some symmetry other than the expected instantaneous point symmetry. The inversion spectrum of ammonia can be studied in the radio-frequency range. For such studies, the ammonia molecule must be treated within the $\mathbf{D}_{3h}$ point group. The experimental measurement of the absolute entropy of ethane and dimethyl-acetylene reveals that they behave as if they belong to a symmetry group of a higher order than either the $\mathbf{D}_{3h}$ or $\mathbf{D}_{3d}$ point groups. In the ammonia case, the plane through which the molecule inverts must be considered as a symmetry element. In the ethane and dimethylacetylene cases, rotations of the methyl groups with respect to each other must be considered as symmetry elements. Methods for handling symmetry groups containing such elements have been developed by Longuet-Higgins and by Altmann, and have been extended by various other workers. The developments are very similar; however, Longuet-Higgins approaches the symmetry groups for nonrigid molecules from the point of view of permutation groups, while Altmann defines actual physical operations (*iso-dynamic operations*) for the group rotations, and so on. Both approaches have their advantages and limitations. We will, however, follow the method of Altmann, since the operations are more intuitively obvious.

Isodynamic Operations

We shall define an isodynamic operation as an operation that takes a nonrigid molecule into an *energetically equivalent* orientation by some *physically reasonable* process such as a rotation about a bond (as in ethane) or a molecular inversion (as in ammonia). These isodynamic operations cannot, in general, be represented by a change of axes as ordinary point symmetry operations can. As examples, the inversion shown in Eq. 6.51 is the only isodynamic operation, other than the identity, for ammonia. For staggered ethane we have the set of threefold rotations shown in Eq. 6.52, and the corresponding rotations of the other methyl group. Note that we are using a convention of script $\mathscr{C}$'s to indicate isodynamic rotations. We shall use script $\mathscr{I}$'s to indicate molecular or group inversions.

The set of isodynamic operations, with the identity, forms a group. We shall restrict the members of the isodynamic group, $\mathbf{I}$, to those isodynamic operations that do not destroy any of the symmetry elements of the point group of the molecule.

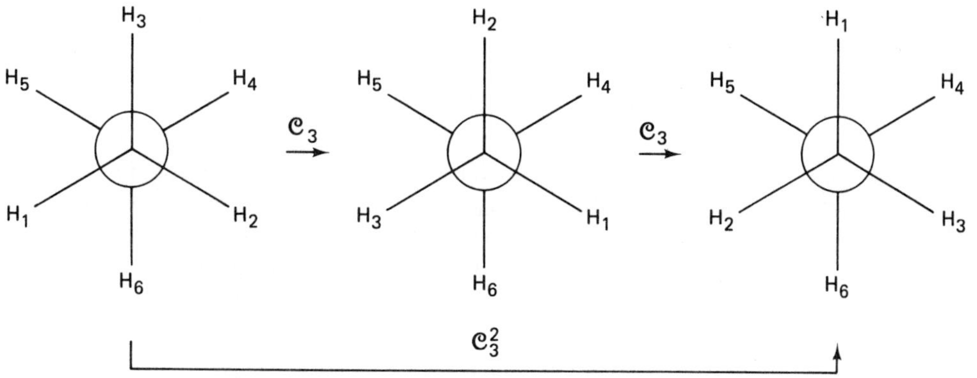

(6.52)

For the case of ethane, this restriction seems redundant, since any rotation other than 120° would lead to an energetically different conformation. In the case of dimethylacetylene, however, where there is probably no detectable energy difference between the $\mathbf{D}_{3h}$, $\mathbf{D}_{3d}$, and $\mathbf{D}_3$ conformations, it is not redundant. The isodynamic group must be defined with respect to one particular point group. This restriction gives two important properties to $\mathbf{I}$: the isodynamic configurations all belong to the same point symmetry group, and the isodynamic group is invariant with respect to conjugation with the elements of the point group.

The Schrödinger Supergroup

The symmetry group of a nonrigid molecule, which, following Altmann, we shall call the *Schrödinger supergroup*, is defined as the product of the isodynamic group and the point group (the Schrödinger group),

$$\mathbf{S} = \mathbf{I} \wedge \mathbf{G} \tag{6.53}$$

The semidirect product indicated in Eq. 6.53 is the general relationship; however, for certain isodynamic groups and point groups, the direct product relationship may hold. We shall proceed now with some examples of supergroups.

Ammonia

Let us illustrate the construction of the Schrödinger supergroup for several molecules. In the case of ammonia, the point group is $\mathbf{C}_{3v}$ and, considering inversion as the allowed isodynamic operation, the isodynamic group is

$$\mathbf{I} = \{E, \mathscr{I}\} \tag{6.54}$$

The supergroup is

$$\mathbf{S} = \{E, \mathscr{I}\}\{E, 2C_3, 3\sigma_v\} \tag{6.55}$$

$$= \{E, 2C_3, 3\sigma_v, \mathscr{I}, 2S_3, 3\sigma_v'\} \tag{6.55a}$$

In this case, the isodynamic operation $\mathscr{I}$ commutes with all of the elements of $\mathbf{C}_{3v}$. Thus, the group product can be written as a direct product,

$$\mathbf{S} = \mathscr{I} \times \mathbf{C}_{3v} = \mathbf{C}_{3v} \times \mathscr{I} \tag{6.56}$$

This group is isomorphic to $\mathbf{D}_{3h}$ (which is $\mathbf{C}_{3v} \times \mathbf{C}_s$). The structure of its character table would be identical to that of $\mathbf{D}_{3h}$. Thus, the spectroscopic treatments of the inversion of ammonia which are based upon a $\mathbf{D}_{3h}$ point symmetry are actually working from a point group that is isomorphic to its supergroup.

Methanol

As a second example, let us consider methanol CH_3OH. The molecule is capable of three different types of conformation, two having $\mathbf{C}_s$ symmetry and one with

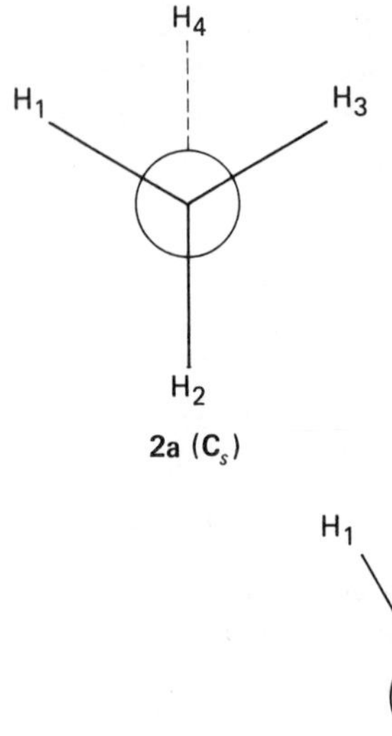

2a ($\mathbf{C}_s$)

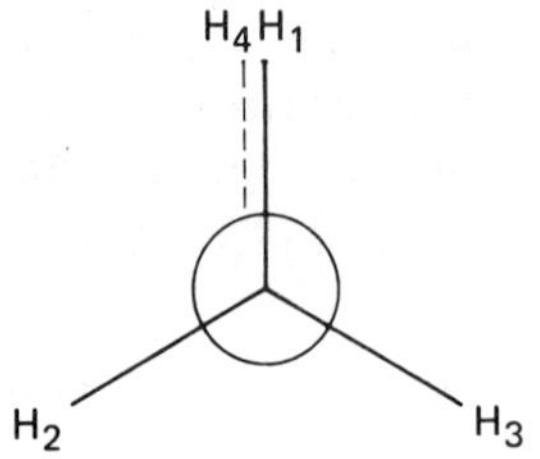

2b ($\mathbf{C}_s$)

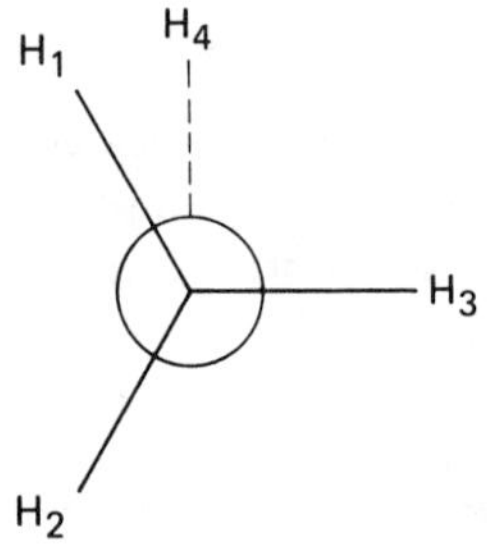

2c ($\mathbf{C}_1$)

only $\mathbf{C}_1$ symmetry (**2a**, **2b**, and **2c**). For structures **2a** and **2b**, with $\mathbf{C}_s$ symmetry, the only isodynamic operation is a $\mathscr{C}_3$. The supergroup is, thus,

$$\mathbf{S} = \mathscr{C}_3 \wedge \mathbf{C}_s \tag{6.57}$$

In this case, $\mathscr{C}_3$ and σ do not commute:

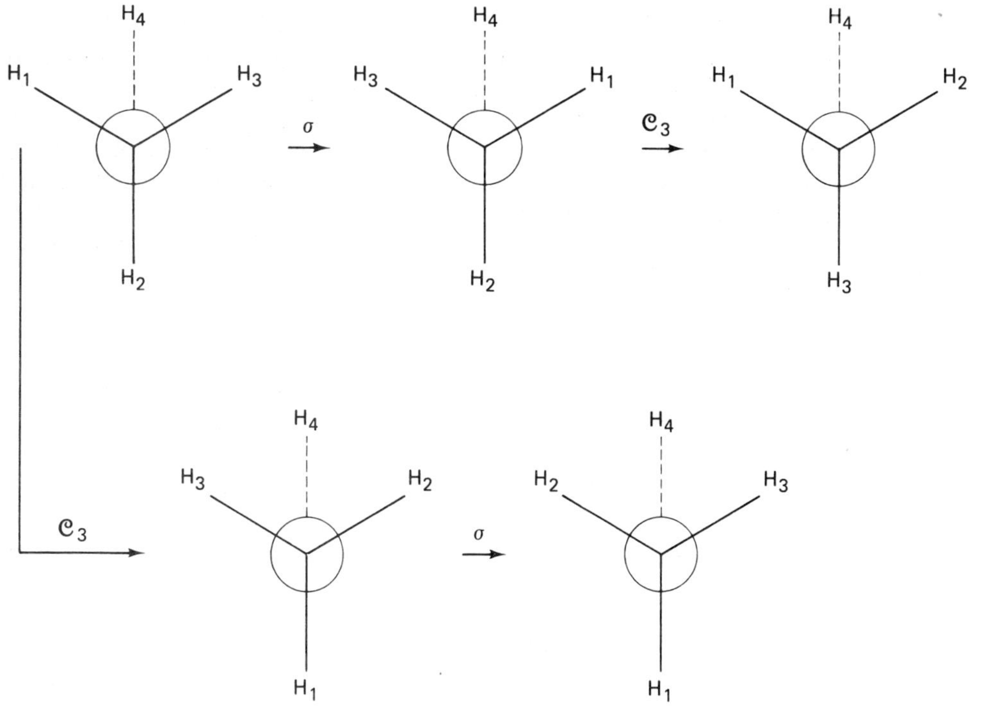

(6.58)

Consequently, the semidirect product is correct. The supergroup is isomorphic to $\mathbf{C}_{3v}$. Both $\mathbf{C}_s$ conformations yield the same supergroup. Consider, however, the $\mathbf{C}_1$ conformation. There are no point symmetry operations, but there is another isodynamic operation other than $\mathscr{C}_3$. Structure **2d** has the same relative orientations of atoms as **2c**, and consequently, must have the same energy. There are no point symmetry elements in **2c**; consequently, none have been destroyed. Thus, the operation that carries the conformation **2c** to **2d** must be an allowed isodynamic

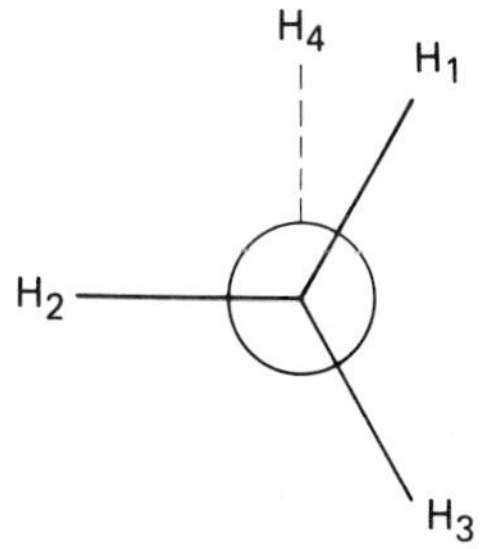

2d

operation. This operation, which we shall call a *switch*, should be carefully defined to avoid problems with its commutation properties. The switch, U, differs from all other symmetry and isodynamic operations which we have discussed in that it requires some vector to "remember where it came from" after any other operation. A switch can be defined as a rotation of some vector by an angle 2θ through some plane, where θ is the angle of the vector from the reference plane. After some other operation, the magnitude of θ may be changed; however, the same vector is rotated by 2θ (where θ may have the new value) through the same plane any time the switch is called for. This is best illustrated by example. The switch required to go from **2c** to **2d** can be considered as a rotation of the vector from C to H_1 through the plane C—O—H_4 by twice its angle from that plane:

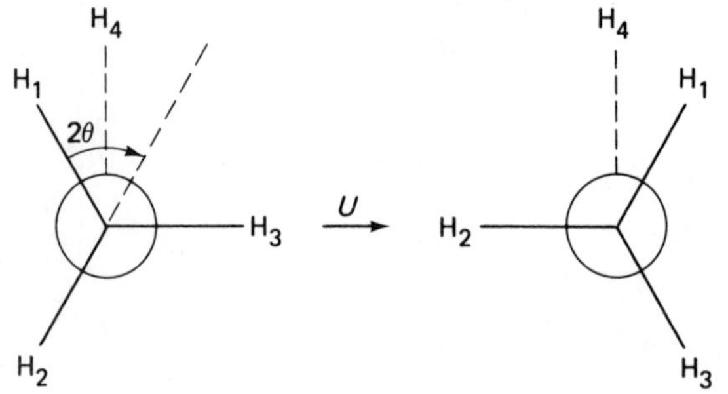

2c **2d** (6.59)

After $\mathscr{C}_3$, the angle θ has been increased by 120°, and we have

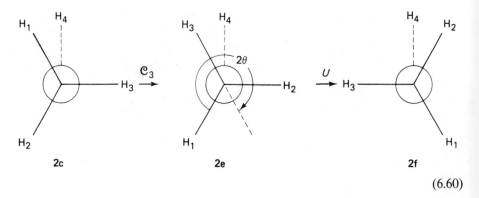

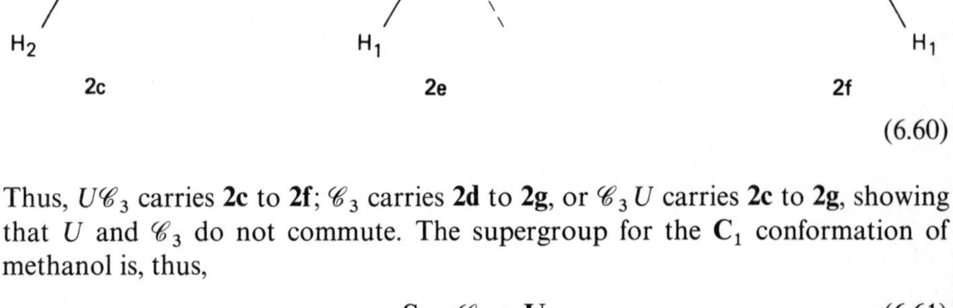

2c **2e** **2f**

(6.60)

Thus, $U\mathscr{C}_3$ carries **2c** to **2f**; $\mathscr{C}_3$ carries **2d** to **2g**, or $\mathscr{C}_3 U$ carries **2c** to **2g**, showing that U and $\mathscr{C}_3$ do not commute. The supergroup for the $\mathbf{C}_1$ conformation of methanol is, thus,

$$\mathbf{S} = \mathscr{C}_3 \wedge \mathbf{U} \tag{6.61}$$

This group is isomorphic to $\mathbf{C}_{3v}$ and to the supergroups of the $\mathbf{C}_s$ conformations.

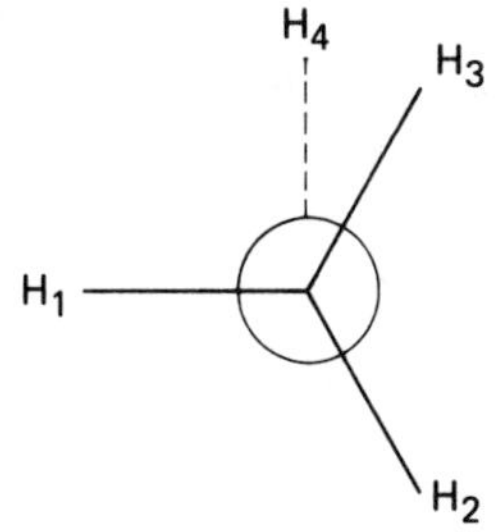

2g

Propane

As a final example of a Schrödinger supergroup, let us consider propane, C_3H_8. This molecule is capable of exhibiting several point symmetries. Among these are two $\mathbf{C}_{2v}$ conformations (all bonds on adjacent carbons staggered or all bonds on adjacent carbons eclipsed), one $\mathbf{C}_s$ conformation (the bonds on C_1 and C_2 staggered with those on C_2 and C_3 eclipsed, or vice versa), a number of $\mathbf{C}_2$ conformations (the terminal carbons skewed from the $\mathbf{C}_{2v}$ structures in such a way that the planes of symmetry are destroyed but the C_2 is retained), and a number of $\mathbf{C}_1$ conformations with random orientations of the two methyl groups. We will confine our attention to one $\mathbf{C}_{2v}$ conformation and one $\mathbf{C}_2$ conformation.

The $\mathbf{C}_{2v}$ structure of propane, shown as **3**, is the most stable conformation. The planes of symmetry are defined by H_7—C—H_8 and H_3—C—C—C—H_6.

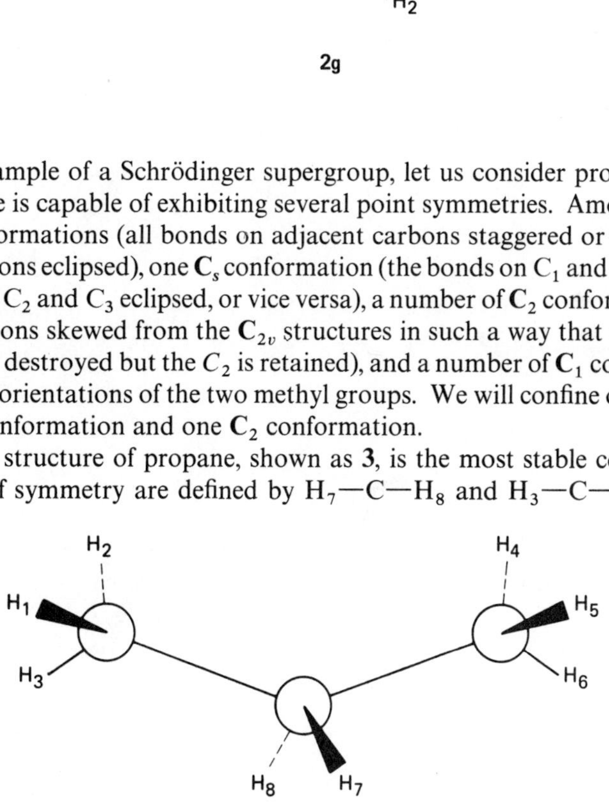

3

The symmetry axis is the intersection of these planes. The only isodynamic operations are the $\mathscr{C}_3$ operations for each methyl group. These are independent; consequently, the isodynamic group is

$$\mathbf{I} = \mathscr{C}_3 \times \mathscr{C}'_3 \tag{6.62}$$

and the supergroup is

$$\mathbf{S} = (\mathscr{C}_3 \times \mathscr{C}'_3) \wedge \mathbf{C}_{2v} \tag{6.63}$$

There is no point group to which this group is isomorphic.

The C_2 operation of $\mathbf{C}_{2v}$ commutes with the $\mathscr{C}_3$'s; however, the planes of symmetry do not. For the H_3—C—C—C—H_6 plane of symmetry, this can be seen in the sequences

$$\mathbf{3} \xrightarrow{\sigma} \mathbf{3a} \xrightarrow{\mathscr{C}_3} \mathbf{3b} \text{ and } \mathbf{3} \xrightarrow{\mathscr{C}_3} \mathbf{3c} \xrightarrow{\sigma} \mathbf{3d}$$

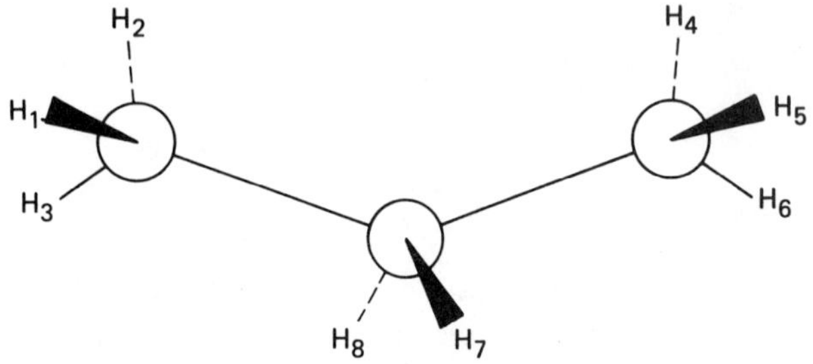

3

σ

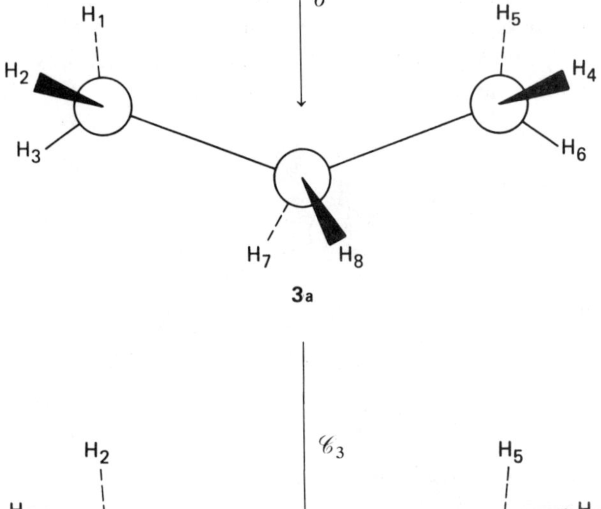

3a

$\mathscr{C}_3$

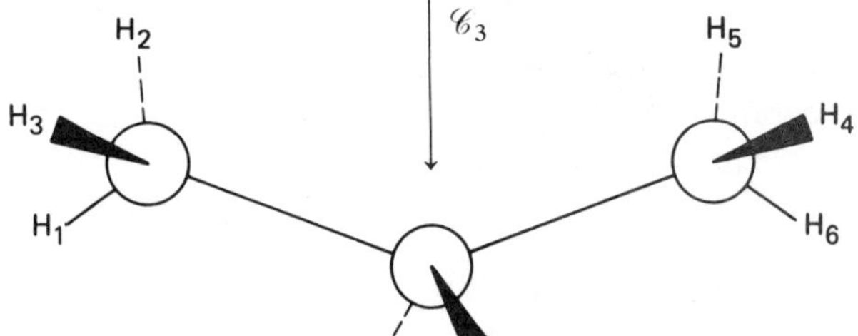

3b

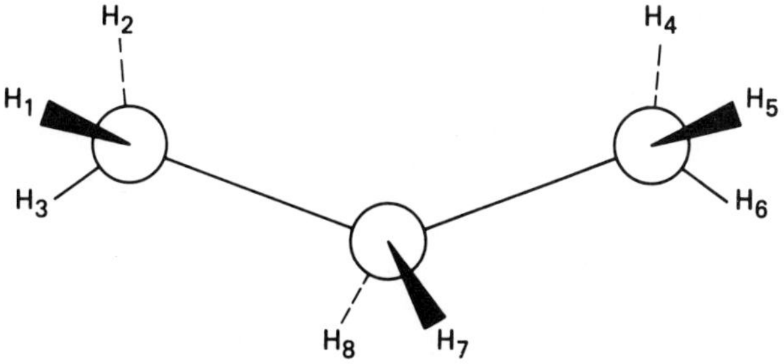

3

$\mathscr{C}_3$

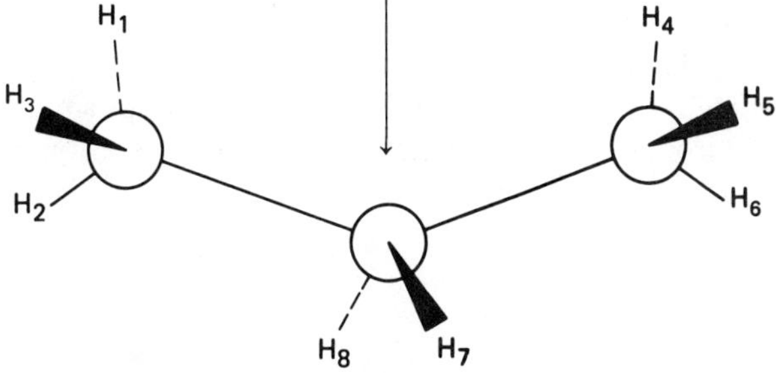

3c

σ

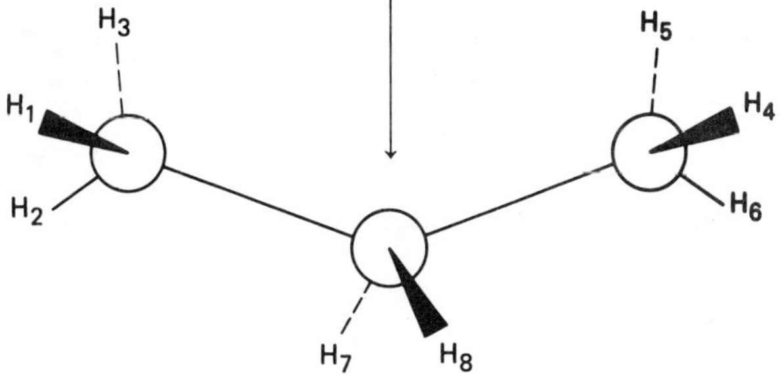

3d

The group structure is, thus,

$$\mathbf{S} = (\mathscr{C}_3 \times \mathscr{C}'_3 \times \mathbf{C}_2) \wedge \mathbf{C}_s \tag{6.63a}$$

One pair of carbons in a $\mathbf{C}_2$ conformation is shown in **4a**. The hydrogens on the other terminal carbon are oriented such that the C_2 element rotates H_1 into

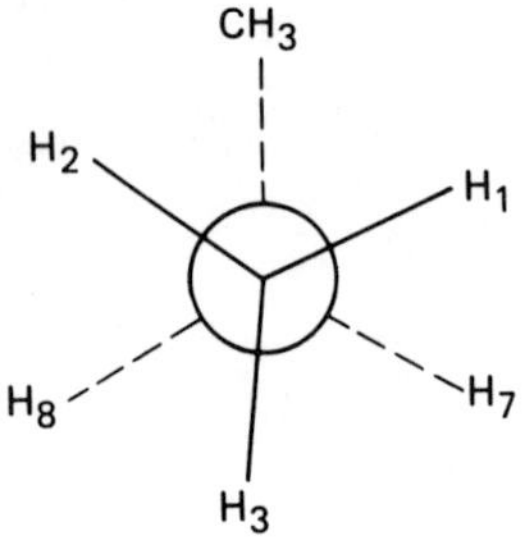

4a

H_4, H_2 into H_5, and H_3 into H_6. In addition to the $\mathscr{C}_3$'s there is an isodynamic switch, V, which switches both methyl groups simultaneously. The hydrogens on the front carbon are switched to the conformation of **4b**, while those on the other

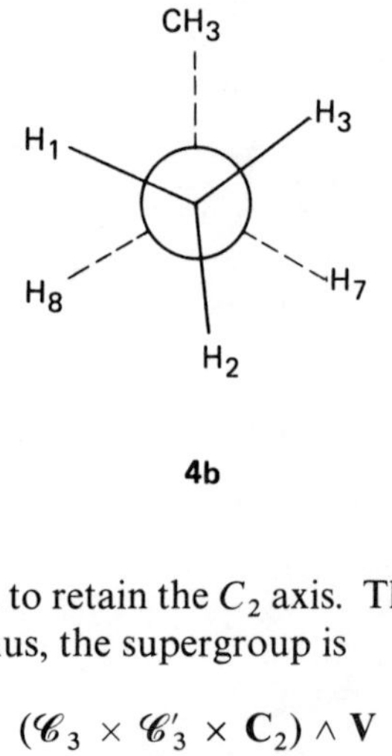

4b

terminal carbon are switched to retain the C_2 axis. This switch commutes with the C_2 but not with the $\mathscr{C}_3$'s. Thus, the supergroup is

$$(\mathscr{C}_3 \times \mathscr{C}'_3 \times \mathbf{C}_2) \wedge \mathbf{V} \tag{6.64}$$

This supergroup is isomorphic to that shown in Eq. 6.63.

Exercise 6.12*:

(a) Find the supergroup for CH_3BF_2 (planar boron) in the $\mathbf{C}_s$ and $\mathbf{C}_1$ conformations. To what point group is it isomorphic?

(b) Find the supergroup for CH_3NH_2 (nonplanar nitrogen) in the $\mathbf{C}_s$ and $\mathbf{C}_1$ conformations. (Note that although the nitrogen can invert, this meets the requirements for an isodynamic operation only in the $\mathbf{C}_1$ conformation.)

(c) Find the supergroup for *p*-dinitrobenzene in the $\mathbf{D}_{2h}$ conformation. (Assume free rotation of the nitro groups.)

The Character Table for the Supergroup of Propane

The construction of the character tables for nonrigid molecules is basically the same as that outlined in Chapter 5 for point groups. As an example of the construction of a character table for a nonrigid molecule, let us consider a propane molecule as previously numbered in **3**. The supergroup has the structure $(\mathscr{C}_3 \times \mathscr{C}'_3) \wedge \mathbf{C}_{2v}$. If the isodynamic rotation of the methyl group bearing hydrogens 1, 2 and 3 is denoted by $\mathscr{C}_3$ and that for the other methyl group by $\mathscr{C}'_3$, we have for the multiplication table for the direct product,

(6.65)

$\mathscr{C}'_3$ \ $\mathscr{C}_3$	E	$\mathscr{C}_3$	$\mathscr{C}_3^2$
E	E	$\mathscr{C}_3$	$\mathscr{C}_3$
$\mathscr{C}'_3$	$\mathscr{C}'_3$	$\mathscr{C}'_3\mathscr{C}_3$	$\mathscr{C}'_3\mathscr{C}_3^2$
$\mathscr{C}'^2_3$	$\mathscr{C}'^2_3$	$\mathscr{C}'^2_3\mathscr{C}_3$	$\mathscr{C}'^2_3\mathscr{C}_3^2$

The multiplication table for the semidirect product is

(6.66)

$\mathscr{C}'_3 \times \mathscr{C}_3$ \ $\mathbf{C}_{2v}$	E	C_2	σ_v	σ'_v
E	${}^aE$	${}^gC_2$	${}^f\sigma_v$	${}^l\sigma'_v$
$\mathscr{C}_3$	${}^b\mathscr{C}_3$	${}^h\mathscr{C}_3C_2$	${}^f\mathscr{C}_3\sigma_v$	${}^l\mathscr{C}_3\sigma'_v$
$\mathscr{C}_3^2$	${}^b\mathscr{C}_3^2$	${}^h\mathscr{C}_3^2C_2$	${}^f\mathscr{C}_3^2\sigma_v$	${}^l\mathscr{C}_3^2\sigma'_v$
$\mathscr{C}'_3$	${}^c\mathscr{C}'_3$	${}^i\mathscr{C}'_3C_2$	${}^f\mathscr{C}'_3\sigma_v$	${}^l\mathscr{C}'_3\sigma'_v$
$\mathscr{C}'_3\mathscr{C}_3$	${}^d\mathscr{C}'_3\mathscr{C}_3$	${}^j\mathscr{C}'_3\mathscr{C}_3C_2$	${}^f\mathscr{C}'_3\mathscr{C}_3\sigma_v$	${}^l\mathscr{C}'_3\mathscr{C}_3\sigma'_v$
$\mathscr{C}'_3\mathscr{C}_3^2$	${}^e\mathscr{C}'_3\mathscr{C}_3^2$	${}^k\mathscr{C}'_3\mathscr{C}_3^2C_2$	${}^f\mathscr{C}'_3\mathscr{C}_3^2\sigma_v$	${}^l\mathscr{C}'_3\mathscr{C}_3^2\sigma'_v$
$\mathscr{C}'^2_3$	${}^c\mathscr{C}'^2_3$	${}^i\mathscr{C}'^2_3C_2$	${}^f\mathscr{C}'^2_3\sigma_v$	${}^l\mathscr{C}'^2_3\sigma'_v$
$\mathscr{C}'^2_3\mathscr{C}_3$	${}^e\mathscr{C}'^2_3\mathscr{C}_3$	${}^k\mathscr{C}'^2_3\mathscr{C}_3C_2$	${}^f\mathscr{C}'^2_3\mathscr{C}_3\sigma_v$	${}^l\mathscr{C}'^2_3\mathscr{C}_3\sigma'_v$
$\mathscr{C}'^2_3\mathscr{C}_3^2$	${}^d\mathscr{C}'^2_3\mathscr{C}_3^2$	${}^j\mathscr{C}'^2_3\mathscr{C}_3^2C_2$	${}^f\mathscr{C}'^2_3\mathscr{C}_3^2\sigma_v$	${}^l\mathscr{C}'^2_3\mathscr{C}_3^2\sigma'_v$

Construction of the table of conjugates reveals that there are 12 classes of operations (the elements of these are indicated by *a* through *l* in Eq. 6.66), $\{E, 2\mathscr{C}_3, 2\mathscr{C}'_3, 2\mathscr{C}_3\mathscr{C}'_3, 2\mathscr{C}_3^2\mathscr{C}'_3, 9\sigma_v, C_2, 2\mathscr{C}_3C_2, 2\mathscr{C}'_3C_2, 2\mathscr{C}_3\mathscr{C}'_3C_2, 2\mathscr{C}_3^2\mathscr{C}'_3C_2, 9\sigma'_v\}$. The character table will also have 12 irreducible representations. The character table can be constructed from the multiplication tables of the component groups. The group $(\mathscr{C}'_3 \times \mathscr{C}_3)$ has the character table

$\varepsilon = e^{2\pi i/3}$

$\mathscr{C}'_3 \times \mathscr{C}_3$	E	$\mathscr{C}_3$	$\mathscr{C}_3^2$	$\mathscr{C}'_3$	$\mathscr{C}_3'^2$	$\mathscr{C}'_3\mathscr{C}_3$	$\mathscr{C}_3'^2\mathscr{C}_3^2$	$\mathscr{C}'_3\mathscr{C}_3^2$	$\mathscr{C}_3'^2\mathscr{C}_3$
$A'A$	1	1	1	1	1	1	1	1	1
$A'E_a$	1	ε	ε^*	1	1	ε	ε^*	ε^*	ε
$A'E_b$	1	ε^*	ε	1	1	ε^*	ε	ε	ε^*
$E'_a A$	1	1	1	ε	ε^*	ε	ε^*	ε	ε^*
$E'_b A$	1	1	1	ε^*	ε	ε^*	ε	ε^*	ε
$E'_a E_a$	1	ε	ε^*	ε	ε^*	ε^*	ε	1	1
$E'_b E_b$	1	ε^*	ε	ε^*	ε	ε	ε^*	1	1
$E'_b E_a$	1	ε	ε^*	ε^*	ε	1	1	ε	ε^*
$E'_a E_b$	1	ε^*	ε	ε	ε^*	1	1	ε^*	ε

$$(6.67)$$

where the representation notation is indicative of the appropriate representations in the individual $\mathscr{C}_3$ groups. The a and b subscripts indicate the components of the separable E representations. The $\mathbf{C}_{2v}$ character table is

$\mathbf{C}_{2v}$	E	C_2	σ_v	σ'_v
A_1	1	1	1	1
A_2	1	1	-1	-1
B_1	1	-1	1	-1
B_2	1	-1	-1	1

$$(6.68)$$

The product table for the elements was given in Eq. 6.66. That for the irreducible representations is

$\mathscr{C}'_3 \times \mathscr{C}_3$ $\diagdown$ $\mathbf{C}_{2v}$	A_1	A_2	B_1	B_2
$A'A$	A_1	A_2	A_3	A_4
$A'E_a$ $A'E_b$	$\begin{pmatrix} E_1 \\ E_1 \end{pmatrix}$	$\begin{pmatrix} E_1 \\ E_1 \end{pmatrix}$	$\begin{pmatrix} E_5 \\ E_5 \end{pmatrix}$	$\begin{pmatrix} E_5 \\ E_5 \end{pmatrix}$
$E'_a A$ $E'_b A$	$\begin{pmatrix} E_2 \\ E_2 \end{pmatrix}$	$\begin{pmatrix} E_2 \\ E_2 \end{pmatrix}$	$\begin{pmatrix} E_6 \\ E_6 \end{pmatrix}$	$\begin{pmatrix} E_6 \\ E_6 \end{pmatrix}$
$E'_a E_a$ $E'_b E_b$	$\begin{pmatrix} E_3 \\ E_3 \end{pmatrix}$	$\begin{pmatrix} E_3 \\ E_3 \end{pmatrix}$	$\begin{pmatrix} E_7 \\ E_7 \end{pmatrix}$	$\begin{pmatrix} E_7 \\ E_7 \end{pmatrix}$
$E'_b E_a$ $E'_a E_b$	$\begin{pmatrix} E_4 \\ E_4 \end{pmatrix}$	$\begin{pmatrix} E_4 \\ E_4 \end{pmatrix}$	$\begin{pmatrix} E_8 \\ E_8 \end{pmatrix}$	$\begin{pmatrix} E_8 \\ E_8 \end{pmatrix}$

$$(6.69)$$

The characters for the E_3 representation, for example, arise from the sum of $E'_a E_a A_1$ and $E'_b E_b A_1$, and are

$\mathscr{C}'_3 \times \mathscr{C}_3$	$E'_a E_a$	$E'_b E_b$	$\mathbf{C}_{2v}$ / A_1	E	C_2	σ_v	σ'_v
			A_1	1	1	1	1
E	1	1		$1 + 1$	$1 + 1$	$1 + 1$	$1 + 1$
$\mathscr{C}_3$	ε	ε^*		$\varepsilon + \varepsilon^*$	$\varepsilon + \varepsilon^*$	$\varepsilon + \varepsilon^*$	$\varepsilon + \varepsilon^*$
$\mathscr{C}_3^2$	ε^*	ε		$\varepsilon^* + \varepsilon$	$\varepsilon^* + \varepsilon$	$\varepsilon^* + \varepsilon$	$\varepsilon^* + \varepsilon$
$\mathscr{C}'_3$	ε	ε^*		$\varepsilon + \varepsilon^*$	$\varepsilon + \varepsilon^*$	$\varepsilon + \varepsilon^*$	$\varepsilon + \varepsilon^*$
$\mathscr{C}_3'^2$	ε^*	ε		$\varepsilon^* + \varepsilon$	$\varepsilon^* + \varepsilon$	$\varepsilon^* + \varepsilon$	$\varepsilon^* + \varepsilon$
$\mathscr{C}'_3\mathscr{C}_3$	ε^*	ε		$\varepsilon^* + \varepsilon$	$\varepsilon^* + \varepsilon$	$\varepsilon^* + \varepsilon$	$\varepsilon^* + \varepsilon$
$\mathscr{C}_3'^2\mathscr{C}_3^2$	ε	ε^*		$\varepsilon + \varepsilon^*$	$\varepsilon + \varepsilon^*$	$\varepsilon + \varepsilon^*$	$\varepsilon + \varepsilon^*$
$\mathscr{C}'_3\mathscr{C}_3^2$	1	1		$1 + 1$	$1 + 1$	$1 + 1$	$1 + 1$
$\mathscr{C}_3'^2\mathscr{C}_3$	1	1		$1 + 1$	$1 + 1$	$1 + 1$	$1 + 1$

(6.70)

The other representations can be constructed analogously. The final character table is presented in Table 6.2. Interestingly, the supergroups for all higher unbranched saturated hydrocarbons are isomorphic to that for propane. All have either $\mathbf{C}_{2v}$ or $\mathbf{C}_{2h}$ for their point symmetry, and the $\mathscr{C}_3$ operations as their only isodynamic operations. Any other apparent isodynamic operation for the $\mathbf{C}_{2v}$ or $\mathbf{C}_{2h}$ conformations can actually be expressed as an Euclidian rotation of the entire molecule. Thus, since $\mathbf{C}_{2v}$ and $\mathbf{C}_{2h}$ are isomorphic, the supergroups are isomorphic.

Table 6.2. Character table for the supergroup of propane

$_3 \times \mathscr{C}'_3) \wedge \mathbf{C}_{2v}$	E	$2\mathscr{C}_3$	$2\mathscr{C}'_3$	$2\mathscr{C}_3\mathscr{C}'_3$	$2\mathscr{C}_3^2\mathscr{C}'_3$	$9\sigma_v$	C_2	$2\mathscr{C}_3 C_2$	$2\mathscr{C}'_3 C_2$	$2\mathscr{C}_3\mathscr{C}'_3 C_2$	$2\mathscr{C}_3^2\mathscr{C}'_3 C_2$	$9\sigma'_v$	
A_1	1	1	1	1	1	1	1	1	1	1	1	1	z, x^2, y^2, z^2
A_2	1	1	1	1	1	−1	1	1	1	1	1	−1	R_z, xy
A_3	1	1	1	1	1	1	−1	−1	−1	−1	−1	−1	x, R_y, xz
A_4	1	1	1	1	1	−1	−1	−1	−1	−1	−1	1	y, R_x, yz
E_1	2	−1	2	−1	−1	0	2	−1	2	−1	−1	0	
E_2	2	2	−1	−1	−1	0	2	2	−1	−1	−1	0	
E_3	2	−1	−1	−1	2	0	2	−1	−1	−1	2	0	
E_4	2	−1	−1	2	−1	0	2	−1	−1	2	−1	0	
E_5	2	−1	2	−1	−1	0	−2	1	−2	1	1	0	
E_6	2	2	−1	−1	−1	0	−2	−2	1	1	1	0	
E_7	2	−1	−1	−1	2	0	−2	1	1	1	2	0	
E_8	2	−1	−1	2	−1	0	−2	1	1	−2	1	0	

Exercise 6.13:

(a) Find the character table for the supergroup of *p*-dinitrobenzene.

(b) Find the supergroup and character table for 1,3,5-trinitrobenzene.

PROBLEMS

1. Construct the indicated products within $\mathbf{R}_h(3)$ or $\mathbf{R}(3)$:

(a) $D_g^{(1)} \times D_u^{(1)}$ (b) $D_u^{(2)} \times D_u^{(3)}$

(c) $D^{(3/2)} \times D^{(1/2)}$ (d) $D^{(3/2)} \times D^{(1)}$

2. Reduce the indicated representations of $\mathbf{R}_h(3)$ to $\mathbf{D}_{\infty h}$:

(a) $D_g^{(2)}$ (b) $D_u^{(1)}$

(c) $D_g^{(0)}$ (d) $D_u^{(3)}$

(e) $D_g^{(3)}$

3. Reduce the indicated representations of $\mathbf{R}_h(3)$ to $\mathbf{O}_h$.

(a) $D_g^{(0)}$ (b) $D_u^{(1)}$

(c) $D_g^{(2)}$ (d) $D_u^{(3)}$

(e) $D_g^{(3)}$

4. Reduce the indicated representations of $\mathbf{R}_h(3)$ to $\mathbf{C}_{4v}$,

(a) $D_g^{(0)}$ (b) $D_u^{(1)}$

(c) $D_g^{(2)}$ (d) $D_u^{(3)}$

(e) $D_g^{(3)}$

5. Construct the double groups for the following point groups:

(a) $\mathbf{D}_3$ (b) $\mathbf{D}_{3d}$

(c) $\mathbf{T}_d$ (d) $\mathbf{O}_h$

6. Find the classes and irreducible representations of $\mathbf{S}(8)$ and $\mathbf{S}(9)$.

7. Find the dimensions of the irreducible representations of $\mathbf{S}(8)$ and $\mathbf{S}(9)$.

8. Construct the group product structure and character table for the supergroup of cyclohexane. To what point group is it isomorphic?

BIBLIOGRAPHY

Three-dimensional rotation group and double groups

HEINE, V., *Group Theory in Quantum Mechanics*, Pergamon Press, Inc., New York, 1960.

HERZBERG, G., *Electronic Spectra and Electronic Structure of Polyatomic Molecules*, Van Nostrand Reinhold Company, New York, 1966.

HOCHSTRASSER, R., *Molecular Aspects of Symmetry*, W. A. Benjamin, Inc., Menlo Park, Calif., 1966.

WEYL, H., *The Theory of Groups and Quantum Mechanics*, Dover Publications, Inc., New York, 1950.

WIGNER, E. P., *Group Theory*, Academic Press, Inc., New York, 1959.

WYBOURNE, B. G., *Classical Groups for Physicists*, John Wiley & Sons, Inc., New York, 1974.

Symmetric permutation group

CHISHOLM, C. D. H., *Group Theoretical Techniques in Quantum Chemistry*, Academic Press, Inc., New York, 1976.

COLEMAN, A. J., "The Symmetric Group Made Easy," in *Advances in Quantum Chemistry*, Vol. 4, ed. P. O. Löwdin, Academic Press, Inc., New York, 1968.

HAMERMESH, M., *Group Theory*, Addison-Wesley Publishing Company, Inc., Reading, Mass., 1962.

HIGMAN, B., *Applied Group-Theoretic and Matrix Methods*, Dover Publications, Inc., New York, 1964.

KAPLAN, I. G., *Symmetry of Many-Electron Systems*, Academic Press, Inc., New York, 1975.

LITTLEWOOD, D. E., *The Theory of Group Characters and Matrix Representations of Groups*, Oxford University Press, New York, 1940.

WEYL, H., *The Theory of Groups and Quantum Mechanics*, Dover Publications, Inc., New York, 1950.

WIGNER, E. P., *Group Theory*, Academic Press, Inc., New York, 1959.

WYBOURNE, B. G., *Classical Groups for Physicists*, John Wiley & Sons, Inc., New York, 1974.

Symmetry groups of nonrigid molecules

ALTMANN, S. L., *Induced Representations in Crystals and Molecules*, Academic Press, Inc., New York, 1977.

BUNKER, P. R., *Molecular Symmetry and Spectroscopy*, Academic Press, Inc., New York, 1979.

LONGUET-HIGGINS, H. C., *Mol. Phys.*, **6**, 445 (1963).

7

Quantum Mechanics

7.1 BASIC POSTULATES

Our review of quantum mechanics will be primarily a review of concepts. A number of applications will be presented later in our discussions of other topics.

There were two essentially independent and simultaneous derivations of modern quantum mechanics. The one more familiar to chemists is the Schrödinger development, which started with the deBroglie postulate of the wave nature of matter and proceeded with a development that closely paralleled classical wave mechanics. The second development by Heisenberg was a development based on matrix mechanics. The overall results of the two methods are virtually identical in every way, and it is relatively simple to point out the equivalence of the various expressions in the two developments. For our purposes, one development will be more convenient in some cases and the other in others. For this reason we will be rather inconsistent in our usage.

The basic postulate of quantum mechanics is that any system can exist only in specific states (*eigenstates*), and that each state is characterized by a state vector called an *eigenvector* (Heisenberg development) or a wave function called an *eigenfunction* (Schrödinger development). As chemists, we usually think of these only in terms of energy states; however, in principle, the state may be determined with respect to any observable quantity.

If certain constraints are placed on the system, then the values of the observable that determine the state may assume only certain distinct allowed values, all other values being not allowed. When this occurs, the states are said to be *quantized.* These allowed values may be spaced relatively far apart, or they may be so closely spaced as to be, for all practical purposes, nearly continuous. If the system does not have constraints on it, the allowed values of the state observable may vary in a truly continuous fashion. In either case, whatever value the state observable assumes, it has a specific state vector or wave function associated with it. Sometimes more than one state vector or wave function may have the same value of the state observable associated with it. Such states are said to be *degenerate.* In principle, the determination of *all commuting observables* for a system would remove all degeneracies. When considering single-particle energy states only, we work with momentum and position in a three-dimensional coordinate space and possibly with a "spin" coordinate. Energies have degeneracies imposed upon them by this three- or four-dimensional space.

Once a system is in a particular state, it must remain in that state until it is acted on by some outside influence. If, however, the states of a system are quantized, the system can interact with the perturbing influence only if the perturbation is of a proper magnitude to put the system in another allowed state. If this condition is not met, there will be no interaction with the system, no matter how intense the perturbation is. This, for example, is why atoms and molecules exhibit definite discrete spectral transitions.

The complete set of eigenvalues of a system is referred to as its *spectrum* of eigenvalues. If the eigenvectors, $\boldsymbol{\psi}_j$, are normalized, then the scalar product of any two of these obeys the vector relationship

$$\boldsymbol{\psi}_i^\dagger \boldsymbol{\psi}_j = \boldsymbol{\psi}_i^* \cdot \boldsymbol{\psi}_j = \delta_{ij} \tag{7.1}$$

Thus, they form a complete set of *basis vectors* in some n-dimensional vector space. In a similar fashion, the eigenfunctions of the wave mechanical development obey the integral equation

$$\int \psi_i^* \psi_j \, dv = \delta_{ij} \tag{7.2}$$

where the integration variable, dv, indicates integration over all space. These eigenfunctions can be said to form a set of *basis functions.* Matrix and vector quantities can be constructed with reference to the set of basis functions. The significance of the quantities so constructed is the same as if they had been constructed with reference to the basis vectors in the Heisenberg representation.

7.2 OBSERVABLES, EXPECTATION VALUES, AND MATRICES

For every state defining observable, p, of a system, there exists an operator, $\hat{p}$, such that

$$\hat{p}\boldsymbol{\psi}_i = p_i \boldsymbol{\psi}_i \tag{7.3a}$$

or in wave notation,

$$\hat{p}\psi_i = p_i\psi_i \tag{7.3b}$$

That is, the result of operating on the state function or vector with the operator produces the value of the property for that particular state (the eigenvalue) times the state function or vector. Frequently, there are quantities that correspond to physically observable properties but do not lead to eigenvalue equations, either because they do not sufficiently well define the system, or because they are incompatible with the particular set of states chosen to define the system. The *expectation values* of these properties can be found by the relationships

$$\langle p \rangle_i = \boldsymbol{\psi}_i^\dagger \hat{p} \boldsymbol{\psi}_i \tag{7.4a}$$

or

$$\langle p \rangle_i = \int \psi_i^* \hat{p} \psi_i \, dv \tag{7.4b}$$

The expectation value of a property is defined as the most probable or average value of the property when the system is in the ith state.

Consider now the relationship

$$\boldsymbol{\psi}_i^\dagger \hat{p} \boldsymbol{\psi}_j = p_{ij} \tag{7.5a}$$

or

$$\int \psi_i^* \hat{p} \psi_j \, dv = p_{ij} \tag{7.5b}$$

The expectation values of p between pairs of the eigenstates can be used to set up an $n \times n$ matrix, $\mathbf{P}$. This matrix is called the *matrix representation* of the operator $\hat{p}$ in the basis ψ. If the operator satisfies the eigenvalue equation, then

$$p_{ij} = p_{jj}\delta_{ij} \tag{7.6}$$

There can be no off-diagonal elements in $\mathbf{P}$. The matrix $\mathbf{P}$ can be broken down into its individual columns (or rows). Each of these $\mathbf{p}_i$ will lie along one of the vectors of the basis set and give a specific value of p along that basis vector (or function).

One frequently used procedure for solving a quantum mechanical problem is to obtain the matrix of some operator (usually the energy operator, or *Hamiltonian*) with reference to some arbitrary set of basis functions or vectors, and then to diagonalize this matrix by the use of a unitary transformation. Transforming the starting basis set with this same unitary transformation converts it into a set of eigenfunctions or eigenvectors of the starting operator. In other words, if the eigenvalue equation can be written

$$\hat{H}\boldsymbol{\Psi} = \boldsymbol{\Psi}\mathbf{E} \tag{7.7}$$

where $\boldsymbol{\Psi}$ is the matrix composed of the complete set of the basis vectors which are eigenvectors of $\hat{H}$, and if $\boldsymbol{\Phi}$ is the matrix of some *arbitrary* set of orthogonal basis vectors, the **H** matrix with reference to **Φ** is

$$\mathbf{H} = \mathbf{\Phi}^\dagger \hat{H} \mathbf{\Phi} \tag{7.8}$$

Now let **T** represent a unitary transformation that converts **H** into the diagonal form, **H**′,

$$\mathbf{H}' = \mathbf{T}^\dagger \mathbf{H} \mathbf{T} \tag{7.9}$$

$$= \mathbf{T}^\dagger \mathbf{\Phi}^\dagger \hat{H} \mathbf{\Phi} \mathbf{T} \tag{7.9a}$$

If Eq. 7.9a is multiplied from the left by **ΦT**, we have

$$\mathbf{\Phi} \mathbf{T} \mathbf{H}' = \mathbf{\Phi} \mathbf{T} \mathbf{T}^\dagger \mathbf{\Phi}^\dagger \hat{H} \mathbf{\Phi} \mathbf{T} \tag{7.10a}$$

or

$$\hat{H} \mathbf{\Phi} \mathbf{T} = \mathbf{\Phi} \mathbf{T} \mathbf{H}' \tag{7.10b}$$

Equation 7.10b has the form of an eigenvalue equation with the eigenvalue matrix corresponding to the diagonal **H**′ matrix (the individual elements are the eigenvalues), and **ΦT** to the matrix of eigenvectors. These are not necessarily the same as **Ψ**; consequently, **H**′ does not necessarily equal **E**. The same relationships are valid if the **H** matrix is constructed from a set of basis functions rather than vectors. The same procedure can be carried through using a nonorthogonal but normalized starting basis set for **Φ**. If we multiply Eq. 7.10b from the left by $\mathbf{\Phi}^\dagger$, we have

$$\mathbf{\Phi}^\dagger \hat{H} \mathbf{\Phi} \mathbf{T} = \mathbf{\Phi}^\dagger \mathbf{\Phi} \mathbf{T} \mathbf{H}' \tag{7.11}$$

This can be rewritten

$$\mathbf{H} \mathbf{T} = \mathbf{S} \mathbf{T} \mathbf{H}' \tag{7.12}$$

where **S** equals $\mathbf{\Phi}^\dagger \mathbf{\Phi}$, or, in terms of individual elements,

$$S_{ij} = \boldsymbol{\phi}_i^\dagger \boldsymbol{\phi}_j \tag{7.13}$$

Equation 7.12 is the usual matrix form of the Schrödinger equation for linear combination of atomic orbitals (L.C.A.O.)-type problems (**H**′ being set equivalent to **E**):

$$\mathbf{H} \mathbf{T} = \mathbf{S} \mathbf{T} \mathbf{E} \tag{7.14}$$

7.3 DIRAC NOTATION

To avoid the duplication of writing an equation both as a vector equation and as an integral equation, we will at this time adopt Dirac's notation. As originally suggested, this was to be a vector notation; however, it has been generalized to represent either state vectors or wave functions. The quantity $|a\rangle$ represents a state vector in column form. The quantity $\langle a|$ is the conjugate transpose of $|a\rangle$. Thus, $\langle a|b\rangle$ represents the scalar product $\mathbf{a}^\dagger \mathbf{b}$. The generalization to functions is that $|a\rangle$ represents a function, $\langle a|$ its complex conjugate, and $\langle a|b\rangle$ is equivalent to $\int a^*b\,dv$. When operators are employed, the relations are

$$\hat{P}\mathbf{a} = \hat{P}|a\rangle = \hat{P}a \tag{7.15a}$$

$$\mathbf{a}^\dagger\hat{P} = \langle a|\hat{P} = a^*\hat{P} \tag{7.15b}$$

$$\mathbf{a}^\dagger\hat{P}\mathbf{b} = \langle a|\hat{P}|b\rangle = \int a^*\hat{P}b\,dv \tag{7.15c}$$

7.4 ORBITAL THEORY OF ATOMS AND MOLECULES

Quantum theory leads to a usable description of the electronic structure of atoms, molecules, and solids. Unfortunately, the equations for describing such systems are too complicated to be solved exactly, with our presently available mathematical tools, for any system more complicated than the hydrogen atom. For this reason, a number of different approximate methods have been employed to obtain approximate solutions to the problems. When used with sufficient refinement, these methods all give reasonable numerical values for the various desired quantities. The orbital theory for describing atoms and molecules, and the band theory for describing solids, are the most useful of these approximations for our purposes in that they can easily be related to the total symmetry of the system under consideration.

According to orbital theory, each energy eigenvalue for an electron in an atom or molecule defines an *orbital* (a one-electron wave function in a three- or four-dimensional space) of the system. These orbitals are described by the corresponding eigenfunctions. The orbital functions extend over the entire system being described; thus, as we shall see later, the orbitals can be described in terms of the same symmetry operations that describe the system as a whole. Atomic orbitals are usually labeled by a series of *quantum numbers* that arise from the solution of the quantum mechanical equations for the atom. Three quantum numbers arise from the spatial description of the atom. A fourth is required to account for the spin (or, more properly, angular momentum) properties of the electron. The *Pauli principle* states that no two electrons in a system can have the same value for all four quantum numbers. The *orbital occupancy* or *configuration* of an atom in a given electronic state is determined by assigning appropriate quantum numbers to the various electrons present while keeping the Pauli principle in mind. The *ground configuration* corresponds to the lowest energy assignment. Other configurations are referred to as *excited configurations.* If incompletely filled *degenerate* orbitals (different orbitals corresponding to the same energy eigenvalue) are involved in a configuration, the same configuration can give rise to different energy *states.* The *ground state* is the lowest possible energy state. All other states are excited states.

In principle, there is no upper limit to the value a spatial quantum number can take. Thus, the eigenvalue spectrum for an atom can contain an infinite number of terms. Its eigenvectors define an infinite-dimensional vector space. Such a space is referred to as a *Hilbert space.* A direct solution of a molecular problem in terms of molecular orbitals would yield a similar situation—an infinite number of possible energy eigenvalues and an infinite number of molecular orbitals (M.O.'s). Configurations and states for molecules are completely analogous to those for atoms.

A common approximation for molecules, which is entirely adequate for our purposes, is to describe the molecular orbitals in terms of a limited (truncated) basis set of atomic orbitals derived from the constituent atoms. This leads to the familiar *linear combination of atomic orbitals* (L.C.A.O.) description of molecular orbitals. If the molecular orbitals are designated ϕ_i and the atomic orbitals χ_μ, then the general equation for an L.C.A.O.-M.O. is

$$\phi_i = \sum_\mu c_{i\mu}\chi_\mu \tag{7.16}$$

(Note the similarity of this to a vector constructed with reference to some basis set.) This will lead to as many independent solutions for ϕ_i as there were χ_μ's in the starting basis set. (The most usual procedure is to choose only those atomic orbitals that can reasonably be expected to contribute to bonding; thus, a very specific truncation.) The symmetry properties of L.C.A.O.-M.O.'s can be simply determined from the sign and magnitude of the L.C.A.O. coefficients and the symmetry properties of the atomic orbitals. The occupancy of molecular orbitals for various electronic states is determined analogously to that for atomic orbitals.

The simplest of the L.C.A.O.-M.O. approximations is the *Hückel method* as applied to π-electron systems. In this approximation, only the $2p$ π orbitals of the constituent atoms are used in the starting basis set. Further, integrals in the Hamiltonian matrix are not explicitly evaluated. The $H_{\mu\mu}$ elements are designated as α_μ integrals. The $H_{\mu\nu}$ elements are designated as $\beta_{\mu\nu}$ integrals when μ and ν come from atoms that are directly bonded, and set equal to zero otherwise. The χ_μ's form a nonorthogonal basis set; however, the **S** matrix is usually assumed to be equal to the identity matrix. All α integrals from carbon orbitals are assumed to be equal, as are all β integrals that involve only carbon orbitals. Further, the α for carbon is usually chosen as the energy zero and β as the energy unit. The α and β values for other atoms are estimated empirically and expressed as

$$\alpha_x = \alpha_C + h_x\beta \tag{7.17}$$

$$\beta_{xy} = k_{xy}\beta \tag{7.18}$$

Values of energies and charge distributions as estimated by the Hückel method are very crude, but the symmetry properties of π orbitals obtained in this fashion are correct. As a consequence of this, we shall make use of Hückel results for describing the symmetry aspects of electronic spectra.

Exercise 7.1*: When the carbon atoms of the allyl radical are numbered sequentially, the Hückel **H** matrix is

$$\begin{bmatrix} \alpha & \beta & 0 \\ \beta & \alpha & \beta \\ 0 & \beta & \alpha \end{bmatrix}$$

The L.C.A.O. wave functions are

$$\phi_1 = \tfrac{1}{2}\chi_1 + 1/\sqrt{2}\chi_2 + \tfrac{1}{2}\chi_3$$
$$\phi_2 = 1/\sqrt{2}\chi_1 - 1/\sqrt{2}\chi_3$$
$$\phi_3 = \tfrac{1}{2}\chi_1 - 1/\sqrt{2}\chi_2 + \tfrac{1}{2}\chi_3$$

Find the eigenvalues of **H** in terms of α and β.

7.5 BAND THEORY OF SOLIDS

The band theory of solids is less familiar to most chemists than is the orbital theory. We shall, therefore, consider some of the arguments leading to the development of the theory before qualitatively presenting the results. When an atom or a molecule exists in a crystalline solid, not only does it possess its own local symmetry, but there is also the repetitive symmetry of all the other equivalent positions in the crystal. Consider a unit cell represented as in Fig. 7.1. The vectors representing the nearest translations to reach equivalent positions in the three dimensions, known as primitive translation vectors, are $\mathbf{t}_1$, $\mathbf{t}_2$, and $\mathbf{t}_3$. The vectors $\mathbf{t}_n$ from a given point to equivalent positions in the crystal can be expressed as

$$\mathbf{t}_n = n^1\mathbf{t}_1 + n^2\mathbf{t}_2 + n^3\mathbf{t}_3 \tag{7.19}$$

where n^1, n^2, and n^3 are integers. Because of the periodicity of the crystal (i.e., the equivalence of periodically recurring points) the potential function in the crystal at any point must equal the function at any equivalent position. This may be expressed for a general function of **r**, $\Theta(\mathbf{r})$, as

$$\Theta(\mathbf{r}) = \Theta(\mathbf{r} + \mathbf{t}_n) \tag{7.20}$$

or more formally

$$\{E|\mathbf{t}_n\}\Theta(\mathbf{r}) = \Theta(\mathbf{r} + \mathbf{t}_n) \tag{7.21}$$

where the symbol $\{E|\mathbf{t}_n\}$ is used to represent an operator that translates the function through a displacement $\mathbf{t}_n$ with no rotation or reflection (see Chapter 4).

The translation operators all commute among themselves. They also commute with the Hamiltonian. All other symmetry operations also commute with the Hamiltonian. This means that wave functions can be chosen which simultaneously diagonalize the symmetry operations and the Hamiltonian. (The translational operations lead directly to a diagonal matrix.) The implication of all of this with reference to the wave function of a crystal is that the most that can

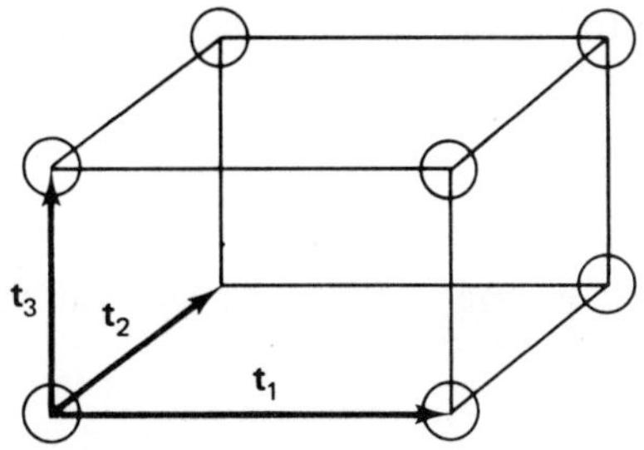

Fig. 7.1. Primitive translation vectors in a unit cell.

happen to the wave function if it is translated by $\mathbf{t}_1$ is that it be multiplied by some constant. If it is translated by $\mathbf{t}_2$, it can be multiplied by another constant, and if by $\mathbf{t}_3$, a third constant. If the wave function is translated by $n^1\mathbf{t}_1$, it would be multiplied by the appropriate constant raised to the n^1 power. A similar relationship would hold for $n^2\mathbf{t}_2$ and $n^3\mathbf{t}_3$. However, for the wave function to be normalized both before and after the translations, the constants must all have a magnitude of unity. The most general form that the constant can have is e raised to some imaginary power. There exists, then, some vector $\mathbf{k}$ such that the constants can be written as $e^{i\mathbf{k}\cdot\mathbf{t}_1}$, $e^{i\mathbf{k}\cdot\mathbf{t}_2}$, and $e^{i\mathbf{k}\cdot\mathbf{t}_3}$. This means that the constant for a general translation $\mathbf{t}_n$, which has components along $\mathbf{t}_1$, $\mathbf{t}_2$, and $\mathbf{t}_3$, is $e^{i\mathbf{k}\cdot\mathbf{t}_n}$, where $\mathbf{t}_n$ is as previously defined. The overall solutions to the periodic potential problem thus may be expressed in such a form that the value of the function at a point which is displaced from a given point in a given unit cell by the vector $\mathbf{t}_n$ equals the value of the function at the undisplaced point multiplied by the factor $e^{i\mathbf{k}\cdot\mathbf{t}_n}$. The vector $\mathbf{k}$ is a real constant vector referred to as the wave vector or propagation constant. (In certain instances, such as in the study of surfaces, $\mathbf{k}$ can be complex. This leads to complications that need not concern us for our purposes.) The relationship for a translated wave function is thus

$$\psi(\mathbf{r} + \mathbf{t}_n) = e^{i\mathbf{k}\cdot\mathbf{t}_n}\psi(\mathbf{r}) \tag{7.22}$$

Notice that the factor multiplying $\psi(\mathbf{r})$ in Eq. 7.22 is the character of a translation element in a space group, as defined in Section 5.7. A useful form for $\psi(\mathbf{r})$ is

$$\psi(\mathbf{r}) = e^{i\mathbf{k}\cdot\mathbf{r}}w(\mathbf{r}) \tag{7.23}$$

This requires that

$$w(\mathbf{r} + \mathbf{t}_n) = w(\mathbf{r}) \tag{7.24}$$

That is, $w(\mathbf{r})$ is a periodic function of $\mathbf{r}$ having the same value in each unit cell of the crystal.

The most general solution for $w(\mathbf{r})$ is to express it in terms of a three-dimensional Fourier expansion. Each of the terms of the Fourier expansion may be considered to be a plane wave, having a definitely determined wave vector. The most familiar form of a plane wave is

$$\sin 2\pi\left(\nu t + \frac{lx + my + nz}{\lambda}\right) \tag{7.25}$$

however, the exponential form we will use is more general.

Consider a vector,

$$\mathbf{K}_h = 2\pi(h_1\mathbf{b}^1 + h_2\mathbf{b}^2 + h_3\mathbf{b}^3) \tag{7.26}$$

where the $\mathbf{b}^i$ are the reciprocals of the $\mathbf{t}_i$, and the h_i are again integers. The $\mathbf{b}^i$ are defined such that

$$\mathbf{t}_i \cdot \mathbf{b}^j = \delta_i^j \tag{7.27}$$

(Notice that $\mathbf{K}_h$ represents a translation vector in reciprocal space.) The quantity $e^{i\mathbf{K}_h \cdot (\mathbf{r} + \mathbf{t}_n)}$ obeys the following relationships:

$$\exp\{i\mathbf{K}_h \cdot (\mathbf{r} + \mathbf{t}_n)\} = \exp\{i\mathbf{K}_h \cdot \mathbf{t}_n\} \exp\{i\mathbf{K}_h \cdot \mathbf{r}\} \tag{7.28}$$

but because of the definitions of $\mathbf{t}_n$ and $\mathbf{K}_h$,

$$\exp\{i\mathbf{K}_h \cdot \mathbf{t}_n\} = \exp\{2\pi i(h_1 n^1 + h_2 n^2 + h_3 n^3)\} \tag{7.29}$$

Since the h_i and n^i are all integers, Eq. 7.29 equals unity; therefore,

$$e^{i\mathbf{K}_h \cdot (\mathbf{r} + \mathbf{t}_n)} = e^{i\mathbf{K}_h \cdot \mathbf{r}} \tag{7.30}$$

In other words, the function $e^{i\mathbf{K}_h \cdot \mathbf{r}}$ has the required periodicity for $w(\mathbf{r})$. Multiplying this by $e^{i\mathbf{k} \cdot \mathbf{r}}$ (see Eq. 7.23) yields $e^{i(\mathbf{k} + \mathbf{K}_h) \cdot \mathbf{r}}$. This is the functional part of the plane wave. It must reflect the symmetry of the system. The overall plane-wave expansion for the wave function of the crystal is

$$\psi(\mathbf{k}, \mathbf{r}) = \sum_{\mathbf{K}_h} v(\mathbf{k} + \mathbf{K}_h) e^{i(\mathbf{k} + \mathbf{K}_h) \cdot \mathbf{r}} \tag{7.31}$$

where the summation is over all possible $\mathbf{K}_h$, and the $v(\mathbf{k} + \mathbf{K}_h)$ represent the amplitude of each term. The relative magnitudes of the $v(\mathbf{k} + \mathbf{K}_h)$ depend upon the form of the potential function the electron experiences as it moves through the crystal.

If we consider a crystal from a completely abstract point of view, it can, in principle, extend infinitely in each direction. In order for a function of the form of Eq. 7.31 to be normalized, however, it must have finite boundaries. If the function has sufficiently large finite boundaries, its behavior near the center of the bounded region is essentially independent of the boundaries. The procedure for solving the Schrödinger equation, then, is to choose boundaries at $N^1\mathbf{t}_1$, $N^2\mathbf{t}_2$, and $N^3\mathbf{t}_3$, where the N^i are large integers. If an infinite extension of the crystal is considered, these boundaries are periodically recurring; hence, this choice is referred to as a choice of periodic boundary conditions. The choice of periodic boundary conditions leads to a fundamental volume containing $N^1N^2N^3$, or N, unit cells.

Since a translation by $N^1\mathbf{t}_1$ must yield a wave function equal to the original value, $e^{i\mathbf{k}\cdot N^1\mathbf{t}_1}$ must equal unity. A similar relationship holds for $N^2\mathbf{t}_2$ and $N^3\mathbf{t}_3$. This condition is satisfied if we write $\mathbf{k}$ as

$$\mathbf{k} = 2\pi(p_1\mathbf{b}^1 + p_2\mathbf{b}^2 + p_3\mathbf{b}^3) \tag{7.32}$$

where the $\mathbf{b}^i$ are as previously defined (the reciprocals of the $\mathbf{t}_i$), and the p_i are equal to integers divided by N^i. The interior of the unit cell in reciprocal space is contained in the range $0 \leq p_i < 1$. This means that p_i can assume the values 0, $1/N^i, 2/N^i, \ldots, (N-1)/N^i$. In other words, in a unit cell in reciprocal space (or $\mathbf{k}$ space) we have a closely spaced lattice of allowable values of $\mathbf{k}$. The volume in which all the $\mathbf{k}$ vectors from a common origin lie is referred to as the *central Brillouin zone*. There will be N of these allowable lattice points distributed uniformly. Since N is normally chosen to be very large, the distribution is almost continuous. If a value of infinity could have been chosen for N, the spacing would be completely continuous.

When the plane-wave expansion is substituted into the Schrödinger equation, an eigenvalue spectrum is obtained for each allowed value of $\mathbf{k}$, each eigenvalue corresponding to a different value of $\mathbf{K}_h$. The energy spacings with respect to $\mathbf{K}_h$ are of the same general order of magnitude as the spacings found in atomic and molecular problems. The spacings with respect to $\mathbf{k}$, however, are so close as to be nearly a continuum. The net overall effect, then, is that there are bands of very closely spaced energy levels with energy gaps between them (hence the name "band theory"). Each plane wave may be occupied by two electrons, or each band by $2N$ electrons. The electron occupancy of these energy bands determines the electrical conductivity of the solid. Substances with partially filled bands are conductors, while those with only completely filled energy bands are insulators. Semiconductors result when impurities with more or fewer electrons than the host are incorporated into the crystal sites of an insulator, or when the energy gap is small enough for thermal population of a normally vacant band to occur.

7.6 TRANSLATION, ROTATION, AND VIBRATION

We have thus far discussed only electronic wave functions. Actually, there are also energy eigenstates for atoms and molecules arising from translation, rotation, and vibration. The total wave function of an atom or molecule should be the product of the electronic, vibrational, rotational, and translational wave functions,

$$\Psi_T = \psi_{\text{el}}\psi_{\text{vib}}\psi_{\text{rot}}\psi_{\text{tr}} \tag{7.33}$$

The product arises because of the fact that a wave function is a probability function. The probability of two events occurring together is the product of the individual independent probabilities. Equation 7.33 implies that the individual wave functions are mutually independent. In actual fact, this is not the case. This can be intuitively realized by considering the fact that rotations can cause centrifugal distortions which shift the equilibrium positions of the atoms in molecules and, consequently, produce a distortion of the electronic and vibrational eigenstates. Vibrations produce a continually changing set of atomic positions that should lead to a continually changing set of electronic eigenstates. Only translation through free space is independent of the other factors. It has been shown by Born and Oppenheimer, however, that the magnitudes of the vibronic (vibrational–electronic) interactions are small (on the order of the ratio of the electron to nuclear mass).

The *Born–Oppenheimer approximation* states that the quantum mechanical equations for the nuclear and electronic motion may be solved separately. The averaged positions of the electrons contribute to the potential energy experienced by the nuclei when solving for nuclear motion, while the converse is true when solving for the motions of electrons. The most usual procedure for solving for electronic motion is to assume a completely fixed nuclear orientation for a given calculation. For solving for nuclear motion, some simple empirical potential, such as the Hooke's law potential,

$$V = \tfrac{1}{2}k(\Delta q)^2 \tag{7.34}$$

(where Δq is the displacement of the internuclear coordinate from equilibrium and k is the force constant), is usually used to approximate the net effect of all the contributions to the potential energy experienced by the nuclei.

The solutions to the wave function for nuclear motion are more often determined in terms of vibrational frequencies than in terms of energy. These frequencies, which are for the entire molecule, correspond directly to the frequencies observed in infrared and Raman spectra. When the problem is handled in this fashion, the set of independent frequency eigenstates are referred to as the *normal modes of vibration* for the molecule. (There are $3N - 5$ of these for a linear N-atomic molecule, and $3N - 6$ for a nonlinear molecule.) The transformed basis set, which is an eigenfunction of the vibrational matrix, corresponds to the *normal coordinates* of the system. One normal coordinate corresponds to each of the normal modes. When constructed from ordinary three-dimensional space, the normal coordinates directly reveal the nuclear motions of each vibration. They exhibit the same symmetry properties as the corresponding vibrational wave functions.

Just as with any other eigenvalue problem, vibrational eigenvalues can be degenerate. When this occurs, the normal coordinates of the degenerate eigenvalues cannot be uniquely defined. Any linear combination of allowed solutions is also a solution.

Any atomic or molecular system that is capable of rotating has associated with it a rotational wave function and a spectrum of rotational eigenstates. These eigenstates are quantized due to the necessity for the quantization of angular momentum. The solutions to the rotational wave functions are in terms of spherical harmonics (i.e., their angular dependence is like that of the hydrogenic orbitals). The energy eigenvalues give rise to the microwave spectra of gas molecules.

7.7 SYMMETRY PROPERTIES OF THE SCHRÖDINGER EQUATION

Let us now turn our attention to the symmetry properties of the quantum mechanical description of a system. The Schrödinger equation for a system may be written

$$\hat{H}|\psi_i\rangle = E_i|\psi_i\rangle \tag{7.35}$$

where $\hat{H}$ is the Hamiltonian operator, containing the operators for kinetic and for potential energy (Eqs. 7.36, in atomic units).

$$\hat{H} = \hat{T} + \hat{V} \tag{7.36}$$

$$= \sum_{\mu=1}^{n} -\frac{1}{2m_\mu}\nabla_\mu^2 + \hat{V} \tag{7.36a}$$

The ∇_μ^2 operator is the *Laplacian operator*, representing the second partial derivative with respect to each coordinate,

$$\nabla_\mu^2 = \frac{\partial^2}{\partial x_\mu^2} + \frac{\partial^2}{\partial y_\mu^2} + \frac{\partial^2}{\partial z_\mu^2} \tag{7.37}$$

m_μ is the mass of particle μ, and the summation is over all particles in the system. The potential-energy operator, $\hat{V}$, is a function of the instantaneous positions of the particles. The point-group operations, when applied to a system, change the positions of the particles with respect to an external coordinate system. They do not change the positions with respect to an internal coordinate system. Since, in the absence of external forces, the potential energy depends only upon the internal coordinates, the potential is unaffected by an application of the symmetry operations. That is,

$$R\hat{V}(\mathbf{r}) = \hat{V}(R\mathbf{r}) = \hat{V}(\mathbf{r}) \tag{7.38}$$

If we make use of the periodic boundary conditions, the same result holds for translational symmetry elements. If the potential operator is operating on some arbitrary function f, we have

$$R(\hat{V}f) = \hat{V}(Rf) \tag{7.39}$$

That is, since the symmetry operator does not affect the potential operator, the two commute.

Let us now consider the kinetic-energy operator expressed in terms of the three generalized coordinates, X_1, X_2, and X_3:

$$\hat{T}(X_1, X_2, X_3) = \sum_{\mu=1}^{n} -\frac{1}{2m_\mu}\nabla_\mu^2 \tag{7.40}$$

where the Laplacian operator is as defined in Eq. 7.37. The effect of a symmetry operator on $\hat{T}$ would be to change it to a function of the transformed coordinates X'_1, X'_2, and X'_3,

$$R\hat{T}(X_1, X_2, X_3) = \hat{T}'(X'_1, X'_2, X'_3) \tag{7.41}$$

In order to find the form of the transformed operator, let us consider the effect of the operator R and the ∇^2 operator on some arbitrary function $f(X_1, X_2, X_3)$:

$$Rf(X_1, X_2, X_3) = f'(X'_1, X'_2, X'_3) \tag{7.42}$$

The primed coordinates of Eqs. 7.41 and 7.42 can be expressed as linear combinations of the original coordinates,

$$X'_i = \sum_{j=1}^{3} s_{ij} X_j \tag{7.43a}$$

or, equivalently,

$$X_i = \sum_{j=1}^{3} r_{ij} X'_j \tag{7.43b}$$

Further, let these be constructed so that they remain orthogonal,

$$\sum_{j=1}^{3} r_{ij} r_{kj} = \delta_{ik} \tag{7.44}$$

If we now operate on the function f by the Laplacian, and on the result by R, we have

$$R\nabla^2 f(X_1, X_2, X_3) = \nabla'^2 f'(X'_1, X'_2, X'_3) \tag{7.45}$$

$$= \nabla'^2 Rf(X_1, X_2, X_3) \tag{7.45a}$$

Equation 7.45a has the form $\nabla'^2 g(X_1, X_2, X_3)$; therefore,

$$R\nabla^2 f(X_1, X_2, X_3) = \nabla'^2 g(X_1, X_2, X_3) \tag{7.46}$$

The result may be expanded by differentiating Eq. 7.46 twice with respect to the X'_i. On the first differentiation, we have

$$\frac{\partial g}{\partial X'_i} = \frac{\partial g}{\partial X_1}\frac{\partial X_1}{\partial X'_i} + \frac{\partial g}{\partial X_2}\frac{\partial X_2}{\partial X'_i} + \frac{\partial g}{\partial X_3}\frac{\partial X_3}{\partial X'_i} \tag{7.47}$$

From Eq. 7.43b we see that

$$\frac{\partial X_k}{\partial X'_i} = r_{ki} \tag{7.48}$$

Thus,

$$\frac{\partial g}{\partial X'_i} = r_{1i}\frac{\partial g}{\partial X_1} + r_{2i}\frac{\partial g}{\partial X_2} + r_{3i}\frac{\partial g}{\partial X_3} \tag{7.49}$$

$$= \sum_{k=1}^{3} r_{ki}\frac{\partial g}{\partial X_k} \tag{7.49a}$$

On differentiating again, we find that

$$\frac{\partial^2 g}{\partial X_i'^2} = \sum_{j=1}^{3} \sum_{k=1}^{3} r_{ki} r_{ji} \frac{\partial}{\partial X_j} \left(\frac{\partial g}{\partial X_k} \right) \tag{7.50}$$

Summing over i from 1 to 3 yields

$$\nabla'^2 g = \sum_{i=1}^{3} \sum_{j=1}^{3} \sum_{k=1}^{3} r_{ki} r_{ji} \frac{\partial}{\partial X_j} \left(\frac{\partial g}{\partial X_k} \right) \tag{7.51}$$

However, due to the orthogonality conditions of Eq. 7.44, the cross terms of Eq. 7.51 vanish, and the r product of the remaining terms equals unity, so that

$$\nabla'^2 g = \sum_{i=1}^{3} \frac{\partial^2 g}{\partial X_i^2} \tag{7.52}$$

$$= \nabla^2 g \tag{7.52a}$$

Since g equals Rf, we have that

$$R\nabla^2 f(X_1, X_2, X_3) = \nabla^2 Rf(X_1, X_2, X_3) \tag{7.53}$$

The equality of Eq. 7.53 holds for the coordinates of each particle in the system. Thus,

$$R(\hat{T}f) = \hat{T}(Rf) \tag{7.54}$$

or, in other words, the kinetic-energy operator commutes with the symmetry operators.

Since the symmetry operators commute with both the potential- and kinetic-energy operators and since the Hamiltonian operator is the sum of the kinetic- and potential-energy operators, the Hamiltonian and the symmetry operators must commute,

$$R(\hat{H}f) = \hat{H}(Rf) \tag{7.55}$$

This means that for the Schrödinger equation, we have

$$R\hat{H}|\psi_i\rangle = RE_i|\psi_i\rangle \tag{7.56a}$$

or

$$\hat{H}|R\psi_i\rangle = E_i|R\psi_i\rangle \tag{7.56b}$$

Thus, the function $R\psi_i$ is an eigenfunction of $\hat{H}$ having the same eigenvalue E_i as ψ_i. If E_i is a nondegenerate eigenvalue and ψ_i is its corresponding normalized eigenfunction, $R\psi_i$ must also be a normalized eigenfunction. Thus,

$$R\psi_i = \pm 1 \times \psi_i \tag{7.57}$$

for *every symmetry element* of the group describing the symmetry of the system. This describes a one-dimensional representation of the system which is, of necessity, irreducible. If E_i is the eigenvalue corresponding to a degenerate eigenfunction, we have

$$\hat{H}|R\psi_{il}\rangle = E_i|R\psi_{il}\rangle \tag{7.58}$$

where ψ_{il} is any one of the set of degenerate eigenfunctions. The function $R\psi_{il}$ can be expressed as a linear combination of the degenerate eigenfunctions

$$R\psi_{il} = \sum_{j=1}^{k} r_{lj}\psi_{ij} \tag{7.59}$$

where k is the order of the degeneracy. Consider now the operator S corresponding to some other symmetry operation. The function $S\psi_{ij}$ can also be expressed as a linear combination of the degenerate eigenfunctions,

$$S\psi_{ij} = \sum_{m=1}^{k} s_{jm}\psi_{im} \tag{7.60}$$

The product

$$Q = SR \tag{7.61}$$

must also be a symmetry element of the group. The function $SR\psi_{il}$ must equal $Q\psi_{il}$, giving

$$Q\psi_{il} = SR\psi_{il} \tag{7.62}$$

$$= S\sum_{j=1}^{k} r_{lj}\psi_{ij} \tag{7.62a}$$

or

$$\sum_{m=1}^{k} q_{lm}\psi_{im} = \sum_{j=1}^{k}\sum_{m=1}^{k} s_{jm}r_{lj}\psi_{im} \tag{7.63}$$

This means that

$$q_{lm} = \sum_{j=1}^{k} s_{mj}r_{lj} \tag{7.64}$$

This is just the defining equation for a matrix **Q**, which is the product **RS**. The set of $(k \times k)$ matrices **Q** derived from the products of all the operations S and R describe the transformations of the k degenerate eigenfunctions. This leads to a k-dimensional irreducible representation of the group.

The discussion we have presented indicates that the eigenfunctions corresponding to the various eigenstates of a system must transform under the symmetry operations as one of the irreducible representations of the system. (There is a very important generalization of this result, due to Wigner, which states that the solutions of the Schrödinger equation for a system define a set of irreducible representations in the function space defined by these solutions.) No restriction has been made as to whether the wave function is rotational, vibrational or electronic, or whether it is an exact or an approximate wave function. The results are general for all cases. This has important implications for both theoretical and experimental descriptions of systems. From a theoretical standpoint, an advance knowledge of the possible symmetry properties of a wave function introduces simplifications into the problem of calculating the wave function. From an experimental point of view, the selection rules which we will later encounter in spectroscopy are directly related to the symmetry properties of the eigenstates in question.

Exercise 7.2*: Find the irreducible representations for the indicated normal modes of vibration (i.e., vibrational wave functions) for the indicated molecules.

(a) Water:

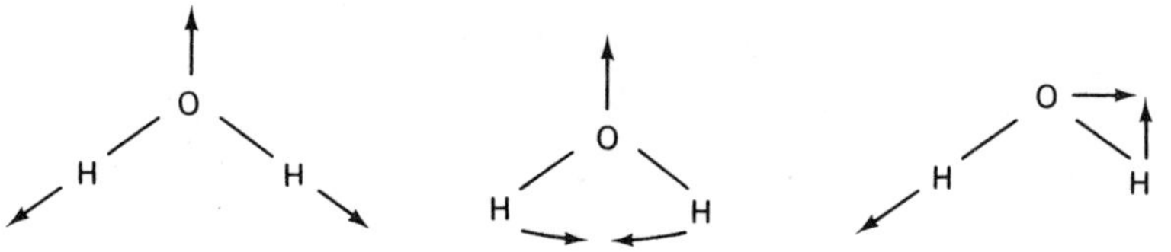

Symmetrical stretch Bend Antisymmetrical stretch

(b) Cyclopropane (carbons only):

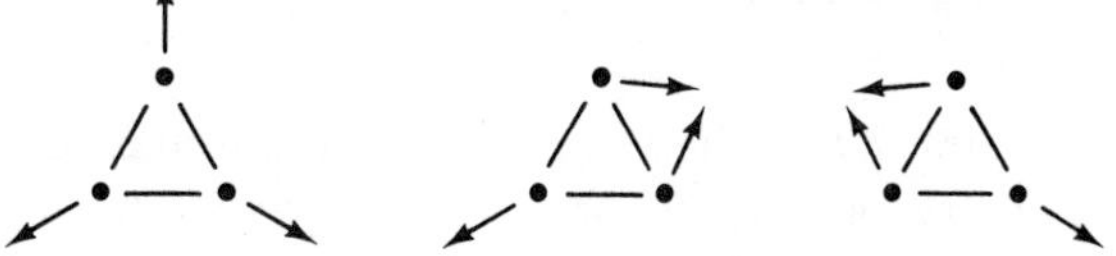

v_1 v_2 v_3

(Note that by subtracting the vectors of $\mathbf{v}_3$ from those of $\mathbf{v}_2$, we obtain  .)

(c) *Trans*-2-butene (carbons only):

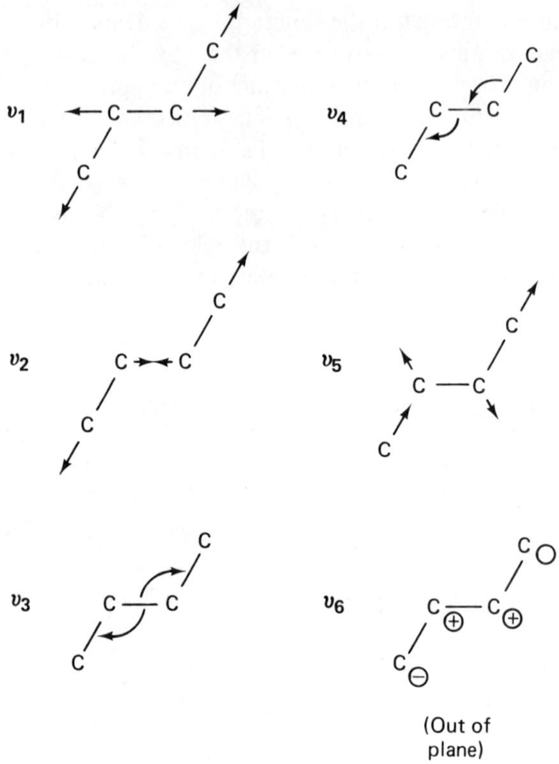

Exercise 7.3: Formaldehyde has a total of four occupied bonding molecular orbitals. Two of these are a_1, one is b_1, and one is b_2 in symmetry. Sketch their expected shapes.

7.8 SYMMETRY RESTRICTIONS ON INTEGRALS

In Section 7.7 we showed that the Hamiltonian of a system was invariant under all symmetry operations, and that the eigenfunctions all transform as irreducible representations of the group of the system. In fact, the symmetry of the Hamiltonian determines the symmetry of the system. The Hamiltonian thus transforms as the totally symmetric irreducible representation of the appropriate group. The energy of the system in a particular state may be written (assuming ψ_i to be normalized) as

$$E_i = \langle \psi_i | \hat{H} | \psi_i \rangle \tag{7.65}$$

The energy is a scalar quantity and, quite obviously, is invariant under all symmetry operations of the system. However, *any* quantum mechanical integral that yields a scalar must be invariant under all symmetry operations of the appropriate group. That is, if integration is carried out over all coordinates of all particles that are included in ψ_i, ψ_j, and $\hat{p}$, then $\langle\psi_i|\hat{p}|\psi_j\rangle$ is a scalar and, consequently, must be invariant under all symmetry operations. As a consequence of this, *for an integral to be nonvanishing, it must transform as the totally symmetric irreducible representation of the group describing the system.* This is a rather severe restriction which is very useful. Much effort can be saved if symmetry alone can be used to determine which integrals must be nonvanishing.

From the discussion of the products of irreducible representations found in Section 5.6, it can be seen that the totally symmetric representation occurs *only* when the product of a representation with itself is taken. Thus, if Γ_i, Γ_j, and Γ_p are the irreducible representations according to which ψ_i, ψ_j, and $\hat{p}$ transform, the representation for the integral will be

$$\Gamma = \Gamma_i \times \Gamma_p \times \Gamma_j \tag{7.66}$$

This will contain the totally symmetric irreducible representation if and only if the product of two of the representations contains the third:

$$\Gamma_i \times \Gamma_j \supset \Gamma_p \tag{7.67a}$$

$$\Gamma_i \times \Gamma_p \supset \Gamma_j \tag{7.67b}$$

or

$$\Gamma_p \times \Gamma_j \supset \Gamma_i \tag{7.67c}$$

There is an additional restriction if i and j represent the same function. If this is the case, it seems trivial to point out that the integral must be invariant to an interchange of i and j; however, it is not trivial from the point of view of the group theory. If Γ_i (and, thus, Γ_j) is degenerate, the representation produced by the product $\Gamma_i \times \Gamma_j$ is reducible. Only the *symmetrized product* (or *symmetrized direct square*) contributes to the nonvanishing matrix element. The symmetrized direct square is the square of the representation with the totally antisymmetric representation of the group (or the isomorphic proper group, or the largest proper subgroup—whichever is applicable) subtracted out. For example, if the expectation value of some property of ammonia with respect to an e orbital is desired, the product $E \times E$ gives $A_1 + A_2 + E$; however, A_2 is the totally antisymmetric representation. Therefore, the integral is nonvanishing only if the operator transforms according to the A_1 or the E representation. The symmetrized product is frequently indicated in tables of rules of products of representations.

7.9 THE VARIATIONAL PRINCIPLE

The fact that the most stable state of a system is its lowest energy state can be coupled with the calculus of variations to obtain approximate solutions to quantum mechanical problems for which exact solutions are not possible.

The expectation value of a Hamiltonian with respect to an arbitrary wave function gives the energy of the system described by the Hamiltonian when the motions of the particles are described by the wave function. If the wave function is exact, the energy will be exact. This is unfortunately not usually the case; consequently, the calculated energy will be higher than the true energy. If, however, the wave function contains some parameters that can be varied, the calculated energy can be improved by minimizing it with respect to each of the parameters in the wave function. There are no restrictions on the form that the wave function can take, as long as it has the usual properties of a "well-behaved" wave function. The most common approximation is probably to express the wave function as a linear combination of other functions, with the mixing coefficients being the variational parameters.

Let us illustrate the variational principle with a simple Hückel molecular orbital problem, the π-electron system of butadiene. The Hückel Hamiltonian is a one-electron Hamiltonian. The π-electron Hückel approximation approximates molecular orbitals with a basis set consisting of one $p\pi$ type function on each atomic center. Thus, we have only four basis functions for butadiene. These will give rise to four linear combinations, the four π molecular orbitals of butadiene. These have the form

$$\phi_i = \sum_{\mu} c_{i\mu} \chi_{\mu} \tag{7.68}$$

where the $c_{i\mu}$ are the coefficients and the χ_{μ} are the basis functions. The energies of the orbitals are approximated by

$$e_i = \langle \phi_i | \hat{h} | \phi_i \rangle \tag{7.69}$$

where $\hat{h}$ is the one-electron Hückel Hamiltonian. Substituting in Eq. 7.68, we have

$$e_i = \sum_{\mu} \sum_{\nu} c_{i\mu} c_{i\nu} \langle \chi_{\mu} | \hat{h} | \chi_{\nu} \rangle = \sum_{\mu} \sum_{\nu} c_{i\mu} c_{i\nu} h_{\mu\nu} \tag{7.70}$$

where the obvious definition of $h_{\mu\nu}$ has been made. The Hückel approximation defines $h_{\mu\nu}$ as α if μ and ν are the same, as β if they are on directly bonded atoms, and as zero otherwise. Expanding Eq. 7.70 with these approximations yields

$$e_i = c_{i1}^2 \alpha + 2c_{i1}c_{i2}\beta + c_{i2}^2 \alpha + 2c_{i2}c_{i3}\beta + c_{i3}^2 \alpha + 2c_{i3}c_{i4}\beta + c_{i4}^2 \alpha \tag{7.71}$$

We must minimize Eq. 7.71 with respect to the coefficients, subject to the constraint that the orbitals remain orthonormal:

$$\langle \phi_i | \phi_j \rangle = \delta_{ij} \tag{7.72}$$

Thus, we must set the variation

$$\delta\{e_i - \varepsilon\langle \phi_i | \phi_j \rangle\} = 0 \tag{7.73}$$

where $-\varepsilon$ is a Lagrangian multiplier. Expanding $\langle\phi_i|\phi_j\rangle$ within the Hückel approximation, where $\langle\chi_\mu|\chi_\nu\rangle$ equals $\delta_{\nu\mu}$, gives

$$\delta\{c_{i1}^2(\alpha-\varepsilon)+2c_{i1}c_{i2}\beta+c_{i2}^2(\alpha-\varepsilon)+2c_{i2}c_{i3}\beta + c_{i3}^2(\alpha-\varepsilon)+2c_{i3}c_{i4}\beta+c_{i4}^2(\alpha-\varepsilon)\}=0 \quad (7.74)$$

This gives the set of equations,

$$\begin{array}{lllll} 2c_{i1}(\alpha-\varepsilon)+2c_{i2}\beta & +0 & +0 & & =0\\ 2c_{i1}\beta & +2c_{i2}(\alpha-\varepsilon)+2c_{i3}\beta & +0 & & =0\\ 0 & +2c_{i2}\beta & +2c_{i3}(\alpha-\varepsilon)+2c_{i4}\beta & & =0\\ 0 & +0 & +2c_{i3}\beta & +2c_{i4}(\alpha-\varepsilon) & =0 \end{array} \quad (7.75)$$

For these equations to be nonvanishing requires that the determinant

$$\begin{vmatrix} \alpha-\varepsilon & \beta & 0 & 0\\ \beta & \alpha-\varepsilon & \beta & 0\\ 0 & \beta & \alpha-\varepsilon & \beta\\ 0 & 0 & \beta & \alpha-\varepsilon \end{vmatrix} = 0 \quad (7.76)$$

This gives four roots for ε (α and β are intrinsically negative, so the energy order is $\varepsilon_1 < \varepsilon_2 < \varepsilon_3 < \varepsilon_4$),

$$\begin{aligned} \varepsilon_4 &= \alpha - 1.618\beta\\ \varepsilon_3 &= \alpha - 0.618\beta\\ \varepsilon_2 &= \alpha + 0.618\beta\\ \varepsilon_1 &= \alpha + 1.618\beta \end{aligned} \quad (7.77)$$

The one-electron wave functions corresponding to these can be found by substituting the energy eigenvalues, one at a time, into Eqs. 7.75 and 7.72, and solving for the $c_{i\mu}$. The results are

$$\begin{aligned} \phi_4 &= 0.3717\chi_1 - 0.6015\chi_2 + 0.6015\chi_3 - 0.3717\chi_4\\ \phi_3 &= 0.6015\chi_1 - 0.3717\chi_2 - 0.3717\chi_3 + 0.6015\chi_4\\ \phi_2 &= 0.6015\chi_1 + 0.3717\chi_2 - 0.3717\chi_3 - 0.6015\chi_4\\ \phi_1 &= 0.3717\chi_1 + 0.6015\chi_2 + 0.6015\chi_3 + 0.3717\chi_4 \end{aligned} \quad (7.78)$$

The same approach is applicable any time a wave function is being approximated by a linear expansion. The individual terms in the expansion can be either one-particle functions or many-particle functions. They may even be, themselves, linear combinations of other functions.

Exercise 7.4: Set up and solve the Hückel problem for the allyl system (three $p\pi$ orbitals in a chain).

7.10 PERTURBATION THEORY

One of the most useful methods for obtaining approximate solutions to complicated quantum mechanical problems is *perturbation theory*. The concept of perturbation theory is based upon the assumption that there exists a model system, related to the true system under study, for which an "exact" quantum mechanical solution can be obtained. This "exact" solution can either be a solution corresponding to a real physical system, or it can be a solution in terms of a highly truncated and highly approximate basis set. The eigenfunctions for the model system are not, in general, eigenfunctions for the true system; however, they define a function space from which the eigenfunctions for the true system can be constructed.

The Hamiltonian for the true system is expressed as the model Hamiltonian, $\hat{H}^0$, plus a perturbation, $\hat{H}'$,

$$\hat{H} = \hat{H}^0 + \hat{H}' \tag{7.79}$$

The same is true for the eigenfunctions and energies:

$$\psi_i = \psi_i^0 + \psi_i' \tag{7.80}$$

$$E_i = E_i^0 + E_i' \tag{7.81}$$

Frequently, $\hat{H}'$ and ψ_i' are broken down into first-order, second-order, and so on, terms. For our purposes, it will be sufficient to decompose $\hat{H}'$ according to the source of the perturbation and to retain ψ_i' as a single term (expanded, however, in terms of the ψ_i^0). The energy and other properties are calculated as expectation values.

$$E_i = N^2 \langle \psi_i | \hat{H} | \psi_i \rangle \tag{7.82}$$

where N is a normalizing constant. Equation 7.82 contains terms of the type

$$E_i^0 = \langle \psi_i^0 | \hat{H}^0 | \psi_i^0 \rangle \tag{7.83a}$$

$$E_i^1 = \langle \psi_i^0 | \hat{H}' | \psi_i^0 \rangle \tag{7.83b}$$

$$E_i^2 = \langle \psi_i' | \hat{H}^0 | \psi_i' \rangle \tag{7.83c}$$

$$E_i^3 = \langle \psi_i' | \hat{H}' | \psi_i' \rangle \tag{7.83d}$$

The E_i^0 term is the zeroth-order approximation. Inclusion of E_i^1 leads to the first-order approximation (*first-order perturbation theory*), while the terms E_i^2 and E_i^3 are usually included together in the second-order approximation (*second-order perturbation theory*). In most treatments, the expansion for ψ_i' is chosen so that E_i^2 vanishes.

Group theory is particularly useful in applications of perturbation theory. The nonvanishing rule discussed in Section 7.8 applies to each of the integrals of Eqs. 7.83. Normally, the higher the symmetry of a system, the easier it is to obtain an "exact" solution. The symmetry of the system is generally the same as or lower than that of $\hat{H}^0$, and is, in fact, generally determined by $\hat{H}'$.

7.11 MANY-PARTICLE SYSTEMS

The discussions we have included up to now have been strictly valid only for single particles or for particles acting completely independently of each other (the *independent particles model*). According to this model, the total wave function for a many-particle system is made up as a product of one-particle functions

$$\Psi = \prod_i \phi(i) \tag{7.84}$$

where the product is over all the particles of the system.

For systems consisting of more than one particle, Eq. 7.84 is incorrect on two counts. The first of these can be easily grasped on an intuitive basis. The Ψ of Eq. 7.84 does not explicitly include the distance of separation between the particles; consequently, in its description, the motion of each particle is completely independent of that of the other particles. Physically, we realize that the motion of a given charged particle will affect and be affected by the motions of other charged particles. For systems of electrons, this effect is called the *correlation effect*, and the energy correction that its inclusion would give is called the *correlation energy*. Correlation effects do not place any symmetry restrictions on a system; however, group theory can be very useful in determining nonvanishing integrals when trying to calculate the correlation energy.

The other deficiency in Eq. 7.84 is that it does not properly take into account permutational symmetry. According to the *Pauli exclusion principle*, the total wave function of a system must be totally antisymmetric with respect to the interchange of any two electrons. In fact, the principle is more general than originally stated by Pauli. The Pauli principle holds for *any* system of *fermions*, particles with half-integer values ($\frac{1}{2}$, 3/2, . . .) of intrinsic angular momentum. (Electrons, protons, and neutrons are fermions.) On the other hand, systems of particles with integer values (0, 1, 2, . . .) of intrinsic angular momentum, called *bosons*, have associated with them wave functions that must be *symmetric* with respect to interchange of any two bosons. Deuterons, α particles, most molecules (taken as entities), and virtually all macroscopic physical objects are bosons. The antisymmetry or symmetry requirement places severe restrictions on the system. Certain apparently reasonable states are allowed, while others are forbidden to exist. Group theory allows us to decide which states are allowed and which are forbidden. We will refer to these as *Pauli-allowed* and *Pauli-forbidden states*, respectively.

The correct form for the group describing a many-particle system is that of a product group involving the appropriate spatial symmetry group for each particle and the permutation group describing the permutations among equivalent particles. (Briefly, the argument is that the group describing the system is constructed from the operations under which the Hamiltonian is invariant. These are the spatial symmetry operations for each particle and the permutations among equivalent particles. This leads to the group just described.) The spatial groups for the equivalent particles are the same; consequently, the spatial portion of the total group for n equivalent particles is $[\mathbf{G}_s]^n$, where $\mathbf{G}_s$ is the group describing the spatial symmetry. The permutational symmetry is described by $\mathbf{S}(n)$, and the total group is

$$\mathbf{G} = [\mathbf{G}_s]^n \cdot \mathbf{S}(n) \tag{7.85}$$

Since all powers of every element of a group are elements of the group, $[\mathbf{G}_s]^n$ is isomorphic to $\mathbf{G}_s$; consequently, for many applications, $\mathbf{G}_s$ is used without ever recognizing that Eq. 7.85 is the correct form. We will use only $\mathbf{G}_s$ in many applications; however, one should always be aware that Eq. 7.85 is the true form.

The product $[\mathbf{G}_s]^n$ will contain elements of the form

$$R = A^a B^b C^c \ldots \tag{7.86}$$

where $A, B, C, \ldots$ are elements of $\mathbf{G}_s$ and

$$a + b + c + \ldots = n \tag{7.87}$$

The characters of the elements in the allowed representations can be obtained by considering the permutational properties. For bosons, the permutational representation of $[\mathbf{G}_s]^n$ must be the same as the appropriate representation of $\mathbf{S}(n)$, since only the product of a representation with itself contains the totally symmetric representation. For fermions, the permutational representation of $[\mathbf{G}_s]^n$ must be the *conjugate* of the appropriate representation of $\mathbf{S}(n)$, since only the product of a representation with its conjugate contains the totally antisymmetric representation. The conjugate of a representation from $\mathbf{S}(n)$ is that representation which has the rows and columns of its Young diagram interchanged from that of the original representation.

The allowed representations of $\mathbf{S}(n)$ for a system of n particles are those representations having at most $2j + 1$ rows in their Young diagrams, where j is the value of the intrinsic angular momentum of the particles. For example, for $j = 0, \frac{1}{2}$, and 1, the allowed Young diagrams have a maximum of 1, 2, and 3 rows, respectively. For a system of four electrons (fermions, $j = \frac{1}{2}$), we have

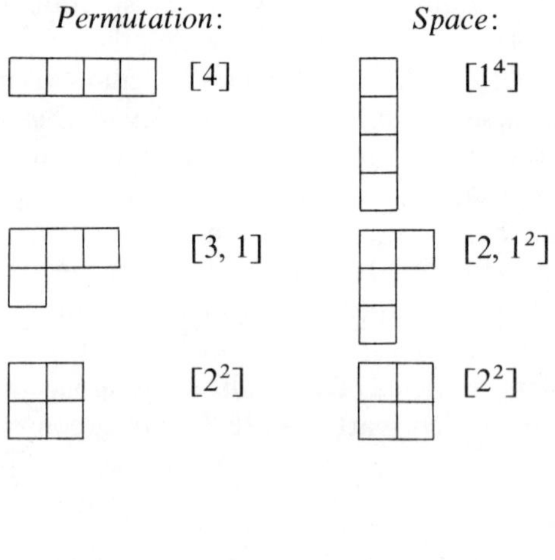

(7.88)

For a system of four deuterons (bosons, $j = 1$), we have

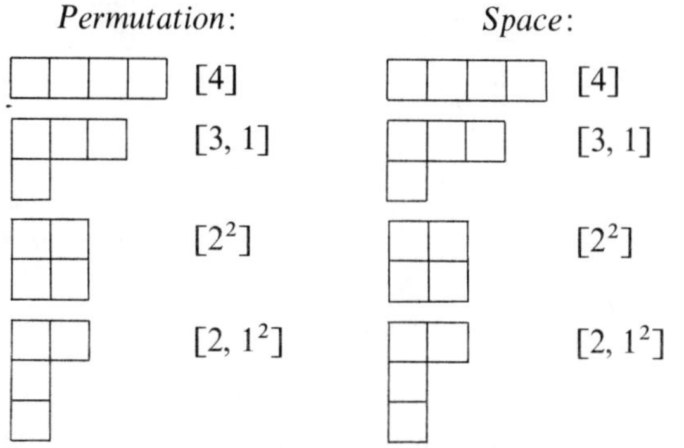

(7.89)

The resultant j values for electrons can be determined from the Young diagrams for the permutational symmetry by assigning the boxes in the first row a value of $\frac{1}{2}$, the value of the intrinsic j of the electron, and those in the second row a value of $-\frac{1}{2}$, and summing over the boxes. Thus, for four electrons, the resultant j values for [4], [3, 1], and $[2^2]$ are 2, 1, and 0, respectively. These are frequently referred to as *quintet*, *triplet*, and *singlet* states.

The allowed representations of $[\mathbf{G}_s]^n$, which will be the same as the allowed representations for a many-particle spatial function in $\mathbf{G}_s$, can be obtained by use of the character table for $\mathbf{S}(n)$. As previously mentioned, the elements of $[\mathbf{G}_s]^n$ have the form of Eq. 7.86. The explicit form of the $A, B, C, \ldots$ and the values of the $a, b, c, \ldots$ are deduced from the class structure of $\mathbf{S}(n)$. The characters of the permutational symmetry adapted representations in $\mathbf{G}_s$ obey the relationship

$$\chi^{[\Gamma]\alpha}(R) = \frac{1}{n!} \sum_i g_i \times \chi^{[\Gamma]}(P_i) \times \left\{ \prod_{a=0}^{n} [\chi(R^{p_a})]^a \right\} \tag{7.90}$$

where $\chi^{[\Gamma]\alpha}(R)$ is the character of element R in the allowed product representation α which is adapted to permutational representation $[\Gamma]$ of $\mathbf{S}(n)$. The i summation is over the classes of permutations of $\mathbf{S}(n)$, g_i is the order of the class, and $\chi^{[\Gamma]}(P_i)$ is the character of the permutation in the ith class. If the permutation cycle structure is written

$$P_i = \prod_{a=0}^{n} p_a^a \tag{7.91}$$

where p_a is the cycle order and a is the number of times a cycle of order p_a appears in P_i, then the product, a and p_a in Eq. 7.90, has the same meaning as in Eq. 7.91. $\chi(R^{p_a})$ is the character of the element R (of $\mathbf{G}_s$) raised to the power p_a. This character itself is then raised to the power a.

A simple example will make the meaning of the terms of Eq. 7.90 more obvious. Consider two electrons in a field of spherical symmetry and each in an orbital characterized by the $D^{(1)}$ representation of $R(3)$ [e.g., the $(1s)^2$ $(2s)^2$ $(2p)^2$ configuration of carbon]. The appropriate permutation group is $\mathbf{S}(2)$. The irreducible representations of **S**(2) are [2] and $[1^2]$. Both are permissible for the electron. The permutational representation [2] must have a representation from $[\mathbf{R}(3)]^2$, which transforms as $[1^2]$, associated with it. The representation $[1^2]$ from **S**(2) must be associated with a spatial function that transforms as [2]. The character table for **S**(2) is

S(2)	(1^2)	(2)
[2]	1	1
$[1^2]$	1	-1

(7.92)

Consider the spatial function that transforms as [2]. The character of the $C(\phi)$ operation is sufficient to determine the representations within **R**(3). From Eq. 7.90, we have

$$\chi^{[2]\alpha}(C(\phi)) = \tfrac{1}{2}\{1 \times 1 \times [\chi(C(\phi))]^2 + 1 \times 1 \times [\chi(C(\phi)^2)]\} \tag{7.93}$$

For $D^{(1)}$, we have

$$\chi(C(\phi)) = 1 + 2\cos\phi \tag{7.94a}$$

$$\begin{aligned}[\chi(C(\phi))]^2 &= 1 + 4\cos\phi + 4\cos^2\phi \\ &= 3 + 4\cos\phi + 2\cos 2\phi\end{aligned} \tag{7.94b}$$

$$\chi(C(\phi)^2) = 1 + 2\cos 2\phi \tag{7.94c}$$

$$\chi^{[2]\alpha}(C(\phi)) = 2 + 2\cos\phi + 2\cos 2\phi \tag{7.95}$$

By inspection, we see that this must arise from a representation

$$\Gamma_{\alpha}^{[2]} = D^{(0)} + D^{(2)} \tag{7.96}$$

Similarly, for the $[1^2]$ spatial representation (which is associated with the [2] permutational representation), we have

$$\begin{aligned}\chi^{[1^2]\alpha}(C(\phi)) &= \tfrac{1}{2}\{1 \times 1 \times [\chi(C(\phi))]^2 - 1 \times 1 \times [\chi(C(\phi)^2)]\} \\ &= 1 + 2\cos\phi\end{aligned} \tag{7.97}$$

Thus,

$$\Gamma_{\alpha}^{[1^2]} = D^{(1)} \tag{7.98}$$

What we have just done is to show that an atom having a p^2 electronic configuration ($[D^{(1)}]^2$) can exist as a ^3P state ($D^{(1)}$ spatial symmetry, [2] permutational symmetry) or as ^1S or ^1D states ($[1^2]$ permutational symmetry and $D^{(0)}$ or $D^{(2)}$ spatial symmetry).

For the binary product $D^{(j)} \times D^{(j)}$ within the **R**(3) or $\mathbf{R}_h(3)$ group, there is a simple rule for symmetrized and antisymmetrized products. The even-indexed representations in the result are totally symmetric and the odd-indexed representations are totally antisymmetric if j is an integer. If j is a half-integer, the converse is true. For example, in the product $D^{(1)} \times D^{(1)}$ the symmetrized product is $D^{(0)} + D^{(2)}$, while the antisymmetrized product is $D^{(1)}$. For the product $D^{(1/2)} \times D^{(1/2)}$ the symmetrized product is $D^{(1)}$ and the antisymmetrized product is $D^{(0)}$.

PROBLEMS

1. In orbital theory, the integral $\langle \phi_i | \hat{H} | \phi_j \rangle$, where ϕ_i and ϕ_j are different energy eigenfunctions and $\hat{H}$ is the Hamiltonian, vanishes. Show, from group theory alone, that this must be the case for atoms when ϕ_i and ϕ_j have different l values. (The statement is true for any system, but the general proof is not by group theory.)

2. Find the symmetry-induced restrictions on the following integrals (note that the numbers in parentheses are the labels of the particles associated with the one-particle function or the one- or two-particle operator):

   (a) $\langle \phi_i(1) | \hat{O}(1) | \phi_j(1) \rangle$

   (b) $\langle \phi_i(1)\phi_j(2) | \hat{O}(1, 2) | \phi_k(1)\phi_l(2) \rangle$

   (c) $\langle \phi_i(1)\phi_j(2)\phi_k(3) | \hat{O}(1, 2) | \phi_l(1)\phi_m(2)\phi_n(3) \rangle$

3. Set up the π-electron Hückel matrix for

   (a) Hexatriene

   (b) Benzene

   (c) Naphthalene

4. A general potential function for a homonuclear diatomic molecule can have the form

$$V(x) = a + bx + cx^2 + dx^3 + ex^4 + \ldots$$

   Show, on the basis of symmetry, which terms in the expansion must vanish.

5. Perform the indicated adaptations of point-group representations to symmetric-group representations:

   (a) E of $\mathbf{C}_{3v}$ to $[1^2]$ of $\mathbf{S}(2)$

   (b) E of $\mathbf{C}_{4v}$ to $[2]$ of $\mathbf{S}(2)$

   (c) E_g of $\mathbf{O}_h$ to $[1^2]$ of $\mathbf{S}(2)$

   (d) T_{1u} of $\mathbf{O}_h$ to $[2, 1]$ of $\mathbf{S}(3)$

   (e) T_{2g} of $\mathbf{O}_h$ to $[3]$ of $\mathbf{S}(3)$

BIBLIOGRAPHY

BARROW, G. M., *Introduction to Molecular Spectroscopy*, McGraw-Hill Book Company, New York, 1962.

CHISHOLM, C. D. H., *Group Theoretical Techniques in Quantum Chemistry*, Academic Press, Inc., New York, 1976.

FLURRY, R. L., JR., *Molecular Orbital Theories of Bonding in Organic Molecules*, Marcel Dekker, Inc., New York, 1968.

HAMERMESH, M., *Group Theory*, Addison-Wesley Publishing Company, Inc., Reading, Mass., 1962.

KAPLAN, I. G., *Symmetry of Many-Electron Systems*, Academic Press, Inc., New York, 1975.

KING, G. W., *Spectroscopy and Molecular Structure*, Holt, Rinehart and Winston, Inc., New York, 1964.

LAWDEN, D. F., *The Mathematical Principles of Quantum Mechanics*, Methuen Company Ltd., London, 1967.

SLATER, J. C., *Quantum Theory of Molecules and Solids*, Vol. I, McGraw-Hill Book Company, New York, 1963; Vol. II, 1965.

8

The Interaction of Radiation and Matter

8.1 SPECTROSCOPY

The study of the absorption of energy from or the emission of energy to the electromagnetic radiation field by some system is known as *spectroscopy*. Such a study provides much useful information about the structure of the system being studied. Frequently, spectroscopy is used in a qualitative manner as when, for example, a complicated organic molecule is identified by comparing its infrared spectrum to that of a known sample of the same material. On the other hand, when the molecules under consideration are relatively simple, very detailed information about the structure of the molecule can be obtained. For example, an analysis of a high-resolution infrared spectrum of gaseous hydrogen chloride can yield, among other things, the force constant for the stretching of the hydrogen–chlorine bond, the moment of inertia of the molecule, the bond length for both the ^{35}Cl- and the ^{37}Cl-containing molecules, and in addition the isotopic ratio of ^{35}Cl to ^{37}Cl. Usually, neither of these types of applications directly involve group theory; however, group theory and symmetry considerations can aid in other cases. For example, symmetry-imposed selection rules can frequently aid in deciding between possible structures for a molecule. In certain cases, the geometries of excited electronic states may be deduced from a detailed symmetry analysis of electronic absorption spectra. We shall primarily confine our attention to the symmetry aspects of spectral studies.

Electromagnetic radiation is conventionally divided into several wavelength ranges. The ranges commonly used in spectroscopy are summarized in Table 8.1. The indicated boundaries between spectral regions are somewhat arbitrary. Table 8.1 also indicates the types of spectral transitions found in the various spectral regions. At the extremes of the regions there may be overlapping of the types of transitions. This is particularly true in the near infrared, where there occur both vibrational transitions (primarily "overtone" bands) and electronic transitions (especially in metal-ion complexes).

Except for paramagnetic resonance, the transitions listed in Table 8.1 involve transitions among the quantized states that would occur in an isolated molecule in the absence of any external forces. The magnetic resonance experiments involve a study of the transitions of paramagnetic nuclei or unpaired electrons in the presence of an external magnetic field. Most of our discussion will center on rotational, vibrational, and electronic spectroscopy.

Since vibrational transitions occur at considerably higher energies than rotational transitions (the energy spacings between vibrational eigenstates are greater than those between rotational eigenstates) it might be expected that a vibrational transition could be accompanied by many different rotational transitions. This is found to be the case. Similarly, since most electronic transitions occur at considerably higher energies than do most vibrational transitions, it might be expected that an electronic transition could be accompanied by many different vibrational transitions, each of which could be accompanied by many different rotational transitions. Again, this is found to be the case. The situation is illustrated schematically in Fig. 8.1. In principle, a transition can occur from any rotational state of any vibrational state of any electronic state to any other rotational state of any (the same or different) vibrational state of any (the same or different) electronic state by the absorption or emission of energy from a beam of electromagnetic radiation. Actually, as we will discuss later, there are selection rules in addition to the symmetry selection rules which prevent some of these from being possible. Thus, a microwave spectrum should be a pure rotational spectrum,

Table 8.1. Electromagnetic radiation

Name	Approximate Wavelength (cm)	Frequency (sec^{-1})	Energy Per Photon (eV)	Spectroscopy
	2×10^6	1.5×10^4	6.2×10^{-11}	
Radio				NMR
	4×10^3	7.5×10^6	3.1×10^{-8}	
Microwave				Molecular rotations, EPR
	3.3×10^{-2}	9×10^{11}	3.7×10^{-3}	
Infrared				Molecular vibrations
	8×10^{-5}	3.8×10^{14}	1.6	
Visible light				Atomic and molecular electronic transitions
	4×10^{-5}	7.5×10^{14}	3.1	
Ultraviolet				Atomic and molecular electronic transitions
	1.2×10^{-6}	2.5×10^{16}	1.0×10^2	
Extreme ultraviolet				Atomic and molecular electronic transitions
	5×10^{-7}	6×10^{16}	2.5×10^2	
X rays				Atomic and molecular electronic transitions
	1.2×10^{-9}	2.5×10^{19}	1.0×10^5	
Gamma rays				Intranuclear transitions
	1×10^{-12}	3×10^{22}	1.2×10^8	

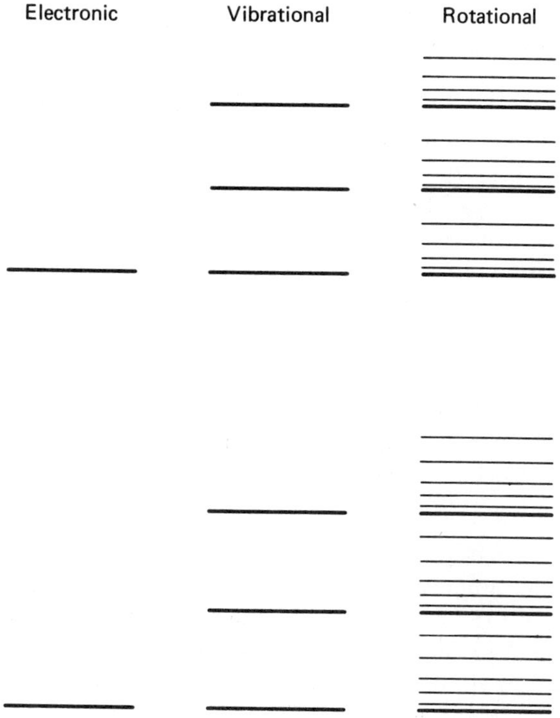

Fig. 8.1. Schematic representation of the superposition of electronic, vibrational, and rotational eigenstates.

an infrared spectrum a vibrational spectrum with rotational fine structure superposed on the spectral bands, and an ultraviolet spectrum an electronic spectrum with vibrational and rotational fine structure superposed on the spectral bands. With sufficiently high resolution, gas-phase spectra do indeed show all these features. In condensed phases, however, collisional broadening and other effects usually obscure the fine structure, and all that is seen are broadened spectral bands corresponding to the particular type of transition appropriate to the region under consideration.

In our initial definition of spectroscopy we included both energy-absorption and energy-emission processes. The absorption processes correspond to ordinary absorption spectroscopy. This is the most common type of study undertaken for molecular systems. When the term "spectrum" is used in connection with the study of a molecule without qualifying it with "absorption" or "emission," it can usually be assumed that "absorption spectrum" is implied. In molecular studies, normal direct emission spectroscopy most commonly involves electronic transitions and is usually given the special name *fluorescence spectroscopy*. (Vibrational emission spectra have also been studied to some extent.) *Phosphorescence emission* is a time-delayed emission involving a (forbidden) change in spin multiplicity during the emission process. The symmetry restrictions on molecular absorption and fluorescence spectroscopy are the same; consequently, in our discussion, unless one or the other is explicitly mentioned, the considerations will apply equally to both. Since phosphorescence involves a change in spin multiplicity, the transition occurring is theoretically forbidden within the context of the usual quantum mechanical description of a system. Symmetry restrictions can add to this forbidden nature; however, features other than symmetry are usually the determining factor as to whether or not phosphorescence can be observed. When symmetry selection rules are applicable, they are the same as for absorption and fluorescence spectroscopy.

8.2 CLASSICAL DESCRIPTION OF ELECTROMAGNETIC RADIATION

When a beam of electromagnetic radiation impinges upon a bit of matter, a number of phenomena can occur. The effect of these phenomena can produce changes in both the matter and the radiation. There are direct relationships between the changes in the matter and the changes in the radiation. By observing the radiation and by studying the changes produced in it by its interaction with the matter, we can obtain much valuable information about the nature of the matter. In fact, these phenomena provide most of the direct experimental information we have about the structure of atoms and molecules. Much of the utility of group theory arises from the application of symmetry and group theory to the interpretation of this information. Before we can proceed intelligently in this direction, however, we must investigate the relationships involved when these interactions take place.

A wave interpretation of electromagnetic radiation will be sufficient for most of our purposes. In this interpretation, a beam of *plane-polarized radiation* may be considered to consist of an oscillating electric field vector **E** and an oscillating magnetic field vector **H** at right angles to the electric field vector. (Note the deviation from our usual notation. These vectors are being represented by capital letters.) The oscillations are of the same frequency and the same phase, and are propagated through space in a third direction which is perpendicular to both of them. The two vectors and the propagation direction may be thought of as describing an orthogonal coordinate system (Fig. 8.2). For certain topics, such as a discussion of optical activity, it is necessary to resolve the electric or magnetic field vector of the plane wave of Fig. 8.2 into two equal and constant components rotating in opposite directions (*circularly polarized radiation*). This is represented schematically in Fig. 8.3 for the electric field vector. Notice that the resultant of the two rotating vectors is a vector whose motion is confined to a plane and whose magnitude varies sinusoidally (i.e., it describes the plane-wave vector motion represented in Fig. 8.2).

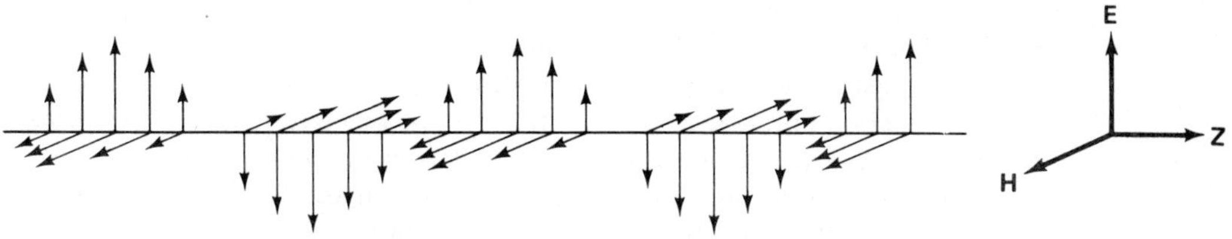

Fig. 8.2. Oscillation of the electric and magnetic field vectors in electromagnetic radiation.

The equations for the propagation of electromagnetic radiation are obtained from a solution of *Maxwell's equations*. In particular, **E** must satisfy the wave equation

$$\nabla^2 \mathbf{E} - \frac{1}{c^2}\frac{\partial^2 \mathbf{E}}{\partial t^2} = 0 \tag{8.1}$$

where c is the speed of light. For propagation through a vacuum, the solution of this is

$$\mathbf{E} = \mathbf{E}^0 \exp\left[i(\omega t - \alpha - \mathbf{k} \cdot \mathbf{r})\right] \tag{8.2}$$

where $\mathbf{E}^0$ is the magnitude of the electric field vector, or, for propagation through matter,

$$\mathbf{E} = \mathbf{E}^0 \exp(-\mathbf{a} \cdot \mathbf{r}) \exp\left[i(\omega t - \alpha - \mathbf{k} \cdot \mathbf{r})\right] \tag{8.3}$$

where ω is the *angular frequency* $2\pi\nu$, α the *phase angle*, **r** the distance the wave has traveled, **k** a propagation vector of magnitude $2\pi/\lambda$ (λ being the *wavelength*), and **a** the *absorption coefficient* (expressed here as a vector, emphasizing the fact that this may have directional properties).

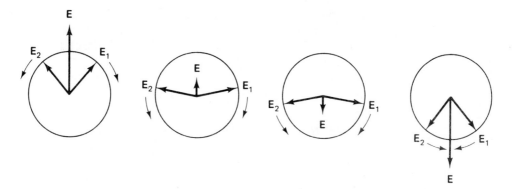

Fig. 8.3. Resolution of a plane wave into two circularly polarized components. The center vector **E** in each case represents the resultant of the two rotating vectors, $\mathbf{E}_1$ and $\mathbf{E}_2$.

Equations 8.2 and 8.3 are the equations for one of the circular components of Fig. 8.3. The plane wave results from constructing the real part of two exponentials, one with a positive and the other with a negative sign for the exponent. The result of the interaction of radiation with matter may be reflected in any of the terms in the exponent in Eq. 8.3. For example, ordinary *absorption spectroscopy* measures the value of the absorption coefficient, **a**, for a system as a function of wavelength or frequency. Inelastic scattering of light, such as in *Raman spectroscopy*, produces a change in the frequency (ω or ν) of the radiation. Scattering itself represents a change in the direction of the **r** vector. *Optical activity*, the rotation of plane-polarized light, occurs via a change in the phase angle α as the radiation transgresses the medium. The information on atomic positions as obtained from *X-ray diffraction* measurements comes from subtle changes in the propagation vector **k** as the radiation interacts with the recurring space symmetry of the crystal. In general, when radiation interacts with matter, all the parameters of the wave equation will be changed to some extent. The experiments are usually designed to optimize the effect that is to be studied.

The quantum mechanical description of radiation (in terms of photons) leads to results qualitatively very similar to Eq. 8.2. Each photon has associated with it a wave function with a functional form similar to that of Eq. 8.2. A beam of radiation would be represented by a summation of such terms. Thus, an absorption of radiation would be expressed as a decrease in the number of photons, rather than as a decrease in amplitude. The results are similar enough that Eq. 8.3 will be sufficient for our purposes.

8.3 TIME-DEPENDENT SCHRÖDINGER EQUATION

Let us turn our attention to a theoretical description of the interaction of radiation and matter. Since the ultimate information desired is information about the matter, it is advantageous to develop this treatment in terms of the quantum mechanical description of the matter. The interactions we are considering are time-dependent processes; consequently, the results must be obtained by a use of the *time-dependent Schrödinger equation*,

$$i\hbar \frac{\partial}{\partial t} |\psi_i\rangle = E_i |\psi_i\rangle \tag{8.4a}$$

where $\hbar = h/2\pi$. In terms of the Hamiltonian operator, this is

$$i\hbar \frac{\partial}{\partial t} |\psi_i\rangle = \hat{H} |\psi_i\rangle \tag{8.4b}$$

The effect of the electromagnetic radiation on the system is to introduce time-dependent electric and magnetic fields, which in turn introduce time-dependent terms into the potential-energy part of the Hamiltonian. The solutions to Eqs. 8.4

must be in terms of time-dependent wave functions. (Note that if the wave function were not time-dependent, the only solution to Eq. 8.4a would be the trivial solution, E_i equals zero.) The most general formal solution of Eq. 8.4a is

$$\psi_i(x, t) = \exp\left(-\frac{iE_i t}{\hbar}\right)u_i(x) \tag{8.5}$$

where $u_i(x)$ is a time-independent function, and the exponential term gives the time dependence of the wave function.

8.4 TIME-DEPENDENT PERTURBATION THEORY

Direct solutions to Eqs. 8.4 and 8.5 are impractical, if not impossible. As a consequence of this, approximate solutions are usually obtained in terms of *time-dependent perturbation theory*. Time-dependent perturbation theory makes use of the stationary-state solutions of time-independent perturbation theory (Section 7.10). If there is some complete set of wave functions that are solutions to the time-independent Schrödinger equation,

$$\hat{H}^0|u_i\rangle = E_i^0|u_i\rangle \tag{8.6}$$

these may be considered to completely span a function space. That is, they may be said to form a complete set of basis functions such that any other function may be constructed as a linear combination of these basis functions. This is analogous to the situation encountered in three-dimensional Cartesian space, where any vector can be represented as a linear combination of unit vectors lying on the x, y, and z axes. For example, if some new Hamiltonian is used such that

$$\hat{H}|v_j\rangle = E_j|v_j\rangle \tag{8.7}$$

the v_j can be constructed as linear combinations of the u_i,

$$v_j = \sum_i c_i u_i \tag{8.8}$$

the summation running over the entire set of u_i. The most general time-independent perturbation theory makes use of this type of expansion to obtain approximate solutions to quantum mechanical problems that cannot be solved exactly. The set of eigenfunctions for a problem that can be solved are used to approximate the solution to a problem that cannot be solved. The Hamiltonian for the problem under consideration is constructed as a perturbation of that for the exactly solvable problem,

$$\hat{H} = \hat{H}^0 + \hat{H}' \tag{8.9}$$

where $\hat{H}'$ is the perturbation.

For a time-dependent situation, the resulting wave function must be time-dependent. A general time-dependent wave equation may be constructed as a sum of terms similar to the right-hand side of Eq. 8.5,

$$\psi_i = \sum_j c_j \exp\left(-\frac{iE_j^0 t}{\hbar}\right) u_j \tag{8.10}$$

where the u_j are a complete set of time-independent functions. The most obvious choice of the u_j in Eq. 8.10 is to choose these as the solutions of the time-independent description of the system under study. There are several reasons for this. First, these wave functions, or state vectors, correspond to the observable stationary states of the system, thereby leading to a description of the time-dependent process in terms of the observable states of the system. This is especially appropriate for a description of spectral transitions in that the transitions can be interpreted as transitions between the particular states under consideration. Another reason for this choice is that normally, in perturbation theory calculations, the unperturbed Hamiltonian should be as similar as possible to the perturbed Hamiltonian. This is because the summation over the unperturbed states cannot usually be carried to completion; there are, in general, an infinite number of possible solutions to the exact Schrödinger equation for a system. The more nearly the individual terms of the summation are to eigenfunctions of the perturbed system, the fewer the number of terms that are required for a reasonably accurate solution to the problem.

The form of the time-dependent perturbation that is used is

$$\hat{H}'(\mathbf{r}, t) \simeq \sum_\mu \frac{iZ_\mu \hbar}{m_\mu} (\mathbf{A}(\mathbf{r}_\mu) \cdot \mathbf{\nabla}_\mu) \tag{8.11}$$

where $\mathbf{A}$ is the vector potential of the electric field and $\mathbf{\nabla}$ the first derivative with respect to each of the coordinates, expressed as a vector. Using this form for the perturbation and the expansion of Eq. 8.10 for the wave function, the time-dependent Schrödinger equation (Eq. 8.4b) becomes

$$(\hat{H}^0 + \hat{H}')\left|\sum_j c_j \exp\left(-\frac{iE_j^0 t}{\hbar}\right) u_j\right\rangle = i\hbar \frac{\partial}{\partial t}\left|\sum_j c_j \exp\left(-\frac{iE_j^0 t}{\hbar}\right) u_j\right\rangle \tag{8.12}$$

The spatial dependence of this may be removed by taking the product from the left with some particular u_m, and integrating over all space, to yield

$$i\hbar \frac{dc_m}{dt} = \sum_j c_j \exp\left[\frac{i(E_m^0 - E_j^0)t}{\hbar}\right] H'_{mj} \tag{8.13}$$

where

$$H'_{mj} = \langle u_m | \hat{\mathbf{H}}' | u_j \rangle \tag{8.14}$$

$$= \langle u_m | \sum_\mu \frac{iZ_\mu \hbar}{m_\mu} (\mathbf{A}(\mathbf{r}_\mu) \cdot \mathbf{\nabla}_\mu) | u_j \rangle \tag{8.14a}$$

The functional form of the vector potential, $\mathbf{A}$, is the same as that of the electric field vector $\mathbf{E}$ (see Eq. 8.2):

$$\mathbf{A} = \mathbf{A}^0 \exp\,[i(\omega t - \alpha - \mathbf{k}\cdot\mathbf{r})] \tag{8.15}$$

Considering only the plane-wave resultant of two oppositely rotating vectors, we can take the real sine or cosine form of this:

$$\mathbf{A} = \mathbf{A}^0 \cos\,(\omega t - \alpha - \mathbf{k}\cdot\mathbf{r}) \tag{8.16}$$

$$= \tfrac{1}{2}\mathbf{A}^0\{\exp\,[i(\omega t - \alpha - \mathbf{k}\cdot\mathbf{r})] + \exp\,[-i(\omega t - \alpha - \mathbf{k}\cdot\mathbf{r})]\} \tag{8.16a}$$

If the wavelength, λ, of the radiation is large compared to the dimensions of the system being studied, $\mathbf{k}\cdot\mathbf{r}$, which equals $2\pi/\lambda$ times $\mathbf{r}$, can be neglected compared to ωt and α, and the vector potential $\mathbf{A}$ can be considered to be spatially invariant over the region of space occupied by the system:

$$\mathbf{A} \simeq \tfrac{1}{2}\mathbf{A}^0\{\exp\,[i(\omega t - \alpha)] + \exp\,[-i(\omega t - \alpha)]\} \tag{8.16b}$$

This is the situation encountered in spectral studies. The shortest wavelength normally used in spectral studies is around 2000 Å. Most molecules have dimensions of around 10 Å or less. Even polymers seldom reach more than 100 to 200 Å in any dimension. If, on the other hand, the wavelength of the radiation is of the same magnitude as atomic and molecular dimensions, the variation of $\mathbf{A}$ with position must be considered. This is the situation encountered in X-ray diffraction. Here the wavelengths range from a fraction of an angstrom to a few angstroms. The information about atomic positions obtained from X-ray diffraction is transmitted via the variation of $\mathbf{A}$ with position.

Let us consider first the situation where $\mathbf{A}$ can be considered to be spatially invariant. In this case, H'_{mj} can be expressed as

$$H'_{mj} = \sum_{\mu} \mathbf{A} Z_\mu \langle u_m |\, \frac{i\hbar}{m_\mu}\, \nabla_\mu | u_j \rangle \tag{8.17}$$

By making use of a series of quantum mechanical identities, it can be shown that Eq. 8.17 equals

$$H'_{mj} = \frac{i(E_j^0 - E_m^0)}{\hbar}\, \mathbf{A}\langle u_m | \sum_{\mu} Z_\mu \mathbf{r}_\mu | u_j \rangle \tag{8.18}$$

The integral in Eq. 8.18 is the *transition dipole*. It is the dipole moment of the system, $\sum_\mu Z_\mu \mathbf{r}_\mu$, averaged between two stationary states of the system. If we express this as a vector, $\boldsymbol{\mu}_{mj}$, Eq. 8.18 becomes

$$H'_{mj} = \frac{i(E_j^0 - E_m^0)}{\hbar}\, \mathbf{A}\cdot\boldsymbol{\mu}_{mj} \tag{8.19}$$

Substituting Eq. 8.19 into Eq. 8.13 and multiplying through by $-i/\hbar$, and making the definition

$$h\nu_{mj} = E_m^0 - E_j^0 \tag{8.20}$$

we have

$$\frac{dc_m}{dt} = -\sum_j c_j \frac{4\pi^2 \nu_{mj}}{h} \mathbf{A} \cdot \boldsymbol{\mu}_{mj} \exp(2\pi i \nu_{mj} t) \tag{8.21}$$

Before interaction with radiation, our system is in one particular eigenstate corresponding to one particular time-independent solution of the Schrödinger equation. Thus, all the coefficients in Eq. 8.21 except one are zero. That one, corresponding to some particular state, say n, of the system, is unity. Thus, in the initial state of the system, we have

$$\frac{dc_m}{dt} = -\frac{4\pi^2 \nu_{mn}}{h} \mathbf{A} \cdot \boldsymbol{\mu}_{mn} \exp(2\pi i \nu_{mn} t) \tag{8.22}$$

In treatments involving the interaction of radiation and matter, it is usually assumed that the time dependence is determined mainly by the initial state of the system. Thus, Eq. 8.22 is said to represent the rate of interaction of the mth state with the nth state under the influence of electromagnetic radiation. Statements made by spectroscopists to the effect that "transition A borrows intensity from transition B" simply imply that other terms in the summation of Eq. 8.21 are important.

The time dependence of **A**, as expressed in Eq. 8.16b, can be substituted into Eq. 8.22 and the result integrated with respect to time to obtain

$$c_m = \frac{\pi i \nu_{mn}}{h} \mathbf{A}^0 \cdot \boldsymbol{\mu}_{mn} \left\{ \exp(-i\alpha) \frac{\exp[2\pi i(\nu + \nu_{mn})t]}{\nu + \nu_{mn}} - \exp(i\alpha) \frac{\exp[-2\pi i(\nu - \nu_{mn})t]}{\nu - \nu_{mn}} \right\} + \text{integration constant} \tag{8.23}$$

Evaluating this between the limits zero and t yields

$$c_m = \frac{\pi i \nu_{mn}}{h} \mathbf{A}^0 \cdot \boldsymbol{\mu}_{mn} \left\{ \exp(-i\alpha) \frac{\exp[2\pi i(\nu + \nu_{mn})t] - 1}{\nu + \nu_{mn}} - \exp(i\alpha) \frac{\exp[-2\pi i(\nu - \nu_{mn})t] - 1}{\nu - \nu_{mn}} \right\} \tag{8.24}$$

If state m is higher in energy than state n, ν_{mn} is positive and we are considering an energy-absorption process. If state m is lower in energy than state n, ν_{mn} is negative and we are referring to an energy-emission process. Equation 8.24 is for a fixed frequency ν. We know from quantization conditions that energy can be absorbed or emitted only in discrete quanta (i.e., electromagnetic radiation can be absorbed only if ν matches ν_{mn}). Actually, because of the Heisenberg principle, there will be a small, but finite, spread of frequencies with ν near ν_{mn} where such a transition can occur. Depending upon whether the process is absorption or emission, either $(\nu - \nu_{mn})$ or $(\nu + \nu_{mn})$ will be very near zero. The term having the appropriate one of these terms in the denominator will be large compared to the other term. Thus, for absorption, the c_m is determined by the second term in braces, while for emission, it is determined by the first term. For an absorption process, then, we have

$$c_m = \frac{\pi i \nu_{mn}}{h} \mathbf{A}^0 \cdot \boldsymbol{\mu}_{mn} \exp(i\alpha) \frac{\exp[-2\pi i(\nu - \nu_{mn})t] - 1}{\nu - \nu_{mn}} \tag{8.25}$$

Remembering the probability interpretation of the wave function, we know that the probability of the system being transferred from state n to state m by an absorption of radiation is proportional to $\psi^*\psi$. We have already carried out an integration to remove the time-independent part of the wave function; consequently,

$$\psi^*\psi = c_m^* c_m = \frac{4\pi^2\nu_{mn}^2}{h^2} (\mathbf{A}^0 \cdot \boldsymbol{\mu}_{mn})^2 \frac{\sin^2 \pi(\nu - \nu_{mn})t}{(\nu - \nu_{mn})^2} \tag{8.26}$$

This is, however, the probability for this transition to occur at a fixed frequency ν. To find the total transition probability, we must integrate over all frequencies. If we let $[\pi(\nu - \nu_{mn})t]$ be our integration variable, the integral can be evaluated and our transition probability is

$$c_m^* c_m = \frac{4\pi^4\nu_{mn}^2}{h^2} (\mathbf{A}^0 \cdot \boldsymbol{\mu}_{mn})^2 t \tag{8.27}$$

Starting with the emission term of Eq. 8.24, we obtain the same final expression.

If plane-polarized radiation is interacting with a crystalline substance having definitely aligned transition dipoles, Eq. 8.27 must be used in some form retaining the product of vectors. If, however, the substance is in a fluid medium, if the radiation is nonpolarized, or both, all possible orientations of the vector potential with the transition dipole become possible. In these cases, the orientations can be averaged and scalar quantities used for A^0 and μ_{mn}. The average of $\cos^2 \theta$ (the square of the direction cosine of the dot product) over all possible values of θ is $\frac{1}{3}$. This gives, for the transition probability,

$$c_m^* c_m = \frac{4\pi^4\nu_{mn}^2}{3h^2} A^{02}\mu_{mn}^2 t \tag{8.28}$$

Transition probabilities are more commonly expressed in terms of *energy density*. The total integrated energy density in terms of the electromagnetic potential vector is

$$\rho = \tfrac{1}{2}\pi\nu^2 A^{02} \tag{8.29}$$

In terms of energy density, the transition probability becomes

$$c_m^* c_m = \frac{8\pi^3}{3h^2} \mu_{mn}^2 \rho t \tag{8.30}$$

$$= B_{mn}\rho t \tag{8.30a}$$

where the quantity B_{mn} is *Einstein's coefficient of induced absorption* (B_{mn} equals B_{nm}). The rate of energy transfer between state m and state n induced by interaction with electromagnetic radiation is

$$\frac{dN_n}{dt} = -\frac{dN_m}{dt} = \frac{d}{dt}(-N_m + N_n)c_m^* c_m = (-N_m + N_n)B_{mn}\rho \qquad (8.31)$$

(where N_i is the number of systems in state i). In an emission process there is a radiation-independent *coefficient of spontaneous emission* (the Einstein A term). For emission only, the expression is

$$\frac{-dN_n}{dt} = N_n(A + B\rho) \qquad (8.32)$$

In order to reproduce the A coefficient theoretically, the classical wave treatment of the radiation is no longer sufficient. The radiation field itself must be quantized. Such a treatment is beyond the scope of the present work; however, the value of A is directly proportional to B, the ratio being

$$\frac{B}{A} = \frac{c^3}{8\pi h\nu^3} \qquad (8.33)$$

where c is the speed of light. Notice that this ratio is frequency-dependent. In the regions where fluorescence spectra are most commonly taken (ultraviolet and short-wavelength regions of the visible), the A term actually predominates. On the other hand, in the infrared and microwave spectral regions, the B term predominates in emission processes. In any case, we shall confine our attention to the B term. If we explicitly need the A term, we can obtain it from Eq. 8.33.

8.6 SYMMETRY RESTRICTIONS ON THE TRANSITION DIPOLE

Let us consider the restrictions that symmetry places on the radiation-induced transition rate between two states. We can see from Eq. 8.30 that the transition probability can be nonzero if and only if the magnitude of the transition dipole $\boldsymbol{\mu}_{mn}$ is nonzero. This transition dipole is the integral

$$\boldsymbol{\mu}_{mn} = \langle u_m | \sum_\alpha Z_\alpha \mathbf{r}_\alpha | u_n \rangle \qquad (8.34)$$

as previously defined in Eq. 8.18. As defined here, this is a vector quantity. It can be resolved into three components corresponding to the Cartesian coordinates x, y, and z,

$$\boldsymbol{\mu}_{mn} = \mu_{mn}^x \mathbf{i} + \mu_{mn}^y \mathbf{j} + \mu_{mn}^z \mathbf{k} \qquad (8.35)$$

where

$$\mu_{mn}^x = \langle u_m | \sum_\alpha Z_\alpha x_\alpha | u_n \rangle \tag{8.36}$$

$$\mu_{mn}^y = \langle u_m | \sum_\alpha Z_\alpha y_\alpha | u_n \rangle \tag{8.37}$$

$$\mu_{mn}^z = \langle u_m | \sum_\alpha Z_\alpha z_\alpha | u_n \rangle \tag{8.38}$$

The quantities μ_{mn}^x, μ_{mn}^y, and μ_{mn}^z are scalar quantities (numbers) characteristic of the system under consideration. Since they are numbers and not functions or vectors, they must be invariant under all symmetry operations (see Section 7.8). That is,

$$R\mu_{mn}^x = \mu_{mn}^x \tag{8.39}$$

$$R\mu_{mn}^y = \mu_{mn}^y \tag{8.40}$$

$$R\mu_{mn}^z = \mu_{mn}^z \tag{8.41}$$

for all symmetry operations R of the point group of the system. This means that

$$R\langle u_m | \hat{\mu}^i | u_n \rangle = \langle u_m | \hat{\mu}^i | u_n \rangle \tag{8.42}$$

where $\hat{\mu}^i$ is one component of the dipole operator. The integral $\langle u_m | \hat{\mu}^i | u_n \rangle$ must transform as the totally symmetric irreducible representation of the system in order not to vanish. The transformation properties (i.e., the symmetry representation) of the integral may be found from the triple product of the representations of the individual parts of the integral, since symmetry operations commute with the integration operation

$$\Gamma(\mu_{mn}^i) = \Gamma(u_m) \times \Gamma(\hat{\mu}^i) \times \Gamma(u_n) \tag{8.43}$$

We already know that the individual wave functions must transform as one of the irreducible representations of the system. If $\Gamma(\hat{\mu}^i)$ is reducible, it can be resolved into a combination of irreducible representations. Of the products of irreducible representations, only the product of a representation with itself contains the totally symmetric irreducible representation; consequently, for Eq. 8.43 to contain the totally symmetric representation, Eq. 8.44 must hold:

$$\Gamma(\hat{\mu}^i) \subset \Gamma(u_m) \times \Gamma(u_n) \tag{8.44}$$

In other words, *the product of the irreducible representations of the eigenfunctions corresponding to the states between which the transition is occurring must transform, or have a component that transforms, as one of the components of the dipole operator for the transition dipole to be nonvanishing* and, consequently, observable.

Exercise 8.1*:

(a) To what irreducible representations do vectors along the positive x axis, the positive y axis, and the positive z axis belong in the $\mathbf{C}_{2v}$ point group? (These will also be the representations to which μ^x, μ^y, and μ^z belong.)

(b) Find the symmetry-allowed transitions among the three normal vibrations of the water molecule, assuming the molecule to lie in the xz plane with the z axis bisecting the bond angle.

Exercise 8.2: Find the symmetry-allowed vibrational transitions for the carbon skeleton of cyclopropane.

8.7 INDUCED DIPOLES AND POLARIZABILITY

Radiation impinging on matter can cause phenomena other than the absorption or emission of radiation and the accompanying change of energy of the system. If we reconsider Eq. 8.23 under conditions such that the incident frequency is not near the resonance frequency, ν_{mn}, we have a situation in which c_m is varying sinusoidally with time. The magnitude of the perturbation caused by the electromagnetic radiation under these conditions will be very small. The coefficients of all terms but one in the wave function will be very small, while that one, corresponding to the eigenstate of the unperturbed system, will be very near unity. Thus, to a good degree of approximation, the time-dependent wave function under these conditions will be

$$\psi = \sum_j c_j \exp\left(-\frac{iE_j^0 t}{\hbar}\right)u_j \tag{8.45}$$

$$= \exp\left(-\frac{iE_n^0 t}{\hbar}\right)u_n + \sum_{j\neq n} c_j \exp\left(-\frac{iE_j^0 t}{\hbar}\right)u_j \tag{8.45a}$$

$$= \exp\left(-\frac{iE_n^0 t}{\hbar}\right)\left\{u_n + \sum_{j\neq n} c_j \exp(-2\pi i\nu_{nj})u_j\right\} \tag{8.45b}$$

$$= \exp\left(-\frac{iE_n^0 t}{\hbar}\right)\left\{u_n + \sum_{j\neq n} \frac{\pi i\nu_{nj}}{h}\mathbf{A}^0\cdot\boldsymbol{\mu}_{nj}u_j\right.$$
$$\left.\times\left[\exp(-i\alpha)\frac{\exp(2\pi i\nu t)}{\nu+\nu_{nj}} - \exp(i\alpha)\frac{\exp(-2\pi i\nu t)}{\nu-\nu_{nj}}\right]\right\} \tag{8.45c}$$

where Eq. 8.24 has been substituted for c_j in Eq. 8.45b. Let us consider the expectation value of the x component of the dipole moment with respect to this wave function. This yields

$$\langle\psi|\hat{\mu}^x|\psi\rangle = \langle u_n|\hat{\mu}^x|u_n\rangle + \sum_{j\neq n}\frac{\pi i\nu_{nj}}{h}A_x\mu_{nj}^x\langle u_n|\hat{\mu}^x|u_j\rangle$$
$$\times\left[\exp(-i\alpha)\frac{\exp(2\pi i\nu t)}{\nu+\nu_{nj}} - \exp(i\alpha)\frac{\exp(2\pi i\nu t)}{\nu-\nu_{nj}}\right] \tag{8.46}$$
$$+ \text{ complex conjugate and higher-order crossed terms}$$

The first term of this is the x component of the permanent dipole moment of the system in the nth eigenstate. The integral in the summation is equal to the x component of the transition dipole. Using this and the sine equivalent of the exponential terms, we have for this term (the *induced dipole*)

$$\mu_{\text{ind}}^{x} = \sum_{j \neq n} \frac{|\mu_{nj}^{x}|^2}{h} 2\pi\nu_{nj} A_x^0 \sin(2\pi\nu t - \alpha)\left(\frac{-1}{\nu + \nu_{nj}} - \frac{1}{\nu - \nu_{nj}}\right) \tag{8.47}$$

$$= \sum_{j \neq n} \frac{|\mu_{nj}^{x}|^2}{h} 2\nu_{nj} 2\pi\nu A_x^0 \sin(2\pi\nu t - \alpha) \frac{1}{\nu_{nj}^2 - \nu^2} \tag{8.48}$$

The x component of the electric field vector $\mathbf{E}$ is, however,

$$E_x = 2\pi\nu A_x^0 \sin(2\pi\nu t - \alpha) \tag{8.49}$$

Thus,

$$\mu_{\text{ind}}^{x} = \left[\sum_{j \neq n} \frac{|\mu_{nj}^{x}|^2}{h} \frac{2\nu_{nj}}{\nu_{nj}^2 - \nu^2}\right] E_x \tag{8.50}$$

This is an oscillating component of the dipole moment that oscillates with the electric field. Similar relations hold for the y and z components. The bracketed term is the *polarizability* of the system. The more common expression is

$$\mu = \alpha E \tag{8.51}$$

The polarizability and the induced dipole are responsible for diverse phenomena such as the deviation of the refractive index of a substance from unity and the Raman effect.

From Eq. 8.50 it is apparent that the operator corresponding to a polarizability perturbation must be the square of the dipole operator. In three-dimensional Cartesian space this will have the components x^2, y^2, z^2, xy, xz, and yz. The symmetry restrictions for this perturbation to be nonvanishing require that some direct product $\Gamma(u_n) \times \Gamma(u_j)$ must contain an irreducible representation that transforms as one of these. For the occurrence of an induced dipole, this is not a very strict restriction, since the summation of Eq. 8.48 is over all the eigenstates of the system. If, on the other hand, a Raman transition is being considered, a transition between two particular states is involved. In this case there are symmetry restrictions placed on the transition.

8.8 SCATTERING

Another important phenomenon that occurs when radiation interacts with matter is *scattering*. We have already seen that when an oscillating electromagnetic field interacts with a system, it can perturb the system even if energy is not absorbed from the field. The qualitative effect is to induce an oscillating dipole in the system.

In order for this to occur, the electronic motion in the system must be disturbed. Classically, an oscillating electric dipole emits an oscillating electromagnetic field whose frequency matches that of the oscillator. This emitted radiation is dispersed with equal intensities in all directions. The equation for an electric field vector generated by an oscillating dipole is

$$\mathbf{E} = -\boldsymbol{\mu}^0 \frac{\omega^2}{rc^2} \exp\left[i(\omega t - \alpha - \mathbf{k}\cdot\mathbf{r})\right] \tag{8.52}$$

The oscillating dipole we are concerned with, however, is the induced dipole of Eqs. 8.50 and 8.51; thus,

$$\boldsymbol{\mu}^0 = \alpha \mathbf{E}^0 \tag{8.53}$$

where $\mathbf{E}^0$ is the amplitude of the incident electromagnetic radiation. The equation for the scattered electric field is then

$$\mathbf{E}_s = -\alpha \mathbf{E}^0 \frac{\omega^2}{rc^2} \exp\left[i(\omega t - \alpha - \mathbf{k}\cdot\mathbf{r})\right] \tag{8.54}$$

$$= -\alpha \frac{\omega^2}{rc^2} \mathbf{E}_{\text{incident}} \tag{8.54a}$$

(Note the two different meanings of the symbol α in Eq. 8.54.) The total intensity (energy density per unit time) of the radiation scattered by a single particle can be found by

$$I_s = \int_{t=0}^{1\text{ sec}} \int_{r=0}^{c} \int_{\theta=0}^{2\pi} \int_{\phi=0}^{\pi} \frac{|\mathbf{E}_s|^2}{4\pi} r^2 \sin\theta \, dr \, d\theta \, d\phi \, dt \tag{8.55}$$

(The integration limits of zero to c for r arise because this is the distance the radiation would travel in 1 sec.) The final result is

$$I_s = \frac{8\pi\alpha^2\omega^4}{3c^4} I_0 \tag{8.56}$$

where I_0 is the intensity of the incident light.

If two or more particles are present, the scattered waves can interfere with each other. This is illustrated schematically in Fig. 8.4 for some particular instant in time. The radiating circles are drawn at increments of one wavelength and represent the maxima of the scattered wave. The intersections of these circles will give *constructive interference. Destructive interference* occurs between these intersections. At some later instant in time, the scattered wave fronts will have moved farther out, and all the points of intersection will also have moved. Those points along the vector $\mathbf{s}'$ will have moved in the direction of $\mathbf{s}'$, and all the others will have swept out an angle as well as having moved radially. An observer along the direction $\mathbf{s}'$ would see an oscillating wave pattern in phase with the incident waves. Along any other direction, no such pattern would be observed. (Notice that another scattered wave front in phase with, and moving in the direction of, the incident wave will also occur.)

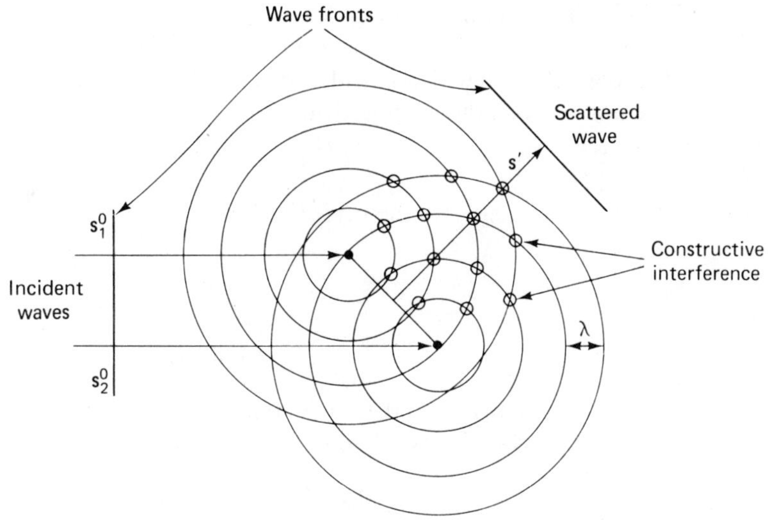

Fig. 8.4. Interference pattern for scattering from two particles.

By considering the vector relation between the propagation vectors, $\mathbf{s}_1^0$ or $\mathbf{s}_2^0$, and the scattered vectors, $\mathbf{s}_1$ or $\mathbf{s}_2$, we can find limitations on the angle at which the scattered waves from two particles can be in phase with each other. To visualize this, let us consider another figure with a more general relationship of the incident and scattered propagation vectors. In Fig. 8.5, P_1 and P_2 are two points that scatter the incident radiation. Their separation is represented by the vector $\mathbf{d}$. The incident radiation has the propagation vector $a\mathbf{s}_0$, where a is a scalar and $\mathbf{s}_0$ is now a unit vector. We will consider scattered radiation in the direction of $\mathbf{s}$ with a propagation vector $b\mathbf{s}$, where $\mathbf{s}$ is again a unit vector. The difference in the distance that rays A and B travel to form a wave front in the direction $\mathbf{s}$ is found by the difference in the projections of $\mathbf{d}$ on $\mathbf{s}_0$ and $\mathbf{s}$:

$$\Delta\mathbf{r} = \mathbf{d}\cdot\mathbf{s}_0 - \mathbf{d}\cdot\mathbf{s} \tag{8.57}$$

$$= \mathbf{d}\cdot(\mathbf{s}_0 - \mathbf{s}) \tag{8.57a}$$

$$= \mathbf{d}\cdot\mathbf{S} \tag{8.57b}$$

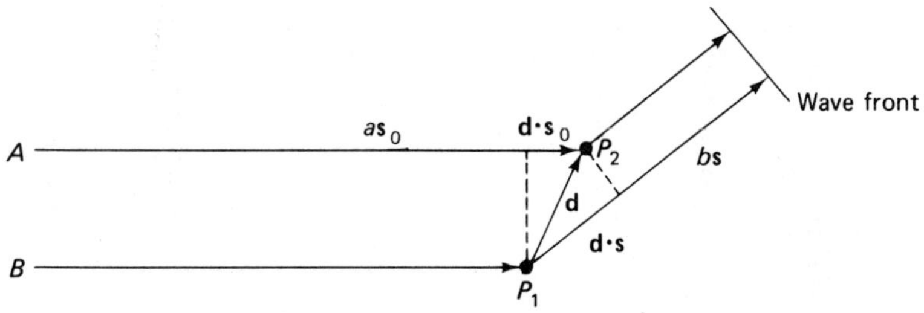

Fig. 8.5. Two generalized propagation vectors for scattering by two points.

To an observer along the direction of **s**, this difference shows up as a difference in phase (ϕ) of the two rays. The vector **S** is normal to a plane that would cause the observed reflection with an incidence (and reflection) angle of θ (Fig. 8.6). If $\mathbf{s}_0$ and **s** are unit vectors, the magnitude of **S** is

$$|\mathbf{S}| = 2 \sin \theta \tag{8.58}$$

The phase difference for the rays A and B is

$$\phi = \frac{2\pi}{\lambda} \mathbf{d} \cdot \mathbf{S} \tag{8.59}$$

$$= \mathbf{k}(\mathbf{d} \cdot \mathbf{S}) \tag{8.59a}$$

In order for the rays A and B to be in phase at the wave front, this must equal an integer multiple of 2π (i.e., $2\pi n$) or, in terms of **k**,

$$n\mathbf{k}\lambda = 2\pi n = \phi = \mathbf{k}(\mathbf{d} \cdot \mathbf{S}) \tag{8.60}$$

giving

$$n\lambda = \mathbf{d} \cdot \mathbf{S} = 2|\mathbf{d}| \sin \theta \tag{8.61}$$

Equation 8.61 is the *Bragg equation* of X-ray diffraction.

If radiation is to be scattered by a many-particle system, there are two situations that must be considered. The particles may be either highly ordered (such as the atoms in a crystal), or they may be completely disordered. In the first case, the particles are all at fixed regular distances from each other; consequently, the scattering for the system obeys Eq. 8.61 for each unique interparticle distance that occurs in the assembly. If λ is very much larger than **d** (e.g., if λ is for light of optical wavelengths and **d** is of the order of atomic dimensions), then the value of $\sin \theta$ for low-order (low values of n) scattering is very small and, for all practical purposes, no scattering is observed. This is why, for example, when light is passing through a large transparent crystal with flat faces, no scattered light is observed when

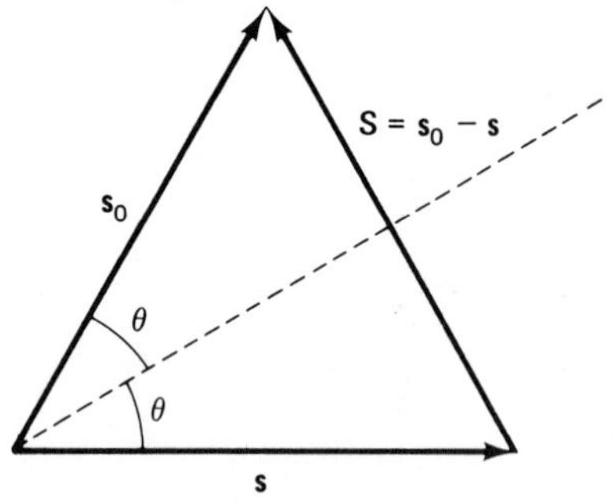

Fig. 8.6. Reflecting plane normal to S.

viewing the crystal from the side. If, on the other hand, λ is of the order of magnitude of $\mathbf{d}$, scattering is observed in accordance with Eq. 8.61. This leads to the whole field of X-ray diffraction and many other diffraction phenomena as well.

If the scattering system consists of randomly distributed particles, scattering can be observed at all angles, irrespective of the wavelength of the radiation. The reason for this can be rather simply understood from crude intuitive considerations. If the scattered rays from two particles are in phase, constructive interference occurs and the amplitudes are additive:

$$A_2 = 2A_1 \tag{8.62}$$

where A_2 is the total amplitude of the two rays and A_1 is the amplitude of a single ray. The intensities, however, are the squares of the amplitudes; consequently,

$$I_2 = 4I_1 \tag{8.63}$$

If destructive interference is occurring, on the other hand, the scattered intensity from the two particles is zero. If a second particle takes all possible random orientations with respect to a given fixed particle, it may be assumed that a constructive interference and a destructive interference occur with equal probability; thus, the net average intensity per particle for two-particle scattering will be

$$(I_2)_{\text{av per pair}} = \tfrac{1}{2}(4I_1 + 0) \tag{8.64}$$

$$= 2I_1 \tag{8.64a}$$

or

$$(I_2)_{\text{av per particle}} = I_1 \tag{8.65}$$

The argument can be extended to N particles to find that the total scattering for N particles will be N times the scattering for a single particle:

$$(I_s)_{\text{total}} = \frac{8\pi\alpha^2\omega^4 N}{3c^4} I_0 \tag{8.66}$$

The scattering of visible light from randomly oriented gas molecules is the reason we see a sky over us in the daytime. Its blue color is due to the fourth-power dependence of the intensity on the frequency, the high-frequency blue end of the spectrum being scattered with more intensity than is the red end.

The discussions we have presented about the interaction of radiation with matter have been general. In the use of the time-dependent perturbation theory, no restrictions are placed on the time-independent solutions. They were implicitly assumed to represent the total wave function for the system in the indicated state. In our applications we place restrictions on these. The restrictions employed yield the conditions for the particular property to be studied.

PROBLEMS

1. Find the general symmetry restrictions on the transition dipole operator between two states differing in one orbital for an atomic system.

2. Find the general symmetry restrictions on the polarizability operator between two states differing in one orbital for an atomic system.

BIBLIOGRAPHY

BARROW, G. M., *Introduction to Molecular Spectroscopy*, McGraw-Hill Book Company, New York, 1962.

EYRING, H., J. WALTER, AND G. E. KIMBALL, *Quantum Chemistry*, John Wiley & Sons, Inc., New York, 1944.

HAMEKA, H. F., *Advanced Quantum Chemistry*, Addison-Wesley Publishing Company, Inc., Reading, Mass., 1965.

KAUZMANN, W., *Quantum Chemistry*, Academic Press, Inc., New York, 1957.

SLATER, J. C., *Quantum Theory of Atomic Structure*. Vol. I, McGraw-Hill Book Company, New York, 1960.

SLATER, J. C., *Quantum Theory of Molecules and Solids*, Vol. 3, McGraw-Hill Book Company, New York, 1967.

9

Atoms and Linear Molecules

9.1 INTRODUCTION

The group theory of atoms has a large and highly developed literature. Most of the definitive work is based upon the Lie group and Lie algebra descriptions of angular momentum, rather than upon point groups. To a lesser extent, the same is true for linear molecules. These groups have not been developed in the present work; consequently, this chapter presents a rather brief discussion of atoms and linear molecules based upon point groups. More advanced treatments can be found in the works listed in the bibliography to this chapter.

9.2 ATOMIC QUANTUM NUMBERS

Before we look at molecular electronic spectra, it will be helpful to briefly review the quantum mechanical selection rules for radiation-induced electronic transitions in atoms. The eigenstates of the electrons in an atom can be characterized by four *quantum numbers*: n, the *principal quantum number*; l, the *angular momentum* or *orbital quantum number*; m, the *azimuthal quantum number* (giving the component of the angular momentum vector along some arbitrary axis); and s, the *spin* (or *intrinsic angular momentum*) *quantum number*. This is usually reported as m_s, the component of s along the axis chosen for m. The only value that s can have for electrons is $\frac{1}{2}$, whereas m_s can have the values $\pm\frac{1}{2}$. In the hydrogen atom, with only one electron, for all practical purposes only the first three of these need be considered if no external forces are acting on the system. In polyelectron atoms, however, the spin angular momentum and orbital angular momentum interact with each other. The resulting total angular momentum determines the selection rules in atomic spectra. This total angular momentum **J** may conveniently be obtained as a vector quantity by vectorially adding the allowed values of the individual orbital angular momentum and spin angular momentum vectors for the various electrons in the atom. The particular method of doing this depends upon whether the magnitudes of the interactions between the spin angular momentum and the orbital angular momentum for a particular electron are greater than or smaller than the magnitudes of the interactions between the various orbital angular momenta and between the various spin angular momenta. The former case (referred to as *jj coupling*) occurs for atoms of heavy elements. The latter case (**LS** coupling or *Russell–Saunders coupling*) occurs for atoms of light elements. For intermediate elements the two types of interaction are of comparable magnitude; consequently, the construction of **J** vectors is much more complicated. For our purposes, a consideration of the **LS** coupling case will be sufficient to illustrate the principles of the application of group theory to atomic spectra.

9.3 THE HYDROGEN ATOM

The quantum mechanical solution of the hydrogen atom problem can be obtained completely with group theoretical techniques by using the four-dimensional rotation group **R**(4). The treatment more familiar to most chemists involves a separation of the problem into radial and angular variables in a three-dimensional coordinate system.

If we consider the hydrogen atom in spherical polar coordinates, its wave function ψ_{nlm} can be expressed as a product of a radial part $R_{nl}(r)$, and an angular part $Y_{lm}(\theta, \phi)$

$$\psi_{nlm}(r, \theta, \phi) = R_{nl}(r) Y_{lm}(\theta, \phi) \tag{9.1}$$

The radial part is dependent upon the principal quantum number n and the angular momentum quantum number l, while the angular function depends upon the angular momentum and azimuthal quantum numbers (l and m). The form of the $R_{nl}(r)$ function is a decaying exponential in r/n times a polynomial in r. The first term in each polynomial is a constant. The first term in the transition dipole between two states of differing n contains the integral

$$\left\langle \exp\left(-\frac{r}{n_1}\right) \middle| r \middle| \exp\left(-\frac{r}{n_2}\right) \right\rangle = \int_0^{\infty} r^3 \exp\left[-\left(\frac{1}{n_1} + \frac{1}{n_2}\right) r\right] dr \tag{9.2}$$

No value of n can make this integral vanish; consequently, there are no selection rules imposed on the allowed values of n in a transition. To reach the same conclusion by symmetry arguments, we realize that the r coordinate in spherical polar coordinates has no angular dependence [i.e., it transforms as the totally symmetric representation, $D^{(0)}$ in the $\mathbf{R}(3)$ point group]. The radial part of the wave function is also totally symmetrical (i.e., has no angular dependence), no matter what value of n is considered. Thus, $\mu_{nn'}$, $R_{nl}(r)$, and $R_{n'l}(r)$ all have the same irreducible representation in the $\mathbf{R}(3)$ point group, the one-dimensional $D^{(0)}$ representation. The requirement that $\mu_{nn'}$ not vanish requires that the product $\Gamma(R_{nl}) \times \Gamma(R_{n'l})$ contain $\Gamma(\mu)$. However, by the Clebsch-Gordan formula,

$$\Gamma(R_{nl}) \times \Gamma(R_{n'l}) = D^{(0)} \times D^{(0)} = D^{(0)} = \Gamma(\mu) \tag{9.3}$$

Thus, transitions involving any change of n are allowed.

Let us now consider the l values. For a given l value there are $(2l + 1)$ possible m values, all of which are degenerate (except when l equals zero). The irreducible representation corresponding to a given l value should therefore have a $(2l + 1)$ dimensionality. From Table 6.1 we see that $D^{(l)}$ is $(2l + 1)$-dimensional. Thus, the irreducible representation corresponding to a given value of l is $D_p^{(l)}$ (where p represents the g or u on inversion). The general position vector $\mathbf{r}$ is three-dimensional; therefore, the angular portion of $\boldsymbol{\mu}$ must transform as the three-dimensional $D_u^{(1)}$. For a transition between two states characterized by l and l' to be allowed, then, the product $D_p^{(l)} \times D_{p'}^{(l')}$ must contain $D_u^{(1)}$. However,

$$D_p^{(l)} \times D_{p'}^{(l')} = D_{p''}^{(|l-l'|)} + D_{p''}^{(|l-l'|+1)} + \ldots + D_{p''}^{(l+l'-1)} + D_{p''}^{(l+l')}$$

where $p'' = g$ if p and p' are the same, and u otherwise. In order for this to contain $D_u^{(1)}$, l must equal l' or $(l' \pm 1)$ [if l' is zero, only the $(l' \pm 1)$ condition is allowed]. Furthermore, if l equals l', the behavior to inversion is wrong. Thus, the l selection rules for a hydrogenic spectral transition are

$$\Delta l = \pm 1 \tag{9.4}$$

In actual fact, the inversion restriction is often violated and the $\Delta l = 0$ transition is seen. A radiation-induced spectral transition (or a spontaneous emission) in hydrogen can therefore involve any change in n; however, excitations that arise from the $1s$ ground state of hydrogen ($l = 0$) must go to an np state ($l = 1$). An excitation or an emission arising from an excited $np(l = 1)$, $nd(l = 2)$, $nf(l = 3)$, and so on, state can go to a state of an adjacent orbital type.

9.4 POLYELECTRON ATOMS

Let us now turn our attention to a polyelectron atom. The total wave function for an N electron atom is usually approximated by the product of the individual orbital functions of each electron:

$$\Psi = \psi_1(r_1, \theta_1, \phi_1)\psi_2(r_2, \theta_2, \phi_2) \ldots \psi_N(r_N, \theta_N, \phi_N) \tag{9.5}$$

The (perhaps reducible) representation for the total wave function must be the product of the irreducible representations of the individual one-electron functions:

$$\Gamma(\Psi) = \Gamma(\psi_1) \times \Gamma(\psi_2) \times \ldots \times \Gamma(\psi_N) \tag{9.6}$$

In addition, the permutational symmetry must be properly accounted for (see Section 7.11). We have already seen that the radial part of the wave function transforms as the totally symmetric representation; consequently, if, for the moment, we neglect spin, anything other than a totally symmetric representation could arise only from the l values of the various electrons. In other words,

$$\Gamma(L) = D^{(l_1)} \times D^{(l_2)} \times \ldots \times D^{(l_N)} \tag{9.7}$$

For the specific example of a two-electron case we have

$$\begin{aligned}\Gamma(L) &= D^{(l_1)} \times D^{(l_2)} = D^{(l_1 - l_2)} + D^{(l_1 - l_2 + 1)} + \ldots \times D^{(l_1 + l_2)} \\ &= \sum_L D^{(L)}\end{aligned} \tag{9.8}$$

where L can have any integer value from $|l_1 - l_2|$ to $l_1 + l_2$. If, however, the two electrons are associated with the same degenerate orbital function, permutational symmetry places limitations on the allowed L values. The total spatial symmetry of the various atomic states can be defined in terms of the L values. Each of the L values corresponds to a particular spectroscopic *term* (a word used to designate the components of angular momentum of a spectroscopic state). For polyelectron atoms in which Russell–Saunders coupling is applicable, the overall L values are constructed directly by chaining the direct products as in Eq. 9.7. The selection rules for changes in L in a spectral transition are the same as those for l shown in Eqs. 9.4, except that $\Delta L = 0$ is also allowed, since, in polyelectron atoms, different electronic configurations can give rise to the same L value, but with different behavior on inversion.

If electron spin is considered, the even-dimensioned $D^{(i)}$ representations are also required, owing to the fact that for an isolated electron, there are two possible equivalent spin states (having m_s values of $\pm\frac{1}{2}$). The total spin representation for a system of N unpaired spins involving Russell-Saunders coupling is

$$D^{(1/2)} \times D^{(1/2)} \times D^{(1/2)} \times \ldots = \sum_S D^{(S)} \tag{9.9}$$

where S can have values of zero to $N/2$ for even N or $\frac{1}{2}$ to $N/2$ for odd N. In the absence of an external magnetic field, pure spin transitions cannot be induced by electromagnetic radiation. Thus, the selection rule for such transitions is ΔS equals zero. If the spin and spatial parts of the wave function are considered together, the representation that it generates (again in the Russell–Saunders scheme) is

$$D^{(L)} \times D^{(S)} = \sum_J D^{(J)} \tag{9.10}$$

where J can have any value from $|L - S|$ to $(L + S)$. The values of J represent the total angular momentum (spin as well as orbital) of the system. Consideration of the selection rules again reveals that ΔJ must equal zero or ± 1 (but only ± 1 if J equals zero) for a transition to be symmetry-allowed. In summary, then, the selection rules for an atom for which Russell–Saunders coupling holds are

$$\Delta S = 0 \tag{9.11}$$

$$\begin{aligned} \Delta L &= 0, \pm 1 \quad \text{if } L \neq 0 \\ &= \pm 1 \quad \text{if } L = 0 \end{aligned} \tag{9.12}$$

$$\begin{aligned} \Delta J &= 0, \pm 1 \quad \text{if } J \neq 0 \\ &= \pm 1 \quad \text{if } J = 0 \end{aligned} \tag{9.13}$$

If spin-orbit interactions are so great that the LS coupling scheme breaks down, then the selection rules for ΔS and ΔL may be violated (this, for example, is why heavy atom systems sensitize singlet–triplet transitions in photochemical experiments). The selection rules for ΔJ are always valid, however, no matter what the coupling scheme is for orbital and spin angular momenta.

9.5 TERM SYMBOLS

Before leaving our discussion of atomic spectra, we might point out that the term symbols used by atomic spectroscopists (e.g., ${}^1S_0$, ${}^3P_0$, ${}^4F_{3/2}$, etc.) are notations of the values of S, L, and J for the particular state of the atom under consideration. The letter indicates the L value: S corresponds to an L value of zero, P to 1, D to 2, F to 3, and so on. The superscript equals $(2S + 1)$, the spin multiplicity. Thus, 1 indicates an S value of zero, 3 a value of 1, 4 a value of $\frac{3}{2}$, and so on. The subscript is the value of J.

When a number of terms can arise from a given ground-state electronic configuration, *Hund's rule* tells us that the most stable state will have the highest spin multiplicity. If more than one L value can be associated with a given S, the largest L corresponds to the most stable state. For cases with more than one J value for a given S and L, the largest J is the most stable if the electronic configuration is such that the incompletely filled level is more than half-filled, while the smallest J is the most stable if it is less than half-filled. Thus, the carbon ground state, with a $(1s)^2(2s)^2(2p)^2$ configuration, has singlet and triplet states (S of 0 and 1) and L values of 0, 1, or 2 (S, P, or D states). As we saw in Section 7.11, the Pauli-allowed states are ${}^3P$, ${}^1S$, and ${}^1D$. Including J values leads to ${}^3P_0$, ${}^3P_1$, ${}^3P_2$, ${}^1S_0$, and ${}^1D_2$ for the possible terms. The *ground state* (lowest energy) term is ${}^3P_0$, since the $2p$ level is less than half-filled. For oxygen, with a ground-state configuration of $(1s)^2(2s)^2(2p)^4$, the same term symbols are possible. Here, the ground state term is $^3P_2$, since the $2p$ level is more than half-full. [Note that, in general, if a level can accommodate N electrons, then the configurations with n and $(N - n)$ electrons give rise to the same terms. This is the *hole formalism*, and is valid not only for atoms, but for molecules and crystals as well.]

As a fairly complex detailed example of the construction of term symbols, let us consider element 23 (vanadium). Vanadium has a $(3d)^3$ electronic configuration in its ground state. All electrons below the $3d$ level are in closed shells; consequently, the allowed term symbols will be determined by the d electrons. The d orbitals transform as $D^{(2)}$ within $\mathbf{R}(3)$. We must properly adapt a product of three $D^{(2)}$ representations to the $\mathbf{S}(3)$ group (see Section 7.11). If we confine our attention to the lowest-energy state, we know it will have the maximum spin value of $\frac{3}{2}$. This corresponds to the [3] representation of $\mathbf{S}(3)$; thus, we must adapt $D^{(2)}$ to the complementary $[1^3]$ representation. The E and $C(\phi)$ characters of $\mathbf{R}(3)$ are all that are required. The $[1^3]$ representation is

$\mathbf{S}(3)$	(1^3)	$3(2, 1)$	$2(3)$
$[1^3]$	1	-1	1

(9.14)

The $D^{(2)}$ representation is

$\mathbf{R}(3)$	E	$C(\phi)$
$D^{(2)}$	5	$1 + 2\cos\phi + 2\cos 2\phi$

(9.15)

Thus, we have for the character of the identity

$$\begin{aligned}\chi^{[1^3]\alpha}(E) &= \tfrac{1}{6}\{(\chi(E))^3 - 3(\chi(E^2))(\chi(E)) + 2(\chi(E^3))\}\\ &= \tfrac{1}{6}\{125 - 75 + 10\} \\ &= 10\end{aligned} \tag{9.16}$$

For the character of the $C(\phi)$, we have

$$\chi^{[1^3]\alpha}(C(\phi)) = \tfrac{1}{6}\{(\chi(C(\phi)))^3 - 3(\chi(C(\phi)^2))(\chi(C(\phi))) + 2(\chi(C(\phi)^3))\} \tag{9.17}$$

The polynomials in $\cos n\phi$ can best be handled by taking the exponential equivalents

$$2\cos n\phi = e^{in\phi} + e^{-in\phi} \tag{9.18}$$

For example, if we let

$$X = 2\cos\phi = e^{i\phi} + e^{-i\phi} \tag{9.19}$$

$$Y = 2\cos 2\phi = e^{i2\phi} + e^{-i2\phi} \tag{9.20}$$

then

$$\begin{aligned}(\chi(C(\phi)))^3 &= (1 + X + Y)^3 \\ &= (1 + 3X + 3Y + 6XY + 3X^2 + 3Y^2 \\ &\quad + 3X^2Y + 3XY^2 + X^3 + Y^3)\end{aligned} \tag{9.21}$$

The individual terms are easily evaluated. Consider XY^2:

$$\begin{aligned}XY^2 &= (e^{i\phi} + e^{-i\phi})(e^{i2\phi} + e^{-i2\phi})^2 \\ &= e^{i5\phi} + e^{i3\phi} + 2e^{i\phi} + 2e^{-i\phi} + e^{-i3\phi} + e^{-i5\phi} \\ &= 4 \cos \phi + 2 \cos 3\phi + 2 \cos 5\phi\end{aligned} \tag{9.22}$$

The final result for $\chi^{[1^3]\alpha}(C(\phi))$ is

$$\begin{aligned}\chi^{[1^3]\alpha}(C(\phi)) &= \tfrac{1}{6}\{12 + 24 \cos \phi + 12 \cos 2\phi + 12 \cos 3\phi\} \\ &= 2 + 4 \cos \phi + 2 \cos 2\phi + 2 \cos 3\phi\end{aligned} \tag{9.23}$$

By inspection we see that, since the last term contains 2 cos 3ϕ, this must contain $D^{(3)}$. Subtracting this out, we have

$$\chi^{[1^3]\alpha}(C(\phi)) - \chi^{D^{(3)}}(C(\phi)) = 1 + 2 \cos \phi = \chi^{D^{(1)}}(C(\phi))$$

Thus, the allowed states with a spin of $\frac{3}{2}$ (quartet states) are ^4F and ^4P. Of these, the ^4F will be lower in energy, since it corresponds to the larger L value. For the ^4F state, J can range from $\frac{9}{2}$ down to $\frac{3}{2}$. A d^3 configuration is less than half-filled, so the term for the ground state of a neutral vanadium atom should be $^4F_{3/2}$.

Consider now the spectrum of vanadium. Transitions from $^4F_{3/2}$ to any of the ^4P levels are forbidden on the basis of ΔL, which would have to change by 2 units. The lowest directly observed transition must, then, involve a different electronic configuration. The energetically nearest orbitals are the $4p$ orbitals; consequently, the transition should be $4p \leftarrow 3d$. The excited-state configuration is now $(3d)^2(4p)$. To find the allowed term symbols for this, the two equivalent $3d$ electrons must be adapted to S(2); however, the $4p$ electron is no longer equivalent to any others. As a result, all combinations resulting from the coupling of the $4p$ electron are allowed. Transitions in which S changes are forbidden, so we must confine our attention to quartet states. This means that our two d electrons must be coupled to give triplets and the resulting triplets coupled with the $4p$ electron. For the d^2 configuration we can use the simple rule that in the $D^{(j)} \times D^{(j)}$, the even-indexed representations in the result are totally symmetrical and the odd-indexed representations are totally antisymmetrical if j is integer, while the converse is true if j is half-integer. Thus, since

$$D^{(2)} \times D^{(2)} = D^{(0)} + D^{(1)} + D^{(2)} + D^{(3)} + D^{(4)} \tag{9.24}$$

$D^{(1)}$ and $D^{(3)}$ are the antisymmetrical components of the product. These are the ones we want, since the triplet spin state is symmetrical. For the d^2 part of the configuration, we have ^3P and ^3F. If we couple these with the $4p$ electron, we have, for the orbital angular momentum,

$$\begin{aligned} D^{(1)} \times D^{(3)} &= D^{(2)} + D^{(3)} + D^{(4)} \\ p \text{ coupled to } F \rightarrow &\quad D + F + G \end{aligned} \tag{9.25}$$

$$\begin{aligned} D^{(1)} \times D^{(1)} &= D^{(0)} + D^{(1)} + D^{(2)} \\ p \text{ coupled to } P \rightarrow &\quad S + P + D \end{aligned} \tag{9.26}$$

The $(3d)^2(4p)$ configuration thus leads to ^4S, ^4P, ^4D, ^4F, and ^4G terms with appropriate J values. The lowest energy of these is probably $^4G_{5/2}$, although the ordering for excited states is not as regular as for ground states. The transition $^4G_{5/2} \leftarrow {}^4F_{9/2}$ is allowed on the basis of ΔS and ΔL, but forbidden on ΔJ. Transitions to $^4G_{7/2}$ or $^4G_{11/2}$ are completely allowed. Transitions to the other allowed states would also occur near in energy to this one.

Exercise 9.1*: If an atom is initially in the state given by the listed term, to which of the other states listed can it go by a normal spectral transition? Give the reasons for any that are forbidden.

Initial					
$^1S_0$	$^3S_1$	$^3P_0$	$^1P_1$	$^1D_2$	$^3P_1$
$^2D_{3/2}$	$^2D_{5/2}$	$^2S_{1/2}$	$^2P_{1/2}$	$^2F_{7/2}$	$^4P_{5/2}$
$^4S_{3/2}$	$^2S_{1/2}$	$^4P_{1/2}$	$^4D_{1/2}$	$^4P_{5/2}$	$^2P_{3/2}$
$^4P_{1/2}$	$^4P_{5/2}$	$^4D_{7/2}$	$^4D_{1/2}$	$^2P_{3/2}$	$^2S_{1/2}$

9.6 CRYSTAL-FIELD THEORY

The simplest theoretical model for describing the spectra of transition-metal complexes, *crystal-field theory*, is a simple perturbed atomic orbital theory. The relevant group theory involves no more than mapping the orbital representations of the central metal ion from the $\mathbf{R}_h(3)$ group onto the appropriate finite symmetry group of the complex. The splitting of the energy levels is then deduced from the electronic repulsion between the electrons on the ligands and those on the central metal. The model is extremely crude in that it neglects all bonding interactions between the metal and the ligands and all interactions among the ligands, yet it explains the most important features of the spectra and of the magnetism of such complexes.

The transition metals and their ions have partially filled d orbitals. The most important structure for the complexes is the octahedral structure. Mapping the

$D_g^{(2)}$ representation, the representation of the d orbitals in $\mathbf{R}_h(3)$, onto the **O** subgroup of the group of the octahedron, we have

O	E	$8C_3$	$6C_2'$	$6C_4$	$3C_2$
$D_g^{(2)}$	5	$1 + 2\cos 120° + 2\cos 240°$	$1 + 2\cos 180° + 2\cos 360°$	$1 + 2\cos 90° + 2\cos 180°$	$1 + 2\cos 180° + 2\cos 360°$
	(5	−1	1	−1	1)

(9.27)

This reducible representation reduces to $E + T_2$. The *gerade* behavior of $D_g^{(2)}$ requires the levels to be e_g and t_{2g}. Thus, the set of fivefold-degenerate d orbitals yield twofold and threefold degeneracies in $\mathbf{O}_h$. If the same treatment is carried out for $\mathbf{T}_d$, another important structure for transition-metal complexes, the mapping yields e and t_2 for the d-orbital representations.

If the magnetic moments of a series of octahedral complexes with differing numbers of d electrons are measured, the results indicate that three unpaired electrons must always be present before any pairing occurs. This indicates that the t_{2g} level must be lower in energy than the e_g level. For metal ions having four to seven d electrons, the magnetic moment depends upon the ligand. For example, for certain ligands a four-electron configuration will have a magnetic moment corresponding to two unpaired electrons which must arise from a $(t_{2g})^4$ configuration, while for other ligands there will be four unpaired electrons that must arise from a $(t_{2g})^3e_g$ configuration. This implies that with certain *strong-field ligands* the *crystal-field splitting* is greater than the *pairing energy* while with other *weak-field ligands*, the pairing energy is greater than the crystal-field splitting. This conclusion is in general agreement with the spectra. The strong-field ligands lead to higher-energy *d–d* electronic transitions on a given metal than do the weak-field ligands.

The experiments show that in tetrahedral complexes the e levels are lower in energy than the t_2 levels. With this modification, the magnetic and spectroscopic behavior with respect to strong-field and weak-field ligands parallels that for octahedral complexes.

The relative splitting of the levels in both cases can be rationalized from consideration of a representation of the metal d orbitals in a Cartesian coordinate system along with the geometric orientation of the ligands. Checking the character tables for $\mathbf{O}_h$ and $\mathbf{T}_d$, we see that d_{z^2} and $d_{x^2-y^2}$ orbitals transform as E_g or E representations, while d_{xz}, d_{yz}, and d_{xy} orbitals transform as T_{2g} or T_2. If the central metal atom were centered in a cube with the origin at the center, the d_{z^2} and $d_{x^2-y^2}$ orbitals (the e orbitals) would have their maxima directed toward the centers of the faces of the cube, while the t_2 orbitals (d_{xz}, d_{yz}, and d_{xy}) would have their maxima directed toward the midpoints of the edges. In an octahedral complex, the ligands are located in the centers of the faces of a cube (see Fig. 9.1). Thus, in an octahedral complex, electrons in e_g orbitals would be more repelled by electrons on the ligands than would electrons in t_{2g} orbitals. In a tetrahedral complex, none of the

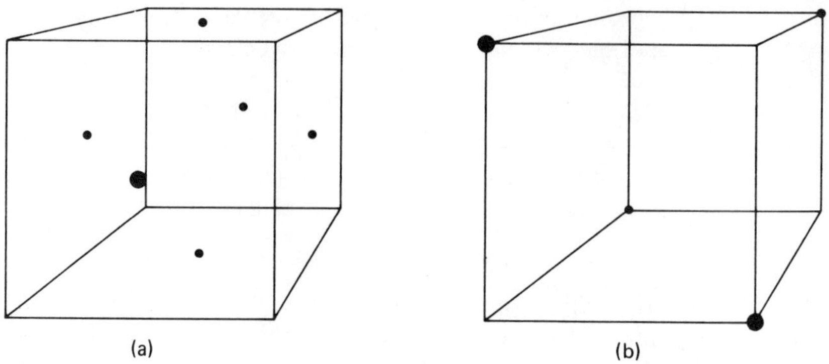

Fig. 9.1. Positions of ligands for (a) an octahedral complex and (b) a tetrahedral complex with reference to a cube.

orbitals are "pointed toward" the ligands, which are located on alternate corners of a cube. However, midpoints of edges are closer to corners than are centers of faces (by a factor of $2^{-1/2}$); therefore, electrons in t_2 orbitals are repelled more by the ligand electrons than are those in e orbitals.

Exercise 9.2*: Into what symmetries would d orbitals split in a field of $\mathbf{D}_{4h}$ symmetry? Try to deduce the order of the levels.

For an atom or ion having more than one electron in a degenerate level, the energy states in a crystal field are more complicated. If the term symbols for the atom or ion are known, the simplest way of finding the possible states in the crystal field is to map the representations of $\mathbf{R}_h(3)$ corresponding to the L values of the term symbols onto the point group of the crystal field. For example, in the last section we saw that a d^3 configuration allows ^4F and ^4P terms in spherical symmetry. The appropriate angular momentum representations are $D_g^{(3)}$ and $D_g^{(1)}$. The *gerade* behavior is due to the *gerade* behavior of the d orbitals. Mapping these onto an octahedral field ($\mathbf{O}_h$) yields

$$\mathbf{R}_h(3): \quad \mathbf{O}_h:$$

$$^4F \rightarrow {}^4A_{2g} + {}^4T_{1g} + {}^4T_{2g} \tag{9.28}$$

$$^4P \rightarrow {}^4T_{1g} \tag{9.29}$$

These are the possible quartet states for a d^3 configuration in an octahedral field. However, nothing is known about the relative energy ordering, except that the ground state is probably one of the states arising from the ^4F mapping.

An alternative approach is to deduce the electronic configuration in the crystal field. In an octahedral field, the three electrons of a d^3 configuration should all occupy t_{2g} orbitals in the lowest-energy state. If the T_{2g} representation is adapted to $[1^3]$ from $\mathbf{S}(3)$, the result is A_{2g}. Thus, the $^4A_{2g}$ state is the ground state. The other states arising from the mapping of the terms onto $\mathbf{O}_h$ arise from other configurations. The $(t_{2g})^2(e_g)$ configuration leads to T_{1g} and T_{2g} states, while the $(t_{2g})(e_g)^2$ configuration leads to a T_{1g} state.

9.7 THE WIGNER–ECKART THEOREM

Introduction

Although its development is beyond the scope of this text, the *Wigner–Eckart theorem* is extremely important in the group theoretical treatment of atoms, of crystal-field theory, and also of nuclear theory. Basically, the theorem provides a systematic method for coupling angular momenta. Many of the results were derived by Condon and Shortley in their 1935 book, *The Theory of Atomic Spectra*, without the explicit use of group theory.

In spherical symmetry, any operator can be expressed in terms of radial and angular parts. The angular part can be related to the spherical harmonics. It is convenient to define the operators as *tensor operators*. A one-electron tensor operator, T^l_m, where l is the rank and m is a specified component, has the same angular behavior as the spherical harmonic $Y_{lm}(\theta, \phi)$ (i.e., the angular behavior of atomic orbitals), but it may have a radial dependence. The l is analogous to an angular momentum quantum number, and the m to its z component.

The m dependence of an integral involving a tensor operator, T^k_q, is given by the Wigner–Eckart theorem. If we symbolically represent a one-electron function as $|\alpha jm\rangle$, where j is the angular momentum, m its z component, and α represents any other applicable quantum numbers, then

$$\langle \alpha_1 j_1 m_1 | T^k_q | \alpha_2 j_2 m_2 \rangle = (-1)^{j_1 - m_1} \begin{pmatrix} j_1 & k & j_2 \\ -m_1 & q & m_2 \end{pmatrix} \langle \alpha_1 j_1 \| T^k \| \alpha_2 j_2 \rangle \qquad (9.30)$$

In Eq. 9.30, $\langle \alpha_1 j_1 \| T^k \| \alpha_2 j_2 \rangle$ is referred to as a *reduced matrix element*, and is independent of m. The quantity in parentheses is commonly called a $3j$ *symbol*. We will use the term $3jm$ *symbol*, since it expresses an m dependence of one-electron angular momentum states labeled by the j's. Extensive tabulations of $3jm$ symbols are available in the literature (see the book by Rotenberg and coworkers listed in the bibliography). They are closely related to the V coefficients of Fano and Racah, and to the Clebsch-Gordan coefficients of Condon and Shortley. In fact, the phase choice of Eq. 9.30 is chosen to agree with the results of Condon and Shortley.

In addition to their utility in evaluating matrix elements in terms of reduced matrix elements, the $3jm$ symbols allow the coupling of two one-electron functions to give a properly symmetry adapted two-electron function. If the one-electron functions are written as $|j_i m_i\rangle$ and the two-electron functions as $|j_1 j_2; JM\rangle$, where J and M are the resultant total angular momentum and total z component, respectively, the relation is

$$|j_1 j_2; JM\rangle = \sum_{m_1} \sum_{m_2} |j_1 m_1\rangle |j_2 m_2\rangle (-1)^{j_2 - j_1 - M} (2J + 1)^{1/2} \begin{pmatrix} j_1 & j_2 & J \\ m & m & -M \end{pmatrix} \qquad (9.31)$$

This represents the coupling of two functions of given j to give a resultant function with a specified J and M. The j's and J are representation indices within $\mathbf{R}(3)$, while the M is a representation label in the two-dimensional rotation group, $\mathbf{R}(2)$. Thus, the adaptation involves the assigning of representation labels in two groups, one of which is a subgroup of the other. In recent years, the technique has been extended to include adaptation to the finite point groups.

Higher-order coupling coefficients can be defined for coupling more than two angular momenta. For example, $6j$ symbols give the coupling of three angular momenta, $9j$ symbols give the coupling of four, and so on. (These are closely related to the W and X coefficients, respectively, of Racah.)

We will present two applications of $3jm$ symbols: the coupling of two p electrons in an atom to give the allowed states, and the crystal-field splitting of an electron in a d orbital by an octahedral field. The reader is referred to the books in the bibliography for more detail and other applications.

The Coupling of Two p Electrons

The allowed states are ^3P, ^1D, and ^1S. We will consider the ^3P state. The possible overall M values from the orbital portion of this are 1, 0, and -1. We can symbolically represent these states as $|pp;11\rangle$, $|pp;10\rangle$, and $|pp;1\bar{1}\rangle$, respectively. (For notational convenience, the minus sign is placed over the M value.) Using Eq. 9.31, the first of these becomes (placing the minus signs over the m values)

$$\begin{aligned}
|pp;11\rangle = {} & |p1\rangle|p1\rangle(-1)^{(1-1-1)}(3)^{1/2}\begin{pmatrix} 1 & 1 & 1 \\ 1 & 1 & \bar{1} \end{pmatrix} \\
& + |p1\rangle|p0\rangle(-1)^{(1-1-1)}(3)^{1/2}\begin{pmatrix} 1 & 1 & 1 \\ 1 & 0 & \bar{1} \end{pmatrix} \\
& + |p1\rangle|p\bar{1}\rangle(-1)^{(1-1-1)}(3)^{1/2}\begin{pmatrix} 1 & 1 & 1 \\ 1 & \bar{1} & \bar{1} \end{pmatrix} \\
& + |p0\rangle|p1\rangle(-1)^{(1-1-1)}(3)^{1/2}\begin{pmatrix} 1 & 1 & 1 \\ 0 & 1 & \bar{1} \end{pmatrix} \\
& + |p0\rangle|p0\rangle(-1)^{(1-1-1)}(3)^{1/2}\begin{pmatrix} 1 & 1 & 1 \\ 0 & 0 & \bar{1} \end{pmatrix} \\
& + |p0\rangle|p\bar{1}\rangle(-1)^{(1-1-1)}(3)^{1/2}\begin{pmatrix} 1 & 1 & 1 \\ 0 & \bar{1} & \bar{1} \end{pmatrix} \\
& + |p\bar{1}\rangle|p1\rangle(-1)^{(1-1-1)}(3)^{1/2}\begin{pmatrix} 1 & 1 & 1 \\ \bar{1} & 1 & \bar{1} \end{pmatrix} \\
& + |p\bar{1}\rangle|p0\rangle(-1)^{(1-1-1)}(3)^{1/2}\begin{pmatrix} 1 & 1 & 1 \\ \bar{1} & 0 & \bar{1} \end{pmatrix} \\
& + |p\bar{1}\rangle|p\bar{1}\rangle(-1)^{(1-1-1)}(3)^{1/2}\begin{pmatrix} 1 & 1 & 1 \\ \bar{1} & \bar{1} & \bar{1} \end{pmatrix}
\end{aligned} \tag{9.32}$$

The $3jm$ symbols represent allowed couplings; therefore, the usual coupling rules must be satisfied in order for them to be nonvanishing. This means that J must be between $|j_1 - j_2|$ and $j_1 + j_2$ (zero and 2, in this case) and that $m_1 + m_2 + \bar{M}$ must equal zero (i.e., only states with $\sum m_i = M$ are allowed). The J values are satisfied for all terms in Eq. 9.32; however, only the second and fourth terms in the summation satisfy the M rule and are nonvanishing. From tables of $3jm$ symbols (see the collection by Rotenberg), we find that

$$\begin{pmatrix} 1 & 1 & 1 \\ 1 & 0 & \bar{1} \end{pmatrix} = -\frac{1}{\sqrt{6}} \tag{9.33a}$$

$$\begin{pmatrix} 1 & 1 & 1 \\ 0 & 1 & \bar{1} \end{pmatrix} = \frac{1}{\sqrt{6}} \tag{9.33b}$$

Thus, our desired function is

$$\begin{aligned} |pp;11\rangle &= \frac{\sqrt{3}}{\sqrt{6}}|p1\rangle|p0\rangle - \frac{\sqrt{3}}{\sqrt{6}}|p0\rangle|p1\rangle \\ &= \frac{1}{\sqrt{2}}(|p1\rangle|p0\rangle - |p0\rangle|p1\rangle) \end{aligned} \tag{9.34}$$

The other two can be constructed similarly, and are

$$|pp;10\rangle = \frac{1}{\sqrt{2}}(|p\bar{1}\rangle|p1\rangle - |p1\rangle|p\bar{1}\rangle) \tag{9.35}$$

$$|pp;1\bar{1}\rangle = \frac{1}{\sqrt{2}}(|p0\rangle|p\bar{1}\rangle - |p\bar{1}\rangle|p0\rangle) \tag{9.36}$$

These are, then, the two-electron ^3P states constructed as linear combinations of the appropriate one-electron p orbitals. The ^1S and ^1D states can be constructed similarly.

Octahedral Crystal-Field Splitting of a d Orbital

Crystal-field splitting is assumed to arise by the perturbation of an orbital by a collection of six point charges arranged in an octahedron around the central ion. We first need to find the form of the perturbation. Consider first one dimension, say x. A point charge, e, at a distance a along the positive x direction would contribute a potential of the form

$$V(a, x) = \frac{e}{[(x-a)^2]^{1/2}} \tag{9.37}$$

while one at a distance a along the negative x direction would contribute

$$V(\bar{a}, x) = \frac{e}{[(x+a)^2]^{1/2}} \tag{9.38}$$

The total perturbation would be the sum of the two. In three dimensions, a charge at a in the positive x direction would give

$$V((a, x), y, z) = \frac{e}{[(x - a)^2 + y^2 + z^2]^{1/2}} \tag{9.39}$$

while one at a along the negative x direction would give

$$V((\bar{a}, x), y, z) = \frac{e}{[(x + a)^2 + y^2 + z^2]^{1/2}} \tag{9.40}$$

Similar terms would arise for the y and z directions. The overall octahedral perturbation would be the sum of the resulting six terms:

$$\begin{aligned} V(x, y, z) = {} & V((a, x), y, z) + V((\bar{a}, x), y, z) + V(x, (a, y), z) + V(x, (\bar{a}, y), z) \\ & + V(x, y, (a, z)) + V(x, y, (\bar{a}, z)) \end{aligned} \tag{9.41}$$

(where $\bar{a}$ signifies that the charge is along the negative coordinate direction). Each of the terms can be expanded in a Taylor's series. For example,

$$V((\bar{a}, x), y, z) = \frac{e}{a}\left(1 - \frac{x}{a} - \frac{r^2}{2a^2} + \frac{3x^2}{2a^2} + \dots\right) \tag{9.42}$$

If such an expansion is carried out for each term, and the results are combined in terms of like-order polynomials, the odd-powered terms cancel because of having opposite signs in the a and $\bar{a}$ terms. The quadratic term will have spherical symmetry. The first term not having spherical symmetry will be the fourth-order polynomial

$$V^4(x, y, z) = \frac{35e}{4a^5}(x^4 + y^4 + z^4 - \tfrac{3}{5}r^4) \tag{9.43}$$

If, now, x, y, and z are replaced by their r, θ, and ϕ equivalents, we can find, after some manipulation of trigonometric identities, that

$$x^4 + y^4 + z^4 - \tfrac{3}{5}r^4 = \frac{4\sqrt{\pi}r^4}{15}[Y_{40} + (\tfrac{5}{14})^{1/2}(Y_{44} + Y_{4\bar{4}})] \tag{9.44}$$

where the Y_{lm} are the spherical harmonics (in terms of θ and ϕ). Thus, our perturbation contains r, a, and some numerical factors, all multiplied times the angular dependence of Eq. 9.44. We will express it as

$$V^4 = B_4[T^4_0 + (\tfrac{5}{14})^{1/2}(T^4_4 + T^4_{\bar{4}})] \tag{9.45}$$

where the T^k_q are tensor operators, and the B_4 absorbs the radial dependence and the numerical constants.

The problem is now to evaluate the expectation value of V^4 with respect to a set of d orbitals. Equation 9.30 can be used directly. The d orbitals correspond to a j value of 2. The m values can range from -2 to 2. The j selection rule for the $3jm$

symbol tells us that the matrix element is nonvanishing for $0 \le k \le 4$. Higher-order contributions cannot occur. The m selection rule tells us that if m_1 equals m_2, q must equal zero, or that if $m_1 \ne m_2$, q must equal $m_1 - m_2$. Thus, the only allowed matrix elements are $\langle 22|T_0^4|22\rangle$, $\langle 2\bar{2}|T_0^4|2\bar{2}\rangle$, $\langle 21|T_0^4|21\rangle$, $\langle 2\bar{1}|T_0^4|2\bar{1}\rangle$, $\langle 20|T_0^4|20\rangle$, $\langle 22|T_4^4|2\bar{2}\rangle$, and $\langle 2\bar{2}|T_4^4|22\rangle$. Furthermore, the symmetry properties of the $3jm$ symbols show that the terms $\langle j_1 m_1|T_q^k|j_2 m_2\rangle$ and $\langle j_1 \bar{m}_1|T_{-q}^k|j_2 \bar{m}_2\rangle$ are equal. We are thus left with only four terms to evaluate. These are as follows:

$$\begin{aligned}\langle 22|T_0^4|22\rangle &= (-1)^{(2-2)}\begin{pmatrix}2 & 4 & 2\\ \bar{2} & 0 & 2\end{pmatrix}\langle 2\|T^4\|2\rangle \\ &= \frac{1}{\sqrt{2\cdot 9\cdot 5\cdot 7}}\langle 2\|T^4\|2\rangle\end{aligned} \tag{9.46}$$

$$\begin{aligned}\langle 21|T_0^4|21\rangle &= (-1)^{(2-1)}\begin{pmatrix}2 & 4 & 2\\ \bar{1} & 0 & 1\end{pmatrix}\langle 2\|T^4\|2\rangle \\ &= \frac{-2\sqrt{2}}{\sqrt{9\cdot 5\cdot 7}}\langle 2\|T^4\|2\rangle \\ &= -4\langle 22|T_0^4|22\rangle\end{aligned} \tag{9.47}$$

$$\begin{aligned}\langle 20|T_0^4|20\rangle &= (-1)^{(2-0)}\begin{pmatrix}2 & 4 & 2\\ 0 & 0 & 0\end{pmatrix}\langle 2\|T^4\|2\rangle \\ &= \frac{\sqrt{2}}{\sqrt{5\cdot 7}}\langle 2\|T^4\|2\rangle \\ &= 6\langle 22|T_0^4|22\rangle\end{aligned} \tag{9.48}$$

$$\begin{aligned}\left(\frac{5}{14}\right)^{1/2}\langle 22|T_4^4|22\rangle &= \left(\frac{5}{14}\right)^{1/2}(-1)^{(2-2)}\begin{pmatrix}2 & 4 & 2\\ \bar{2} & 4 & \bar{2}\end{pmatrix}\langle 2\|T^4\|2\rangle \\ &= (\tfrac{5}{14})^{1/2}\,\tfrac{1}{3}\langle 2\|T^4\|2\rangle \\ &= 5\langle 22|T_0^4|22\rangle\end{aligned} \tag{9.49}$$

Note that two of these, $\langle 21|T_0^4|21\rangle$ (which is degenerate with $\langle 2\bar{1}|T_0^4|2\bar{1}\rangle$) and $\langle 20|T_0^4|20\rangle$, will correspond to independent energy levels. The others lead to a 2×2 secular determinant involving the $|22\rangle$ and $|2\bar{2}\rangle$ states. The energy quantity $\langle B_4\rangle\langle 22|T_0^4|22\rangle$, where $\langle B_4\rangle$ is the expectation value of B_4, is defined as D_q. (The experimental definition is that $10D_q$ is the energy splitting between the e_g and t_{2g} levels in an octahedral field.) The roots of the determinant are $6D_q$, associated with a state that is $(1/\sqrt{2})(|22\rangle + |2\bar{2}\rangle)$, and $-4D_q$ for the state $(1/\sqrt{2})(|22\rangle - |2\bar{2}\rangle)$. Thus, the triply degenerate t_{2g} level has an energy of $-4D_q$, while the doubly degenerate e_g level has an energy of $6D_q$. The energies and one-electron states are tabulated in Table 9.1.

Table 9.1. Crystal-field states and energies for a d^1 electronic configuration in an octahedral field

Energy[a]	O_h Symmetry Label	State in Terms of L and M[b]
$6D_q$	E_g	$\|20\rangle$
		$\frac{1}{\sqrt{2}}(\|22\rangle + \|2\bar{2}\rangle)$
$-4D_q$	T_{2g}	$\|21\rangle$
		$\|2\bar{1}\rangle$
		$\frac{1}{\sqrt{2}}(\|22\rangle - \|2\bar{2}\rangle)$

[a] Frequently, the difference between these, $10D_q$, is referred to as Δ.

[b] Any linear combination of the degenerate states is also an acceptable state.

To handle other symmetries, the form of the perturbation in the appropriate field would have to be determined. For orbitals of higher l than the d orbitals, terms involving higher-order polynomials would be required. Otherwise, the procedure would be the same as outlined.

9.8 LINEAR MOLECULES

The $D_{\infty h}$ and $C_{\infty v}$ Point Groups

For describing the electronic spectra of molecules it is convenient to describe the total molecular electronic wave function as a product of one-electron functions similar to the atomic case shown previously (Eq. 9.5):

$$\Psi_{\text{molecular}} = \psi_1^{\text{MO}}(x_1, y_1, z_1)\psi_2^{\text{MO}}(x_2, y_2, z_2)\ldots\psi_N^{\text{MO}}(x_N, y_N, z_N) \tag{9.50}$$

These one-electron functions can be assumed to describe molecular orbitals which are completely analogous to the atomic orbitals we have discussed. The representation for the total molecular wave function is the product of the representations of the individual orbitals:

$$\Gamma(\Psi) = \Gamma(\psi_1^{\text{MO}}) \times \Gamma(\psi_2^{\text{MO}}) \times \ldots \Gamma(\psi_N^{\text{MO}}) \tag{9.51}$$

This will again have to be adapted to permutational symmetry. Molecules are not spherically symmetrical. As a consequence of this, the wave functions cannot, in general, be separated into radial and angular portions. Consequently, any selection rules must usually take into account all three coordinates of some convenient coordinate system. The only exceptions to this are for linear molecules. All linear molecules belong to one of two point groups: $\mathbf{D}_{\infty h}$ or $\mathbf{C}_{\infty v}$ (those having a plane of symmetry perpendicular to the molecular axis and those not having such a plane of symmetry). These groups include all diatomic molecules as well as a number of important polyatomic molecules, such as carbon dioxide, hydrogen cyanide, and acetylene.

For direct quantum mechanical calculations of the electronic wave functions of diatomic molecules, the elliptical coordinate system is usually the most convenient system to use. For describing the symmetry properties of the electronic wave functions of these as well as all other linear molecules, however, the cylindrical coordinate system is more convenient. The coordinates in the cylindrical system are z, a line extending in both positive and negative directions from some origin (in linear molecules this contains the molecular axis and usually has the origin at the center of the molecule); r, the perpendicular distance from z; and ϕ, the angle of rotation about z (see Fig. 9.2). The allowed values of z run from $-\infty$ to $+\infty$, those of r from 0 to ∞, and ϕ from 0 to 2π. Just as in the atomic case, r has no directional properties, and hence can cause no restrictions on the selection rules. Both z and ϕ do have directional properties, however. The z coordinate changes sign at the origin, while the ϕ coordinate describes angular motion parallel to the xy plane. The z coordinate (and consequently, the z component of the transition dipole) must transform as a one-dimensional irreducible representation. The ϕ coordinate (which determines both the x and y components of the transition dipole) must transform as a two-dimensional irreducible representation.

Tables 9.2 and 9.3 give the character tables for the $\mathbf{D}_{\infty h}$ and $\mathbf{C}_{\infty v}$ point groups. These are infinite-dimensional, since any angle ϕ represents an allowed symmetry element. Notice that in both cases there are one-dimensional representations designated by the symbol Σ, while all the other representations are two-dimensional. The one-dimensional representations have 1 for the character of the $C(\phi)$ element. The two-dimensional representations have $2 \cos \lambda\phi$ for the character of $C(\phi)$, where λ is a positive integer (note that if λ were zero, $\cos \lambda\phi$ would equal unity). The $2C(\phi)$ for the class refer to rotations in the $+$ and $-$ directions. The number λ is analogous to the index of the representations in the $\mathbf{R}(3)$ group. Physically, molecular orbitals having symmetries corresponding to different values of λ have different values of angular momentum about the z axis similar to the l values of

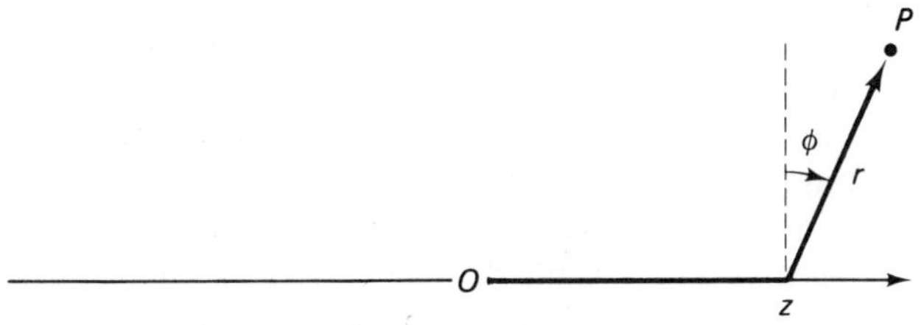

Fig. 9.2. Schematic representation of a point P with cylindrical coordinates Z, r, and ϕ.

Table 9.2. Character table for the $\mathbf{D}_{\infty h}$ point group

$\mathbf{D}_{\infty h}$	E	$2C(\phi)$	C_2	σ_h	$2S(\phi)$	i	σ_v
Σ_g^+	1	1	1	1	1	1	1
Σ_u^+	1	1	-1	-1	-1	-1	1
Σ_g^-	1	1	-1	1	1	1	-1
Σ_u^-	1	1	1	-1	-1	-1	-1
Π_g	2	$2\cos\phi$	0	-2	$-2\cos\phi$	2	0
Π_u	2	$2\cos\phi$	0	2	$2\cos\phi$	-2	0
Δ_g	2	$2\cos 2\phi$	0	2	$2\cos 2\phi$	2	0
Δ_u	2	$2\cos 2\phi$	0	-2	$-2\cos 2\phi$	-2	0
Φ_g	2	$2\cos 3\phi$	0	-2	$-2\cos 3\phi$	2	0
Φ_u	2	$2\cos 3\phi$	0	2	$2\cos 3\phi$	-2	0
Γ_g^λ	2	$2\cos\lambda\phi$	0	$(-1)^\lambda \times 2$	$(-1)^\lambda \times 2\cos\lambda\phi$	2	0
Γ_u^λ	2	$2\cos\lambda\phi$	0	$(-1)^{(\lambda-1)} \times 2$	$(-1)^{(\lambda-1)} \times 2\cos\lambda\phi$	-2	0

Table 9.3. Character table for the $\mathbf{C}_{\infty v}$ point group

$\mathbf{C}_{\infty v}$	E	$2C(\phi)$	$\infty\sigma_v$
Σ^+	1	1	1
Σ^-	1	1	-1
Π	2	$2\cos\phi$	0
Δ	2	$2\cos 2\phi$	0
Φ	2	$2\cos 3\phi$	0
$\vdots$			
Γ^λ	2	$2\cos\lambda\phi$	0

atomic orbitals. The notations Σ, Π, Φ, and so on, for the irreducible representations in the $\mathbf{D}_{\infty h}$ and $\mathbf{C}_{\infty v}$ point groups are generalizations of the S, P, D, F, and so on, notation from atomic spectroscopy. The $+$ and $-$ superscripts refer, respectively, to symmetric and antisymmetric behavior with respect to the σ_v's. As usual, the g and u subscripts in the representations of the $\mathbf{D}_{\infty h}$ point group refer to symmetric and antisymmetric behavior with respect to the point of inversion.

9.9 MOLECULAR ELECTRONIC STATES

In molecular electronic spectroscopy almost all of the usually observed transitions are between the ground electronic state (the lowest-energy state) of the molecule and an excited state that arises from the promotion of one electron from some particular molecular orbital to a higher-energy molecular orbital. In constructing the orbital occupancy for the ground state of a molecule, the *aufbau* (building up) principle holds just as it does in atoms. That is, each succeedingly higher-energy molecular orbital is filled, in accordance with the Pauli principle (two electrons in the same spatial orbital must have opposing spins), until all the electrons have been accounted for. Most common stable molecules have singlet ground electronic states (no unpaired electrons or $\sum m_s = 0$), although there are important exceptions such as O_2 (triplet) and NO_2 (doublet). For molecules with singlet ground states, every occupied spatial orbital is doubly occupied. The molecule is said to be a *closed-shell system.* This means that, in the direct product representation of the molecular electronic wave function within the point group of the molecule, if a given representation appears once, it must appear a second time. Thus, the product representation is a series of products of direct squares. This means that the electronic wave function for a molecule with a singlet ground state must transform as the totally symmetric representation within the point group of the molecule. In molecules with one or more partially occupied orbitals (*open shells*), such as molecules whose ground states have a spin multiplicity of other than unity and excited states of molecules with a singlet ground state, the representation describing the overall symmetry of the state is the product of the representations of the singly occupied spatial orbitals. For example, in its ground state, the hydrogen molecule has a doubly occupied σ_g^+ orbital. The symmetry of this state is the totally symmetric Σ_g^+. (Note that, by convention, orbital symmetries are represented by lowercase symbols while uppercase symbols are reserved to express the overall symmetry of the system. The orbitals can also be classified according to their angular momentum, or λ, values and the states according to total angular momentum, or Λ.) In the first excited state, one of the electrons is promoted to an orbital of σ_u^+ symmetry. The state symmetry is then

$$\begin{aligned}\Gamma &= \Gamma(\sigma_g^+) \times \Gamma(\sigma_u^+) \\ &= \Sigma_u^+\end{aligned} \tag{9.52}$$

This promotion represents a transition that is allowed via μ_{nm}^z. By convention, in writing such transitions the higher-energy state is listed first and the direction of the transition by an arrow (i.e., $\Sigma_u^+ \leftarrow \Sigma_g^+$). In the ground state of the oxygen molecule there is a degenerate pair of π_g orbitals containing two electrons. That is, two electrons are in singly occupied orbitals, each of π_g symmetry. All of the other orbitals are doubly occupied. The irreducible representation is

$$\Gamma(O_2) = \Gamma(\pi_g) \times \Gamma(\pi_g) \tag{9.53}$$

If this direct product is constructed, the representation becomes

$\mathbf{D}_{\infty h}$	E	$2C(\phi)$	C_2	σ_h	$2S(\phi)$	i	σ_v
$\Gamma(O_2)$	4	$4\cos^2\phi$	0	4	$4\cos^2\phi$	4	0

or

$\Gamma(O_2)$	4	$2 + 2\cos 2\phi$	0	4	$2 + 2\cos 2\phi$	4	0

(9.54)

where in the second version of the representation, $4\cos^2\phi$ has been resolved into the indicated trigonometric identity. It can be seen by inspection that

$$\Gamma(O_2) = \Sigma_g^+ + \Sigma_g^- + \Delta_g \tag{9.55}$$

These represent the three spatial symmetries that the $(\pi_g)^2$ configuration of oxygen can have. Consideration of the spins yields the possibility of singlet and triplet states. The assignment of these involves a simple, straightforward application of the methods of Section 7.11. Since we already know the possible representations, we need only determine $\chi(C(\phi))$ to distinguish between the Σ and Δ states and $\chi(\sigma_v)$ to distinguish between the Σ^+ and Σ^- states. Furthermore, since only singlet and triplet states are possible, once one of these is determined, the remaining representations will belong to the other.

Consider the singlet state. The permutational symmetry is antisymmetric; consequently, the spatial function must be symmetric (i.e., it must transform under the operations of **S**(2) as the representation [2]). Application of Eq. 7.90 yields, for $\chi^{[2]\alpha}(C(\phi))$,

$$\begin{aligned}\chi^{[2]\alpha}(C(\phi)) &= \tfrac{1}{2}\{1 \times 1 \times [\chi(C(\phi))]^2 + 1 \times 1 \times [\chi(C(\phi)^2)]\} \\ &= \tfrac{1}{2}\{1 \times 1 \times [2 \cos \phi]^2 + 1 \times 1 \times [2 \cos 2\phi]\} \\ &= \tfrac{1}{2}\{4 \cos^2 \phi + 2 \cos 2\phi\} \\ &= 1 + 2 \cos 2\phi\end{aligned} \tag{9.56a}$$

using the identity $2 \cos^2 \phi = 1 + \cos 2\phi$. For $\chi^{[2]\alpha}(\sigma_v)$, we have

$$\begin{aligned}\chi^{[2]\alpha}(\sigma_v) &= \tfrac{1}{2}\{1 \times 1 \times [\chi(\sigma_v)]^2 + 1 \times 1 \times [\chi(E)]\} \\ &= \tfrac{1}{2}\{0 + 2\} \\ &= 1\end{aligned} \tag{9.56b}$$

From 9.56a we see that the singlet states are Σ and Δ, and from 9.56b, that the Σ state is Σ^+. Thus, the $(\pi_g)^2$ states of O_2 are ${}^1\Sigma_g^+$, ${}^1\Delta_g$, and ${}^3\Sigma_g^-$. Of these, the ${}^3\Sigma_g^-$ state is of the lowest energy, as would be expected from Hund's rule.

As previously mentioned, the different λ values for the molecular orbitals correspond to different values of orbital angular momentum about the molecular axis. This is very analogous to the l quantum number in atomic systems. The angular "shape" of molecular orbitals with various λ values, when viewed down the molecular axis, matches the angular shape of atomic orbitals with corresponding l values. Thus, an atomic orbital with an l value of zero (an s orbital) is spherically symmetrical; a molecular orbital with a λ value of zero (a σ orbital) is cylindrically symmetrical. An atomic orbital with an l value of 1 (a p orbital) has one angular node and is antisymmetric with respect to reflection through the origin; a molecular orbital with a λ value of 1 (a π orbital) has one angular node and is antisymmetric with respect to reflection through the molecular plane. The correlation is similar for higher l and λ values. The concept of σ, π, δ, and so on, molecular orbitals for diatomic molecules has been generalized to polyatomic systems. If a molecular orbital has σ (or π or δ, etc.) symmetry between two adjacent atoms in a molecule, it is designated as a σ (or π or δ, etc.) orbital even though it may extend over many atoms in a molecule which has much lower symmetry than $\mathbf{D}_{\infty h}$ or $\mathbf{C}_{\infty v}$.

9.10 REPRESENTATIONS OF THE DIPOLE OPERATOR AND SELECTION RULES

The dipole moment operator can be conveniently divided into its x, y, and z components. These three components individually transform as the respective Cartesian coordinates,

$$\hat{\mu} = \hat{\mu}^x + \hat{\mu}^y + \hat{\mu}^z \tag{9.57}$$

A transition between two states will be allowed if the expectation value of any one of these between the two states does not equal zero (see Section 8.6). In transforming to cylindrical coordinates the z coordinate is still an independent variable; consequently, μ_{nm}^z may be determined separately from the other components. The x and y coordinates, however, are not mutually independent. They both depend on r and ϕ; consequently, they must be handled together. The z component of the transition dipole transforms as a one-dimensional irreducible representation. This must be one of the Σ representations. The z coordinate, being a line, must be symmetric with respect to σ_v; consequently, the representation is Σ^+. This is sufficient to determine the representation in the $\mathbf{C}_{\infty v}$ point group. There are, however, other symmetry elements in the $\mathbf{D}_{\infty h}$ point group. If the origin of the z coordinate is contained in the σ_h element (as it is in the most symmetrical choice of a coordinate system), it changes sign on inversion. Consequently, the irreducible representation corresponding to μ_{nm}^z in the $\mathbf{D}_{\infty h}$ point group is Σ_u^+. Thus, a transition from state n to state m is allowed via μ_{nm}^z if the product $\Gamma(\Psi_n) \times \Gamma(\Psi_m)$ contains Σ_u^+ when the molecule belongs to the $\mathbf{D}_{\infty h}$ point group; or Σ^+ when the molecule belongs to the $\mathbf{C}_{\infty v}$ point group.

If, in transforming from Cartesian to cylindrical coordinates, the positive x axis is taken to be the origin for ϕ, the x component of r is $r \cos \phi$. If the positive y axis had been chosen as the origin, the y component of r would have been $r \cos \phi$. Thus, x and y must transform on rotation by ϕ as $\cos \phi$. This means that the x and y coordinates, and consequently, μ_{nm}^x and μ_{nm}^y, must transform as a Π representation. This is sufficient to classify these in the $\mathbf{C}_{\infty v}$ point group. In the $\mathbf{D}_{\infty h}$ point group the behavior with respect to inversion must be considered. Both x and y change sign on inversion; consequently, they transform as the Π_u representation. An electronic transition is allowed via μ_{nm}^x and μ_{nm}^y if the product $\Gamma(\Psi_n) \times \Gamma(\Psi_m)$ contains Π_u when the molecule belongs to the $\mathbf{D}_{\infty h}$ point group; or Π when it belongs to the $\mathbf{C}_{\infty v}$ point group.

The Σ^+ representation is the totally symmetric representation within the $\mathbf{C}_{\infty v}$ point group. For the product $\Gamma(\Psi_n) \times \Gamma(\Psi_m)$ to contain this, the representation of μ^z, $\Gamma(\Psi_n)$ must equal $\Gamma(\Psi_m)$ (since the only direct product containing the totally symmetric representation is the direct square). In other words, for a transition to be allowed via μ_{nm}^z, $\Delta\Lambda$ must equal zero. For determining the selection rules for μ_{nm}^x and μ_{nm}^y, we must find the limitations on the direct products that will yield a representation containing Π. This can be done by considering the product of the characters of $C(\phi)$. This product must contain $\cos \phi$ or $\cos(-\phi)$ for the product representation to contain Π. The product of these characters for states n and m will be of the form $\cos n\phi \cos m\phi$. If, however, we set m equal to $(n - a)$, we have, by trigonometric identity,

$$\cos n\phi \cos (n - a)\phi = \tfrac{1}{2}[\cos a\phi + \cos (2n - a)\phi] \tag{9.58}$$

The only general way that this product can contain $\cos \phi$ or $\cos(-\phi)$ is for a to equal ± 1. Thus, the selection rule for a transition to be allowed via μ_{nm}^x or μ_{nm}^y is

$$\Delta\Lambda = \pm 1 \tag{9.59}$$

The selection rules within the $\mathbf{D}_{\infty h}$ point group can be found analogously. For a transition to be allowed via μ_{nm}^z, Eq. 9.58 must contain a constant (ϕ-independent) term. This can only happen if a equals zero ($\cos a\phi$ equals unity). Thus, again for a μ_{nm}^z transition to be allowed, $\Delta\Lambda$ must equal zero. Similarly, for x- and y-polarized transitions, $\Delta\Lambda$ must equal ± 1. This is not enough to fully determine the selection rules in this case, however. The transition dipole operators all belong to *ungerade* representations; consequently, the product representation $\Gamma(\Psi_n) \times \Gamma(\Psi_m)$ must be *ungerade*. This can only happen if either Ψ_n or Ψ_m is *gerade* and the other is *ungerade*. Thus, the two states involved in the transition *must* have *different behavior with respect to the point of inversion.* In any molecular system, the spin selection rule is the same as in atomic systems: ΔS must equal zero (unless there are heavy atoms present to cause a breakdown of the selection rules).

9.11 POLARIZATION OF TRANSITIONS

We have stated that a spectral transition may be allowed via the x, y, or z component of the transition dipole. These can actually be experimentally distinguished from one another. If the spectral study is being conducted with plane-polarized light, the radiation can only interact with the components of the dipole vectors oriented parallel to the electric field vectors of the radiation. If the substance being studied is in a fluid medium (liquid or gas), there will always be a certain fraction of the dipole vectors oriented in a proper direction to interact with the radiation field vector. If, however, the substance being studied is in the crystalline state, it might be possible to line the crystal up in such a fashion that the x, y, and z components can be separately brought into parallel with the plane of the electric field vectors. In this case, the component of the transition dipole causing the interaction can be identified. When a given transition is allowed via only a particular component of the dipole vector, it is said to be *polarized* along the corresponding coordinate (i.e., x-polarized, y-polarized, or z-polarized).

Exercise 9.3: State which of the following molecular states can be reached from the indicated starting state and give the polarization of each allowed transition.

From	To				
$^1\Sigma_g^+$	$^1\Sigma_g^+$,	$^1\Sigma_u^+$,	$^1\Pi_g$,	$^3\Pi_u$,	$^1\Delta_u$
$^1\Pi_u$	$^1\Sigma_g^+$,	$^1\Sigma_u^+$,	$^1\Pi_g$,	$^3\Pi_u$,	$^1\Delta_u$
$^3\Delta_g$	$^1\Sigma_g^+$,	$^3\Sigma_u^+$,	$^3\Pi_g$,	$^3\Pi_u$,	$^3\Delta_u$
$^3\Sigma^-$	$^3\Sigma^-$,	$^1\Sigma^+$,	$^3\Pi$,	$^3\Delta$,	$^3\Phi$
$^1\Phi$	$^1\Phi$,	$^1\Pi$,	$^1\Delta$,	$^1\Sigma^+$,	$^3\Delta$
$^2\Delta$	$^2\Delta$,	$^4\Sigma^+$,	$^2\Pi$,	$^2\Phi$,	$^2\Sigma^-$

9.12 ROTATIONAL SPECTRA

Since molecules are not spherically symmetrical, they are capable of rotating about one or more axes to yield a net angular momentum. This net angular momentum is quantized; consequently, molecules are capable of existing in different rotational states. The quantum mechanical solution to the problem of a rigid rotor with a moment of inertia I (a reasonable approximation of a diatomic molecule) yields the energy expression

$$E_J = \frac{h^2}{8\pi^2 I} J(J+1) \tag{9.60}$$

in terms of the quantum number J. The functional form of the rotational wave function is exactly the same as the angular dependence of the electronic wave function of the hydrogen atom. Thus, as might be expected, the symmetry restrictions on radiation-induced transitions between rotational energy levels can be deduced from the use of the **R**(3) point group and the Clebsch–Gordan formula. The requirement is that the direct product $\Gamma(\psi_J) \times \Gamma(\psi_{J'})$ must contain $D^{(1)}$, just as for the previous cases. However,

$$\Gamma(\psi_J) \times \Gamma(\psi_{J'}) = D^{(J)} \times D^{(J')} \tag{9.61}$$

$$= D^{(J+J')} + D^{(J+J'-1)} + \ldots + D^{|J-J'|} \tag{9.61a}$$

As before, the summation of Eq. 9.61a contains $D^{(1)}$ only if ΔJ equals zero or ± 1. For molecules with only one moment of inertia (i.e., linear molecules), a ΔJ value of zero means that there is no change of rotational state; that is, it corresponds to no transition at all. Thus, the only meaningful selection rule for such rotational transitions is

$$\Delta J = \pm 1 \tag{9.62}$$

The rotational energy states are sufficiently close in energy that there is significant thermal population of excited rotational levels. As a consequence, transitions to both higher and lower J values occur with high probability. Also, the transitions do not all originate from a common state but from a thermal distribution of states. This makes microwave spectra considerably more complicated than might at first be thought.

Within the rigid rotor approximation, changes in the rotational state produce no changes in the internal coordinates of any of the particles (nuclei or electrons) of the molecule. Consequently, the transition dipole is equal to the permanent dipole moment of the molecule. This means that unless the molecule has a permanent dipole moment, the magnitude of the transition dipole is zero. In such cases (which include all molecules belonging to the $\mathbf{D}_{\infty h}$ point group), there can be no mechanism for direct interaction of the radiation with the rotational states of the molecule. In other words, no microwave spectrum can be observed if the molecule does not have a permanent dipole moment. For $\mathbf{C}_{\infty v}$ molecules a spectrum occurs, and the rotational selection rule is $\Delta J = \pm 1$, where J is the angular momentum quantum number. Rotational spectra of $\mathbf{D}_{\infty h}$ molecules can be observed by Raman techniques.

9.13 VIBRATIONAL SPECTRA

A convenient way to describe the symmetry properties of the vibrational states of a molecule is in terms of a set of parallel internal Cartesian coordinate systems, one system centered on each atom of the molecule. Any motion of the system can be defined in terms of the displacements of the atoms along these coordinates. Such a system for a diatomic molecule is shown in Fig. 9.3. Translations of the entire molecule are represented by equal translations along each coordinate of each atom. Rotations can be represented by combinations of motions in the various planes defined by the axes or as rotations about the axes of still another coordinate system located at the center of mass of the molecule. For a diatomic molecule as in Fig. 9.3, the rotations can be resolved into only two independent rotations: that within the xz plane (about y), and that within the yz plane (about x). The only possible vibration for a diatomic molecule is the "in–out" motion of the two nuclei, represented in Fig. 9.3 by a positive displacement of one atom-centered z axis occurring with a negative displacement of the other. The symmetry of this vibration can be obtained by considering how this combination of displacements transforms under the various symmetry elements of the point group of the molecule. The displacements are unchanged by any of the symmetry operations of the $\mathbf{C}_{\infty v}$ point group; consequently, its representation is the totally symmetric Σ^+ representation. Within the $\mathbf{D}_{\infty h}$ point group, the vibration is also symmetric with respect to inversion, S, and C_2 since the positive and negative displacements that are interchanged by these operations also change sense, so that the net result is unchanged. Thus, in the $\mathbf{D}_{\infty h}$ point group the vibration belongs to the totally symmetric Σ_g^+ representation.

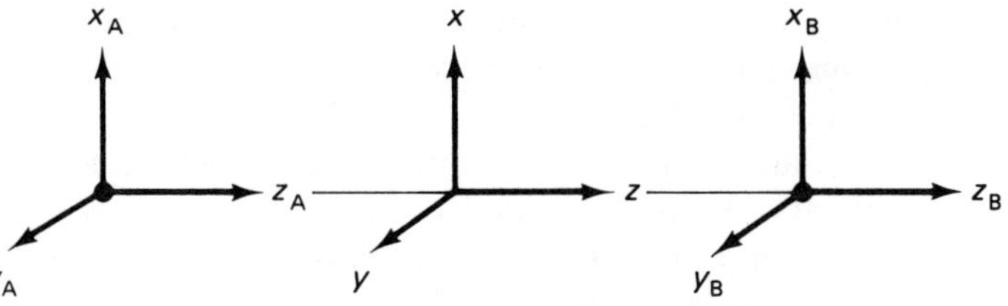

Fig. 9.3. Atom-centered and center-of-mass coordinate systems for a diatomic molecule.

The operational definition of a point-symmetry operation of a system is that it is an operation which carries the system into a configuration that is indistinguishable from the original configuration (i.e., all characters for the symmetry operations acting on the original system must be $+1$). As a consequence of this, the ground vibrational state of a molecule must belong to the totally symmetric irreducible representation of the point group of the molecule. This means that any vibrational excitation originating from the ground vibrational state is an excitation from a totally symmetric state to a state having the appropriate symmetry of the excited state. The direct product of the ground-state representation and the excited-state representation is just the representation of the excited state:

$$\Gamma(\psi_{v=0}) \times \Gamma(\psi_{v=v'}) = \Gamma(\psi_{v=v'}) \tag{9.63}$$

If the potential-energy function describing a vibration is assumed to be a simple Hooke's law function,

$$V(x) = \tfrac{1}{2}k(x - x_0)^2 \tag{9.64}$$

where x_0 is the equilibrium configuration for the nuclei, the vibrating molecule becomes a harmonic oscillator problem. The quantum mechanical solution to this gives a vibrational wave function in terms of the Hermite polynomial. The energy levels turn out to be

$$E_v = \left(v + \frac{1}{2}\right)\frac{h}{2\pi}\sqrt{\frac{k}{\mu}} \tag{9.65}$$

where v is the vibrational quantum number, k the force constant, and μ the reduced mass. Contrary to the situation we encountered in the electronic spectra of one-electron systems, where no restriction was placed on the possible changes in the energy-dependent quantum number, there is a restriction on Δv for vibrational transitions. This restriction, which arises from the form of the Hermite polynomial rather than from spatial symmetry considerations, is

$$\Delta v = \pm 1 \tag{9.66}$$

In actual practice, the harmonic oscillator approximation breaks down and higher values of Δv are observed. These are much less intense transitions than the

$\Delta v = \pm 1$ transition, however. The spacings for these higher transitions (or *overtones*) are also slightly different from the predictions based on the harmonic oscillator approximation.

In addition to the quantum mechanical selection rule, there can also be symmetry-imposed selection rules. For example, if we consider a heteronuclear diatomic molecule ($\mathbf{C}_{\infty v}$ point group), the vibration is Σ^+. The direct product of this representation with the ground-state representation is also Σ^+. This also happens to be the irreducible representation that describes the z component of the transition dipole; consequently, a transition from the ground vibrational level with $v = 0$ to an excited Σ^+ level with $v = 1$ is allowed and z-polarized. By similar reasoning, the excited vibrational level in a homonuclear diatomic molecule ($\mathbf{D}_{\infty h}$) has a Σ_g^+ representation. None of the Cartesian coordinates transform as Σ_g^+ in the $\mathbf{D}_{\infty h}$ point group; consequently, no direct square of representations is obtained and the transition dipole vanishes. No direct radiation-induced transition can be observed in this case.

We have previously shown (Section 8.7) that when Raman scattering occurs, the perturbation operator to be averaged between the two states is the square of the dipole operator, $(e\mathbf{r})^2$. If this is expanded in terms of Cartesian coordinates, we find terms of the type x^2, y^2, z^2, xz, xy, and yz. If an irreducible representation that transforms as any of these or any combination of these is contained in the direct product of the ground- and excited-state representations, the transition is Raman-allowed. In the $\mathbf{C}_{\infty v}$ point group, z^2 and the combination $x^2 + y^2$ transform as Σ^+; consequently, the Σ^+ vibration is Raman-allowed as well as direct-radiation (or infrared)-allowed. In the $\mathbf{D}_{\infty h}$ point group, z^2 and $x^2 + y^2$ transform as Σ_g^+; consequently, although the Σ_g^+ vibrational transition is not infrared-active, it is Raman-active.

When it is necessary to know how the various coordinates and their products transform in order to determine selection rules, it is possible to work out the transformation properties directly as we have thus far done. It is not usually necessary to go through this, however. Most sets of character tables include this information. Table 9.4 again shows the $\mathbf{C}_{\infty v}$ character table along with the coordinate transformation properties. This information is contained in the two columns after the characters. The first column gives the coordinate or rotation

Table 9.4. The $\mathbf{C}_{\infty v}$ character table with coordinate transformations

$\mathbf{C}_{\infty v}$	E	$2C_\phi$	$\infty\sigma_v$	Coordinate Transformations	
Σ^+	1	1	1	z	$x^2 + y^2, z^2$
Σ^-	1	1	-1	R_z	
Π	2	$2\cos\phi$	0	$(x, y)\ (R_x, R_y)$	(xz, yz)
Δ	2	$2\cos 2\phi$	0		$(x^2 - y^2, xy)$
Φ	2	$2\cos 3\phi$	0		
$\vdots$					
Γ^λ	2	$2\cos\lambda\phi$	0		

(R_x, R_y, or R_z), which transforms as the given irreducible representation. The next column gives the binary product of coordinates. Note that for the two-dimensional representations there are pairs of entries enclosed in parentheses. This indicates that both of these together transform as the indicated two-dimensional representation. In the cubic point groups there are instances of three entries being coupled.

The treatment of the vibrations of linear polynuclear molecules is similar to that for diatomics, except that there is more than one possible type of vibration. Figure 9.4 shows the possible independent modes of vibration for carbon dioxide. Any other vibratory motion can be resolved into combinations of these. Such independent modes of vibration, which transform as irreducible representations of the point group of the system, are referred to as *normal modes of vibration*. These normal modes of carbon dioxide can be shown by inspection to have the indicated symmetries within the $\mathbf{D}_{\infty h}$ point group. Note that ν_3 and ν_4 are completely equivalent; consequently, they are degenerate and must belong to a two-dimensional representation. By consulting the $\mathbf{D}_{\infty h}$ point group we can see that ν_1 is infrared-inactive, but Raman-active; ν_2 is infrared-active (z-polarized) and

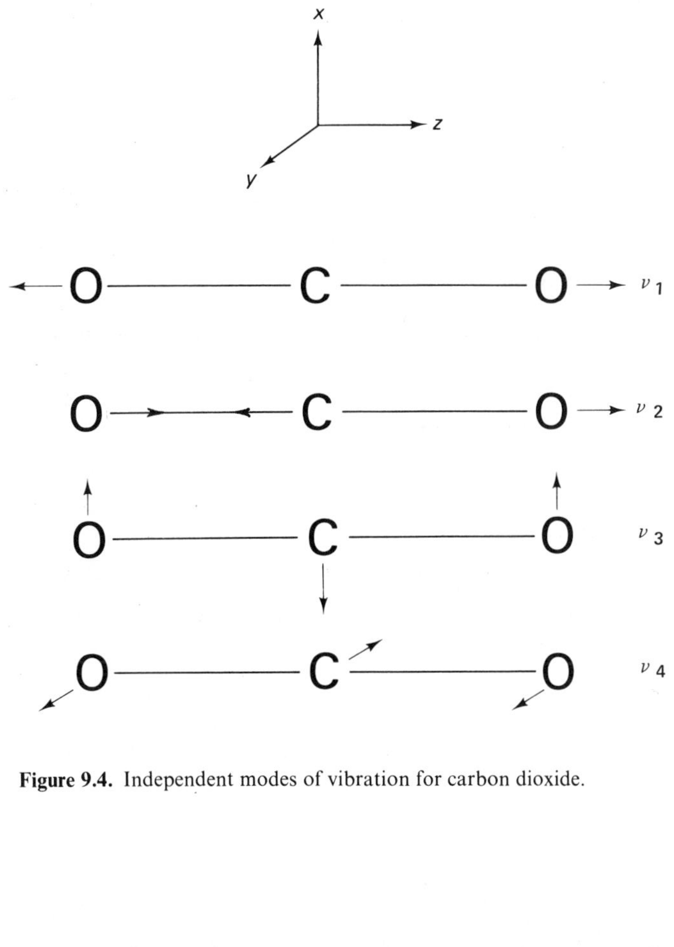

Figure 9.4. Independent modes of vibration for carbon dioxide.

Raman-inactive; and the degenerate pair of ν_3 and ν_4 are infrared-active (x and y transform together as π_u; consequently, if the incident radiation has any component along either of these axes, the transition can occur) and Raman-inactive. Note that no band is both infrared- and Raman-active. This mutual exclusiveness holds for all molecules possessing a point of inversion. Experimentally, the three predicted bands are observed, ν_2 and ν_3 by direct infrared techniques at 2349.3 cm^{-1} and 667.3 cm^{-1}, and ν_1 by Raman techniques at 1388.3 cm^{-1}.

PROBLEMS

1. Construct the ground-state-term symbols for the first 10 atoms of the periodic table.

2. Construct the ground-state-term symbols for the first transition series (elements 21 to 30).

3. Find the symmetry of the ground electronic state of a d^2 and of a d^4 configuration in the following point symmetries (use the strong-field limit for d^4):

(a) $\mathbf{D}_{\infty h}$ (b) $\mathbf{O}_h$

(c) $\mathbf{T}_d$ (d) $\mathbf{D}_{4h}$

(e) $\mathbf{D}_{2d}$ (f) $\mathbf{C}_{4v}$

4. Find the symmetry of the ground electronic state of a homonuclear diatomic molecule that has a δ^2 electronic configuration.

5. The Stark effect involves spectroscopy in an electric field. The electric field imposes a perturbation, having the symmetry of the field ($\mathbf{C}_{\infty v}$), on the system. Map the singlet states of carbon (arising from the p^2 configuration) onto $\mathbf{C}_{\infty v}$ and find the selection rules for transitions between these levels.

6. Describe the microwave spectrum of a linear molecule in an electric field.

BIBLIOGRAPHY

CONDON, E. U., AND G. H. SHORTLEY, *The Theory of Atomic Spectra*, Cambridge University Press, New York, 1935.

FANO, U., AND G. RACAH, *Irreducible Tensorial Sets*, Academic Press, Inc., New York, 1959.

GRIFFITH, J. S., *The Irreducible Tensor Method for Molecular Symmetry Groups*, Prentice-Hall, Inc., Englewood Cliffs, N.J., 1962.

HERZBERG, G., *Atomic Spectra and Atomic Structure*, Dover Publications, Inc., New York, 1944.

HERZBERG, G., *Spectra of Diatomic Molecules*, 2nd ed., Van Nostrand Reinhold Company, New York, 1950.

KAPLAN, I. G., *Symmetry of Many-Electron Systems*, Academic Press, Inc., New York, 1975.

KING, G. W., *Spectroscopy and Molecular Structure*, Holt, Rinehart and Winston, Inc., New York, 1964.

ORCHIN, M., AND H. H. JAFFÉ, *Symmetry, Orbitals, and Spectra*, Wiley–Interscience, New York, 1970.

ROTENBERG, M., R. BIVENS, N. METROPOLIS, AND J. K. WOOTEN, *The 3j and 6j Symbols*, The MIT Press, Cambridge, Mass., 1964.

SLATER, J. C., *Quantum Theory of Atomic Structure*, Vol. I, McGraw-Hill Book Company, New York, 1960; Vol. II, 1960.

WYBOURNE, B. G., *Classical Groups for Physicists*, John Wiley & Sons, Inc., New York, 1974.

10

Electronic Structure and Spectra of Nonlinear Molecules

10.1 INTRODUCTION

Most chemists find group theory most useful for describing the properties of nonlinear polyatomic molecules. The groups employed here are the discrete point groups that we have discussed in detail in the earlier chapters. For molecules possessing any degree of symmetry, the use of group theory offers aid in all problems involving quantum chemical calculations of any kind and in the classification and interpretation of all kinds of spectra. In this chapter and those following it, we will illustrate a number of applications. The emphasis will be upon obtaining the maximum amount of information from the group theory with a minimum consideration of numerical computation.

10.2 L.C.A.O. MOLECULAR ORBITALS

When considering the symmetry restrictions on the electronic transitions of nonlinear polyatomic molecules, the overall symmetry properties of the molecular orbitals must be known. In most cases these cannot be classified in terms of only the orbital angular momentum as was the case for linear molecules; consequently, in order to find the selection rules, something must be known about the actual form of the molecular orbital wave function. The most common approximate method of constructing molecular orbitals is the linear combination of atomic orbitals (L.C.A.O.) method or some modification of it (see Section 7.4). As implied by the name, the method describes molecular orbitals as a linear sum of functions which are centered on the various atoms of the molecules

$$\phi_i = \sum_{\mu} c_{i\mu}\chi_{\mu} \tag{10.1}$$

where the ϕ_i is the ith molecular orbital, χ_μ is the μth atomic function, and the $c_{i\mu}$ are weighting coefficients determining the relative contribution of each of the χ_μ to ϕ_i. In the simplest approximations, the χ_μ are a suitable approximation to the atomic orbitals occupied by the valence electrons of the atoms in the molecule. In many cases (e.g., organic π-electron systems) only a limited number of the valence orbitals are used. For more exact calculations on a system, all the electrons are considered and the individual χ_μ's may be combinations of functions (either atomic orbitals or some mathematically more convenient function such as Gaussian functions. For our purposes, for determining the representations of the molecular orbitals within the point group of the molecule, the simplest approximation is sufficient. In fact, all that is required are the relative signs of the $c_{i\mu}$ and the symmetry properties of the χ_μ. For example, if we consider a homonuclear diatomic molecule that uses only a single s orbital on each atom for bonding (such as H_2), the possible L.C.A.O.-M.O. wave functions arising from the two atomic s orbitals would be

$$\phi_1 = c_{11}s_1 + c_{12}s_2 \tag{10.2a}$$

$$\phi_2 = c_{21}s_1 - c_{22}s_2 \tag{10.2b}$$

where the c's themselves are chosen to be positive numbers. The s orbitals have no directional properties; consequently, they transform as a constant. These two orbitals are represented schematically in Fig. 10.1. If we consider the symmetry properties of these within the $\mathbf{D}_{\infty h}$ point group, we see that ϕ_1 has σ_g^+ symmetry while ϕ_2 has σ_u^+ symmetry. Within the $\mathbf{C}_{\infty v}$ point group, both orbitals would have σ^+ symmetry.

For a second example, let us consider the π-type orbitals of ethylene. The molecule has a p-type valence orbital on each carbon, which is perpendicular to the molecular plane and which is not utilized in forming the σ-type molecular orbitals. These two p orbitals can be combined to form two π-type molecular orbitals. The mathematical form of these is the same as in the previous example:

$$\phi_1 = c_{11}p_1 + c_{12}p_2 \tag{10.3a}$$

$$\phi_2 = c_{21}p_1 - c_{22}p_2 \tag{10.3b}$$

These are shown schematically in Fig. 10.2. (Note that, if the molecule lies in the yz plane, the transformation properties of the p orbitals are the same as for a unit vector parallel to the x axis.) The ethylene molecule belongs to the $\mathbf{D}_{2h}$ point

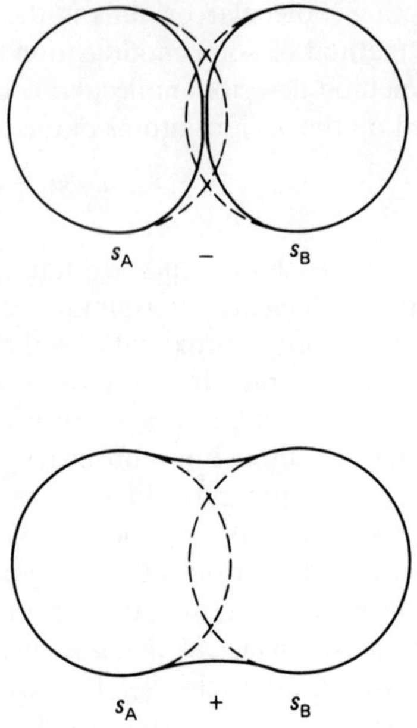

Fig. 10.1. Schematic representation of the two molecular orbitals of a diatomic molecule arising from a linear combination of s orbitals.

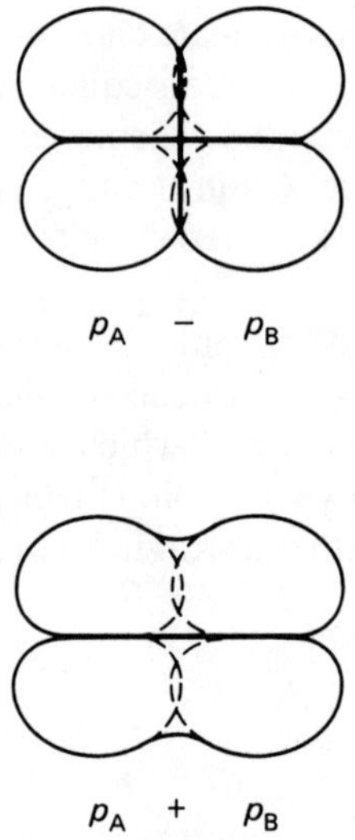

Fig. 10.2. Schematic representation of the two π molecular orbitals of ethylene arising from a linear combination of p orbitals.

group. The symmetries of the molecular orbitals may be found by considering how the orbitals behave with respect to the symmetry elements of the point group. If the C—C bond lies along the z axis (this choice is conventionally made for ethylene to emphasize its relationship to diatomic molecules), the results are

$\mathbf{D}_{2h}$	E	$C_2(z)$	$C_2(y)$	$C_2(x)$	i	$\sigma(xy)$	$\sigma(xz)$	$\sigma(yz)$
$B_{3u} = \Gamma(\phi_1)$	1	−1	−1	1	−1	1	1	−1
$B_{2g} = \Gamma(\phi_2)$	1	−1	1	−1	1	−1	1	−1

(10.4)

The b_{3u} orbital has the lower energy of the two orbitals. The ground state of the ethylene molecule (closed-shell) has two electrons in the b_{3u} orbital and none in the b_{2g} orbital. (The symmetry of the ground state is A_g.) The lowest-energy transition represents the promotion of one of the electrons in the b_{3u} orbital to the b_{2g} orbital. The symmetry of this excited state is $b_{3u} \times b_{2g} = B_{1u}$. The lowest singlet electronic transition is ${}^1B_{1u} \leftarrow {}^1A_g$. The transition is allowed and z-polarized. It is experimentally observed at 40,015 cm^{-1}.

10.3 GEOMETRIC DERIVATION OF REPRESENTATIONS

The symmetries of the possible molecular orbitals arising from a given set of valence atomic orbitals can be derived from a set of independent tensors centered on the atoms that transform as the valence orbitals under question. The total representation arising from these tensors can be resolved into irreducible representations corresponding to the symmetries of the molecular orbitals that can arise from the starting basis orbitals. The atomic s orbitals give rise to zero-order tensors, or scalars; the p orbitals to first-order tensors, or vectors; the d orbitals give rise to second-order tensors, and so on. For simple applications, the problem can be handled geometrically; however, for more complicated applications and for applications involving tensors of order 2 or higher, the matrix representations of the operations and the full representation of the orbital tensors are needed. The tensors for higher l-value atomic orbitals can be constructed from the appropriate products of the vectors. (In these cases, a site-symmetry treatment is usually much easier, however.) If we carry through the procedure geometrically for the π orbitals of ethylene, we need the transformation properties of the two independent x vectors shown in Fig. 10.3 under the operations of the $\mathbf{D}_{2h}$ point group. The identity operation and the $\sigma(xz)$ operation leave the vectors unchanged, the $C_2(z)$

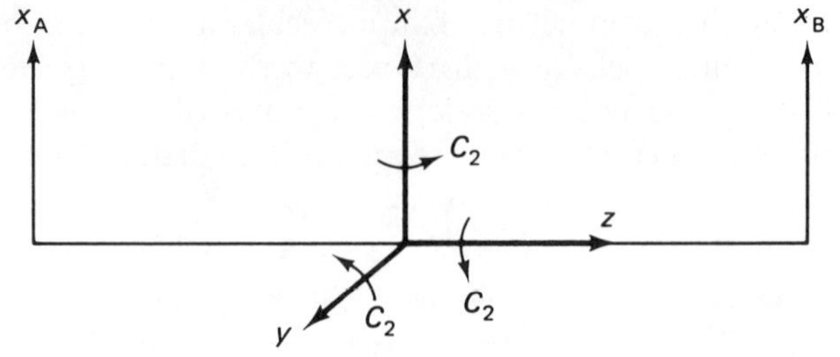

Fig. 10.3. Vectors for finding the transformation properties of *p*-type atomic orbitals within the $\mathbf{D}_{2h}$ molecular point group.

and the $\sigma(yz)$ operations change the sign of both vectors while all the other operations move the vectors from their original positions and, consequently, contribute nothing to the representation. The reducible π representation is then

$\mathbf{D}_{2h}$	E	$C_2(z)$	$C_2(y)$	$C_2(x)$	i	$\sigma(xy)$	$\sigma(xz)$	$\sigma(yz)$
$\Gamma(\pi)$	2	-2	0	0	0	0	2	-2

(10.5)

It can easily be seen by inspection that this representation is the sum of the two representations shown in Eq. 10.4. Note, incidentally, that by knowing the symmetry properties of the molecular orbital and of the atomic orbitals, the qualitative "shape" of the molecular orbitals can be constructed. The π orbitals of ethylene, as of any molecule, are antisymmetric with respect to the plane of the molecule. All that is required in this case are the operations that describe the in-plane rotational symmetry of the system. In the present case, the b_{3u} orbital is symmetric with respect to $C_2(x)$ while the b_{2g} orbital is antisymmetric. This means that the coefficients for the atomic orbitals must be the same for the b_{3u} case, but have opposite signs for the b_{2g} case.

The general geometric procedure for finding the representation arising from an equivalent set of basis functions requires the construction of matrices to represent the transformations. For the π system of ethylene, this is almost trivial, but it affords an instructive example. If we designate the equivalent p orbitals in their original positions by an array as

$\mathbf{M} =$		p_1	p_2
	p_1	1	0
	p_2	0	1

(10.6)

the various symmetry operations yield the following geometric results:

$$\mathbf{EM} = \begin{array}{c|cc} & p_1 & p_2 \\ \hline p_1 & 1 & 0 \\ p_2 & 0 & 1 \end{array} \tag{10.6a}$$

$$C_2(z)\mathbf{M} = \begin{array}{c|cc} & p_1 & p_2 \\ \hline p_1 & -1 & 0 \\ p_2 & 0 & -1 \end{array} \tag{10.6b}$$

$$C_2(y)\mathbf{M} = \begin{array}{c|cc} & p_1 & p_2 \\ \hline p_1 & 0 & -1 \\ p_2 & -1 & 0 \end{array} \tag{10.6c}$$

$$C_2(x)\mathbf{M} = \begin{array}{c|cc} & p_1 & p_2 \\ \hline p_1 & 0 & 1 \\ p_2 & 1 & 0 \end{array} \tag{10.6d}$$

$$i\mathbf{M} = \begin{array}{c|cc} & p_1 & p_2 \\ \hline p_1 & 0 & -1 \\ p_2 & -1 & 0 \end{array} \tag{10.6e}$$

$$\sigma(xy)\mathbf{M} = \begin{array}{c|cc} & p_1 & p_2 \\ \hline p_1 & 0 & 1 \\ p_2 & 1 & 0 \end{array} \tag{10.6f}$$

$$\sigma(xz)\mathbf{M} = \begin{array}{c|cc} & p_1 & p_2 \\ \hline p_1 & 1 & 0 \\ p_2 & 0 & 1 \end{array} \tag{10.6g}$$

$$\sigma(yz)\mathbf{M} = \begin{array}{c|cc} & p_1 & p_2 \\ \hline p_1 & -1 & 0 \\ p_2 & 0 & -1 \end{array} \tag{10.6h}$$

The entries show to what each of the starting basis functions is transformed after each of the operations. For example, Eq. 10.6b implies that $C_2(z)$ takes both the orbitals p_1 and p_2 to their negatives (reverses their direction) while Eq. 10.6c implies that $C_2(y)$ takes p_1 to $-p_2$ and p_2 to $-p_1$. The representation arising from these two p orbitals is obtained from the traces of these matrices. The same procedure can be extended to any number of equivalent basis functions. The only requirement is that the geometrical result of the transformations must be known.

10.4 SITE-SYMMETRY DERIVATION OF REPRESENTATIONS

A much simpler procedure for constructing symmetry-adapted molecular orbitals from atomic basis orbitals having an l value of greater than unity arises from the use of *site symmetries.* The *site-symmetry group* of a given atom is that subgroup of the full point group that contains all symmetry elements that pass through the atom.

We start with the full $\mathbf{R}_h(3)$ symmetry of the free atom and then systematically reduce this to the site symmetry of the atom as it appears in the molecule. The characters for the representations of the various orbitals on the atom can then be obtained from the behavior with respect to the elements of the point group that has the proper site symmetry. Almost without exception the atoms will fall into one of five categories: the full point group of the molecule (occurs only for atoms on the intersection of all the symmetry elements of the molecule); $\mathbf{C}_{\infty v}$ (atoms in linear molecules, but not at the center of symmetry); $\mathbf{C}_{nv}$ (atoms on either the principal axis or a subsidiary axis—usually $\mathbf{C}_{2v}$); $\mathbf{C}_s$ (atoms lying in a plane of symmetry); and $\mathbf{C}_1$ (atoms not lying on any symmetry element). The orbitals on a given atom can contribute to the total representation of the possible molecular orbitals only via the elements of the subgroup corresponding to its site symmetry. (This can be seen by referring to Eq. 10.5. The site symmetry of a carbon atom in ethylene is $\mathbf{C}_{2v}$.) The orbitals on each symmetry-related atom contribute equally to this total representation. Thus, the problem is to find the character of each orbital on each unique atom with respect to each element of the site-symmetry subgroup and to sum the results over all the atoms.

With these ideas in mind, let us work through some examples. As a first example, let us consider the symmetries of the possible molecular orbitals for ammonia (NH_3) which arise from a starting valence orbital basis set consisting of $2s$ and $2p$ orbitals on the nitrogen and $1s$ orbitals on the hydrogens. The point symmetry of ammonia is $\mathbf{C}_{3v}$. The site symmetry of the nitrogen is the full molecular symmetry, while that for the hydrogen is $\mathbf{C}_s$. Let us first consider the central nitrogen atom. The s orbital on nitrogen transforms as the totally symmetric representation; consequently, its representation has unity for each character. The set of p orbitals are triply degenerate in the $\mathbf{R}_h(3)$ point group of the free atom, transforming as $D_u^{(1)}$. Thus, the character of the E element in the p representation is

3. The characters of the rotational elements can be obtained by substituting in the proper angular value for ϕ (120°) into the rotational character for $D_u^{(1)}$ from the $\mathbf{R}_h(3)$ point group. As for all σ operations, the character for σ_v is + 1. The results are

$\mathbf{C}_{3v}$	E	$2C_3$	$3\sigma_v$
Γ_s^{N}	1	1	1
Γ_p^{N}	3	0	1

(10.7)

Note that the s orbital transforms as the totally symmetric A_1 representation of $\mathbf{C}_{3v}$ while the p orbitals transform as $A_1 + E$. Thus, the s orbital can participate in bonding via a molecular orbital of a_1 symmetry while the p orbitals can participate in bonding via one orbital of a_1 symmetry and one degenerate pair of e symmetry.

The s orbitals on the hydrogens transform as the totally symmetric A representation within $\mathbf{C}_s$. There are three equivalent hydrogens. Each lies in only one symmetry element, however. Thus, when mapping the $\mathbf{C}_s$ group onto $\mathbf{C}_{3v}$, we have

$\mathbf{C}_{3v}$	E	$(2C_3)$	σ_v	σ_v'	σ_v''
$\Gamma_s^{\mathrm{H}_1}$	1	0	1	0	0
$\Gamma_s^{\mathrm{H}_2}$	1	0	0	1	0
$\Gamma_s^{\mathrm{H}_3}$	1	0	0	0	1

(10.8)

To combine the σ_v's into the one class of the $\mathbf{C}_{3v}$ group, we must take the average contribution of the hydrogens, giving

$\mathbf{C}_{3v}$	E	$2C_3$	$3\sigma_v$
$\Gamma_s^{3\mathrm{H}}$	3	0	1

(10.9)

Combining this with the orbitals from the nitrogen, we have

$\mathbf{C}_{3v}$	E	$2C_3$	$3\sigma_v$
Γ_s^{N}	1	1	1
Γ_p^{N}	3	0	1
$\Gamma_s^{3\mathrm{H}}$	3	0	1
Γ_{NH_3}	7	1	3

(10.10)

This reduces to

$$\Gamma_{NH_3} = 3A_1 + 2E \tag{10.11}$$

The chosen basis set thus leads to $3a_1$ orbitals and two pairs of degenerate e orbitals. These orbitals can accommodate a total of 14 electrons. Ammonia has only eight valence electrons; consequently, there will be vacant orbitals. Calculations reveal that the order of orbital energies is a_1, a_1, e, e, a_1. All but the last two are fully occupied (two electrons per a_1 orbital and four in the e orbitals).

Electronic excitations can arise from a promotion of electrons from occupied to vacant orbitals. The possible symmetry types of the transitions are $a_1 \leftarrow a_1$, $a_1 \leftarrow e$, $e \leftarrow a_1$, and $e \leftarrow e$. The first of these would lead to excited states of A_1 symmetry, the second and third to E, and the fourth to A_1, A_2, and E. Since both the highest occupied and lowest vacant orbitals are e orbitals, the lowest excited state would be expected to be one of these. The ground electronic state of the molecule has A_1 symmetry. $A_1 \leftarrow A_1$ transitions are symmetry-allowed and z-polarized, $E \leftarrow A_1$ transitions are allowed and x- and y-polarized, while $A_2 \leftarrow A_1$ transitions are forbidden within the $\mathbf{C}_{3v}$ point group. There is an additional complication in ammonia, however. The geometry of the molecule changes on excitation and all excited states that have been characterized belong to the $\mathbf{D}_{3h}$ point group. The state that is A_2 in $\mathbf{C}_{3v}$ becomes A_2'' in $\mathbf{D}_{3h}$. Transitions from the totally symmetric ground state to A_2'' are symmetry-allowed in $\mathbf{D}_{3h}$. Thus, the first electronic transition observed in ammonia is from the A_1 ground state in the $\mathbf{C}_{3v}$ symmetry to the A_2'' excited state in the $\mathbf{D}_{3h}$ symmetry. This transition occurs at 46,136 cm^{-1}.

For a more complicated case, let us find the symmetries of the possible molecular orbitals that can arise for an AB_4 tetrahedral system (such as $FeBr_4^-$) in which *all five atoms* can contribute to bonding via one set each of s, p, and d orbitals. The central atom will have the full $\mathbf{T}_d$ symmetry of the molecule, while the site symmetry of the ligand atoms will be $\mathbf{C}_{3v}$. Let us consider first the central atom. The s orbital on the central atom transforms as the totally symmetric representation; its representation has unity for each character. The set of p orbitals are triply degenerate in the $\mathbf{R}_h(3)$ point group; consequently, the character of the E element in the p representation is 3. The characters of the rotational elements can again be obtained by substituting in the proper angular values for ϕ in the rotational character of $D_u^{(1)}$ from the $\mathbf{R}_h(3)$ point group. Since l is odd, the leading term is negative for the S_4 operation. As for all σ operations for Cartesian coordinates and their polynomials, the character for σ_d is $+1$. The results are as shown.

$\mathbf{T}_d$	E	$8C_3$	$3C_2$	$6S_4$	$6\sigma_d$
Γ_p^c	3	$1 + 2\cos 120°$	$1 + 2\cos 180°$	$-1 + 2\cos 90°$	1
Γ_p^c	3	0	-1	-1	1

(10.12)

This is just the T_2 irreducible representation within the $\mathbf{T}_d$ point group. For the set of d orbitals, l equals 2 and the results are

$\mathbf{T}_d$	E	$8C_3$	$3C_2$	$6S_4$	$6\sigma_d$
Γ_d^c	5	$1 + 2\cos 120° + 2\cos 240°$	$1 + 2\cos\pi + 2\cos 2\pi$	$1 - 2\cos 90° + 2\cos\pi$	1
Γ_d^c	5	-1	1	-1	1

(10.13)

This is not an irreducible representation; however, it can be resolved into an E representation and a T_2 representation. This is also the ligand-field splitting for d orbitals in a field of tetrahedral symmetry. Thus, the s, p, and d orbitals on the central atom can participate in bonding via one molecular orbital of a_1 symmetry, one of e symmetry, and two of t_2 symmetry.

For the s, p, and d orbitals on one of the ligands, we have, within the $\mathbf{C}_{3v}$ subgroup that represents their site symmetry:

$\mathbf{C}_{3v}$	E	$2C_3$	$3\sigma_v$
Γ_s^L	1	1	1
Γ_p^L	3	$1 + 2\cos 120°$	1
Γ_d^L	5	$1 + 2\cos 120° + 2\cos 240°$	1

(10.14)

or

$\mathbf{C}_{3v}$	E	$2C_3$	$3\sigma_v$
Γ_s^L	1	1	1
Γ_p^L	3	0	1
Γ_d^L	5	-1	1

(10.14a)

There are, however, four equivalent ligands; consequently, for the total representation of the ligands this must be multiplied by four:

$\mathbf{C}_{3v}$	E	$2C_3$	$3\sigma_v$
Γ_s^L	4	4	4
Γ_p^L	12	0	4
Γ_d^L	20	-4	4

(10.15)

When transferring these representations to the $\mathbf{T}_d$ point group, the C_3's and σ_d's in the $\mathbf{T}_d$ group must be divided into two sets, since only one pair of the C_3's pass through a given atom and only three of the σ's are associated with a given C_3 operation. Within the $\mathbf{T}_d$ point group the ligand representations are

(10.16)

$\mathbf{T}'_d$	E	$2C_3$	$(6C_3)$	$(3C_2)$	$(6S_4)$	$3\sigma_d$	$(3\sigma'_d)$
Γ^{L}_s	4	4	0	0	0	4	0
Γ^{L}_p	12	0	0	0	0	4	0
Γ^{L}_d	20	−4	0	0	0	4	0

Combining the C_3's and σ_d's, we have

(10.16a)

$\mathbf{T}_d$	E	$8C_3$	$3C_2$	$6S_4$	$6\sigma_d$
Γ^{L}_s	4	1	0	0	2
Γ^{L}_p	12	0	0	0	2
Γ^{L}_d	20	−1	0	0	2

These may be individually resolved to give

$$\Gamma^{\mathrm{L}}_s = A_1 + T_2 \tag{10.17}$$

$$\Gamma^{\mathrm{L}}_p = A_1 + E + T_1 + 2T_2 \tag{10.18}$$

$$\Gamma^{\mathrm{L}}_d = A_1 + 2E + 2T_1 + 3T_2 \tag{10.19}$$

There would be a total of 45 atomic orbitals involved if all of the s, p and d orbitals on each ligand were employed. This should give rise to 45 possible molecular orbitals. The total molecular orbital representation we have obtained is

(10.20)

$\mathbf{T}_d$	E	$8C_3$	$3C_2$	$6S_4$	$6\sigma_d$
Γ^{c}_s	1	1	1	1	1
Γ^{c}_p	3	0	−1	−1	1
Γ^{c}_d	5	−1	1	−1	1
Γ^{L}_s	4	1	0	0	2
Γ^{L}_p	12	0	0	0	2
Γ^{L}_d	20	−1	0	0	2
$\Gamma^{\mathrm{total}}_{\mathrm{M.O.}}$	45	0	1	−1	0

This can be resolved to give

$$\Gamma^{\mathrm{total}}_{\mathrm{M.O.}} = 4A_1 + 4E + 3T_1 + 8T_2 \tag{10.21}$$

Adding the dimensionalities of these gives the correct value of 45. There can thus be four nondegenerate a_1 molecular orbitals, four doubly degenerate e orbitals, three triply degenerate t_1 orbitals, and eight triply degenerate t_2 orbitals. The results give us the possible symmetry types of orbitals we can have. It *does not* yield any information about the orbital occupancy or energy of the various orbitals. The possible symmetry-allowed transitions among orbitals of these symmetries may be obtained in the usual fashion.

For illustrative purposes we adopted a rather extreme example. A more realistic approach to a tetrahedral transition metal halide such as $FeBr_4^-$ would be to include the *s*, *p*, and *d* atomic orbitals of the central metal and the *s* and *p* orbitals of the ligands. With this basis set, the symmetries of our resulting molecular orbitals would be

$$\Gamma_{\text{M.O.}}^{\text{total}} = 3A_1 + 2E + T_1 + 5T_2 \tag{10.22}$$

Even with this smaller set of orbitals, however, we have no way of being certain of their relative energies. Investigations into the spectra and energy levels of such systems are the object of much current research in inorganic chemistry.

Exercise 10.1*: Find the symmetries of *all* the possible molecular orbitals arising from all atomic valence shell orbitals in the following molecules, and find the symmetry-allowed electronic transitions in each case.

(a) Methane
(b) Ethane (staggered conformation)
(c) $CoCl_6^{3-}$ ($\mathbf{O}_h$ point group)

10.5 HYBRIDIZED ORBITALS

The concept of hybridization was introduced by Linus Pauling when he noticed that if he took certain linear combinations of atomic valence orbitals, the resulting "hybridized" orbitals assumed the same geometrical orientation as did the chemical bonds around that atom. Hybridization thus provided an early explanation for the shapes of molecules. The use of hybridized orbitals is necessary for valence bond calculations and for certain types of molecular orbital calculations, and is useful for determining shapes of molecules and for other applications.

Group theory provides the solution for two problems in hybridization: the determination of the hybridization associated with a certain shape and the construction of the appropriate hybrid orbitals from a given basis set. There are several approaches to each of these problems. We will present an approach based upon site symmetry.

In Sections 2.6 and 5.3 we discussed the construction of groups as products of subgroups. One particularly useful construction is to use the group of the site symmetry, $\mathbf{G}_S$, of a particular function, atom, and so on, and the group of interchanges of the equivalent sites, $\mathbf{G}_I$:

$$\mathbf{G} = \mathbf{G}_I \cdot \mathbf{G}_S \tag{10.23}$$

In Eq. 10.23 a "dot" has been used to indicate the product since, depending upon the specific case, either a direct, a semidirect, or a weak direct product may be involved. (A weak direct product occurs when neither of the subgroups is invariant with respect to the other.) If a semidirect product is involved, either $\mathbf{G}_I$ or $\mathbf{G}_S$ may be the invariant subgroup.

In constructing hybridized orbitals, the nature of the atoms attached to the considered atom is usually ignored. Thus, the symmetry defined by the hybrid orbitals is the highest symmetry consistent with the geometric structure. The site symmetry of the hybrid orbitals defines $\mathbf{G}_S$ while the subgroup interchanging them defines $\mathbf{G}_I$. Table 10.1 lists $\mathbf{G}_S$ and $\mathbf{G}_I$ for some selected systems.

Table 10.1. Site symmetry and interchange groups for some selected systems

Point Group	Molecule	Ligand	$\mathbf{G}_S$	$\mathbf{G}_I$
$\mathbf{C}_{3v}$	AX_3	X	$\mathbf{C}_s$	$\mathbf{C}_3$
	AX_3Y	Y	$\mathbf{C}_{3v}$	$\mathbf{C}_1$
$\mathbf{C}_{4v}$	AX_4	X	$\mathbf{C}_s$	$\mathbf{C}_4$
	AX_4YZ	Y(Z)	$\mathbf{C}_{4v}$	$\mathbf{C}_1$
$\mathbf{C}_{nv}$	AX_n	X	$\mathbf{C}_s$	$\mathbf{C}_n$
$\mathbf{D}_{2h}$	$AX_2Y_2Z_2$	X(Y, Z)	$\mathbf{C}_{2v}$	$\mathbf{C}_2$
$\mathbf{D}_{2d}$	AX_2Y_2	X(Y)	$\mathbf{C}_s$	$\mathbf{D}_2$
$\mathbf{D}_{3h}$	AX_3	X	$\mathbf{C}_{2v}$	$\mathbf{C}_3$
	AX_3Y_2	Y	$\mathbf{C}_{3v}$	$\mathbf{C}_2$
$\mathbf{D}_{3d}$	AX_6	X	$\mathbf{C}_s$	$\mathbf{S}_6$
$\mathbf{D}_{4h}$	AX_4	X	$\mathbf{C}_{2v}$	$\mathbf{C}_4$
	AX_4Y_2	Y	$\mathbf{C}_{4v}$	$\mathbf{C}_2$
$\mathbf{D}_{6h}$	X_6	X	$\mathbf{C}_{2v}$	$\mathbf{C}_6$
$\mathbf{T}_d$	AX_4	X	$\mathbf{C}_{3v}$	$\mathbf{D}_2$
$\mathbf{O}_h$	AX_6	X	$\mathbf{C}_{4v}$	$\mathbf{S}_6$
$\mathbf{D}_{\infty h}$	X_2	X	$\mathbf{C}_{\infty v}$	$\mathbf{C}_i$

Once the site symmetry of the hybrid orbitals has been found, the representations in the complete group which are spanned by these can be found immediately by use of the *correlation theorem.* The hybridization is determined directly from the representations by consulting the right-hand side of the character tables to see what basis functions span these representations. The correlation theorem states that the irreducible representations in a group, $\mathbf{G}$, spanned by a function (or set of functions) located at a site of lower symmetry, $\mathbf{G}_S$, can be found by finding the irreducible representations spanned by the function (or functions) in $\mathbf{G}_S$ and then correlating these with the irreducible representations of $\mathbf{G}$. Each function having symmetry Γ' in $\mathbf{G}_S$ will contribute to every Γ in $\mathbf{G}$ that correlates with Γ'. Correlation tables can be constructed by mapping the representations of the full group onto the subgroup, and reducing any of the resulting representations that are not irreducible. Table 10.2 shows the $\mathbf{C}_{3v}$–$\mathbf{T}_d$ correlation table. From this table we see that a function belonging to the A_1 representation in $\mathbf{C}_{3v}$ would contribute to functions having A_1 and T_2 symmetry in $\mathbf{T}_d$; a function transforming as E in $\mathbf{C}_{3v}$ would contribute to E, T_1 and T_2 in $\mathbf{T}_d$, and so on.

Table 10.2. Correlation of $\mathbf{C}_{3v}$ with $\mathbf{T}_d$

$\mathbf{T}_d$	$\mathbf{C}_{3v}$
A_1	A_1
A_2	A_2
E	E
T_1	$A_2 + E$
T_2	$A_1 + E$

For the present purposes, a correlation table is not really needed. The hybrid orbitals transform as the totally symmetric representation within $\mathbf{G}_S$. The totally symmetric representation of a subgroup correlates with those representations from the full group which have nonnegative characters for the symmetry operations of the subgroup. Consider, for example, tetrahedral hybridization. The hybrid orbitals have $\mathbf{C}_{3v}$ site symmetry and transform as A_1 within $\mathbf{C}_{3v}$. The E, C_3, and σ_v operations of $\mathbf{C}_{3v}$ correspond to the E, C_3, and σ_d operations of $\mathbf{T}_d$. The only representations of $\mathbf{T}_d$ having nonnegative entries for these are A_1 and T_2. Thus, these are the representations spanned by the hybrid orbitals. (Note that the results are the same as would have been obtained from Table 10.2.) An s orbital always forms a basis for the totally symmetric representation (A_1 in this case). Consulting the $\mathbf{T}_d$ character table, we see that T_2 is spanned by the set (x, y, z) or by the set (xy, xz, yz). If only an s and p atomic basis set is being used, we see immediately that the hybridization is sp^3 (the set p_x, p_y, p_z corresponding to the set x, y, z). If d orbitals were included in the basis set, the hybridization would correspond to $s(\lambda p + \mu d)^3$, where λ and μ are mixing coefficients that would have to be determined by energy considerations rather than by symmetry.

As a second example, consider the hybridization of a trigonal pyramid such as NH_3 or PH_3 with an s and p atomic basis set. The full point symmetry is $\mathbf{C}_{3v}$, while the site symmetry of the hybrid bond orbitals is $\mathbf{C}_s$. The correlation of the totally symmetric A' representations of $\mathbf{C}_s$ with $\mathbf{C}_{3v}$ yields A_1 and E representations for the hybrid orbitals. Both s and p_z orbitals span A_1 of $\mathbf{C}_{3v}$ while p_x and p_y span E. The resulting hybridization is $(\lambda s + \mu p_z)p^2$. The λ and μ must again be determined by energy considerations. If λ equals μ, the hybridization becomes sp^3 and the bond angles become 109°28′, near the value for NH_3. If λ equals zero, the orbitals become pure p in character leading to a predicted bond angle of 90°, very near the value for PH_3. If μ equals zero, the hybridization becomes sp^2, the hybrids are coplanar with a bond angle of 120°, the structure of the excited electronic states of NH_3.

Let us now consider the actual construction of the hybrid orbitals from the basis set. If we symbolically denote the hybrid orbitals as ϕ_i and the basis orbitals as χ_k, then we have

$$\phi_i = \sum_k c_{ik}\chi_k \tag{10.24}$$

The problem is to find the c_{ik}. Since the basis set and the set of hybrids span the same representations, either can be expressed as a linear combination of the other. Thus, we can validly write the inverse of the transformation of Eq. 10.24:

$$\chi_k = \sum_i c'_{ki}\phi_i \tag{10.25}$$

Since the individual basis orbitals form independent bases for their corresponding irreducible representations, the coefficients of Eq. 10.25 can be determined directly by the use of projection operators. (The appropriate projection operating on χ_k gives it back unchanged.) Equation 10.25 can be written in the form of a matrix transformation of a vector

$$\boldsymbol{\chi} = \boldsymbol{\phi}\mathbf{T} \tag{10.26}$$

where the set of χ_k and ϕ_i are represented as row vectors and each column of $\mathbf{T}$ is one of the sets of coefficients. If the columns of $\mathbf{T}$ are individually normalized, $\mathbf{T}$ becomes unitary and right multiplying by $\tilde{\mathbf{T}}$ yields

$$\boldsymbol{\chi}\tilde{\mathbf{T}} = \boldsymbol{\phi} \tag{10.27}$$

Thus, the form of the hybrid orbitals can be found simply by determining the columns of the vector $\mathbf{T}$ by applying the appropriate projection operators to the set of ϕ_i and then carrying out the inverse transformation of Eq. 10.27. Of course, the χ_i must be ordered in $\boldsymbol{\chi}$ in the order corresponding to the order of the irreducible representations in $\mathbf{T}$.

The use of the group of interchanges $\mathbf{G}_I$, rather than the full point group, greatly simplifies the construction of $\tilde{\mathbf{T}}$. The set of hybrid orbitals spans the *regular representation of* $\mathbf{G}_I$. The regular representation $\Gamma^{(R)}$ of a group is defined as

$$\Gamma^{(R)} = \sum_\Gamma m_\Gamma \Gamma \tag{10.28}$$

where the Γ are the irreducible representations of the group and m_Γ is the dimension of the irreducible representation Γ. Thus, if the m_Γ-dimensional representations are resolved into m_Γ independent representations, there is a one-to-one correspondence between the hybrid orbital combinations and representations of $\mathbf{G}_I$. The combinations can be determined immediately from the character table for $\mathbf{G}_I$. In doing so, two words of caution are in order. First, either the correlation tables or the transformation properties of the bases within $\mathbf{G}_I$ should be used to properly order the χ_i. Second, the orientation of the reference axis system will be determined by $\mathbf{G}_I$. For all common symmetries other than octahedral, the results are the usual set of simplest hybrid orbitals; however, for octahedral hybridization the reference z axis will be a C_3 axis (the principal axis of the $\mathbf{S}_6$ subgroup) rather than the usual orientation along a C_4 axis.

Consider again tetrahedral hybridization. In this case $\mathbf{G}_I$ is $\mathbf{D}_2$. In $\mathbf{D}_2$ an s orbital transforms as A while p_z, p_y, and p_x transform as B_1, B_2, and B_3, respectively. Thus, normalizing the columns of $\mathbf{T}$, we have

$$\boldsymbol{\chi} = \boldsymbol{\phi}\mathbf{T} = (\phi_1 \quad \phi_2 \quad \phi_3 \quad \phi_4)\begin{bmatrix} \frac{1}{2} & \frac{1}{2} & \frac{1}{2} & \frac{1}{2} \\ \frac{1}{2} & \frac{1}{2} & -\frac{1}{2} & -\frac{1}{2} \\ \frac{1}{2} & -\frac{1}{2} & \frac{1}{2} & -\frac{1}{2} \\ \frac{1}{2} & -\frac{1}{2} & -\frac{1}{2} & \frac{1}{2} \end{bmatrix} \tag{10.29}$$

and

$$\boldsymbol{\phi} = \boldsymbol{\chi}\tilde{\mathbf{T}} = (s \quad p_z \quad p_y \quad p_x)\begin{bmatrix} \frac{1}{2} & \frac{1}{2} & \frac{1}{2} & \frac{1}{2} \\ \frac{1}{2} & \frac{1}{2} & -\frac{1}{2} & -\frac{1}{2} \\ \frac{1}{2} & -\frac{1}{2} & \frac{1}{2} & -\frac{1}{2} \\ \frac{1}{2} & -\frac{1}{2} & -\frac{1}{2} & \frac{1}{2} \end{bmatrix} \tag{10.29a}$$

or

$$\phi_1 = \tfrac{1}{2}(s + p_z + p_y + p_x) \tag{10.29b}$$

$$\phi_2 = \tfrac{1}{2}(s + p_z - p_y - p_x) \tag{10.29c}$$

$$\phi_3 = \tfrac{1}{2}(s - p_z + p_y - p_x) \tag{10.29d}$$

$$\phi_4 = \tfrac{1}{2}(s - p_z - p_y + p_x) \tag{10.29e}$$

Note that in Eq. (10.29a) the matrix $\tilde{\mathbf{T}}$ is the character table for $\mathbf{G}_I$ with the rows normalized. This will be the general situation, except that degenerate representations will have to be expressed as independent representations.

Consider the construction of the hybrid orbitals for NH_3. The group of interchanges is $\mathbf{C}_3$. Let

$$\sigma = \lambda s + \mu p_z \tag{10.30}$$

We have

$$(\phi_1 \quad \phi_2 \quad \phi_3) = (\sigma \quad p_x \quad p_y)\begin{bmatrix} 1/\sqrt{3} & 1/\sqrt{3} & 1/\sqrt{3} \\ 2/\sqrt{6} & -1/\sqrt{6} & -1/\sqrt{6} \\ 0 & 1/\sqrt{2} & -1/\sqrt{2} \end{bmatrix} \tag{10.31}$$

$$\phi_1 = 1/\sqrt{3}\sigma + 2/\sqrt{6}p_x \tag{10.31a}$$

$$\phi_2 = 1/\sqrt{3}\sigma - 1/\sqrt{6}p_x + 1/\sqrt{2}p_y \tag{10.31b}$$

$$\phi_3 = 1/\sqrt{3}\sigma - 1/\sqrt{6}p_x - 1/\sqrt{2}p_y \tag{10.31c}$$

In Eq. (10.31) we have constructed two independent real forms for the E representation of $\mathbf{C}_3$.

The construction of any other hybridization scheme is equally simple. The previously mentioned word of caution about the orientation of the reference axis system for an octahedral system should, however, be remembered. In that case, to get the usual orientation of hybrids, one should directly construct the matrix $\mathbf{T}$ from the projection operators of the $\mathbf{O}$ or $\mathbf{O}_h$ point group.

10.6 PROJECTION OPERATORS AND L.C.A.O. MOLECULAR ORBITALS

Symmetry-adapted molecular orbitals can be projected out of a basis set that is composed of atom-centered functions by use of projection operators. In many cases, with limited-size basis sets and high symmetry molecules, the symmetry can completely or almost completely determine the molecular orbitals. Such is the case for the π-electron system of benzene. Another such case is the valence M.O.'s of methane when constructed from carbon $2s$ and $2p$ functions and hydrogen $1s$ functions only. In these cases the orbital occupancy and symmetry of electronic transitions can be derived with a minimum of qualititive quantum mechanical concepts. In the case of the π orbitals of benzene, the principal rotational subgroup of the $\mathbf{D}_{6h}$ molecular point group is sufficient to uniquely determine the symmetry orbitals. The results of the operations of $\mathbf{C}_6$ on one of the carbon $2p\pi$ orbitals of benzene are as follows:

$\mathbf{C}_6$	E	C_6	C_3	C_2	C_3^2	C_6^5
χ_1	χ_1	χ_2	χ_3	χ_4	χ_5	χ_6

(10.32)

Within the $\mathbf{C}_6$ point group, the π molecular orbitals of benzene have the symmetries A, B, E_1, and E_2. (It is, in fact, general that when a regular polygonal system is constructed with one basis function on each center, all the irreducible representations of the corresponding cyclic point group appear once and only once in the function space of the system.)

Projecting out the various symmetry-adapted orbitals, we have

$$P^{(A)}\chi_1 = \chi_1 + \chi_2 + \chi_3 + \chi_4 + \chi_5 + \chi_6 \tag{10.33a}$$

$$P^{(B)}\chi_1 = \chi_1 - \chi_2 + \chi_3 - \chi_4 + \chi_5 - \chi_6 \tag{10.33b}$$

$$P^{(E_1)}\chi_1 = 2\chi_1 + \chi_2 - \chi_3 - 2\chi_4 - \chi_5 + \chi_6 \tag{10.33c}$$

$$P^{(E_2)}\chi_1 = 2\chi_1 - \chi_2 - \chi_3 + 2\chi_4 - \chi_5 - \chi_6 \tag{10.33d}$$

(Notice that in Eqs. 10.33c and 10.33d the real form of the characters of the C_6 and C_3 elements in the E representations were taken from the $\mathbf{D}_{6h}$ character table, rather than using the imaginary forms from the $\mathbf{C}_6$ table. The separable forms from the $\mathbf{C}_6$ table could have been used and the results resolved into real and imaginary components.) Except for normalization, Eqs. 10.33a and 10.33b are the symmetry-adapted a and b orbitals, while Eqs. 10.33c and 10.33d represent one component of degenerate pairs of e_1 and e_2 orbitals. (Within the $\mathbf{D}_{6h}$ point group, these become a_{2u}, b_{2g}, e_{1g}, and e_{2u} when the nodal properties of π orbitals are taken into account.) At the Hückel level of calculation, overlap is explicitly ignored and the normalization factors are $(6)^{-1/2}$ for the a and b orbitals and $(12)^{-1/2}$ for the e orbitals (see Sections 7.4 and 7.9).

The Hückel energy levels for benzene can be calculated directly to give

$$\begin{aligned} E_{a_{2u}} &= \langle (6)^{-1/2}(\chi_1 + \chi_2 + \chi_3 + \chi_4 + \chi_5 + \chi_6)|\hat{H}|(6)^{-1/2} \\ &\quad \times (\chi_1 + \chi_2 + \chi_3 + \chi_4 + \chi_5 + \chi_6)\rangle \\ &= \tfrac{1}{6}(6\alpha + 12\beta) \\ &= \alpha + 2\beta \end{aligned} \tag{10.34a}$$

$$\begin{aligned} E_{b_{2g}} &= \langle (6)^{-1/2}(\chi_1 - \chi_2 + \chi_3 - \chi_4 + \chi_5 - \chi_6)|\hat{H}|(6)^{-1/2} \\ &\quad \times (\chi_1 - \chi_2 + \chi_3 - \chi_4 + \chi_5 - \chi_6)\rangle \\ &= \alpha - 2\beta \end{aligned} \tag{10.34b}$$

$$\begin{aligned} E_{e_{1g}} &= \langle (12)^{-1/2}(2\chi_1 + \chi_2 - \chi_3 - 2\chi_4 - \chi_5 + \chi_6)|\hat{H}|(12)^{-1/2} \\ &\quad \times (2\chi_1 + \chi_2 - \chi_3 - 2\chi_4 - \chi_5 + \chi_6)\rangle \\ &= \alpha + \beta \end{aligned} \tag{10.34c}$$

$$\begin{aligned} E_{e_{2u}} &= \langle (12)^{-1/2}(2\chi_1 - \chi_2 - \chi_3 + 2\chi_4 - \chi_5 - \chi_6)|\hat{H}|(12)^{-1/2} \\ &\quad \times (2\chi_1 - \chi_2 - \chi_3 + 2\chi_4 - \chi_5 - \chi_6)\rangle \\ &= \alpha - \beta \end{aligned} \tag{10.34d}$$

In Eqs. 10.34a to 10.34d the usual Hückel approximations and definitions are made:

$$\langle \chi_\mu|\hat{H}|\chi_\mu\rangle = \alpha \tag{10.35}$$

$$\langle \chi_\mu|\hat{H}|\chi_\nu\rangle = \beta \quad \mu \text{ and } \nu \text{ are directly bonded} \tag{10.36}$$

$$= 0 \quad \text{otherwise} \tag{10.36a}$$

Remembering that β is a negative number, the order of the energy levels is $E_{a_{2u}}$, $E_{e_{1g}}$, $E_{e_{2u}}$, $E_{b_{2g}}$. The π-electron system of benzene contains six electrons; consequently, the a_{2u} orbital is doubly occupied and the doubly degenerate e_{1g} set is occupied by four electrons. The first electronic transition is $e_{2u} \leftarrow e_{1g}$. The ground-state electronic wave function of benzene has A_{1g} symmetry, since all the molecular orbitals are completely occupied. The first excited state will have an odd electron in the e_{1g} orbital and a single electron in the e_{2u} orbital. The symmetry of the excited state will be that resulting from a product of these representations:

$$E_{1g} \times E_{2u} = B_{1u} + B_{2u} + E_{1u} \tag{10.37}$$

If the mutual repulsions of the electrons were neglected, these states would all be degenerate; however, the electronic repulsion actually splits the levels. The net result is that, of the excited singlet states, the ${}^1B_{2u}$ state is the lowest state and the ${}^1E_{1u}$ the highest arising from this orbital transition. Direct transitions from the ground state to the ${}^1B_{2u}$ state are symmetry-forbidden. As we shall see later, however, this transition is experimentally observed (at 38,086 cm^{-1}), owing to the interaction of the electronic and vibrational states. Its intensity is, nevertheless, much less than that of the transition to the allowed ${}^1E_{1u}$ state occurring at about 55,000 cm^{-1}.

Symmetry-adapted orbitals for methane can be constructed by using either the s and p valence orbitals from carbon or a set of four tetrahedrally hybridized orbitals. If the calculations are sufficiently refined, either choice will give identical results. For crude, qualitative treatments, however, the tetrahedrally hybridized set produces more easily interpretable results. The results of projecting out symmetry adapted functions from either the set of tetrahedrally hybridized carbon orbitals or the set of hydrogen 1s orbitals within the **T** subgroup of $\mathbf{T}_d$ are the same as previously found in Exercise 5.5 for a set of four equivalent bond functions. Except for normalization, the hydrogen contributions are

$$\phi_H^a = h_1 + h_2 + h_3 + h_4 \tag{10.38a}$$

$$\phi_H^t = 3h_1 - h_2 - h_3 - h_4 \tag{10.38b}$$

and the carbon contributions are

$$\phi_C^a = T_1 + T_2 + T_3 + T_4 \tag{10.39a}$$

$$\phi_C^t = 3T_1 - T_2 - T_3 - T_4 \tag{10.39b}$$

where the h_i and T_i are the hydrogen 1s and tetrahedral orbitals, respectively. (Within the $\mathbf{T}_d$ group these become a_1 and t_2 in symmetry.) The complete molecular orbitals have the form

$$\phi^{a_1} = c_1^a \phi_H^a \pm c_2^a \phi_C^a \tag{10.40a}$$

$$\phi^{t_2} = c_1^t \phi_H^t \pm c_2^t \phi_C^t \tag{10.40b}$$

The positive sign produces bonding character and the negative sign antibonding character. If the hydrogen and tetrahedral contributions are separately normalized and the Hückel zero-differential-overlap approximation is made, the normalizing constant for the a_1 orbitals is $\frac{1}{2}$, while that for the t_2 orbitals is $(12)^{-1/2}$. The molecular orbitals, and consequently the energies, of methane are thus completely determined by symmetry except for the two constants c_1 and c_2 [or really, their ratio, since $(c_1^2 + c_2^2)$ must equal unity]. The results for the energies are

$$\begin{aligned} E_{a_1} &= \langle \phi^a | \hat{H} | \phi^a \rangle \\ &= \langle c_1^a \phi_H^a \pm c_2^a \phi_C^a | \hat{H} | c_1^a \phi_H^a \pm c_2^a \phi_C^a \rangle \\ &= (c_1^a)^2 \langle \phi_H^a | \hat{H} | \phi_H^a \rangle + (c_2^a)^2 \langle \phi_C^a | \hat{H} | \phi_C^a \rangle \pm 2 c_1^a c_2^a \langle \phi_H^a | \hat{H} | \phi_C^a \rangle \end{aligned} \tag{10.41a}$$

$$\begin{aligned} E_{t_2} &= \langle \phi^t | \hat{H} | \phi^t \rangle \\ &= (c_1^t)^2 \langle \phi_H^t | \hat{H} | \phi_H^t \rangle + (c_2^t)^2 \langle \phi_C^t | \hat{H} | \phi_C^t \rangle \pm 2 c_1^t c_2^t \langle \phi_H^t | \hat{H} | \phi_C^t \rangle \end{aligned} \tag{10.41b}$$

The terms appearing in the a_1 case are

$$\begin{aligned}\langle\phi_{\mathrm{H}}^{a}|\hat{H}|\phi_{\mathrm{H}}^{a}\rangle &= \langle\tfrac{1}{2}(h_1 + h_2 + h_3 + h_4)|\hat{H}|\tfrac{1}{2}(h_1 + h_2 + h_3 + h_4)\rangle \\ &= \tfrac{1}{4}\{\langle h_1|\hat{H}|h_1\rangle + \langle h_2|\hat{H}|h_2\rangle + \langle h_3|\hat{H}|h_3\rangle + \langle h_4|\hat{H}|h_4\rangle\} \\ &= \langle h_1|\hat{H}|h_1\rangle \end{aligned} \tag{10.42a}$$

$$\begin{aligned}\langle\phi_{\mathrm{H}}^{a}|\hat{H}|\phi_{\mathrm{C}}^{a}\rangle &= \langle\tfrac{1}{2}(h_1 + h_2 + h_3 + h_4)|\hat{H}|\tfrac{1}{2}(T_1 + T_2 + T_3 + T_4)\rangle \\ &= \tfrac{1}{4}\{\langle h_1|\hat{H}|T_1\rangle + \langle h_2|\hat{H}|T_2\rangle + \langle h_3|\hat{H}|T_3) + \langle h_4|\hat{H}|T_4\rangle\} \\ &= \langle h_1|\hat{H}|T_1\rangle \end{aligned} \tag{10.42b}$$

$$\begin{aligned}\langle\phi_{\mathrm{C}}^{a}|\hat{H}|\phi_{\mathrm{C}}^{a}\rangle &= \langle\tfrac{1}{2}(T_1 + T_2 + T_3 + T_4)|\hat{H}|\tfrac{1}{2}(T_1 + T_2 + T_3 + T_4)\rangle \\ &= \tfrac{1}{4}\{\langle T_1|\hat{H}|T_1\rangle + \langle T_2|\hat{H}|T_2\rangle + \langle T_3|\hat{H}|T_3\rangle + \langle T_4|\hat{H}|T_4\rangle \\ &\quad + 2\langle T_1|\hat{H}|T_2\rangle + 2\langle T_1|\hat{H}|T_3\rangle + 2\langle T_1|\hat{H}|T_4\rangle \\ &\quad + 2\langle T_2|\hat{H}|T_3\rangle + 2\langle T_2|\hat{H}|T_4\rangle + 2(T_3|\hat{H}|T_4\rangle\} \\ &= \langle T_1|\hat{H}|T_1\rangle + 3\langle T_1|\hat{H}|T_2\rangle \end{aligned} \tag{10.42c}$$

The crossed terms in Eqs. 10.42a and 10.42b vanish within this approximation; however, those in Eq. 10.42c do not, since they represent interactions between two nonorthogonal orbitals on the same atom. The energies of the a_1 molecular orbitals are thus

$$\begin{aligned} E_{a_1} &= (c_1^a)^2\langle h_1|\hat{H}|h_1\rangle + (c_2^a)^2\{\langle T_1|\hat{H}|T_1\rangle + 3\langle T_1|\hat{H}|T_2\rangle\} \\ &\quad \pm 2c_1^a c_2^a\langle h_1|\hat{H}|T_1\rangle \end{aligned} \tag{10.43}$$

The terms in the t_2 case and the energies of the t_2 molecular orbitals are

$$\langle\phi_{\mathrm{H}}^{t}|\hat{H}|\phi_{\mathrm{H}}^{t}\rangle = \langle h_1|\hat{H}|h_1\rangle \tag{10.44a}$$

$$\langle\phi_{\mathrm{H}}^{t}|\hat{H}|\phi_{\mathrm{C}}^{t}\rangle = \langle h_1|\hat{H}|T_1\rangle \tag{10.44b}$$

$$\langle\phi_{\mathrm{C}}^{t}|\hat{H}|\phi_{\mathrm{C}}^{t}\rangle = \langle T_1|\hat{H}|T_1\rangle - \langle T_1|\hat{H}|T_2\rangle \tag{10.44c}$$

$$\begin{aligned} E_{t_2} &= (c_1^t)^2\langle h_1|\hat{H}|h_1\rangle + (c_2^t)^2\{\langle T_1|\hat{H}|T_1\rangle - \langle T_1|\hat{H}|T_2\rangle\} \\ &\quad \pm 2c_1^t c_2^t\langle h_1|\hat{H}|T_1\rangle \end{aligned} \tag{10.45}$$

If numerical estimates of the integrals are available, the energies in each case can be obtained by solving the 2 × 2 determinant which results when the variational principle is applied to Eq. 10.43 or Eq. 10.45. Qualitatively, however, if the c^{a}'s and the c^{t}'s are roughly of the same order of magnitude, the a_1 bonding orbital will lie lower than the t_2 bonding orbital and the a_1 antibonding orbital lower than the t_2 antibonding orbital, since all the integrals are intrinsically negative. Thus, the eight valence electrons in methane completely fill the a_1 and t_2 bonding orbitals. The first electronic transition is $a_1 \leftarrow t_2$ in character, giving rise to a T_2 state for the first excited electronic state. The ${}^1T_2 \leftarrow {}^1A_1$ transition is symmetry-allowed and probably occurs at about 68,700 cm^{-1}. The assignment is uncertain since this energy is sufficiently high to cause disassociation of the molecule.

Exercise 10.2: The L.C.A.O. valence orbital treatment of ethane leads to three molecular orbitals of A_{1g} symmetry, three of A_{2u} symmetry, and two degenerate pairs of each E_g and E_u symmetry. Starting with tetrahedral carbon orbitals and hydrogen 1*s* orbitals, construct the expression for the energies of these in terms of integrals over atomic basis sets and mixing coefficients (analogously to Eqs. 10.43 and 10.45).

10.7 ORBITAL OCCUPANCY IN MOLECULES

We have stated that the orbital occupancy in a molecule cannot be determined with certainty from symmetry arguments. With the aid of simple concepts from quantum mechanics some qualitative information about orbital occupancy can be obtained and, in fact, the occupancy in hydrides containing only one heavier atom can be determined with a fair degree of certainty. To illustrate this, let us consider ammonia (NH_3) as an example. If the atoms were infinitely separated, we would have one nitrogen atom and three hydrogen atoms. The orbital occupancy in these individual atoms can, as we have already discussed, be determined from the *aufbau* principle. If, on the other hand, we could bring the atoms together, passing through the equilibrium molecular geometry, until the nuclei coalesced, we would have a nuclear charge of $+10$. This is the charge on the neon nucleus. The orbital occupancy of neon can again be determined from the *aufbau* principle. The actual ammonia molecule lies somewhere between these extremes. In fact, in this case it lies much nearer to the united neon atom than to the separated atoms. If the symmetries of the occupied orbitals in neon are reduced to the $\mathbf{C}_{3v}$ symmetry of ammonia, the energies of the resulting symmetry orbitals are in the correct order for the occupied molecular orbitals of ammonia. In neon the 1*s* and 2*s* atomic orbitals are doubly occupied. The set of three 2*p* orbitals are fully occupied with six electrons. The totally symmetric *s* orbitals transform as a_1 orbitals in the $\mathbf{C}_{3v}$ point group. The *p* orbitals transform as the three-dimensional $D_u^{(1)}$ in the $\mathbf{R}_h(3)$ point group. In the $\mathbf{C}_{3v}$ point group, the $D_u^{(1)}$ representation reduces to an A_1 and an E representation. When constructed from a given basis set, a nodeless orbital is lower in energy than one with nodes; thus, the a_1 orbital should lie lower than the pair of *e* orbitals. The a_1 molecular orbital arising from the neon 1*s* orbital corresponds to the inner-shell orbital arising from the nitrogen 1*s* orbital in the molecule. The other three orbitals are valence orbitals and occur in the proper order in the molecule. The correlation is shown schematically in Fig. 10.4.

The ordering of the vacant L.C.A.O. molecular orbitals can be obtained by using the fact that molecular orbitals constructed as linear combinations of atomic orbitals usually occur in pairs, one member of the pair being "bonding" and the other "antibonding" with reference to the center of gravity of the energies of the constituent atomic orbitals. Thus, the remaining a_1 and *e* orbitals for ammonia are the antibonding orbitals that pair with the occupied bonding *e* orbitals and the highest occupied a_1 orbital. The amount of destabilization of the antibonding

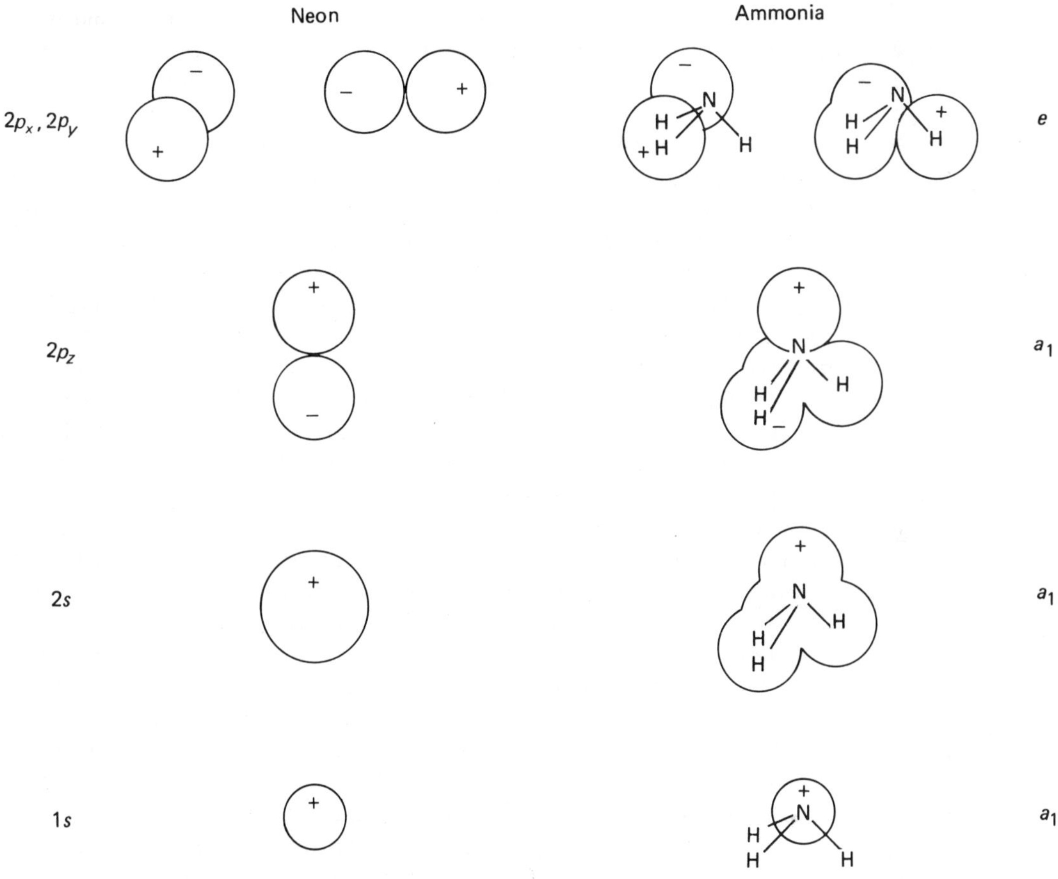

Fig. 10.4. Schematic correlation of the neon atomic orbitals with the molecular orbitals of ammonia. The plus and minus signs are the signs of the wave functions in the indicated regions of space.

orbitals approximately equals the amount of stabilization of the corresponding bonding orbitals. We would therefore expect the vacant *e* orbitals to be lower in energy (less destabilized) than the vacant a_1 orbital since the occupied (bonding) *e* orbitals are higher in energy (less stabilized) than the a_1 orbital. These arguments thus give us the correct order of energy for the L.C.A.O. molecular orbitals of ammonia when they are constructed as linear combinations of the atomic orbitals of the constituent atoms. In fact, the occupied orbitals obtained are in the proper order, no matter what the starting basis set is.

This same scheme will give the ordering of the molecular orbitals arising from any set of equivalent atomic orbitals having σ symmetry with respect to the bonds in the molecule. Thus, in NF_3 the molecular orbitals arising from the nitrogen atomic orbitals and the $2p_\sigma$ orbitals from the fluorines again give rise to a set of molecular orbitals occurring in the order a_1, a_1, e, e, a_1. The molecular orbitals arising from the other atomic orbitals on fluorine give problems, however. The source of the problems is more one of the energies of the individual atomic orbitals and of their interactions than it is one of symmetry. First, the energies of the 2*s* and 2*p* orbitals on fluorine are different. Either can interact with the atomic orbitals on nitrogen and with each other to yield molecular orbitals; however, the energy starting point is different for the two sets of orbitals. Furthermore, owing to the differing spatial shapes, the interaction energies of the two sets will be different. It turns out that due to these effects, the molecular orbitals having a_1 and *e* symmetry arising from the 2*s* fluorine orbitals remain essentially localized on the fluorines and that bonding occurs mainly via the $2p_\sigma$ orbitals. The other 2*p* orbitals from the fluorines can lead to one a_1, one a_2, and two pairs of degenerate *e* molecular orbitals. All told, there are five a_1, one a_2, and five pairs of *e* orbitals arising from the valence atomic orbitals in NF_3. Of these, three a_1 and two pairs of *e* orbitals can be ordered relative to each other from an extensión of the united atom concept as applied to ammonia. The relative energies of the other molecular orbitals are unknown without some additional information.

In ammonia one pair of *e* and two a_1 orbitals are bonding and one pair of *e* and one a_1 are antibonding. The latter would also be expected to be antibonding in NF_3. The NF_3 molecule has 26 valence electrons. The molecular orbitals we have constructed can accommodate at most 32 valence electrons; thus, only the mentioned antibonding orbitals are vacant. All the others are fully occupied. This means that the first electronic transition will arise from a promotion of an electron to an *e* orbital just as it did in ammonia. Since, however, we do not know the energy ordering of all the occupied orbitals, we cannot say which orbital it is promoted from. Even so, a complete characterization of the electronic spectrum of NF_3 could be used with the ordering we have obtained to yield much information about the ordering of the occupied orbitals. Unfortunately, however, the electronic spectrum of NF_3 appears to be unresolvable, yielding only a continuous increase in absorption from about 1800 Å to the ionization limit at about 960 Å.

Another approach to the assignment of the ordering of molecular orbitals is to construct these as a linear combination of bond orbitals. In this treatment, each bond is treated as a pseudo-diatomic, two-atomic-orbital system having a nodeless bonding and a one-node antibonding two-center bond orbital associated with it. (The nodes under consideration are nodes perpendicular to the bond, not nodes along the bond.) These are combined to yield molecular orbitals. The bonding bond orbitals yield bonding molecular orbitals while the antibonding bond orbitals yield antibonding molecular orbitals. This is shown schematically, for two sets of bond orbitals, in Fig. 10.5. There will be interactions between members of the bonding and antibonding sets which correspond to the same irreducible representation; however, these interactions will only increase the bonding or antibonding character of the individual molecular orbitals. The representations of the resulting molecular orbitals are found by considering the

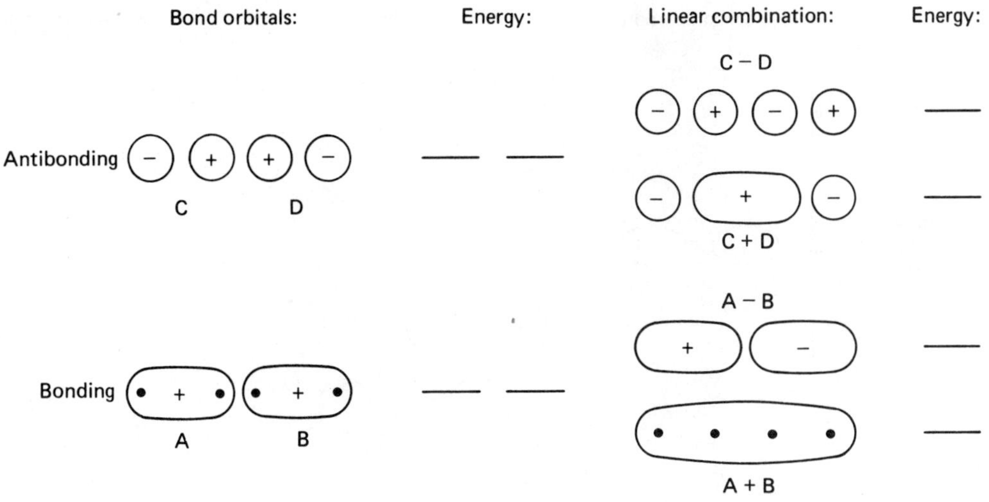

Fig. 10.5. Schematic representation of the linear combination of two sets of bond orbitals. A and B are bonding bond orbitals. C and D are antibonding. Positions of the nuclei are indicated by dots in A, B, and A + B. Signs are the signs of the wave functions in the indicated regions.

transformation properties of the bonds. This method is useful when the molecule contains many equivalent bonds and only a few bond types.

Ethane, having six equivalent CH bonds and one CC bond, presents a good example for this treatment. Let us consider the staggered $\mathbf{D}_{3d}$ conformation (see Fig. 10.6). The nodeless CC bonding orbital transforms as the A_{1g} irreducible representation within $\mathbf{D}_{3d}$ while the antibonding CC orbital, having a node in the center, transforms as A_{2u}. The irreducible representations for the combinations of CH bonding orbitals are A_{1g}, E_g, A_{2u}, and E_u. The representations for the CH antibonding orbitals are the same. (This will always be the case for bonding and antibonding orbitals unless the nodes in the antibonding orbitals lie on a plane of symmetry, a point of inversion, or a C_2' axis in the molecular symmetry group, as was the case for the CC antibonding orbital.) The bonding and antibonding molecular orbitals again occur in pairs having either the same or complementary symmetries. For molecules with a σ_h element, a point of inversion, or a C_2' axis relating equivalent bond orbitals, the relationship is complementary; that is, the a_{1g} bonding orbital pairs with the a_{2u} antibonding orbital, the e_g with the e_u, and so on. The e orbitals are totally CH in character, while the a orbitals contain contributions from both CC and CH. The lowest-energy molecular orbital should be a totally symmetric a_{1g} molecular orbital. (This means that the highest-energy vacant molecular orbital should be a_{2u}.) The a_{2u} bonding orbital should have its energy determined primarily by the CH bond orbitals, since the a_{2u} CC bond orbital is antibonding, and consequently, should lie at considerably higher energy. The A_{2u} representation is symmetric with respect to the C_3 operation,

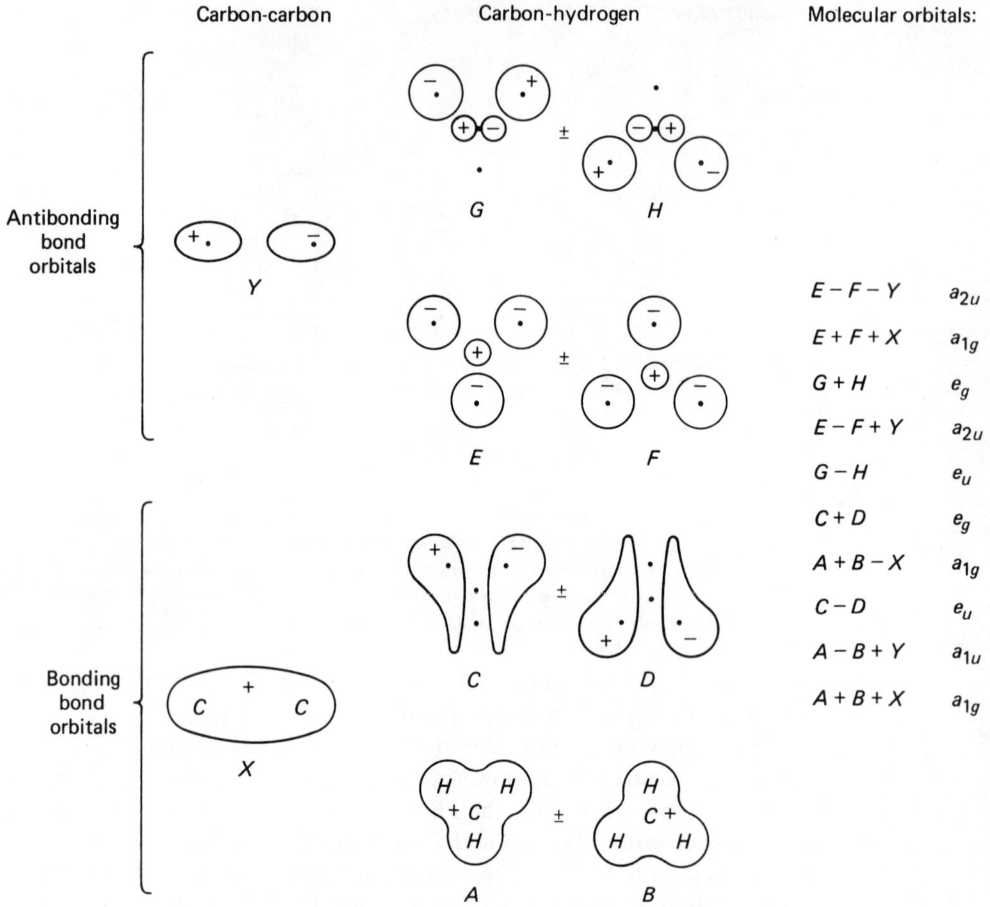

Fig. 10.6. Schematic representation of linear combinations of bond orbitals for staggered ethane. The CH_3 sets are shown end on. Positions of the nuclei are as shown in the first set. The signs are the signs of the wave functions in the indicated regions. The a_{1g} and a_{2u} CH bond orbitals interact with the bonding and antibonding CC bond orbitals to give two overall a_{1g} and two a_{2u} molecular orbitals.

implying that there are no nodes between adjacent hydrogens on the same carbon in the a_{2u} molecular orbital. The e orbitals will have nodes between adjacent hydrogens. The a_{2u} orbital, on the other hand, has a node between the carbons. The e_g orbital also has such a node, while the e_u does not. The e_g orbital, having two nodes, should lie higher in energy than either the a_{2u} or e_u orbitals which have only one node. The e_u orbital should lie higher in energy than the a_{2u} since the node is between bond orbitals in a closer spatial arrangement in the e_u case than in the a_{2u} case. We have thus established the following energy ordering among the bonding molecular orbitals: $a_{1g} < a_{2u} < e_u < e_g$. The only bonding molecular orbital missing in this sequence is the other a_{1g} molecular orbital, arising from the antibonding combination of the CC bonding orbital and the A_{1g} combination of the CH bonding orbitals. The corresponding antibonding orbitals can be ordered by the orbital pairing relationship. Thus, all but two of the occupied and vacant molecular orbitals that can be formed from a linear combination of bond orbitals (and which, in this case, are the same as the L.C.A.O. molecular orbitals) are obtained from symmetry and qualitative bonding arguments. In this particular case, the remaining a_{1g} bonding orbital occurs between the two e bonding orbital sets, and, by pairing arguments, the related a_{2u} vacant orbital occurs between the two sets of vacant e orbitals. The first electronic transition in staggered ethane should result from the promotion of an electron from an e_g orbital to an e_u orbital. This gives rise to an A_{1u} state, an A_{2u} state, and a doubly degenerate E_u state. Unfortunately, the electronic spectrum of ethane is insufficiently resolved to experimentally assign the symmetries of the excited states.

The methods we have outlined can be used to obtain some insight into the molecular orbital occupancy of larger molecules. In these cases, however, the amount of information that can be obtained decreases rapidly as the size of the molecule increases and as its symmetry decreases.

Exercise 10.3*: Find the molecular orbital occupancy in the water molecule by using the united atom concept.

Exercise 10.4: Find the molecular orbital representations for ethylene by using the linear combination of bond orbitals. (Note that there are now three types of bonds: CH, CC_σ, and CC_π. The occupied CC_π lies higher in energy than the occupied CC_σ.)

10.8 VALENCE BOND WAVE FUNCTIONS

A molecular orbital treatment of a molecule based upon an atomic orbital basis set involves the construction of one-electron molecular orbitals as linear combinations of the atomic orbitals. The many-electron wave function for the molecule is then constructed as a product of these one-electron molecular orbitals. The *valence bond* treatment is a many-electron treatment from the start. It starts from products of atomic orbitals that represent the "bonding" in the molecule and then takes linear combinations of these products. In highly refined calculations, the two methods converge on the same results. For more approximate work, each approximation has its advantages and disadvantages.

In the simplest approximation, valence bond theory leads to the description of bonding by Lewis dot structures and to resonance theory as used by organic chemists. These are extremely simple methods which yield much useful information about the ground states of most molecules that have singlet ground states. On the other hand, qualitative interpretations of electronic spectra and excited electronic states are usually easier with the aid of simple molecular orbital theory.

For direct numerical calculations with a given basis set, the valence bond method frequently gives ground-state energies with a higher absolute accuracy, since it partially accounts for *electron correlation* (the tendency of like charged electrons to avoid one another). However, this advantage is often offset by the fact that in *self-consistent field* (S.C.F.) molecular orbital calculations, the *correlation energy* (the energy error due to electron correlation) is similar for similar molecules.

The symmetric permutation group (Section 6.4) is most useful in detailed valence bond calculations. Use is made of the complementarity of the spatial and spin functions, as described in Section 7.11. For a given spin multiplicity, the projection operator for the appropriate spatial representation is applied to a simple product function corresponding to the desired spatial function. This yields the (unnormalized) required linear combination of product functions. Consider as a simple example the valence bond wave function for the H_2 molecule as constructed from 1*s* atomic orbitals. For the singlet ground state, the permutation representation for the two electron spins is $[1^2]$ within **S**(2). This requires the spatial function to transform as [2]. The simple atomic orbital product function is $1s_A(1)1s_B(2)$, where A and B label the 1*s* orbitals on the two atoms. Operating on this with $P^{[2]}$, we have

$$P^{[2]}1s_A(1)1s_B(2) = 1s_A(1)1s_B(2) + 1s_A(2)1s_B(1) \qquad (10.46)$$

This is the well-known valence bond spatial function for the ground state of H_2.

In principle, this procedure can be applied to any valence bond problem not involving *ionic configurations* (configurations with two electrons associated with a given basis spatial orbital); however, complications quickly arise. Only in **S**(2) is the representation corresponding to a singlet spin state nondegenerate, yet for most molecules a singlet ground state is nondegenerate. In actual fact, what the permutation representation produces is a combination of the singlet ground state and the singlet excited states that can be produced by simple product functions. These can be separated by adding weighting coefficients to the various terms in the linear combination and then doing a variational treatment with respect to the weighting coefficients. This will lead to a determinantal equation of the same order as the degeneracy of the representation. The lowest-energy root of this will be the ground-state energy.

Consider, for example, the singlet states of the π-electron system of butadiene. The singlet spin function transforms as $[2^2]$ within **S**(4). This representation is twofold-degenerate and is self-conjugate. Thus, there are two simple product singlet states of the butadiene π system. If we call the $p\pi$ orbitals a, b, c, and d, the first few simple products are $a(1)b(2)c(3)d(4)$, $a(2)b(3)c(4)d(1)$, $a(3)b(4)c(1)d(2)$, and so on. To get the bond structures corresponding to these, it is assumed that the same pair of electrons is bonded in each case. The first and third of these thus correspond, in the valence bond approximation, to structure **1**, while the second

$$C_a{=}C_b{-}C_c{=}C_d$$

1

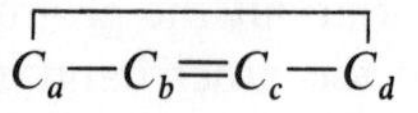

2

corresponds to structure **2**, the "long-bond" structure. All of the other permutations would lead to one or the other of these or to structure **3**. Structures such as **3**, where the bonds overlap, are not allowed valence bond structures.

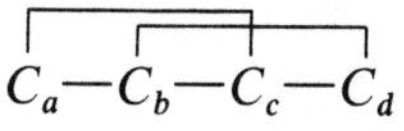

3

Applying the permutations of **S**(4) to $a(1)b(2)c(3)d(4)$, the (1^4) operation leaves it unchanged for a structure of type **1**, the $6(2, 1^2)$ give two structures of each of the three types, the $3(2^2)$ give three of type **1**, the $8(3, 1)$ give four each of types **2** and **3**, and the $6(4)$ all give type **2** structures. Applying the projection operator $P^{[2^2]}$ to a type **1** structure thus gives

$$P^{[2^2]}\Psi_1 = 8\Psi_1 - 4\Psi_2 - 4\Psi_3 \tag{10.47}$$

but since Ψ_3 is not allowed

$${}^1\Psi_{VB} = 8c_1\Psi_1 - 4c_2\Psi_2 \tag{10.48}$$

where the c's are the mixing coefficients which are determined by the variational principle. It turns out that the ground state is predominantly Ψ_1 in character, while the excited singlet state arising from this approximation is predominantly Ψ_2.

These states can also be characterized by their symmetry with respect to the point group of the molecule. There are several ways of doing this. One is to map the representation from **S**(N) onto the *covering group* of the molecule (the simplest group that effects all interchanges of equivalent positions). For butadiene, this is $\mathbf{C}_2$. The $\mathbf{C}_2$ operation corresponds to (2^2); consequently, $[2^2]$ maps onto two A representations of $\mathbf{C}_2$. (For systems with closed-shell ground states, the ground state will always be totally symmetric.)

Let us briefly consider the π-electron system of benzene. The $[2^3]$ representation of **S**(6) is five-dimensional. The five allowed structures are the two Kékulé structures (**1** and **2**) and the three Dewar Structures (**3** to **5**).

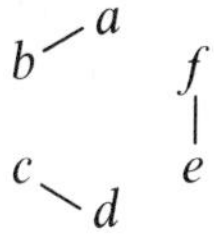

1

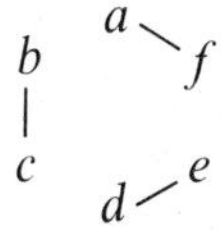

2

3

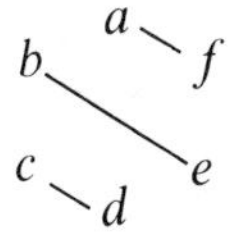

4

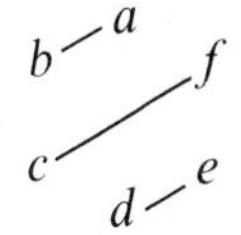

5

(Note that these are all the structures that could be drawn which connect pairs of points without crossing lines. Similar cyclic structures can be drawn for finding the allowed pairing for any valencc bond wave function, whether the molecule is cyclic or not. Such diagrams are called *Rumer diagrams*. For an N-electron singlet, there are $N!/\{(N/2 + 1)!(N/2)!\}$ such structures.) For benzene, there are two sets of degenerate structures. The mapping of $[2^3]$ onto $\mathbf{D}_6$, the covering group for benzene, yields $2A_1 + B_2 + E_2$. These same representations can be obtained from structures **1** to **5**. The two equivalent structures **1** and **2** give rise to the symmetric and antisymmetric combinations (which transform as A_1 and B_2):

$$\Psi_1(A_1) = 1/\sqrt{2}(\Psi_1 + \Psi_2) \tag{10.49}$$

$$\Psi(B_2) = 1/\sqrt{2}(\Psi_1 - \Psi_2) \tag{10.50}$$

The three equivalent structures **3** to **5** combine to give A_1 and E_2 representations:

$$\Psi_2(A_1) = 1/\sqrt{3}(\Psi_3 + \Psi_4 + \Psi_5) \tag{10.51}$$

$$\Psi(E_2) = 1\sqrt{6}(\Psi_3 - \Psi_4 - \Psi_5) \tag{10.52}$$

This additional factorization simplifies the calculations in that only functions transforming as the same representation interact with each other. Thus, the B_2 and E_2 states are completely determined, while the A_1 states lead to a 2×2 determinantal problem.

It is frequently useful to be able to qualitatively find the one-electron molecular orbitals which correspond to valence bond structures. If the ground state of a molecule is fairly well defined by a single valence bond structure or by a combination of equivalent structures, this gives a method of finding the molecular orbitals which are occupied in the ground state. The method of doing this is analogous to the method of bond orbitals presented in Section 10.7. In this case, only the bonding bond orbitals are considered. Thus, for butadiene, considering only the first valence bond structure, we have

$$\phi_1(a) = \chi_{ab} + \chi_{cd} \tag{10.53}$$

$$\phi_2(b) = \chi_{ab} - \chi_{cd} \tag{10.54}$$

where the χ's correspond to the indicated pairs of atomic orbitals. For benzene, considering only the Kékulé structures, we have

$$\chi_{\text{I}}(A) = \chi_{ab} + \chi_{cd} + \chi_{ef} \tag{10.55a}$$

$$\chi_{\text{II}}(A) = \chi_{af} + \chi_{bc} + \chi_{de} \tag{10.55b}$$

$$\chi_{\text{I}}(E) = 2\chi_{ad} - \chi_{bc} - \chi_{ef} \tag{10.56a}$$

$$\chi_{\text{II}}(E) = 2\chi_{de} - \chi_{af} - \chi_{bc} \tag{10.56b}$$

$$\phi(a_1) = \chi_{\text{I}}(A) + \chi_{\text{II}}(A) \tag{10.57a}$$

$$\phi(e_2) = \chi_{\text{I}}(E) + \chi_{\text{II}}(E) \tag{10.57b}$$

Exercise 10.5*: How many singlet nonionic valence bond structures can be drawn for a ten-π-electron system?

Exercise 10.6: Draw the Rumer diagrams for a ten-π-electron system.

Exercise 10.7: Classify the valence bond states according to symmetry for cyclodecapentaene, naphthalene, and azulene.

10.9 CONFIGURATIONS AND CONFIGURATION INTERACTION

An electronic configuration of an atom or a molecule represents an assignment of all the electrons to specific orbitals. In molecules, different molecular orbital occupancies give different configurations. Different valence bond structures also represent different configurations. As was pointed out in Section 9.5, the terms "configuration" and "state" are not synonymous. When partially filled degenerate orbitals are involved, a given configuration can lead to more than one state. The Pauli-allowed states require the proper antisymmetrization of the product representations. Even when a given configuration gives rise to only one state, the calculated energy for this state is usually not the exact energy for the state, because of the necessarily approximate nature of the calculations. An improved energy can be obtained by approximating the many-electron wave function by a linear combination of configurations. This approximation is known as *configuration interaction.* As in any linear expansion problem, this leads to a determinantal equation to be solved.

Group theory can be of considerable aid in configuration interaction (CI) calculations. The integrals involved in the CI determinant are of the form $\langle \Psi_A | \hat{H} | \Psi_B \rangle$, where Ψ_A and Ψ_B are many-electron wave functions for configurations A and B and $\hat{H}$ is the Hamiltonian operator. Since $\hat{H}$ is totally symmetric, the integral vanishes unless Ψ_A and Ψ_B transform as the same irreducible representation of the group of the system, (i.e., only configurations of the same symmetry can interact). For example, in Section 7.9 we derived the π-electron molecular orbitals of butadiene within the Hückel approximation. The symmetries of these would be the same within any other approximation. Relabeling these as symmetry orbitals, we have, in order of increasing energy, $\phi_1(a_u)$, $\phi_1(b_g)$, $\phi_2(a_u)$, and $\phi_2(b_g)$. The lowest-energy four-electron configuration for the π-electrons is

$$\Psi_1(A_g) = (\phi_1(a_u))^2(\phi_1(b_g))^2 \tag{10.58}$$

and leads to an A_g state. There are 18 excited singlet configurations possible, as well as 13 triplets and one quintet. Four of the excited singlets involve one electron being promoted to a higher-energy orbital, nine involve two, four involve three, and one involves all four promoted. Let us confine our attention to the singlets arising from a one-electron promotion. The configurations are

$$\Psi_2(B_u) = (\phi_1(a_u))^2\phi_1(b_g)\phi_2(a_u) \tag{10.59}$$

$$\Psi_3(A_g) = (\phi_1(a_u))^2\phi_1(b_g)\phi_2(b_g) \tag{10.60}$$

$$\Psi_4(A_g) = \phi_1(a_u)(\phi_1(b_g))^2\phi_2(a_u) \tag{10.61}$$

$$\Psi_5(B_u) = \phi_1(a_u)(\phi_1(b_g))^2\phi_2(b_g) \tag{10.62}$$

(Note that, in general, the symmetry of a configuration arising from a one-electron promotion from a closed-shell state is simply the product of the representations of the orbitals from which and to which the electron was promoted.) Thus, the configurations **1**, **3**, and **4** can interact with each other, while **2** and **5** can interact. The determinantal equation will have the form

$$\begin{vmatrix} H_{1,1}-E & H_{1,3} & H_{1,4} & 0 & 0 \\ H_{1,3} & H_{3,3}-E & H_{3,4} & 0 & 0 \\ H_{1,4} & H_{3,4} & H_{4,4}-E & 0 & 0 \\ 0 & 0 & 0 & H_{2,2}-E & H_{2,5} \\ 0 & 0 & 0 & H_{2,5} & H_{5,5}-E \end{vmatrix} = 0 \quad (10.63)$$

Since the 3×3 block and the 2×2 block have no off-diagonal elements connecting them, each can be solved independently. (In actual fact, if the molecular orbitals were self-consistent field orbitals, $H_{1,3}$ and $H_{1,4}$ would also be zero, since *Brillouin's theorem* tells us that an SCF ground state will not interact with any singly excited configurations.)

A complete configuration interaction treatment of butadiene would involve all 19 singlet configurations (eleven of these would be A_g and eight B_u), and all 13 triplets (five A_g and eight B_u). (There is only one A_g quintet configuration.) A complete configuration interaction treatment yields the best possible energy that can be obtained from a given basis set; however, for problems of any size, the determinantal equations become unmanageably large.

Exercise 10.8: Find the symmetries of the singly excited configurations of benzene. Set up the CI determinant for each symmetry type.

PROBLEMS

1. Construct symmetry-adapted L.C.A.O. molecular orbitals for the following π systems (assume that each atom contributes one $p\pi$ orbital):

(a) 

(b) 

(c) 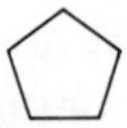

(d) 

(e) 

(f) 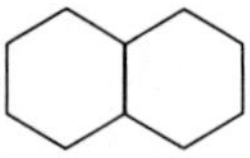

(g) 

(h) 

(i) 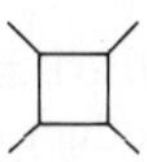

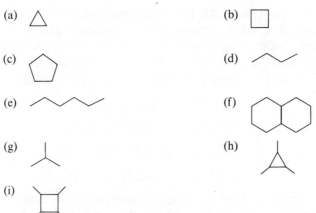

2. Set up symmetry-factored Hückel determinants for the molecules from Problem 1.

3. Find the symmetries of all molecular orbitals arising from the valence orbitals of
   (a) MnO_4^{2-} ($\mathbf{T}_d$ point group)
   (b) $NiCl_4^{2-}$ ($\mathbf{D}_{4h}$ point group)

4. Construct a set of sp^3d hybrid orbitals (use d_{z^2} as the d orbital).

5. Construct a set of sp^3d^2 hybrid orbitals (use d_{z^2} and $d_{x^2-y^2}$ as the d orbitals).

6. Construct the allowed Rumer diagrams and the corresponding valence bond structures for the singlet π states of hexatriene. Set up the symmetry-factored configuration interaction determinant.

7. Construct the symmetry-factored configuration interaction determinant for the singlet states of the π system of the carbonate ion, which involve only single excitations.

8. Deduce the symmetries of all the occupied valence orbitals of the following molecules (assume the highest point symmetry consistent with the structure):
   (a) Propane
   (b) Isobutane
   (c) Prismane 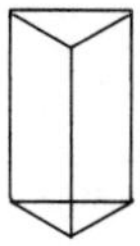

BIBLIOGRAPHY

ATKINS, P. W., *Molecular Quantum Mechanics*, Oxford University Press, New York, 1970.

COTTON, F. A., *Chemical Applications of Group Theory*, 2nd ed., John Wiley & Sons, Inc., New York, 1971.

FLURRY, R. L., JR., *Molecular Orbital Theories of Bonding in Organic Molecules*, Marcel Dekker, Inc., New York, 1968.

HALL, L. H., *Group Theory and Symmetry in Chemistry*, McGraw-Hill Book Company, New York, 1969.

HERZBERG, G., *Electronic Spectra of Polyatomic Molecules*, Van Nostrand Reinhold Company, New York, 1966.

JAFFÉ, H. H., AND M. ORCHIN, *Theory and Applications of Ultraviolet Spectroscopy*, John Wiley & Sons, Inc., New York, 1962.

KING, G. W., *Spectroscopy and Molecular Structure*, Holt, Rinehart and Winston, Inc., New York, 1964.

ORCHIN, M., AND H. H. JAFFÉ, *Symmetry, Orbitals, and Spectra*, Wiley–Interscience, New York, 1970.

SLATER, J. C., *Quantum Theory of Molecules and Solids*, Vol. I, McGraw-Hill Book Company, New York, 1963.

11

Vibrations of Nonlinear Molecules

11.1 INTRODUCTION

Constructing the normal modes of vibration for small linear molecules by inspection is relatively simple. For more complicated molecules, however, inspection methods quickly become insufficient. The irreducible representations to which normal modes belong can, on the other hand, be found directly from group theory. If we had a collection of N independent atoms, each of the atoms would have three degrees of translational freedom (i.e., *each* atom's motion could be described by three independent coordinates, giving, for the system of N atoms, $3N$ independent coordinates). The symmetry of each atom could be described by the $\mathbf{R}_h(3)$ point group; however, the system as a whole would in general have no symmetry. If the N atoms were rigidly joined so that there could be no motion of the atoms with respect to each other, we would, in effect, have gone from an N-particle system to a one-particle system. The one particle would be capable of being translated, the motion of the translation being described by three coordinates (x, y, and z, for example). In addition, the system as a whole would no longer have spherical symmetry; consequently, it would have three (if nonlinear) or two (if linear) degrees of rotational freedom. The rigid system, then, would have six (or five, if linear) independent modes of motion. Its symmetry properties would be those corresponding to the shape of the rigid structure. An actual molecule falls between these two extremes. The forces holding the molecule together are sufficiently rigid to yield a fixed equilibrium, or average, configuration of the atoms with respect to each other. The forces, however, are not rigid enough to prevent all relative motion of the atoms. The result is that we have stable molecules in which the atoms vibrate about their equilibrium positions. Since we have N atoms that can all move, at least to some extent, in any direction, there are still $3N$ degrees of freedom of movement for the total system. Three of these, however, correspond to translations of the entire system. Three (or two in the linear case) correspond to rotations of the entire system. The remaining $3N - 6$ (or $3N - 5$) can only be associated with degrees of vibrational freedom. For example, a diatomic molecule must have $3N - 5$ or 1 degree of vibrational freedom, a linear triatomic four degrees, a bent triatomic three degrees, and so on.

The symmetry properties of the possible vibrations can be obtained by considering the transformation properties of a set of unit displacements along a set of atom-centered Cartesian coordinates (as shown in Fig. 9.3, for example) within the point group of the system. All possible motions of the system can be described by combinations of such a set of displacements. All the vibrational states of the system must transform as irreducible representations within the point group of the system, as must translations and rotations of the system as a whole. The only possible motions of the system are translations, rotations, and vibrations; consequently, the sums of the irreducible representations of the translations, rotations, and vibrations should equal the total representation obtained by operating on the atom-centered coordinates by the elements of the point group. This total motion representation can be constructed directly by either geometric or site-symmetry methods. The irreducible representations corresponding to translation and rotation may be subtracted out. What remains will then be the sum of the irreducible representations of the possible vibrations. This reducible representation can be resolved into its irreducible components, each of which will correspond to one of the *normal modes of vibration* of the system.

11.2 GEOMETRIC TREATMENT

Water

In order to illustrate the geometric method for finding the symmetries of the possible normal modes of vibration of a system, let us consider water as a specific example. Figure 11.1 shows the internal coordinate system for water (aligning the z axes parallel to the symmetry axis of the molecule). The molecule belongs to the $\mathbf{C}_{2v}$ point group. The symmetry elements are E, C_2 (along the z direction), and two σ_v (the x_1z_1 and y_1z_1 planes). The molecule has three atoms; consequently, there are nine displacement vectors. The total displacement representation will be nine-dimensional. After subtracting out for translation and rotation, we will be left with a three-dimensional representation to describe the vibration.

The procedure to follow in finding the displacement representation is to find the components of the displacement vectors along their *original* axes after each of

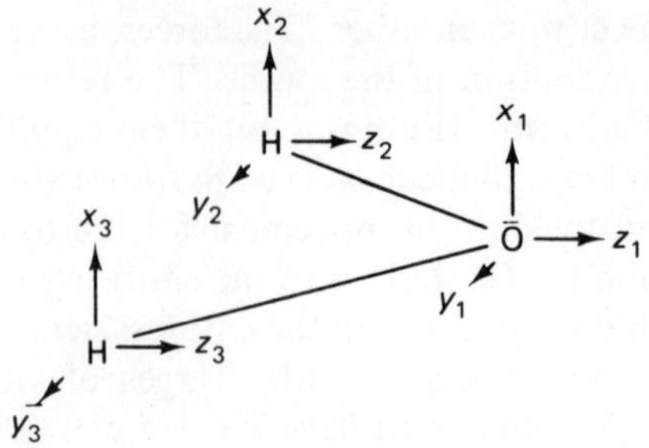

Fig. 11.1. Internal coordinate system for water.

the symmetry operations. This is then the character for that operation. The identity operation does nothing to the system. Each of the nine vectors remains unchanged; consequently,

$$\chi(E) = 9 \tag{11.1}$$

The C_2 operation interchanges the two hydrogens; consequently, the displacements of these no longer lie along the original coordinate system. The displacement vectors centered on the hydrogens contribute nothing to the character of C_2. The vectors on oxygen must thus determine the character of C_2. The z_1 vector is unchanged for a contribution of 1 to this character. The x_1 and y_1 vectors both change their direction and lie along the negative axes after the C_2 operation. They each contribute -1 to the character of C_2. The net result is

$$\chi(C_2) = 1 + 2(-1) = -1 \tag{11.2}$$

The $\sigma_v^{(yz)}$ leaves all y and z unchanged but changes the sign of all x; consequently,

$$\chi(\sigma_v^{(yz)}) = 3 \times 2 - 3 = 3 \tag{11.3}$$

The $\sigma_v^{(xz)}$ interchanges the hydrogens, leaves x_1 and z_1 unchanged, and changes the sign of y_1:

$$\chi(\sigma_v^{(xz)}) = 2 - 1 = 1 \tag{11.4}$$

These operations can again be expressed by the matrices shown in Section 10.3. The array is nine-dimensional, having entries for each coordinate on each atom. We have

(11.5a)

EM =	x_1	y_1	z_1	x_2	y_2	z_2	x_3	y_3	z_3
x_1	1	0	0	0	0	0	0	0	0
y_1	0	1	0	0	0	0	0	0	0
z_1	0	0	1	0	0	0	0	0	0
x_2	0	0	0	1	0	0	0	0	0
y_2	0	0	0	0	1	0	0	0	0
z_2	0	0	0	0	0	1	0	0	0
x_3	0	0	0	0	0	0	1	0	0
y_3	0	0	0	0	0	0	0	1	0
z_3	0	0	0	0	0	0	0	0	1

(11.5b)

$C_2\mathbf{M} =$

	x_1	y_1	z_1	x_2	y_2	z_2	x_3	y_3	z_3
x_1	-1	0	0	0	0	0	0	0	0
y_1	0	-1	0	0	0	0	0	0	0
z_1	0	0	1	0	0	0	0	0	0
x_2	0	0	0	0	0	0	-1	0	0
y_2	0	0	0	0	0	0	0	-1	0
z_2	0	0	0	0	0	0	0	0	1
x_3	0	0	0	-1	0	0	0	0	0
y_3	0	0	0	0	-1	0	0	0	0
z_3	0	0	0	0	0	1	0	0	0

(11.5c)

$\sigma_v^{(xz)}\mathbf{M} =$

	x_1	y_1	z_1	x_2	y_2	z_2	x_3	y_3	z_3
x_1	1	0	0	0	0	0	0	0	0
y_1	0	-1	0	0	0	0	0	0	0
z_1	0	0	1	0	0	0	0	0	0
x_2	0	0	0	0	0	0	1	0	0
y_1	0	0	0	0	0	0	0	-1	0
z_2	0	0	0	0	0	0	0	0	1
x_3	0	0	0	1	0	0	0	0	0
y_3	0	0	0	0	-1	0	0	0	0
z_3	0	0	0	0	0	1	0	0	0

(11.5d)

$\sigma_v^{(yz)}\mathbf{M} =$

	x_1	y_1	z_1	x_2	y_2	z_2	x_3	y_3	z_3
x_1	-1	0	0	0	0	0	0	0	0
y_1	0	1	0	0	0	0	0	0	0
z_1	0	0	1	0	0	0	0	0	0
x_2	0	0	0	-1	0	0	0	0	0
y_2	0	0	0	0	1	0	0	0	0
z_2	0	0	0	0	0	1	0	0	0
x_3	0	0	0	0	0	0	-1	0	0
y_3	0	0	0	0	0	0	0	1	0
z_3	0	0	0	0	0	0	0	0	1

The characters are again the traces of these. The net result is

(11.6)

$\mathbf{C}_{2v}$	E	C_2	$\sigma_v^{(xz)}$	$\sigma_v^{(yz)}$
Γ_{H_2O}	9	-1	1	3

Translations along the x, y, and z axes transform as B_1, B_2, and A_1, respectively, within the $\mathbf{C}_{2v}$ point group, while rotations about x, y, and z transform as B_2, B_1, and A_2. The net translation–rotation representation is

$$\Gamma_{\text{T-R}} = A_1 + A_2 + 2B_1 + 2B_2 \tag{11.7a}$$

or

(11.7b)

$\mathbf{C}_{2v}$	E	C_2	$\sigma_v^{(xz)}$	$\sigma_v^{(yz)}$
$\Gamma_{\text{T-R}}$	6	-2	0	0

Subtracting Eq. 11.7b element by element from Eq. 11.6 we obtain for the vibrational representation, Γ_{vib},

(11.8)

$\mathbf{C}_{2v}$	E	C_2	$\sigma_v^{(xz)}$	$\sigma_v^{(yz)}$
Γ_{vib}	3	1	1	3

This representation is simple enough that it can be resolved into its irreducible components by trial and error. If, however, we carry through the systematic reduction (see Section 5.4) for the vibration representation of water, the order, g, is 4, all characters are real and have for A_1,

$$\begin{aligned} a_{A_1} &= \tfrac{1}{4}(1 \times 3 + 1 \times 1 + 1 \times 1 + 1 \times 3) \\ &= 2 \end{aligned} \tag{11.9}$$

for A_2,

$$\begin{aligned} a_{A_2} &= \tfrac{1}{4}(1 \times 3 + 1 \times 1 - 1 \times 1 - 1 \times 3) \\ &= 0 \end{aligned} \tag{11.10}$$

for B_1,

$$\begin{aligned} a_{B_1} &= \tfrac{1}{4}(1 \times 3 - 1 \times 1 + 1 \times 1 - 1 \times 3) \\ &= 0 \end{aligned} \tag{11.11}$$

and for B_2,

$$\begin{aligned} a_{B_2} &= \tfrac{1}{4}(1 \times 3 - 1 \times 1 - 1 \times 1 + 1 \times 3) \\ &= 1 \end{aligned} \tag{11.12}$$

Thus, the vibrational representation is

$$\Gamma_{\text{vib}} = 2A_1 + B_2 \tag{11.13}$$

This means that the water molecule has two modes of vibration of A_1 symmetr[y] and one of B_2. (Many authors take the xz plane as the molecular plane, giving B as the B representation.) All three of these represent infrared-allowed transition (see Section 8.6). The A_1 transitions are z-polarized while the B_2 transition i

y-polarized (x-polarized if xz is taken as the molecular plane). Relating these to the normal modes of vibration for water, the a_1 vibrations are a symmetrical stretch, ν_1 (both OH distances increasing and decreasing in phase), and a bending mode, ν_2. The b_1 vibration is an unsymmetrical stretch, ν_3 (one OH distance increasing as the other is decreasing). All three transitions are also Raman-active (see Section 8.7). All of these transitions are observed experimentally, ν_1 occurring at 3651.7 cm^{-1}, ν_2 at 1595.0 cm^{-1}, and ν_3 at 3755.8 cm^{-1} in the vapor phase. In addition to these fundamental transitions, a number of overtone and combination bands are also observed. Herzberg reports a total of 19 infrared bands for water.

Boron Trifluoride

Let us consider boron trifluoride as a second example. The internal coordinates can be represented as in Fig. 11.2. Within the $\mathbf{D}_{3h}$ point group, the representation that includes all possible displacements is

$\mathbf{D}_{3h}$	E	$2C_3$	$3C_2$	σ_h	$2S_3$	$3\sigma_v$
Γ_{BF_3}	12	0	-2	4	-2	2

(11.14)

The translational representation for the entire molecule is

$$\Gamma_{tr} = E' + A_2'' \tag{11.15}$$

while the rotational representation is

$$\Gamma_{rot} = A_2' + E'' \tag{11.16}$$

Subtracting these from the total representation, we obtain for Γ_{vib}

$\mathbf{D}_{3h}$	E	$2C_3$	$3C_2$	σ_h	$2S_3$	$3\sigma_v$
Γ_{vib}	6	0	0	4	-2	2

(11.17)

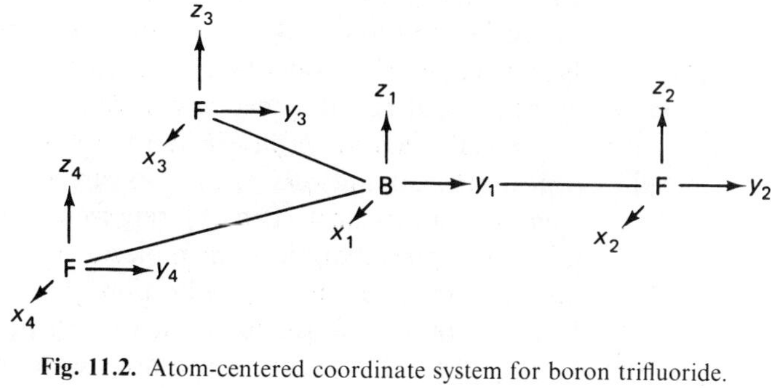

Fig. 11.2. Atom-centered coordinate system for boron trifluoride.

This can be resolved into its component irreducible representations

$$\Gamma_{vib} = A_1' + 2E' + A_2'' \tag{11.18}$$

Thus, the six possible vibrations for the molecule are divided into a vibration with A_1' symmetry, one with A_2'' symmetry, and two pairs of doubly degenerate vibrations of E' symmetry. Of these, the A_1' is predicted to be Raman-active, the E' are all infrared- and Raman-active, and the A_2'' is infrared-active. This should lead to three different observed fundamental frequencies in the infrared (the two pairs of E' transitions occurring at different frequencies, but both members of each pair at the same frequency) and three different observed frequencies in the Raman. Two of the Raman bands should match two of the infrared frequencies (for the E' transitions), while the third should be different. Experimentally, gaseous $^{11}BF_3$ yields bands of sufficient intensity to be fundamental transitions at 480.4 [I (infrared) and R (Raman)], 691.3 (I.), 888 (R.), and 1445.9 cm^{-1} (I.). It is immediately obvious that the band at 480.4 cm^{-1} is of E' symmetry and the one at 888 cm^{-1} is of A_1' symmetry. One of the Raman bands, however, is not observed, in spite of being symmetry-allowed; consequently, we cannot decide on the basis of symmetry alone which of the remaining two bands is of A_2'' symmetry and which is of E'. In this case, the choice can be made on the basis of isotope splitting. (^{10}B and ^{11}B occur naturally in the abundance of 1:4.) From Eq. 9.65 we see that the frequency of a vibration is inversely proportional to the square root of the reduced mass; consequently, $\nu(^{10}B)/\nu(^{11}B)$ should equal $\sqrt{\mu(^{11}B)/\mu(^{10}B)}$. The reduced mass for the A_2'' band is simply $m(B)/[m(B) + 3m(F)]$, while that for the degenerate E' band is more complicated. The 691.3 cm^{-1} band for ^{11}B is accompanied by a band at 719. 5 cm^{-1} for ^{10}B while the 1445.9 cm^{-1} band is accompanied by a band at 1497 cm^{-1}. The frequency ratios for $\nu(^{10}B)/\nu(^{11}B)$ are 1.0408 and 1.0353, respectively. The expected ratio for the A_2'' band is 1.0409; consequently, the 691.3 cm^{-1} band must have A_2'' symmetry, while the 1445.9 cm^{-1} band must have E' symmetry.

Frequently, it is possible to determine something about the actual nature of the motions in the normal modes of vibration from a qualitative inspection of their irreducible representations within the point group of the molecule. This is usually relatively straightforward for one-dimensional representations. For example, the A_1' representation in BF_3 is totally symmetric. The only conceivable set of translation vectors that could be constructed on the atoms and would yield a completely equivalent set after every symmetry operation would be a set of translations of equal magnitude and in the same sense along each B—F bond (i.e., all fluorine atoms moving outward and inward in phase with each other while the boron remains stationary). The A_2'' representation is antisymmetric with respect to σ_h. This implies that, since the molecule is planar, there must be out-of-plane displacements involved in an A_2'' vibration. The only such motion that does not move the center of mass of the molecule or does not involve a rotation of the molecule is for the three fluorines to move downward, remaining coplanar, while the boron moves upward, or vice versa. Since the E' representations are two-dimensional, any number of motions can be devised that will have the proper transformation properties for these. About the only thing that can be said for certain is that, since the E' representations are symmetrical with respect to σ_h, the motions are in the plane of the molecule. In this case these are basically an asymmetric stretching mode (the 1445.9 cm^{-1} band) and an in-plane bend (the 480.4 cm^{-1} band).

Exercise 11.1*: Find the symmetries of the normal vibrations and tell whether or not the transitions are infrared- or Raman-allowed for each of the following:

(a) Hydrogen cyanide
(b) Formaldehyde
(c) Acetylene

Exercise 11.2: In its lowest excited electronic state, the point symmetry of acetylene is $\mathbf{C}_{2h}$ (the molecule is distorted toward a Z-shaped configuration). Find the symmetries and transformation properties of the vibrations in this configuration.

11.3 SITE-SYMMETRY TREATMENT

Water

The use of site symmetries offers considerable simplifications in finding the symmetries of the normal modes of vibration of molecules, just as it does in the determination of molecular symmetry orbitals. The set of three translation vectors for a free atom transform as the three-dimensional $D_u^{(1)}$ of the $\mathbf{R}_h(3)$ point group. The contributions of the various atoms in a molecule to the total motional representation can be obtained by mapping the elements of $\mathbf{R}_h(3)$ onto those of the appropriate site symmetry groups, and these, in turn, onto those of the point group and summing over all atoms. Let us work through the examples of H_2O and BF_3 by this technique.

In water, the site symmetry of the oxygen is the full $\mathbf{C}_{2v}$ symmetry of the molecule, while that of the hydrogens is $\mathbf{C}_s$. We thus have, for the hydrogens:

(11.19)

$\mathbf{C}_s$	E	σ
Γ_H	3	1
Γ_{2H}	6	2

and for the oxygen:

(11.20)

$\mathbf{C}_{2v}$	E	C_2	$\sigma(xz)$	$\sigma(yz)$
Γ_O	3	$1 + 2\cos 180°$	1	1
	(3	-1	1	1)

Mapping the hydrogen representation onto $\mathbf{C}_{2v}$ and combining, we have (recognizing that the hydrogens are in the yz plane as we previously aligned the molecule)

$\mathbf{C}_{2v}$	E	C_2	$\sigma_v(xz)$	$\sigma(yz)$
Γ_O	3	−1	1	1
Γ_{2H}	6	0	0	2
Γ_{H_2O}	9	−1	1	3

(11.21)

This total representation is identical to that obtained previously (Eq. 11.6). The $\Gamma_{T\text{-}R}$ is subtracted out, as before, to yield the vibrational representation.

Boron Trifluoride

In boron trifluoride, the site symmetry of the boron is that of the molecule, $\mathbf{D}_{3h}$, while that of the fluorines is $\mathbf{C}_{2v}$. For the fluorines, we have

$\mathbf{C}_{2v}$	E	C_2	$\sigma(xz)$	$\sigma(yz)$
Γ_F	3	$1 + 2\cos 180°$	1	1
	(3	−1	1	1)
Γ_{3F}	9	−3	3	3

(11.22)

while for the boron we have

$\mathbf{D}_{3h}$	E	$2C_3$	$2C_2$	σ_h	$2S_3$	$3\sigma_v$
Γ_B	3	$1 + 2\cos 120°$	$1 + 2\cos 180°$	1	$-1 + 2\cos 120°$	1
	(3	0	−1	1	−2	1)

(11.23)

When mapping the fluorine representation onto the $\mathbf{D}_{3h}$ point group, the $\sigma(xz)$ and the $\sigma(yz)$ correspond to the σ_h and the σ_v's, respectively (the orientation is immaterial). All three fluorines lie in the horizontal plane of symmetry; however, only one σ_v passes through each fluorine (i.e., only one σ_v is coincident with the corresponding σ of the site symmetry of a particular fluorine). Thus, when mapping the fluorine representation onto $\mathbf{D}_{3h}$,

$$\chi(3\sigma_v) = \tfrac{1}{3}(3 + 0 + 0) = 1 \tag{11.24}$$

Similarly, only one C_2 coincides with each fluorine and $\chi(3C_2)$ equals -1. The final mappings and results are

$\mathbf{D}_{3h}$	E	$2C_3$	$3C_2$	σ_h	$2S_3$	$3\sigma_v$
Γ_{B}	3	0	-1	1	-2	1
$\Gamma_{3\mathrm{F}}$	9	0	-1	3	0	1
Γ_{BF_3}	12	0	-2	4	-2	2

(11.25)

This is again identical to the previous results (Eq. 11.14).

Exercise 11.3: Find the symmetries of the normal vibrations of methane and of ethane in its staggered configuration.

11.4 PROJECTION OPERATORS AND NORMAL MODES OF VIBRATION

Stretches, Bends, and the Like

It is frequently desirable to be able to determine the actual motions for a vibration belonging to a particular irreducible representation. For simple small molecules, this can frequently be accomplished by inspection on the basis of intuition alone; however, since for each additional atom in a molecule there are three additional vibrations, a more systematic procedure is needed. The most systematic procedure is to use projection operators. For molecular vibrations, the projection operator technique can be applied directly to a set of translation vectors aligned along a set of atom-centered Cartesian coordinate systems. This, in fact, yields properly symmetry-adapted vibrational modes. It is frequently more convenient, both from the point of view of visualizing the results and for determining force constants, to use bond stretches and angular deformations as the starting basis functions.

To illustrate the principles of applying projection operators, let us construct the normal modes of vibration for three molecules: water, ammonia, and formaldehyde. The triatomic water molecule has three normal modes of vibration, two of a_1 symmetry and one of b_1 symmetry, within the $\mathbf{C}_{2v}$ point group. A natural choice of basis functions for constructing the normal vibrations for water is the pair of OH stretches, s_1 and s_2, and the HOH angular deformation, α_{12} (Fig. 11.3a). The C_2 operation carries s_1 into s_2, s_2 into s_1, and α_{12} into itself. The in-plane σ_v leaves all functions unchanged, while the out-of-plane σ_v' has the same overall effect as C_2. Thus, the results of the symmetry operations on the various functions

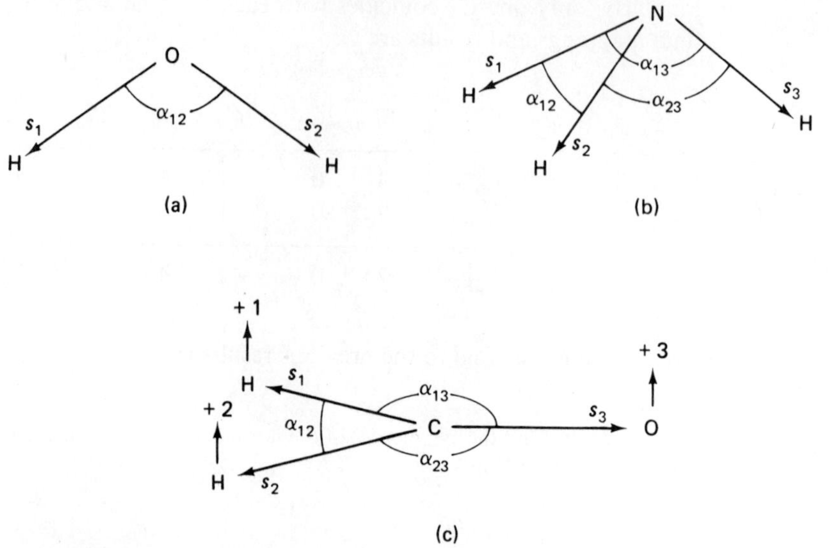

Fig. 11.3. Internal coordinates for the vibrations of (a) water, (b) ammonia, and (c) formaldehyde.

are as shown in Table 11.1. The result of the operation of the projection operator of A_1 symmetry on s_1 yields

$$\begin{aligned} P^{(A_1)}s_1 = \sum_R \chi_R^{*(A_1)} R s_1 &= 1 \times s_1 + 1 \times s_2 + 1 \times s_1 + 1 \times s_2 \\ &= 2(s_1 + s_2) \end{aligned} \tag{11.26}$$

Thus, the function $(s_1 + s_2)$, a symmetrical stretch, is a symmetry-adapted normal vibration for water having the symmetry a_1. The same function results if the projection operator is applied to s_2. Applying the A_1 projection operator to α_{12}, we have

$$\begin{aligned} P^{(A_1)}\alpha_{12} &= 1 \times \alpha_{12} + 1 \times \alpha_{12} + 1 \times \alpha_{12} + 1 \times \alpha_{12} \\ &= 4\alpha_{12} \end{aligned} \tag{11.27}$$

Thus, the bending mode is a normal vibration of water having the symmetry a_1.

Applying the B_1 projection operator to s_1 yields

$$\begin{aligned} P^{(B_1)}s_1 &= 1 \times s_1 - 1 \times s_2 + 1 \times s_1 - 1 \times s_2 \\ &= 2(s_1 - s_2) \end{aligned} \tag{11.28}$$

Table 11.1. The results of applying the symmetry operations of C_{2v} to the internal coordinates of water

$Es_1 = s_1$	$C_2 s_1 = s_2$	$\sigma_v s_1 = s_1$	$\sigma'_v s_1 = s_2$
$Es_2 = s_2$	$C_2 s_2 = s_1$	$\sigma_v s_2 = s_2$	$\sigma'_v s_2 = s_1$
$E\alpha_{12} = \alpha_{12}$	$C_2 \alpha_{12} = \alpha_{12}$	$\sigma_v \alpha_{12} = \alpha_{12}$	$\sigma'_v \alpha_{12} = \alpha_{12}$

the unsymmetrical stretch. Operating on s_2 with this operator yields the same result except for sign. We can also verify that there are no vibrations of other symmetries by the use of projection operators. For example, using the A_2 projection operator with s_1, we have

$$\begin{aligned} P^{(A_2)}s_1 &= 1 \times s_1 + 1 \times s_2 - 1 \times s_1 - 1 \times s_2 \\ &= 0 \end{aligned} \tag{11.29}$$

and similarly for the other basis functions and for the B_2 representation.

The stretches and deformations for ammonia are shown in Fig. 11.3b. The molecule has six normal modes of vibration. These are two a_1 vibrations and two pairs of degenerate e vibrations. The effect of the symmetry operations of $\mathbf{C}_{3v}$ on the basis functions is shown in Table 11.2. The one-dimensional a_1 modes can be

Table 11.2. The results of applying the symmetry operations of C_{3v} to the internal coordinates of ammonia

$Es_1 = s_1$	$C_3\alpha_{12} = \alpha_{23}$	$\sigma_v s_1 = s_1$	$\sigma'_v\alpha_{12} = \alpha_{12}$
$Es_2 = s_2$	$C_3\alpha_{13} = \alpha_{12}$	$\sigma_v s_2 = s_3$	$\sigma'_v\alpha_{13} = \alpha_{23}$
$Es_3 = s_3$	$C_3\alpha_{23} = \alpha_{13}$	$\sigma_v s_3 = s_2$	$\sigma'_v\alpha_{23} = \alpha_{12}$
$E\alpha_{12} = \alpha_{12}$	$C_3^2 s_1 = s_3$	$\sigma_v\alpha_{12} = \alpha_{13}$	$\sigma''_v s_1 = s_3$
$E\alpha_{13} = \alpha_{13}$	$C_3^2 s_2 = s_1$	$\sigma_v\alpha_{13} = \alpha_{12}$	$\sigma''_v s_2 = s_2$
$E\alpha_{23} = \alpha_{23}$	$C_3^2 s_3 = s_2$	$\sigma_v\alpha_{23} = \alpha_{23}$	$\sigma''_v s_3 = s_1$
$C_3 s_1 = s_2$	$C_3^2\alpha_{12} = \alpha_{13}$	$\sigma'_v s_1 = s_2$	$\sigma''_v\alpha_{12} = \alpha_{23}$
$C_3 s_2 = s_3$	$C_3^2\alpha_{13} = \alpha_{23}$	$\sigma'_v s_2 = s_1$	$\sigma''_v\alpha_{13} = \alpha_{13}$
$C_3 s_3 = s_1$	$C_3^2\alpha_{23} = \alpha_{12}$	$\sigma'_v s_3 = s_3$	$\sigma''_v\alpha_{23} = \alpha_{12}$

directly and uniquely constructed from any one of the stretches and any one of the deformations. For example,

$$\begin{aligned} P^{(A_1)}s_1 &= 1 \times s_1 + 1 \times (s_2 + s_3) + 1 \times (s_1 + s_3 + s_2) \\ &= 2(s_1 + s_2 + s_3) \end{aligned} \tag{11.30}$$

and

$$\begin{aligned} P^{(A_1)}\alpha_{23} &= 1 \times \alpha_{23} + 1 \times (\alpha_{13} + \alpha_{12}) + 1 \times (\alpha_{23} + \alpha_{12} + \alpha_{13}) \\ &= 2(\alpha_{12} + \alpha_{13} + \alpha_{23}) \end{aligned} \tag{11.31}$$

These represent a symmetrical stretch and a symmetrical bending mode. Note that in the bending mode the molecule tends to "flatten out" as the angles get larger and to form a higher pyramid as the angles get smaller.

For the doubly degenerate e vibrations, an infinite number of representations are possible. Typical modes can be constructed by using any of the basis functions. For numerical work, however, the functions used in constructing different e representations must belong to the same subgroup of the molecular point group. For example, the functions s_1 and α_{23} belong to the subgroup $\{E, \sigma_v\}$, while s_2 and α_{13} belong to the subgroup $\{E, \sigma'_v\}$ and s_3 and α_{12} to the subgroup $\{E, \sigma''_v\}$. Thus, the two sets of e vibrations could be constructed from s_1 and α_{23}, s_2 and α_{13}, or

s_3 and α_{12}. Mixing of the functions would result in vibrations that were not orthogonal. Linear combinations of the functions could also be used, however. The function $(s_1 + s_2)$ belongs to the same subgroup as α_{12}, while the function $(\alpha_{12} + \alpha_{13})$ belongs to the same subgroup as s_1. Using s_1 and α_{23} as the starting functions and projecting out the E representations, we have

$$\begin{aligned} P^{(E)}s_1 &= 2s_1 - 1 \times (s_2 + s_3) + 0 \times (s_1 + s_3 + s_2) \\ &= 2s_1 - s_2 - s_3 \end{aligned} \tag{11.32}$$

$$\begin{aligned} P^{(E)}\alpha_{23} &= 2\alpha_{23} - 1 \times (\alpha_{13} + \alpha_{12}) + 0 \times (\alpha_{23} + \alpha_{12} + \alpha_{13}) \\ &= 2\alpha_{23} - \alpha_{13} - \alpha_{12} \end{aligned} \tag{11.33}$$

These represent suitable e vibrations: an asymmetric stretch and an asymmetric bend. To obtain the orthogonal component of a given e vibration, another function can be constructed, from the same basis set, which belongs to the same subgroup as the function from which the original component was constructed, but which transforms as a different irreducible representation of the subgroup. Thus, s_1 transforms as the totally symmetric irreducible representation of the $\mathbf{C}_s$ group while the function $(s_2 - s_3)$ transforms as the antisymmetric representation. Applying the $P^{(E)}$ operator to this, we have

$$\begin{aligned} P^{(e)}(s_2 - s_3) &= 2(s_2 - s_3) - 1 \times \{(s_3 - s_1) + (s_1 - s_2)\} \\ &= 3(s_2 - s_3) \end{aligned} \tag{11.34}$$

This does indeed represent a function which is orthogonal to that shown in Eq. 11.32. In a similar fashion, the e vibration orthogonal to that shown in Eq. 11.33 can be constructed from the combination $(\alpha_{12} - \alpha_{13})$ to give

$$P^{(E)}(\alpha_{12} - \alpha_{13}) = 3(\alpha_{12} - \alpha_{13}) \tag{11.35}$$

Formaldehyde (Fig. 11.3c) has two types of bonds, CH and CO, and consequently, two different types of stretching functions and two different types of bending functions. When these functions contribute to vibrations belonging to the same irreducible representation, combinations of the types must be made.

When the symmetry elements of the formaldehyde molecule are aligned so that the σ_v is the molecular plane and the σ_v' is perpendicular to the molecular plane, the vibrations are $3a_1$, $2b_1$, and b_2. The B_2 representation is antisymmetric with respect to the molecular plane; consequently, in addition to the stretches and bends, some sort of out-of-plane motions will be required. If we denote motions of the hydrogens and oxygen as $\oplus 1$, $\oplus 2$, and $\oplus 3$ when the motion is above the plane, and $\ominus 1$, and so on, when it is below the plane, and implicitly assume that the carbon atom will move sufficiently to keep the center of mass constant, we will have a sufficient number of functions to describe the vibrations. Table 11.3 shows the effect of the symmetry operations on the chosen basis functions. The normal coordinates can be constructed by operating on s_1, s_3, α_{12}, α_{13}, $\oplus 1$, and $\oplus 3$ with

Table 11.3. The results of applying the symmetry operations of C_{2v} to the internal coordinates of formaldehyde

$Es_1 = s_1$	$C_2 s_1 = s_2$	$\sigma_v s_1 = s_1$	$\sigma'_v s_1 = s_2$
$Es_2 = s_2$	$C_2 s_2 = s_1$	$\sigma_v s_2 = s_2$	$\sigma'_v s_2 = s_1$
$Es_3 = s_3$	$C_2 s_3 = s_3$	$\sigma_v s_3 = s_3$	$\sigma'_v s_3 = s_3$
$E\alpha_{12} = \alpha_{12}$	$C_2 \alpha_{12} = \alpha_{12}$	$\sigma_v \alpha_{12} = \alpha_{12}$	$\sigma'_v \alpha_{12} = \alpha_{12}$
$E\alpha_{13} = \alpha_{13}$	$C_2 \alpha_{13} = \alpha_{23}$	$\sigma_v \alpha_{13} = \alpha_{13}$	$\sigma'_v \alpha_{13} = \alpha_{23}$
$E\alpha_{23} = \alpha_{23}$	$C_2 \alpha_{23} = \alpha_{13}$	$\sigma_v \alpha_{23} = \alpha_{23}$	$\sigma'_v \alpha_{23} = \alpha_{13}$
$E(\oplus 1) = \oplus 1$	$C_2(\oplus 1) = \ominus 2$	$\sigma_v(\oplus 1) = \ominus 1$	$\sigma'_v(\oplus 1) = \oplus 2$
$E(\oplus 2) = \oplus 2$	$C_2(\oplus 2) = \ominus 1$	$\sigma_v(\oplus 2) = \ominus 2$	$\sigma'_v(\oplus 2) = \oplus 1$
$E(\oplus 3) = \oplus 3$	$C_2(\oplus 3) = \ominus 3$	$\sigma_v(\oplus 3) = \ominus 3$	$\sigma'_v(\oplus 3) = \oplus 3$

the appropriate projection operators. Without going through all the possibilities, we have

$$P^{(A_1)} s_1 = 2(s_1 + s_2) \tag{11.36}$$

$$P^{(A_1)} s_3 = 4 s_3 \tag{11.37}$$

$$P^{(A_1)} \alpha_{12} = 4\alpha_{12} \tag{11.38}$$

$$P^{(A_1)} \alpha_{13} = 2(\alpha_{13} + \alpha_{23}) \tag{11.39}$$

$$P^{(B_1)} s_1 = 2(s_1 - s_2) \tag{11.40}$$

$$P^{(B_1)} \alpha_{13} = 2(\alpha_{13} - \alpha_{23}) \tag{11.41}$$

$$P^{(B_2)} \oplus 1 = 2(\oplus 1 + \oplus 2) \tag{11.42}$$

$$P^{(B_2)} \oplus 3 = 4 \oplus 3 \tag{11.43}$$

All the other projection operators yield zero.

There are a total of eight nonvanishing functions projected out from the starting basis functions. Formaldehyde has only six normal vibrations; consequently, the eight functions we have produced are not all independent. In actual fact, all functions of the same symmetry type will interact to some extent. Owing to the relative magnitudes of the force constants, however, stretches and bends can be treated essentially independently. Thus, the stretches having A_1 symmetry can be combined in a symmetric and an antisymmetric fashion with suitable mixing coefficients to give

$$s_{a_1}^{+} = 4c_1^{+} s_3 + 2c_2^{+}(s_1 + s_2) \tag{11.44}$$

$$s_{a_1}^{-} = 4c_1^{-} s_3 - 2c_2^{-}(s_1 + s_2) \tag{11.45}$$

The A_1 bending functions yield

$$b_{a_1}^{+} = 4c_1^{+}\alpha_{12} + 2c_2^{+}(\alpha_{23} + \alpha_{23}) \tag{11.46}$$

$$b_{a_1}^{-} = 4c_1^{-}\alpha_{12} - 2c_2^{-}(\alpha_{13} + \alpha_{23}) \tag{11.47}$$

Note, however, that the function in Eq. 11.46 represents a physically impossible situation: all three angles increasing or decreasing simultaneously while the molecule remains planar. This function can therefore be discarded. The functions having B_2 symmetry are out-of-plane motions. The combinations will represent out-of-plane bends and are

$$b_{b_2}^{+} = 4c_1^{+} \oplus 3 + 2c_2^{+}(\oplus 1 + \oplus 2) \tag{11.48}$$

$$b_{b_2}^{-} = 4c_1^{-} \oplus 3 - 2c_2^{-}(\oplus 1 + \oplus 2) \tag{11.49}$$

The latter of these represents the oxygen moving up while the hydrogens move down (i.e., it is a rotation of the molecule). Thus, Eq. 11.49 also does not represent an allowed vibration. This leaves us with the six required vibration functions: the combinations of Eqs. 11.44, 11.45, and 11.47 for the a_1 vibrations; the functions of Eqs. 11.40 and 11.41 for the b_1 vibrations; and the combination of Eq. 11.48 for the b_2 vibration. It should be noted that in all these motions the carbon atom will have to move sufficiently to keep the center of mass constant. Also, the magnitudes of the mixing coefficients in the combinations would have to be determined by numerical calculations.

The principles that we have used in our three examples can be used in constructing the normal coordinates for any other molecule. The resulting functions will not be normalized; however, normalization can be accomplished by standard techniques. A warning is in order, however. For complicated molecules, the determination of suitable angle deformations can be very tricky. The book by Wilson, Decius, and Cross, listed in the bibliography to this chapter, goes into this problem in detail.

Atom-Centered Coordinates

In order to illustrate the use of atom-centered coordinates for constructing normal modes of vibration, let us consider methane (point group $\mathbf{T}_d$). The total representation for a set of Cartesian displacement vectors situated on the five atoms can be determined by a site symmetry treatment. This yields $A_1 + E + T_1 + 3T_2$ as the motional representations. Of these, one T_2 represents a translation of the entire molecule. This is the representation of the displacement vectors on the carbon atom. If we ignore the carbon and consider only the motions of the hydrogens relative to the carbon, this T_2 is eliminated from consideration. Of the remaining representations, which can all be obtained from the vectors on the four hydrogens, the T_1 represents a rotation of the entire molecule. The vibrational representations are thus $A_1 + E + 2T_2$.

The point group of the molecule is $\mathbf{T}_d$. If we factor this into a product of the site symmetry and the interchange symmetry, we have

$$\mathbf{T}_d = \mathbf{D}_2 \wedge \mathbf{C}_{3v} \tag{11.50}$$

where $\mathbf{D}_2$ is the interchange group and $\mathbf{C}_{3v}$ is the site-symmetry group. A suitable orientation for the displacement vectors is shown in Fig. 11.4. This has been chosen

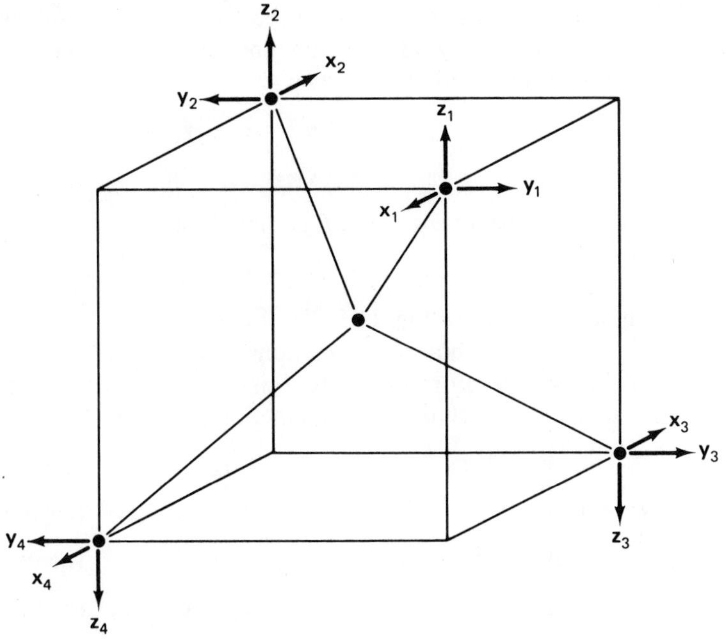

Fig. 11.4. Starting set of hydrogen-centered basis vectors for the normal vibrations of methane.

so that the basis vectors match the site symmetry, and like vectors are interchanged by the interchange group. We can simplify our work by using a correlation table. The correlations of $\mathbf{D}_2$ and $\mathbf{C}_{3v}$ with $\mathbf{T}_d$ are shown in Table 11.4. The vectors on the hydrogens span the A_1 and E representations of the $\mathbf{C}_{3v}$ site symmetry. We see that the A_1 representation of $\mathbf{C}_{3v}$ correlates with the A_1 and T_2 representations of $\mathbf{T}_d$, while the E representation of $\mathbf{C}_{3v}$ correlates with the E, T_1, and T_2 representations. The T_1 representation is the representation of the rotations; therefore, we need not concern ourselves with it.

We now make use of the fact that a projection operator of a group can be expressed as a product of the projection operators of the subgroups of the product

Table 11.4. Correlation of $\mathbf{D}_2$ and $\mathbf{C}_{3v}$ with $\mathbf{T}_d$

$\mathbf{T}_d$	$\mathbf{D}_2$	$\mathbf{C}_{3v}$
A_1	A	A_1
A_2	A	A_2
E	$2A$	E
T_1	$B_1 + B_2 + B_3$	$A_2 + E$
T_2	$B_1 + B_2 + B_3$	$A_1 + E$

structure. The basis vectors can be adapted to the site symmetry, and then the resulting symmetry adapted functions can be combined according to the interchange group. Within $\mathbf{C}_{3v}$ we have

$$P^{(A_1)}\mathbf{x}_1 = \mathbf{x}_1 + \mathbf{y}_1 + \mathbf{z}_1 \equiv \mathbf{r}_1 \tag{11.51}$$

$$P^{(E)}\mathbf{x}_1 = 2\mathbf{x}_1 - \mathbf{y}_1 - \mathbf{z}_1 \equiv \mathbf{e}_1 \tag{11.52}$$

The other component of the E combination is

$$P^{(E)}(\mathbf{y}_1 - \mathbf{z}_1) = \mathbf{y}_1 - \mathbf{z}_1 \equiv \mathbf{p}_1 \tag{11.53}$$

These are shown in Fig. 11.5.

The final vibrational functions are obtained by applying the appropriate projection operators of $\mathbf{D}_2$ to Eqs. 11.51 to 11.53. The results are (only one component of each degenerate function is given)

$$\phi(a_1) = P^{(A)}\mathbf{r}_1 = \mathbf{r}_1 + \mathbf{r}_2 + \mathbf{r}_3 + \mathbf{r}_4 \quad \text{(symmetric stretch)} \tag{11.54}$$

$$\phi_1(t_2) = P^{(B_1+B_2+B_3)}\mathbf{r}_1 = 3\mathbf{r}_1 - \mathbf{r}_2 - \mathbf{r}_3 - \mathbf{r}_4 \quad \text{(asymmetric stretch)} \tag{11.55}$$

$$\phi(e) = P^{(A)}\mathbf{e}_1 = \mathbf{e}_1 + \mathbf{e}_2 + \mathbf{e}_3 + \mathbf{e}_4 \quad \text{(bend)} \tag{11.56}$$

$$\phi_2(t_2) = P^{(B_1+B_2+B_3)}\mathbf{e}_1 = 3\mathbf{e}_1 - \mathbf{e}_2 - \mathbf{e}_3 - \mathbf{e}_4 \quad \text{(bend)} \tag{11.57}$$

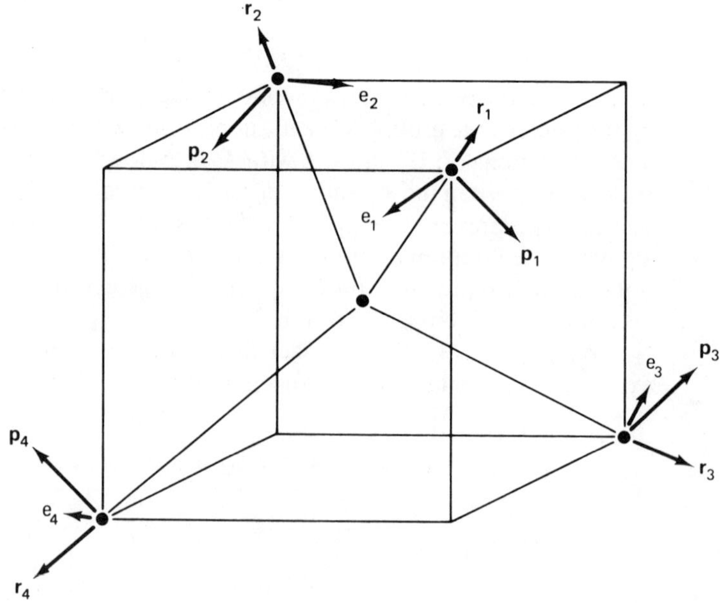

Fig. 11.5. Site-symmetry-adapted hydrogen-centered displacement vectors for methane.

A similar approach can be applied to any system. However, for molecules with less symmetry, it is more difficult to interpret the results in terms of stretches and bends. As an example, let us consider methanol. The point symmetry for the most symmetrical conformation is only $\mathbf{C}_s$; however, we will consider the non-rigid molecular group (see Section 6.5). Starting from the $\mathbf{C}_s$ conformation, the only isodynamic operation is the $\mathscr{C}_3$ rotation of the methyl group.

The supergroup is

$$\mathbf{S} = \mathscr{C}_3 \wedge \mathbf{C}_s \tag{11.58}$$

and is isomorphic to $\mathbf{C}_{3v}$. The character table is shown in Table 11.5, which also includes the transformation properties of the Cartesian coordinates and the rotations. Note that the behavior of these is determined by the point group. This also dictates the orientation of the basis vectors. The atoms lying in the plane of symmetry must have their z axis perpendicular to this plane, and their x and y axes in

Table 11.5. Character table for $\mathscr{C}_3 \wedge \mathbf{C}_s$

$\mathscr{C}_3 \wedge \mathbf{C}_s$	E	$2\mathscr{C}_3$	3σ	
A_1	1	1	1	x, y, R_z
A_2	1	1	-1	z, R_x, R_y
E	2	-1	0	

the plane. The isodynamic operation interchanges the origins of the vectors on the methyl hydrogens, but *keeps their directions constant.* These are shown in Fig. 11.6. Since there is no interchange of any of the atoms in the symmetry plane by the point symmetry, the choice of the orientations of the x and y axes is completely arbitrary. For convenience, we have chosen them all to be parallel.

There are 12 vibrations possible for CH_3OH. The total motional representation is $8A_1 + 4A_2 + 3E$. The rotations and translations account for $3A_1$ and $3A_2$ of these; thus, the vibrational representation is $5A_1 + A_2 + 3E$.

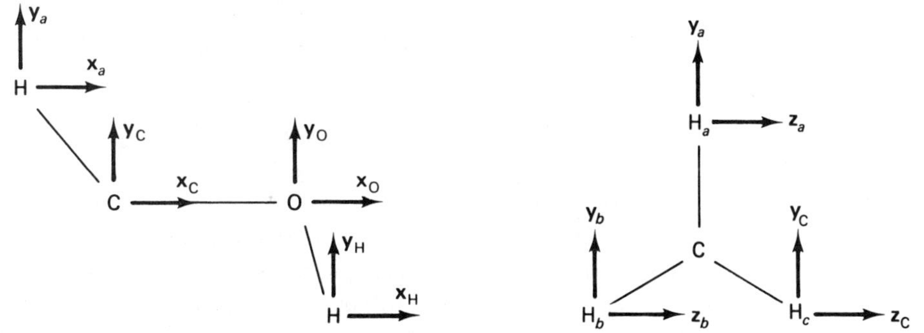

Fig. 11.6. Starting set of atom-centered displacement vectors for methanol.

The site symmetry for the carbon, the oxygen, and the hydroxyl hydrogen (denoted simply H) is the full group. Their interchange symmetry is only the identity. The site symmetry for the methyl hydrogen H_a is $\mathbf{C}_s$, while its interchange symmetry is $\mathscr{C}_3$. The other two hydrogens have only the identity as their site symmetry and the full group as the interchange symmetry; however, their displacements will be generated by the $\mathscr{C}_3$ projection operators operating on H_a, so they need not be considered explicitly. The correlation table for $\mathbf{C}_s$ and $\mathscr{C}_3$ with the full group is shown in Table 11.6.

The x and y coordinates for the atoms in the plane both transform as A' within $\mathbf{C}_s$; therefore, any linear combination of them is suitable. This gives the eight functions

$$\mathbf{p}_{\mathrm{H}}^{\pm} = a\mathbf{x}_{\mathrm{H}} \pm b\mathbf{y}_{\mathrm{H}} \tag{11.59}$$

$$\mathbf{p}_{\mathrm{O}}^{\pm} = c\mathbf{x}_{\mathrm{O}} \pm d\mathbf{y}_{\mathrm{O}} \tag{11.60}$$

$$\mathbf{p}_{\mathrm{C}}^{\pm} = e\mathbf{x}_{\mathrm{C}} \pm f\mathbf{y}_{\mathrm{C}} \tag{11.61}$$

$$\mathbf{p}_{a}^{\pm} = g\mathbf{x}_{a} \pm h\mathbf{y}_{a} \tag{11.62}$$

The corresponding $\mathbf{z}$ vectors by themselves transform as A''. The functions for H, O, and C are already molecular functions since the interchange group contains only the identity. The $\mathbf{p}$'s transform as A_1 and the $\mathbf{z}$'s as A_2 within the supergroup. The $\mathbf{p}_a$ and $\mathbf{z}_a$ must be operated on with the projection operators from $\mathscr{C}_3$. We have

$$P^{(A)}\mathbf{p}_a^{\pm} = \mathbf{p}_a^{\pm} + \mathbf{p}_b^{\pm} + \mathbf{p}_c^{\pm} = g(\mathbf{x}_a + \mathbf{x}_b + \mathbf{x}_c) \pm h(\mathbf{y}_a + \mathbf{y}_b + \mathbf{y}_c) \tag{11.63}$$

$$P^{(A)}\mathbf{z}_a = \mathbf{z}_a + \mathbf{z}_b + \mathbf{z}_c \tag{11.64}$$

$$P^{(E)}\mathbf{p}_a^{\pm} = 2\mathbf{p}_a^{\pm} - \mathbf{p}_b^{\pm} - \mathbf{p}_c^{\pm} = g(2\mathbf{x}_a - \mathbf{x}_b - \mathbf{x}_c) \pm h(2\mathbf{y}_a - \mathbf{y}_b - \mathbf{y}_c) \tag{11.65}$$

$$P^{(E)}\mathbf{z}_a = 2\mathbf{z}_a - \mathbf{z}_b - \mathbf{z}_c \tag{11.66}$$

All vibrations of the same symmetry type can interact with each other, so the final vibrations have the form (except for normalization)

$$\begin{aligned}\phi(a_1) = {} & c_{\mathrm{H}}(a\mathbf{x}_{\mathrm{H}} \pm b\mathbf{y}_{\mathrm{H}}) + c_{\mathrm{O}}(c\mathbf{x}_{\mathrm{O}} \pm d\mathbf{y}_{\mathrm{O}}) + c_{\mathrm{C}}(e\mathbf{x}_{\mathrm{C}} \pm f\mathbf{y}_{\mathrm{C}}) \\ & + c_{\mathrm{Me}}[g(\mathbf{x}_a + \mathbf{x}_b + \mathbf{x}_c) \pm h(\mathbf{y}_a + \mathbf{y}_b + \mathbf{y}_c)]\end{aligned} \tag{11.67}$$

$$\phi(a_2) = c_{\mathrm{H}}\mathbf{z}_{\mathrm{H}} + c_{\mathrm{O}}\mathbf{z}_{\mathrm{O}} + c_{\mathrm{C}}\mathbf{z}_{\mathrm{C}} + c_{\mathrm{Me}}(\mathbf{z}_a + \mathbf{z}_b + \mathbf{z}_c) \tag{11.68}$$

$$\phi_1(e) = g(2\mathbf{x}_a - \mathbf{x}_b - \mathbf{x}_c) \pm h(2\mathbf{y}_a - \mathbf{y}_b - \mathbf{y}_c) \tag{11.69}$$

$$\phi_2(e) = 2\mathbf{z}_a - \mathbf{z}_b - \mathbf{z}_c \tag{11.70}$$

There will be eight a_1 functions, four corresponding to various values and signs for the c's in Eq. 11.67 with all plus signs in the $\mathbf{x}$ and $\mathbf{y}$ combinations, and four with all minus signs. Three of these will be a rotation and two translations. There will be four a_2 functions corresponding to various c's in Eq. 11.68. Three of these will be two rotations and a translation. Equation 11.69 gives two doubly degenerate

Table 11.6. Correlation of $\mathscr{C}_3$ and C_s with $\mathscr{C}_3 \wedge C_s$

$\mathscr{C}_3$	$\mathscr{C}_3 \wedge C_s$	C_s
A	A_1	A'
A	A_2	A''
E	E	$A' + A''$

vibrations, while Eq. 11.70 gives one doubly degenerate function. Except for the *e* vibrations, which can be described in terms of specific motions of the methyl groups, none of the vibrations can be described as simple stretches, bends, and so on.

Exercise 11.4: Use atom-centered coordinates to describe the normal coordinates of NH_3, both including and excluding inversion at the nitrogen in the group.

11.5 VIBRONIC INTERACTIONS

Frequently, an electronic transition that is found to be symmetry-forbidden is experimentally observed in the spectrum of a molecule. For example, the lowest-energy singlet transition in benzene, ${}^1B_{2u} \leftarrow {}^1A_{1g}$, is such a transition. Such transitions are usually made allowed via *vibronic interactions*, the interaction of excited vibrational and electronic states. The most usual detailed treatments of vibronic interactions follow the perturbation theory development first presented by Herzberg and Teller in 1933. This type of treatment allows the intensities to be calculated in terms of the intensities of noncoupled vibrational and electronic transitions. For our purposes, however, an argument based simply on the total symmetries of the states involved will be sufficient.

The source of vibronic transitions can be visualized from the schematic representation of the potential-energy curves for the ground and excited electronic states of a diatomic molecule shown in Fig. 11.7. In general, the equilibrium nuclear configuration for an excited electronic state will be different from that for a ground electronic state. Electronic excitations, however, obey the *Franck–Condon principle*; that is, the time required for an electronic transition to occur is much too short for nuclear reorganization to occur simultaneously. Thus, the nuclear configuration that is directly achieved on electronic excitation is a distorted configuration as far as the excited electronic state is concerned. This nuclear configuration corresponds to an excited vibrational level of the excited electronic state. The overall symmetry of the state achieved is obtained from the electronic-state symmetry and the vibrational-state symmetry. In the approximation we are using, the total wave function is a product of the electronic, vibrational, and rotational wave functions:

$$\Psi = \psi_e \psi_v \psi_r \tag{11.71}$$

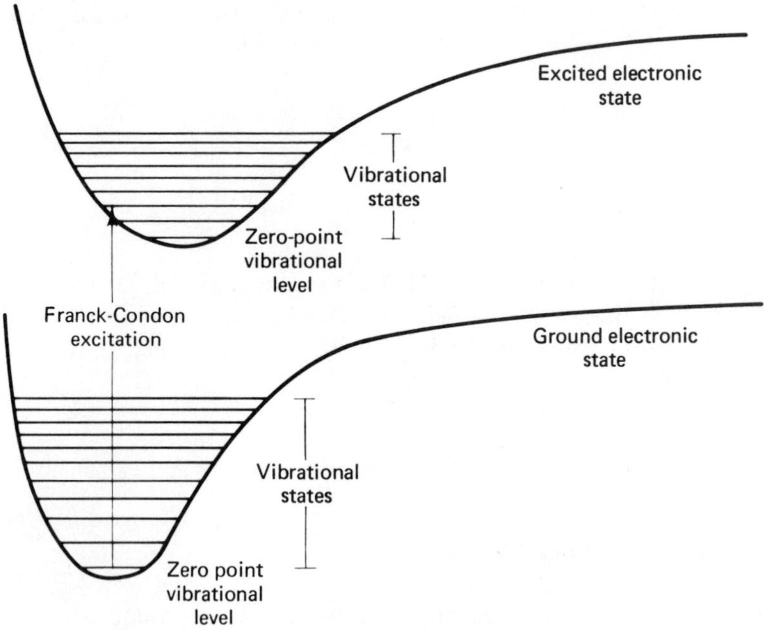

Fig. 11.7. Schematic representation of a Franck–Condon excitation for a diatomic molecule.

The total representation for a particular state will thus be the product of representations corresponding to the irreducible representations of the electronic, vibrational, and rotational wave functions for that state:

$$\Gamma(\text{total}) = \Gamma(\psi_e) \times \Gamma(\psi_v) \times \Gamma(\psi_r) \qquad (11.72)$$

The irreducible representations of the rotational wave functions $\Gamma(\psi_r)$ are derived from the $\mathbf{R}(3)$ point group. For the moment we will ignore these and concentrate our attention on the electronic and vibrational states.

The transition dipole integral to be considered, if a transition between two vibronic states is to be electric-dipole-induced, is

$$\boldsymbol{\mu}_{ij}^{kl} = \langle \psi_e^i \psi_v^j | e\mathbf{r} | \psi_e^k \psi_v^l \rangle \qquad (11.73)$$

For absorption spectra, the starting state (ground state), denoted by i and j, is usually totally symmetrical with respect to both its electronic and vibrational wave functions. The symmetry requirement to make the complete representation of Eq. 11.73 totally symmetric, and thus an observable, is that the product $\Gamma(\mathbf{r}) \times \Gamma(\psi_e^k) \times \Gamma(\psi_v^l)$ must contain the totally symmetric representation. In order for this to occur, the product $\Gamma(\psi_e^k) \times \Gamma(\psi_v^l)$ must, as usual, contain the irreducible representation of at least one of the Cartesian coordinates (i.e., the product must contain a representation that corresponds to a directly observable excited state).

The more general relationship, that the product $\Gamma(\mathbf{r}) \times \Gamma(\psi_e^k) \times \Gamma(\psi_v^l)$ must contain the totally symmetric representation, is more useful for our present purposes, however. Let us first work through the relationships for one-dimensional representations so that we can use equalities. After finding the behavior for this case, we will generalize to the situation where the representations can be two- or three-dimensional.

For one-dimensional representations only, the requirement is that

$$\Gamma(\mathbf{r}) \times \Gamma(\psi_e^k) \times \Gamma(\psi_v^l) = \Gamma_{\text{sym}} \tag{11.74}$$

If the electronic excitation is itself symmetry-allowed,

$$\Gamma(\mathbf{r}) \times \Gamma(\psi_e^k) = \Gamma_{\text{sym}} \tag{11.75}$$

This means that for Eq. 11.74 to be satisfied, $\Gamma(\psi_v^l)$ *must be the totally symmetric irreducible representation.* In other words, for symmetry-allowed electronic excitations, the excited electronic state achieved must be associated with a totally symmetric vibrational state (i.e., the state must have no vibrational excitation, or it must have excitation of totally symmetric vibrational modes; the second situation is the more general case). Under sufficient resolution, the vapor-phase spectrum of such a system would show a band corresponding to the electronic transition, and superimposed on this would be vibrational fine structure corresponding to totally symmetric vibrations of the excited electronic state. The same symmetry requirements are valid for emission; consequently, the fluorescence spectrum corresponding to a symmetry-allowed electronic transition would have, superimposed upon the electronic band, a vibrational fine structure corresponding to totally symmetric vibrations of the ground electronic state. (Fluorescence originates from the ground vibrational level of the excited electronic state.) This can sometimes be a useful method of studying vibrations which cannot be directly observed.

If $\Gamma(\mathbf{r})$ and $\Gamma(\psi_e^k)$ have dimensionalities greater than unity, their product will be reducible. In such a case, if the electronic transition is symmetry-allowed, we have

$$\Gamma(\mathbf{r}) \times \Gamma(\psi_e^k) = \Gamma_{\text{sym}} + \Gamma' + \Gamma'' + \ldots \tag{11.76}$$

where the Γ's on the right-hand side of the equation are the irreducible representations making up the reducible representation of the product. In this case, when we consider the vibronic interaction, we have

$$\Gamma(\mathbf{r}) \times \Gamma(\psi_e^k) \times \Gamma(\psi_v^l) = \Gamma_{\text{sym}} \times \Gamma(\psi_v^l) + \Gamma' \times \Gamma(\psi_v^l) + \ldots \tag{11.77}$$

For situations such as this, totally symmetrical vibrations will contribute to the fine structure via the first term on the right-hand side of Eq. 11.77. Other vibrations can also occur, however, for cases where the $\Gamma(\psi_v^l)$ equals one of the Γ'.

If a transition is symmetry-forbidden as far as the electronic states are concerned, then, for one-dimensional representations,

$$\Gamma(\mathbf{r}) \times \Gamma(\psi_e^k) = \Gamma' \tag{11.78}$$

where Γ' is some irreducible representation other than the totally symmetrical one. We have, on considering vibronic interaction,

$$\Gamma(\mathbf{r}) \times \Gamma(\psi_e^k) \times \Gamma(\psi_v^l) = \Gamma' \times \Gamma(\psi_v^l) \tag{11.79}$$

In order for this transition to be made allowed via vibronic interaction, $\Gamma(\psi_v^l)$ must equal, or be contained in, Γ'.

If the product representation of Eq. 11.78 is reducible, vibronic interaction may occur via any of the irreducible components. Thus, if any component of Γ' equals $\Gamma(\psi_v^l)$, the transition will be made symmetry-allowed via vibronic interaction.

Exercise 11.5*: The first electronic transition in formaldehyde (CH_2O) is $\pi^* \leftarrow n$ in character. The n orbital can be considered to be a p orbital lying in the molecular plane.

(a) Assuming the molecule to lie in the yz plane with z coinciding with the molecular axis and the n orbital to point in the y direction, find the symmetry of the $\pi^* \leftarrow n$ excited state.

(b) Is this $\pi^* \leftarrow n$ transition symmetry-allowed?

(c) Find the symmetries of the normal vibrations of formaldehyde.

(d) If the $\pi^* \leftarrow n$ transition is allowed, which vibrations will contribute to its fine structure, or if it is forbidden, which vibrations will make it allowed by vibronic interaction?

Exercise 11.6: Find the symmetries of the normal vibrations (if any) which would make the indicated forbidden electronic transitions allowed. Give the polarization of the resulting vibronic transition.

Point Group	Transition
$\mathbf{C}_{3v}$	$A_2 \leftarrow A_1$
$\mathbf{D}_{3h}$	$E'' \leftarrow A_1'$
$\mathbf{D}_{3d}$	$E_g \leftarrow A_{1g}$
$\mathbf{C}_{\infty v}$	$\Sigma^- \leftarrow \Sigma^+$
$\mathbf{D}_{\infty h}$	$\Pi_g \leftarrow \Sigma_g^+$
$\mathbf{T}_d$	$E \leftarrow A_1$
$\mathbf{O}_h$	$E_u \leftarrow A_{1g}$

11.6 OVERTONES OF DEGENERATE VIBRATIONS

Overtones to most molecular vibrations can be observed under the proper experimental conditions. If these overtones are of degenerate vibrations, they will lead to more than one excited vibrational state. The representations of these overtone states can be obtained by taking the appropriate products of the representation of the fundamental with itself. If it is a first overtone (i.e., a two-quantum excitation), we have $\Gamma_v \times \Gamma_v$; if a second overtone, $\Gamma_v \times \Gamma_v \times \Gamma_v$, and so on. There is a restriction on these, however. The oscillator Hamiltonian is a boson operator; consequently, the product must be a symmetrized product (in contrast to the antisymmetrized product that was required for many-electron states). Thus, for an n-quantum excitation, we must adapt our vibrational representation to the $[n]$ representation of $\mathbf{S}(n)$ (see Section 7.11).

Consider a triple excitation of a t_2 vibration of methane. We must adapt the T_2 representation of $\mathbf{T}_d$ to the totally symmetric [3] representation of $\mathbf{S}(3)$. For $\mathbf{S}(3)$, we have

$\mathbf{S}(3)$	(1^3)	$3(2, 1)$	$2(3)$
[3]	1	1	1

(11.80)

For $\mathbf{T}_d$, we have

$\mathbf{T}_d$	E	$8C_3$	$3C_2$	$6S_4$	$6\sigma_d$
T_2	3	0	-1	-1	1

(11.81)

For $\chi^{[3]\alpha}(R)$, we have

$$\chi^{[3]\alpha}(R) = \tfrac{1}{6}\{1 \times 1 \times (\chi(R))^3 + 3 \times 1 \times (\chi(R^2))(\chi(R)) + 2 \times 1 \times \chi(R^3)\}. \tag{11.82}$$

For example, for $\chi^{[3]\alpha}(E)$, we have

$$\begin{aligned}\chi^{[3]\alpha}(E) &= \tfrac{1}{6}\{27 + 3 \times 1 \times 3 \times 3 + 2 \times 1 \times 3\}\\ &= 10\end{aligned} \tag{11.83}$$

The final result is

$\mathbf{T}_d$	E	$8C_3$	$3C_2$	$6S_4$	$6\sigma_d$
Γ_{overtone}	10	1	-2	0	2

(11.84)

This reduces to $A_1 + T_1 + 2T_2$. These are the vibrational states arising from a triple excitation of a t_2 vibration.

Exercise 11.7*: Find the vibrational states resulting from the following in methane:

(a) Double excitation of an e mode
(b) Double excitation of a t_2 mode
(c) Triple excitation of an e mode

PROBLEMS

1. (a) Find the symmetries of the normal vibrations of NH_3 ($\mathbf{C}_{3v}$).
   (b) Assign the excitations as infrared-allowed, Raman-allowed, or forbidden.
   (c) Construct the normal modes of vibration.
   (d) Find the vibrational states arising from the first overtone of each fundamental.
   (e) Which overtone states could be reached by infrared excitation from the ground state?

2. Repeat Problem 1 for $NiCl_3^{2-}$($\mathbf{D}_{4h}$).

3. Repeat Problem 1 for SF_6($\mathbf{O}_h$).

4. Repeat Problem 1 for NH_3, including the nitrogen inversion in the group.

5. Find the symmetries of the normal vibrations of propane within its supergroup. Find the selection rules. Construct the normal coordinates.

6. The $E_g \leftarrow T_{2g}$ electronic transition is forbidden in an octahedral complex. What vibrational excitation would make this vibronically allowed?

BIBLIOGRAPHY

BARROW, G. M., *Introduction to Molecular Spectroscopy*, McGraw-Hill Book Company, New York, 1962.

COTTON, F. A., *Chemical Applications of Group Theory*, 2nd ed., John Wiley & Sons, Inc., New York, 1971.

FERRARO, J. R., AND J. S. ZIOMEK, *Introduction to Group Theory*, 2nd ed., Plenum Press, New York, 1975.

HALL, L. H., *Group Theory and Symmetry in Chemistry*, McGraw-Hill Book Company, New York, 1969.

HARMONY, M. D., *Introduction to Molecular Energies and Spectra*, Holt, Rinehart and Winston, Inc., New York, 1972.

HERZBERG, G., *Infrared and Raman Spectra*, Van Nostrand Reinhold Company, New York, 1945.

KING, G. W., *Spectroscopy and Molecular Structure*, Holt, Rinehart and Winston, Inc., New York, 1964.

WILSON, E. B., JR., J. C. DECIUS, AND P. C. CROSS, *Molecular Vibrations*, McGraw-Hill Book Company, New York, 1955.

12

Rotational States and Nuclear Spin States

12.1 MOMENTS OF INERTIA AND TOP CLASSIFICATION

Nonlinear molecules can, in general, have three independent moments of inertia. In molecules with symmetry elements, the rotations from which these arise lie along symmetry axes or in symmetry planes. If there is a symmetry axis of order 3 or higher, two of the rotations become degenerate (two moments of inertia become equal). If there is more than one symmetry axis of order 3 or higher, as in the cubic groups, all three rotations are degenerate. If the highest order of symmetry axis is 2, all three rotations are completely independent and the moments of inertia are all unequal (except for the possibility of accidental degeneracies). The three independent angular momenta couple to give a net angular momentum which is quantized. This net rotational angular momentum, which is labeled with the quantum number J, behaves essentially as any other net angular momentum that we have discussed. Its eigenfunctions transform as the irreducible representations of the $\mathbf{R}_h(3)$ point group. Its selection rules can be derived directly from this group. The selection rules for the individual components of angular momentum are, however, more complicated.

The rotational behavior of molecules is conventionally divided into three classes. Molecules with all three moments of inertia equal are called *spherical tops*. These molecules cannot exhibit microwave spectra since they cannot have a permanent dipole moment. Rotational spectra of such systems can, however, be observed by the rotational Raman technique and by rotational fine structure on vibrational spectra.

Molecules with two moments of inertia equal are referred to as *symmetric tops*. These are further subdivided into prolate tops and oblate tops. *Prolate tops* are those symmetric tops in which the two degenerate moments of inertia are greater than the unique one. In *oblate tops* the degenerate moments are smaller than the unique one. Linear molecules are prolate symmetric tops, while planar symmetric tops are oblate. Symmetric tops may or may not have permanent dipole moments, and consequently, may or may not exhibit microwave spectra.

Molecules that have three different moments of inertia are known as *asymmetric tops*. Such molecules will almost invariably have permanent dipole moments and exhibit microwave spectra.

The moments of inertia of a molecule are, by convention, labeled *a*, *b*, and *c* with $I_a < I_b < I_c$. Thus, for prolate tops, I_b equals I_c, while for oblate tops I_a equals I_b. For prolate tops, the principal symmetry axis is the *a* axis, while for oblate tops it is the *c* axis.

There are two approaches that one uses when applying the principles of molecular group theory to the rotational states of molecules. The most obvious approach is to classify these states within the point group of the molecule. The other approach is to classify the system in terms of the symmetry properties of its moments of inertia, rather than the rotational states. Thus, an asymmetric top has three unique independent moments of inertia. These can be represented by a system of three orthogonal vectors of unequal magnitude (Fig. 12.1). If positive and negative combinations of these are allowed, the system of vectors transforms as the $\mathbf{D}_{2h}$ point group. For a symmetric top, two of the vectors become degenerate. All linear combinations of these vectors which lie in their plane are

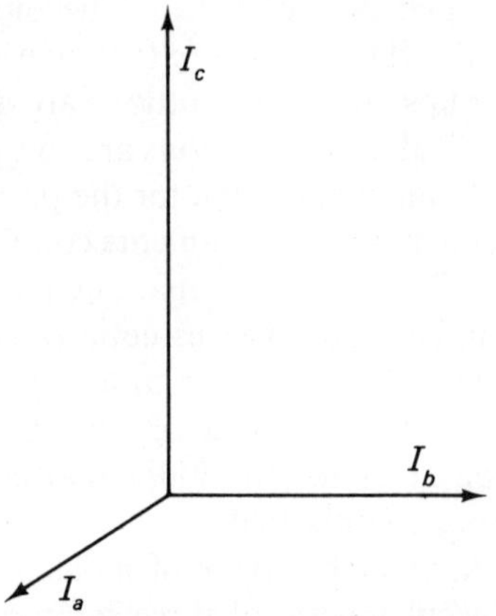

Fig. 12.1. Schematic representation of the moments of inertia of an asymmetric top.

also equivalent. This means that there are no unique directions in the plane of the degenerate vectors. The system of vectors transforms as the $\mathbf{D}_{\infty h}$ point group. Similarly, for spherical tops all three vectors are equivalent, as is any linear combination in any direction. The moments of inertia of the spherical top thus transform according to the $\mathbf{R}_h(3)$ point group.

Both approaches to the symmetry treatment are employed in the analysis of rotational spectra. The first is used to study selection rules, the interaction of rotational states with vibrational, electronic, and spin states, and to determine statistical weights of rotational levels. The second approach allows all tops of a given type to be characterized with the same set of rules. It is used to obtain energy levels and, consequently, structural information (via the moments of inertia of the molecule).

12.2 ROTATIONAL WAVE FUNCTIONS AND ENERGY LEVELS

The detailed description of rotational wave functions is usually based on the Eulerian angles θ, ϕ, and χ (see Fig. 6.1). We shall not go into detail on this development; however, we will retain the basic formalism. The rotational wave function of a symmetric top, $\psi_{JKM}(\theta, \phi, \chi)$, can be expressed

$$\psi_{JKM}(\theta, \phi, \chi) = \theta_{JKM}(\theta)e^{iM\phi}e^{iK\chi} \tag{12.1}$$

In this equation, $\theta_{JKM}(\theta)$ is the external rotation function. Its eigenstates transform as the irreducible representations of the $\mathbf{R}_h(3)$ point group. It is through this function that J quantization and the corresponding selection rules arise. The quantum numbers K and M represent components of angular momentum. They both can range in value from $-J$ to J. The M quantum number is analogous to the m quantum number in the hydrogenic electronic wave function. It gives the component of the total angular momentum along the external z axis. Thus, a rotational state having a given J value is $(2J + 1)$-fold-degenerate, in the absence of an external field, via the degeneracy of the various M levels. This M degeneracy can be removed by the application of an external electric field (the Stark effect) or a magnetic field (the Zeeman effect). The K quantum number is the component of J along the internal principal axis.

The rotational energy levels of a symmetric top, in terms of J and K, are

$$E_{JK} = BJ(J + 1) + (A' - B)K^2 \tag{12.2}$$

where

$$B = \frac{h}{8\pi^2 cI_B} \tag{12.3}$$

and

$$A' = \frac{h}{8\pi^2 cI_{A'}} \tag{12.4}$$

The I_B is one of the equivalent moments of inertia and $I_{A'}$ is the unique one (either I_a or I_c). In the spherical top, where all moments of inertia are equal, the states of differing K, but common J, are degenerate. This, coupled with the M degeneracy, means that all rotational states of spherical tops are $(2J + 1)^2$-fold degenerate.

In symmetric-top molecules, the K degeneracy is partially lifted, to the extent that states of different $|K|$ are nondegenerate. States with $|K|$ greater than zero are doubly degenerate (corresponding to the $+K$ and $-K$ states), while those with $K = 0$ are nondegenerate. In prolate tops, I_a is the unique moment of inertia and is smaller than I_b. Thus, A is larger than B. States having $|K|$ greater than zero will increase in energy as $|K|$ increases. Note that for linear molecules, I_a is zero and A is infinite. This means that a nonzero K state for a linear molecule would have an infinitely high energy and would be unattainable; consequently, the expression given previously, Eq. 9.60, is valid for linear molecules. In oblate tops, I_c is the unique moment of inertia and is greater than I_b. This means that oblate tops having $|K|$ greater than zero will decrease in energy as $|K|$ increases.

In asymmetric tops, the K degeneracy is completely lifted; however, since no axis within the asymmetric top has a special relationship to the others, there is no unique internal axis on which to project the angular momentum. In fact, the motion is such that there is no fixed component of angular momentum along any internal axis. The concept of the K quantum number, which was based on a symmetric top, therefore loses its meaning. It is replaced by a number τ, which is a numerical label rather than a true quantum number. The allowed values of τ are the same as those for K; however, there are no selection rules involving τ. Numbering of the levels is sequential, starting with $\tau = -J$ and going to J.

The energy levels of an asymmetric top are conveniently expressed in terms of an asymmetry parameter κ, where

$$\kappa = \frac{2B - A - C}{A - C} \tag{12.5}$$

Note that κ equals -1 for a prolate top and $+1$ for an oblate top. Classically, rotational energy is given by the expression

$$E = \frac{p_a^2}{2I_a} + \frac{p_b^2}{2I_b} + \frac{p_c^2}{2I_c} = \frac{p_a^2 A + p_b^2 B + p_c^2 C}{\hbar^2} \tag{12.6}$$

where the p_i are the components of angular momentum. Since total angular momentum is conserved, this can be rearranged to give

$$E = \frac{\frac{1}{2}(A + C)p^2 + \frac{1}{2}(A - C)(p_a^2 - p_c^2 + \kappa p_b^2)}{\hbar^2} \tag{12.7}$$

If we make the quantum mechanical substitution of $J(J + 1)\hbar^2$ for p^2 and call the last parenthetical term $\hbar^2 E(\kappa)$, we have

$$E = \tfrac{1}{2}(A + C)J(J + 1) + \tfrac{1}{2}(A - C)E(\kappa) \tag{12.8}$$

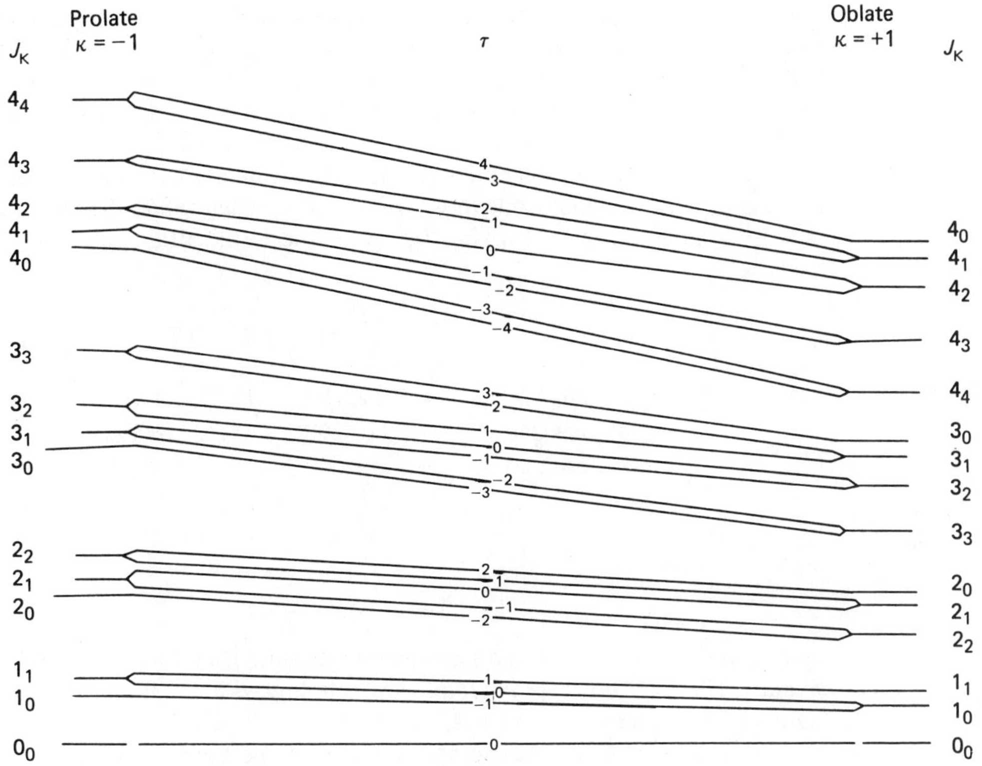

Fig. 12.2. Schematic representation of the energy levels of an asymmetric top in relation to the prolate and oblate symmetric tops.

In applications to spectral data, the $E(\kappa)$ are obtained numerically by expanding the rotational wave function for the asymmetric top as a linear combination of symmetric-top functions. The resulting expansion is substituted into the rotational Schrödinger equation, which is then solved for the allowed energy levels. The energy levels for an asymmetric top are shown schematically in Fig. 12.2.

12.3 GROUP THEORETICAL TREATMENT

Classification of J Values into Irreducible Representations

Let us now turn our attention to the group-theoretical treatment of rotational states. First, let us consider the classification of the rotational states according to the irreducible representations of the molecular point group. As we have previously mentioned, this is accomplished by mapping the irreducible representation, for the J value under consideration, from the $\mathbf{R}_h(3)$ point group onto the point group of the molecule [actually, $\mathbf{R}(3)$ and the rotational subgroups of the point groups are sufficient for rotational states]. As examples of spherical, symmetric, and asymmetric tops, let us consider methane, methyl chloride, and water, respectively. Further, for illustrative purposes, consider the rotational state having a J value of 3 in each case. The rotation functions with odd J values are all *gerade* with respect to the point of inversion, while those with even J are *ungerade*; therefore, we have the $D_g^{(3)}$ representation. Mapping $D_g^{(3)}$ onto the tetrahedral group of methane, we have

$\mathbf{T}_d$	E	$8C_3$	$3C_2$	$6S_4$	$6\sigma_d$
$D_g^{(3)}$	7	$1 + 2\cos 120° + 2\cos 240° + 2\cos 360°$	$1 + 2\cos 180° + 2\cos 360° + 2\cos 540°$	$1 - 2\cos 90° + 2\cos 180° - 2\cos 270°$	-1
	7	1	-1	-1	-1

(12.9)

This reduces to

$$\Gamma_r^{(J=3)} = A_2 + T_1 + T_2 \tag{12.10}$$

Note that these rotational states are degenerate since they correspond to the same J value. They will, however, enter into any coupling with vibrational and electronic states and into any selection rules.

For methyl chloride, the point group is $\mathbf{C}_{3v}$, and the mapping is

$\mathbf{C}_{3v}$	E	$2C_3$	$3\sigma_v$
$D_g^{(3)}$	7	$1 + 2\cos 120° + 2\cos 240° + 2\cos 360°$	-1
	7	1	-1

(12.11)

The reduction to irreducible representations yields

$$\Gamma_r^{(J=3)} = A_1 + 2A_2 + 2E \tag{12.12}$$

Again these states are degenerate. For water, the mapping and the reduction are

$\mathbf{C}_{2v}$	E	C_2	σ_v	$\sigma_{v'}$
$D_g^{(3)}$	7	$1 + 2\cos 180° + 2\cos 360° + 2\cos 540°$	-1	-1
	7	-1	-1	-1

(12.13)

$$\Gamma_r^{(J=3)} = A_1 + 2A_2 + 2B_1 + 2B_2 \tag{12.14}$$

When only rotational states of molecules are being considered, only the rotational subgroup of the point group is required. Thus, methane would be classified according to the group **T**, methyl chloride according to the group $\mathbf{C}_3$, and water according to $\mathbf{C}_2$. Most treatments of rotational states are carried out on the basis of these subgroups. The more complete treatment is required, however, for consideration of the coupling of rotational states to vibrational and electronic states.

Classification of K Values into Irreducible Representations

The K quantum number gives the component of angular momentum along the internal z axis for a symmetric top. States of differing $|K|$ value transform as the irreducible representations of the $\mathbf{D}_{\infty h}$ point group. For symmetric and asymmetric tops, these may be reduced to the point symmetry of the individual molecule. In the case of spherical tops, all K values for a given J value represent degenerate rotational states; consequently, the states of different K cannot be resolved. Consider the $J = 3$ case for the $\mathbf{C}_{3v}$ point group of methyl chloride. The allowed $|K|$ values are 0, 1, 2, and 3. These correspond to Σ_g^-, Π_g, Δ_g, and Φ_g in the $\mathbf{D}_{\infty h}$ point group. The reduction to $\mathbf{C}_{3v}$ is

(12.15)

$\mathbf{D}_{\infty h}$	E	$C(\phi = 120°)$	σ
$\mathbf{C}_{3v}$	E	C_3	σ_v
Σ_g^-	1	1	-1
Π_g	2	2 cos 120°	0
	(2	-1	0)
Δ_g	2	2 cos 240°	0
	(2	-1	0)
Φ_g	2	2 cos 360°	0
	(2	2	0)

Thus, the $K = 0$ state transforms as A_2 within $\mathbf{C}_{3v}$, while $|K| = 1$ and $|K| = 2$ both transform as the E representation, and $|K| = 3$ transforms as $A_1 + A_2$. Similarly, within $\mathbf{C}_{2v}$, $K = 0$ transforms as A_2, $|K| = 1$ and $|K| = 3$ each transform as $B_1 + B_2$, and the $|K| = 2$ state transforms as $A_1 + A_2$.

Selection Rules

For microwave absorption, the J selection rules are the same as they were in the case of linear molecules [i.e., within $\mathbf{R}(3)$, $\Delta J = 0, \pm 1$]. The presence of a permanent dipole moment is also again necessary. Thus, methane, having no permanent dipole moment, will not exhibit a microwave spectrum. Both methyl chloride and water have permanent dipole moments. In both cases, this lies only along the z axis. Thus, if $\Gamma_r^i \times \Gamma_r^f$ contains Γ_{μ_z}, a spectrum can occur. Considering the $(J = 4) \leftarrow (J = 3)$ transition for methyl chloride, we find that

$$\Gamma_r^{(J=4)} = A_1 + 2A_2 + 3E \tag{12.16}$$

The dipole component μ_z transforms as A_1 within $\mathbf{C}_{3v}$ (in fact, for all $\mathbf{C}_n$ and $\mathbf{C}_{nv}$ groups, μ_z transforms as the totally symmetric representation); consequently, $A_1 \leftrightarrow A_1, A_2 \leftrightarrow A_2$, and $E \leftrightarrow E$ transitions are allowed. For the $(J = 3) \leftarrow (J = 2)$ transition, we have

$$\Gamma_r^{(J=2)} = A_1 + 2E \tag{12.17}$$

The transitions $A_1 \leftrightarrow A_1$ and $E \leftrightarrow E$ are allowed.

The K selection rule for direct radiative transitions can be derived from the $\mathbf{D}_{\infty h}$ point group. In this group, μ_z transforms as Σ_u^+; therefore, $\Gamma_r^i \times \Gamma_r^f$ must contain Σ_u^+. In order for a product to contain a Σ representation, the K values must be the same. Furthermore, to obtain an *ungerade* representation, either the initial or final state must be *gerade*, and the other *ungerade*. Thus, in addition to the $\Delta J = 0, \pm 1$ selection rule, we have $\Delta K = 0$ and $g \leftrightarrow u$. The $g \leftrightarrow u$ alternation arises from $J = \pm 1$ but not $J = 0$; therefore, the latter is not allowed for symmetric tops. These rules are in agreement with those deduced in the preceding paragraph, with the additional restriction that the transitions between states of the same representation must arise from the same K value. That is, for the $(J = 4) \leftarrow (J = 3)$ transition, the only $A_2 \leftrightarrow A_2$ transitions allowed are those arising from $K = 0$ to $K' = 0$ and $K = 3$ to $K' = 3$, while those corresponding to $K = 0$ to $K' = 3$, and vice versa, are not allowed.

The $\Delta K = 0$ selection rule causes the $\Delta J = 0$ transitions not to be observable in symmetric-top molecules on energy grounds as well as because of the $g \leftrightarrow u$ alternation. In asymmetric tops, where K is no longer a good quantum number, $\Delta J = 0$ transitions can be observed.

12.4 STATISTICAL WEIGHTS OF ROTATIONAL LEVELS

As mentioned in the discussion of the rotational spectra of diatomic molecules, rotational states are sufficiently close in energy that at normal temperatures there is significant thermal population of excited rotational states. This thermal population follows the exponentially decaying Boltzmann distribution curve. Superimposed upon this is the increase in the degeneracy of a level with increasing J values. The net result is that for a given molecule at a given temperature there will be some rotational state, generally above the ground rotational state, which will have a maximum population. States higher and lower in energy will have lower populations (Fig. 12.3).

Since the intensity of a spectral transition is dependent upon the relative populations of the level from which the transition originates and that to which it

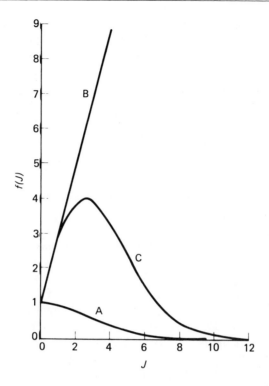

Fig. 12.3. Graph of distribution of rotational states for a linear molecule. A, $\exp[-BJ(J+1)hc/kT]$: B, $(2J+1)$: C, $(2J+1)\exp[-BJ(J+1)hc/kT]$. Calculated for a B value of 10.44 cm^{-1} at 300 K.

goes, the intensities of microwave transitions will be J-dependent. Superimposed upon this will also be a symmetry-induced intensity dependence. Consider, for example the $K = 2$ and $K = 3$ branches of a transition in methyl chloride. The $K = 3$ states transform as $A_1 + A_2$ in the $\mathbf{C}_{3v}$ point group, while the $K = 2$ states transform as the E representation. The magnitude of the transition dipole is that of the permanent dipole moment; consequently, if centrifugal distortions are neglected, it is not J- or K-dependent. Thus, the only factors affecting the intensities of the transitions for a given molecule are statistical factors. Consider now the products $\Gamma_r^i \times \Gamma_{\mu_z} \times \Gamma_r^f$ for the two K values. For $K = 3$ we have

$$(A_1 + A_2) \times A_1 \times (A_1 + A_2) = 2A_1 + 2A_2 \tag{12.18}$$

while for $K = 2$, we have

$$E \times A_1 \times E = A_1 + A_2 + E \tag{12.19}$$

For the $K = 3$ transition the totally symmetric representation occurs twice, while for the $K = 2$ transition it only occurs once. Thus, assuming equal initial populations of the levels, the $K = 3$ transition would be observed with twice the intensity of the $K = 2$ transition. Relative intensities of other transitions in this and other systems can be obtained in a similar fashion. In actual fact, however, this does not give the entire statistical picture. If the molecule contains nuclei with nonzero moments of inertia, the nuclear states and their weights will have to be included to give a complete picture of the statistical weights of the various rotational states and transitions. Nuclear states will be discussed in the next section.

Exercise 12.1*: Find the irreducible representations of all rotational states from $J = 0$ to $J = 4$ for NH_3.

12.5 NUCLEAR SPIN STATES

Clebsch–Gordan Coupling of Nuclear Spins

Atomic nuclei are, to the chemist, composed of protons and neutrons. Both of these particles have angular momenta of a magnitude of $\frac{1}{2}$ in appropriate units. Within the nucleus of an atom these angular momenta couple in some not fully understood manner to give a net angular momentum to the nucleus. These nuclear angular momenta have magnitudes that are multiples of $\frac{1}{2}$ (0, $\frac{1}{2}$, 1, $\frac{3}{2}$, etc.). The nuclear angular momenta for the various nuclei in a molecule couple to give various net nuclear spin states for molecules. These nuclear spin states can be observed in a number of ways. Among others, they impose statistical factors on the rotational energy levels of molecules in addition to those of the pure rotational functions; they are the states that are directly observed in nuclear magnetic resonance (NMR); and they are the source of hyperfine interactions in electron paramagnetic resonance (EPR) and spin-spin coupling patterns in NMR spectra. We shall illustrate two applications of group theory to nuclear spin: the use of the Clebsch–Gordan relationship to obtain splitting patterns in simple paramagnetic resonance experiments, and the use of permutation groups to obtain the irreducible representations of spin states and their interaction with rotational states.

Much information about the nuclear spin states of molecules can be obtained by simply coupling the spin angular momenta of equivalent nuclei by use of the Clebsch–Gordan relationship. For example, CH_3Cl has three equivalent protons, each having a nuclear angular momentum of $\frac{1}{2}$. The net nuclear spin states for the protons are

$$D^{(1/2)} \times D^{(1/2)} \times D^{(1/2)} = 2D^{(1/2)} + D^{(3/2)} \tag{12.20}$$

Because of rapid quadrupole relaxation effects, the chlorine nucleus (angular momentum of $\frac{3}{2}$) does not interact with the proton states. In the presence of a magnetic field, the $D^{(3/2)}$ state would split into four components along the field direction: $-\frac{3}{2}$, $-\frac{1}{2}$, $\frac{1}{2}$, and $\frac{3}{2}$. Each of the $D^{(1/2)}$ states would split into two, $\pm\frac{1}{2}$.

This would lead to four energy states for the proton functions. Those with field components of $\pm\frac{3}{2}$ would be nondegenerate, while those with components of $\pm\frac{1}{2}$ would be threefold-degenerate, with one contribution from the $D^{(3/2)}$ and two from the two $D^{(1/2)}$. If an experiment were carried out to determine the NMR spectrum of CH_3Cl, the sample in the magnetic field would be irradiated with electromagnetic radiation of a proper frequency to produce transitions between the various angular momentum states. As in any other spectrum involving changes in angular momentum or angular momentum components, the selection rules require that the change be zero or ± 1 in angular momentum units. Since the states are all one angular momentum unit from the adjacent states, all energy absorptions would occur at the same frequency. (At the magnetic field strengths usually employed in NMR experiments the energy separations are such that the various states are all nearly equally populated. From the Boltzmann distribution, the excess population for the lower of two adjacent proton states is on the order of parts per million at room temperature.)

Suppose now that we consider CH_3F. The ^{19}F nucleus has a spin angular momentum of $\frac{1}{2}$ which interacts with the angular momenta of the hydrogen nuclei. It is not equivalent to the hydrogens, however. The group for the nuclear spin states is a semidirect product of the group for fluorine and that for the hydrogens. The complete formal treatment is similar to that for constructing the groups for nonrigid molecules. If an NMR experiment is carried out on CH_3F in such a fashion that the energy levels of the fluorine are observed, the fluorine peak will be split because of spin-spin coupling between the fluorine and the hydrogens. Qualitatively, the various angular momentum states of the protons will interact with the two of fluorine, causing slight energy shifts from the value of the fluorine transition in the absence of such interactions. For a situation such as this, where the fundamental resonance frequencies of the differing nuclei have a large separation relative to the magnitude of the interactions of the nuclei, the interactions are conveniently handled by perturbation theory. We will not go into the treatment; however, the perturbation to the Hamiltonian (and, consequently, the energy) has the form $hJ_{HF}M_F M_H$, where J_{HF} is the coupling constant. Note that the sign of this interaction term is the product of the signs of the components of angular momentum of the two sets of nuclei. Thus, the energy scheme for the fluorine is as shown schematically in Fig. 12.4. When studying the fluorine transitions, the selection rules are $\Delta M_F = 0, \pm 1$, $\Delta M_H = 0$, and $\Gamma_i = \Gamma_j$. Thus, when studying the transition from $M_F = -\frac{1}{2}$ to $M_F = \frac{1}{2}$, no change can occur in M_H. Furthermore, as we shall see later, the various states with the same value of M_H and M_F either belong to different irreducible representations within the appropriate point group, or are constructed from orthogonal spin functions; consequently, each lower-energy state can only go to a single higher-energy state. The ^{19}F NMR spectrum of CH_3F would show four peaks of relative intensities (from the statistical weight of the levels) of 1 : 3 : 3 : 1. The splitting between the peaks will be the difference in the splitting of the $\pm\frac{1}{2}$ levels of fluorine. In other words, the ^{19}F resonance reveals the spin

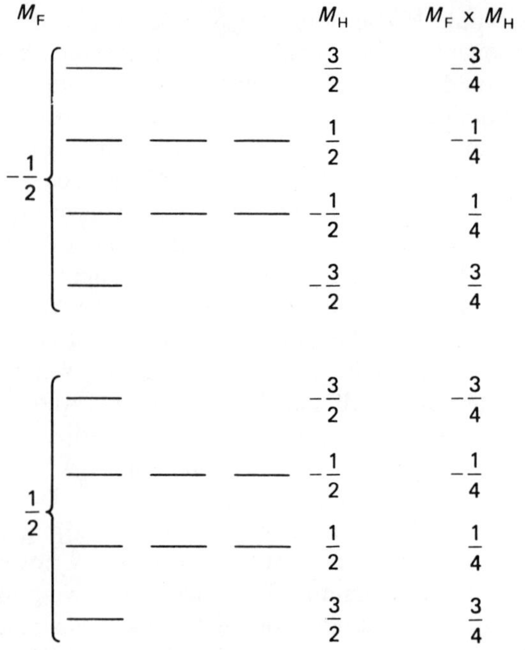

Fig. 12.4. Schematic representation of the nuclear angular momentum energy states for fluorine in CH_3F in a magnetic field.

states of the protons. Conversely, the proton NMR would show two lines from the two possible spin states of the fluorine.

In many molecules, nonequivalent sets of the same nucleus have sufficiently different energies, when in a magnetic field, that this simple treatment can be used for the interpretation of the spectrum. Such a molecule is ethanol, CH_3CH_2OH. The resonances for the three methyl protons, the two methylene protons, and the single hydroxyl proton occur at different frequencies. The spin-spin coupling effects occur both through the chemical bonds in a molecule and through free space, and fall off very rapidly with increasing distance. Thus, in ethanol the hydroxyl proton and the methyl proton resonances are effectively split only by the methylene protons. Under high resolution these signals are seen as triplets with the usual 1 : 2 : 1 statistical ratio. The methylene resonance is split by both the methyl and hydroxyl protons. It turns out, however, that the spin-spin interaction with the methyl protons is greater than that with the hydroxyl proton. The observed methylene resonance is split into a quartet (1 : 3 : 3 : 1), and each of these peaks is further split into a doublet by the hydroxyl proton.

Similar treatments to these can be carried out any time the coupling between nonequivalent nuclei is very small compared to the shift between their resonance frequencies. When the two quantities are comparable in magnitude, however, the interactions become more complicated and an analysis of the NMR splitting patterns requires a relatively complete quantum mechanical treatment of the spin states of the system. These two cases are frequently referred to as "first-order" and "second-order" treatments, respectively.

The treatment of EPR hyperfine splitting patterns is similar. The group under consideration is the product of that for the unpaired electron (or electrons) and that for the equivalent paramagnetic nuclei. For example, the anion radical of *p*-benzoquinone has four equivalent protons. The protonic state is

$$D^{(1/2)} \times D^{(1/2)} \times D^{(1/2)} \times D^{(1/2)} = 2D^{(0)} + 3D^{(1)} + D^{(2)} \qquad (12.21)$$

This leads to a five-line pattern superimposed on the electron resonance. The statistically imposed intensities are 1 : 4 : 6 : 4 : 1.

Exercise 12.2*: Calculate the EPR splitting pattern for the CH_3 radical.

Irreducible Representations of Nuclear Spin States

The most direct way to calculate the irreducible representations of various nuclear spin states within the point group of a molecule is through the use of the permutation group of the nuclei as mapped onto the point group of the molecule. In practice, this amounts to using the permutation notation for the elements of the point group, operating on the various spin states with the permutation operators, and then finding the irreducible representations by the use of projection operators or some other suitable technique. We shall present the method by examples.

As a first example of the application of the method, consider CH_4. In this case the permutation group is isomorphic to the point group of the molecule; consequently, the mapping will be direct and easy to interpret. If the $\pm\frac{1}{2}$ spin states of the protons are denoted only by the sign, and the ordering in a sequence is equated to the numbering of the protons, there will be one molecular spin state of $+4/2$ $(++++)$, four of $+2/2$ $[(+++-), (++-+), (+-++)$, and $(-+++)]$, six of 0 $[(++--)$, etc.], four of $-2/3$ $[(+---)$, etc.], and one of $-4/2$ $(----)$. These are all mutually orthogonal since, for example, integrals over spin functions of the type $\langle \alpha\alpha\alpha\beta \mid \alpha\alpha\beta\alpha \rangle$ vanish. They do not, however, all correspond to irreducible representations within the point group of the molecule or the **S**(4) permutation group. The states corresponding to the various irreducible representations can be constructed by the use of projection operators. To do this, we need the results of operating on each of the functions by the group operators. In the present case, only one member from each total spin set need be used. Furthermore, the representations for the sets with negative net spin will be the same as those with positive net spin. The required results are summarized in Table 12.1. Notice that in both the 2/2 and 0 states, all the other spin functions are generated by the group operation operating on one of the functions. We will find that this is not always the case when the point group is a subgroup of the permutation group.

Since none of the group operations convert any of the spin functions into their negatives [note that $(++--)$ is equivalent to $\alpha(1)\alpha(2)\beta(1)\beta(2)$; its negative is $-(\alpha(1)\alpha(2)\beta(1)\beta(2))$, not $(--++)$], all the spin states will contain the totally symmetric irreducible representation. For the $\pm 4/2$ states this will be the only irreducible representation. The problem thus remains of determining which other representations occur in the other spin states. Applying the projection operator for the E representation of $\mathbf{T}_d$ to the $(+++-)$ function, we obtain

$$\begin{aligned}
P^{(E)}(+++-) = {} & 2 \times (+++-) \\
& - 1 \times [(+++-) + (-+++) + (-+++) + (+-++) \\
& \quad + (+++-) + (+-++) + (++-+) \\
& \quad + (++-+)] \\
& + 2 \times [(++-+) + (+-++) + (-+++)] \\
& + 0 \times [(+++-) + (+++-) + (-+++) + (++-+) \\
& \quad + (+-++) + (+++-)] \\
& + 0 \times [(-+++) + (+-++) + (+-++) + (++-+) \\
& \quad + (++-+) + (-+++)] \\
= {} & 0
\end{aligned} \tag{12.22}$$

Thus, the E representation does not occur in the irreducible representations of the 2/2 nuclear spin state. For the T_1 representation, we have

$$\begin{aligned}
P^{(T_1)}(+++-) = {} & 3 \times (+++-) \\
& - 0 \times [(+++-) + (-+++) + (-+++) + (+-++) \\
& \quad + (+++-) + (+-++) + (++-+) + (++-+)] \\
& - 1 \times [(++-+) + (+-++) + (-+++)] \\
& + 1 \times [(+++-) + (+++-) + (-+++) + (++-+) \\
& \quad + (+-++) + (+++-)] \\
& - 1 \times [(-+++) + (+-++) + (+-++) + (++-+) \\
& \quad + (++-+) + (-+++)] \\
= {} & 6(+++-) - 2(++-+) - 2(+-++) - 2(-+++)
\end{aligned} \tag{12.23}$$

The T_1 irreducible representation does occur in the 2/2 spin state. One possible form of the symmetry-adapted function is, except for normalization, as in Eq. 12.23. In a similar fashion, we find

$$\begin{aligned}
P^{(E)}(++--) = {} & 4(++--) - 2(-++-) - 2(-+-+) - 2(+-+-) \\
& - 2(+--+) + 4(--++),
\end{aligned} \tag{12.24}$$

and

$$P^{(T_1)}(++--) = 4(++--) - 4(--++) \tag{12.25}$$

Table 12.1. Results of operation of the proton spin-product functions of methane with the symmetry operations of T_d.*

	Spin-Product Function		
	$M_s = 2$	$M_s = 1$	$M_s = 0$
Operation	+ + + +	+ + + −	+ + − −
E	+ + + +	+ + + −	+ + − −
$C_3(x, y, z)$	+ + + +	+ − + +	+ − + −
C_3^2	+ + + +	+ + − +	+ − − +
$C_3(-x, -y, z)$	+ + + +	+ + − +	− + − +
C_3^2	+ + + +	− + + +	− + + −
$C_3(x, -y, -z)$	+ + + +	− + + +	− + − +
C_3^2	+ + + +	+ − + +	+ − − +
$C_3(-x, y, -z)$	+ + + +	+ + + −	+ − + −
C_3^2	+ + + +	+ + + −	− + + −
$C_2(z)$	+ + + +	+ + − +	+ + − −
$C_2(x)$	+ + + +	+ − + +	− − + +
$C_2(y)$	+ + + +	− + + +	− − + +
$S_4(z)$	+ + + +	+ − + +	− − + +
S_4^3	+ + + +	− + + +	− − + +
$S_4(x)$	+ + + +	− + + +	− + + −
S_4^3	+ + + +	+ + − +	+ − − +
$S_4(y)$	+ + + +	+ − + +	+ − + −
S_4^3	+ + + +	+ + − +	− + − +
$\sigma(x, y)$	+ + + +	+ + − +	+ + − −
$\sigma(x, -y)$	+ + + +	+ + + −	+ + − −
$\sigma(x, z)$	+ + + +	+ + + −	+ − + −
$\sigma(x, -z)$	+ + + +	− + + +	− + − +
$\sigma(y, z)$	+ + + +	+ − + +	+ − − +
$\sigma(y, -z)$	+ + + +	+ + + −	− + + −

* Numbered sequentially, the hydrogens are in the (+, +, +), (−, −, +), (+, −, −), and (−, +, −) octants of a Cartesian coordinate system centered on the carbon. Note that the $M_s = -1$ and -2 functions can be obtained from the $M_s = +1$ and $+2$ functions by interchanging plus and minus signs.

All the other projection operators on these spin functions yield zero. Thus, for the various states, we have

$$\Gamma^{4/2} = \Gamma^{-4/2} = A_1 \tag{12.26}$$

$$\Gamma^{2/2} = \Gamma^{-2/2} = A_1 + T_1 \tag{12.27}$$

$$\Gamma^{0} = A_1 + E + T_1 \tag{12.28}$$

In Section 12.3 we saw that the $J = 3$ rotational state of methane transformed as $A_2 + T_1 + T_2$ within the $\mathbf{T}_d$ point group. In Section 12.4 we stated that nuclear states would impose statistical factors on the population of rotational states. We are now in a position to find these for methane. If pure rotational states are to be considered, the appropriate group to use is the **T** rotational subgroup of the $\mathbf{T}_d$ group. Our net rotational spin state will transform as representations that result from products of the representations of the rotational and spin states. Within the group **T**, our $J = 3$ rotational representations are $A + 2T$, while our spin representations from $\Gamma^{\pm 4/2}$, $\Gamma^{\pm 2/2}$, and Γ^0 are $5A + E + 3T$. To correspond to an observable state, the net state must transform as the totally symmetric A representation within the rotational group. We have, then, for the rotational states,

$$A(5A + E + 3T) = 5A + E + 3T \tag{12.29}$$

$$\begin{aligned} T(5A + E + 3T) &= 5T + 2T + 3(A + E + 2T) \\ &= 3A + 3E + 13T \end{aligned} \tag{12.30}$$

Since only the A states are observable, we have the statistical factor of 5 : 3 : 3 imposed upon the A and the two T rotational states.

Let us now consider another four-proton molecule, but one in which the point group is not isomorphic to the permutation group. Ethylene, C_2H_4, is such a molecule. The molecule belongs to the $\mathbf{D}_{2h}$ point group. Table 12.2 presents the results of operating on the various spin functions with the operations of the group. Notice that for the spin 0 case, the group operations do not interconvert all the spin functions. As a consequence of this, a sufficient number of spin functions from this set must be included to generate the entire set. Notice also that the point of inversion and planes of symmetry are equivalent to the pure rotation elements in their effect on the spin functions. This means that all nuclear representations will be *gerade*. Applying the projection operators, we find that

$$\Gamma^{4/2} = \Gamma^{-4/2} = A_g \tag{12.31}$$

$$\Gamma^{2/2} = \Gamma^{-2/2} = A_g + B_{1g} + B_{2g} + B_{3g} \tag{12.32}$$

$$\Gamma^0_{(++--)} = A_g + B_{1g} \tag{12.33}$$

$$\Gamma^0_{(+-+-)} = A_g + B_{2g} \tag{12.34}$$

$$\Gamma^0_{(+--+)} = A_g + B_{3g} \tag{12.35}$$

$$\Gamma^0_{\text{total}} = 3A_g + B_{1g} + B_{2g} + B_{3g} \tag{12.36}$$

Applying these methods to systems where the equivalent nuclei have spins of greater than $\frac{1}{2}$ is no more difficult. The only difference is that the permutations will involve more symbols, and there can be more states. For example, for C_2D_4, the deuteron has a spin moment of 1 and can have three states: 1, 0, and -1. The net spin states can have the nine values, from 4 to -4. The relative numbers of states are 1 : 4 : 10 : 16 : 19 : 16 : 10 : 4 : 1. Allowing the + sign to represent the $+1$ state of a single deuteron, the $-$ sign the -1 state, and the 0 the zero state, the $+4$ state of the molecule is $(++++)$; the $+3$ state, $(+++0)$ and its permutations; the $+2$ state, $(+++-)$, $(++00)$, and their permutations; the $+1$ state,

Table 12.2. Results of operating on the proton spin-product functions of ethylene with the symmetry operations of D_{2h}.*

	Spin-Product Function				
			$M_s = 0$		
	$M_s = 2$	$M_s = 1$			
Operation	$++++$	$+++-$	$++--$	$+--+$	$+-+-$
E	$++++$	$+++-$	$++--$	$+--+$	$+-+-$
$C_2(z)$	$++++$	$++-+$	$++--$	$-++-$	$-+-+$
$C_2(y)$	$++++$	$+-++$	$--++$	$-++-$	$+-+-$
$C_2(x)$	$++++$	$-+++$	$--++$	$+--+$	$-+-+$
i	$++++$	$+-++$	$--++$	$-++-$	$+-+-$
$\sigma(x, y)$	$++++$	$-+++$	$--++$	$+--+$	$-+-+$
$\sigma(x, z)$	$++++$	$+++-$	$++--$	$+--+$	$+-+-$
$\sigma(y, x)$	$++++$	$++-+$	$++--$	$-++-$	$-+-+$

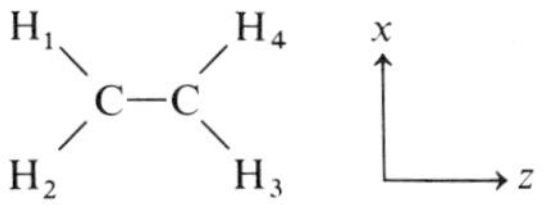

* The z axis is the C—C bond and the xz plane is the molecular plane. Note that the $M_s = -1$ and -2 functions can be obtained from the $M_s = +1$ and $+2$ functions by interchanging plus and minus signs.

$(++0-)$, $(+000)$, and their permutations; the 0 state, $(++--)$, $(+-00)$, (0000), and their permutations; and so on. The final results are

$$\Gamma^4 = \Gamma^{-4} = A_g \tag{12.37}$$

$$\Gamma^3 = \Gamma^{-3} = A_g + B_{1g} + B_{2g} + B_{3g} \tag{12.38}$$

$$\Gamma^2 = \Gamma^{-2} = 4A_g + 2B_{1g} + 2B_{2g} + 2B_{3g} \tag{12.39}$$

$$\Gamma^1 = \Gamma^{-1} = 4A_g + 4B_{1g} + 4B_{2g} + 4B_{3g} \tag{12.40}$$

$$\Gamma^0 = 7A_g + 4B_{1g} + 4B_{2g} + 4B_{3g} \tag{12.41}$$

If a molecule contains more than one type of nucleus with a nonzero angular momentum, the representations for each nuclear type are found separately and the total representations are found from the products of the separate representations.

Exercise 12.3:

(a) Calculate the irreducible representations of all the proton spin states of NH_3.
(b) Find the statistical weights of the various rotational representations for the $J = 3$ rotational state of NH_3, including the proton spin states.
(c) Deduce the complete set of statistically induced relative intensities for the $(J = 3) \leftarrow (J = 2)$ transitions in NH_3.

PROBLEMS

1. Classify the following molecules as spherical top, oblate symmetrical top, prolate symmetrical top, or asymmetrical top:

   (a) NH_3 (b) Benzene

   (c) Ethane (d) SF_6

   (e) Propane

2. The benzene molecule has a C—C distance of 1.40 Å, and a C—H distance of 1.08 Å. Calculate the energy spacings and the statistical weights of the first 15 rotational levels at 300°K.

3. Consider rotovibronic coupling (coupling of rotational, vibrational, and electronic states). What combinations of rotational and vibrational states would make the $B_{1u} \leftarrow A_{1g}$ electronic transition of benzene allowed? (Assume the same geometry in both electronic states—an incorrect assumption.)

4. Calculate the irreducible representations of the proton spin states for

   (a) Ethane (b) Benzene

BIBLIOGRAPHY

GORDY, W., W. V. SMITH, AND R. TRAMBARULO, *Microwave Spectroscopy*, John Wiley & Sons, Inc., New York, 1953.

HARMONY, M. D., *Introduction to Molecular Energies and Spectra*, Holt, Rinehart and Winston, Inc., New York, 1972.

HERZBERG, G., *Infrared and Raman Spectra*, Van Nostrand Reinhold Company, New York, 1945.

KING, G. W., *Spectroscopy and Molecular Structure*, Holt, Rinehart and Winston, Inc., New York, 1964.

TOWNS, C. H., AND A. L. SCHAWLOW, *Microwave Spectroscopy*, McGraw-Hill Book Company, New York, 1955.

13

Symmetry Control of Chemical Reactions

13.1 INTRODUCTION

The idea of symmetry control of chemical reactions was popularized in 1965 by Woodward and Hoffmann. Their results were quickly given symmetry and group-theoretical justification by Longuet-Higgins and Abrahamson. The original treatment is based upon a molecular orbital description of the reacting system. In effect, a symmetry is assumed for the transition state, and an orbital correlation diagram for the reactants and products is constructed with respect to this symmetry. If the occupied orbitals of the reactants correlate only with occupied orbitals of the products, the reaction is considered to be allowed, while if any of the occupied orbitals of the reactants correlate with unoccupied orbitals of the products and vice versa, the reaction is considered to be forbidden. Many other workers have contributed to the field. Our approach will differ from the traditional treatment in a number of respects.

The group of the chemical reaction is defined by the orientation of the reactants and products. The total electronic state of the reacting system is deduced within this group. The allowedness or forbiddenness of a reaction is determined by determining whether or not there is an allowed nuclear motion within this group which connects the reactants to the products. The method is independent of the theoretical description of the system. Any bonding theory that adequately describes the system can be employed. Even Lewis dot structures work for thermal reactions in most cases.

We will approximate the total wave function of the reacting system Ψ as a linear combination of the total wave functions of the reactants Ψ_R and the products Ψ_P:

$$\Psi = C_R\Psi_R + C_P\Psi_P \tag{13.1}$$

where C_R and C_P are linear coefficients which vary as a function of the distance along the "reaction coordinate." The resulting energy will be "exact" for the isolated reactants and products, but will lie above this "exact" energy at intermediate points along the reaction coordinate. Within the Born–Oppenheimer approximation, the energy at any point along the reaction coordinate will be the lowest root of the determinant

$$\begin{vmatrix} H_{RR} - E & H_{RP} - S_{RP}E \\ H_{PR} - S_{PR}E & H_{PP} - E \end{vmatrix} = 0 \tag{13.2}$$

where

$$H_{RR} = \langle \Psi_R | \hat{H} | \Psi_R \rangle \tag{13.3a}$$

$$H_{RP} = H_{PR} = \langle \Psi_R | \hat{H} | \Psi_P \rangle \tag{13.3b}$$

$$S_{RP} = S_{PR} = \langle \Psi_R | \Psi_P \rangle \tag{13.3c}$$

$$H_{PP} = \langle \Psi_P | \hat{H} | \Psi_P \rangle \tag{13.3d}$$

and the Hamiltonian is a function of the reaction coordinate. The roots of this are

$$\begin{aligned} E = (1 - S_{RP}^2)^{-1}\{\tfrac{1}{2}(H_{RR} + H_{PP}) - H_{RP}S_{RP} \pm [H_{RR}H_{PP}S_{RP}^2 \\ - H_{RP}S_{RP}(H_{RR} + H_{PP}) + H_{RP}^2 + \tfrac{1}{4}(H_{RR} - H_{PP})^2]^{1/2}\} \end{aligned} \tag{13.4}$$

If H_{RP} and S_{RP} are zero, the roots are H_{RR} and H_{PP}. H_{RR} will monotonically increase from the energy of the isolated reactants to some higher value as the reaction proceeds along the reaction coordinate. H_{PP} will similarly monotonically decrease from some high value to the energy of the isolated products. This is shown by the solid lines in Fig. 13.1. Such a path would correspond to a forbidden reaction path. If H_{RP} and/or S_{RP} do not equal zero, there would be an energy lowering at intermediate points along the reaction coordinate and the reactants would go smoothly to products, as shown by the dashed lines in Fig. 13.1. Such a path would correspond to an allowed reaction path. Thus, in order to determine whether or not a reaction is allowed, the vanishing or nonvanishing of H_{RP} or S_{RP} must be determined. These can be determined by symmetry.

It should be noted that the nonvanishing of H_{RP} and/or S_{RP} is a necessary, but not sufficient, requirement for the reaction to be allowed by a one-step process. Since no estimate of the activation energy is given by these arguments, the activation energy may be sufficiently high that the reaction may proceed by some other path, or it may not go at all.

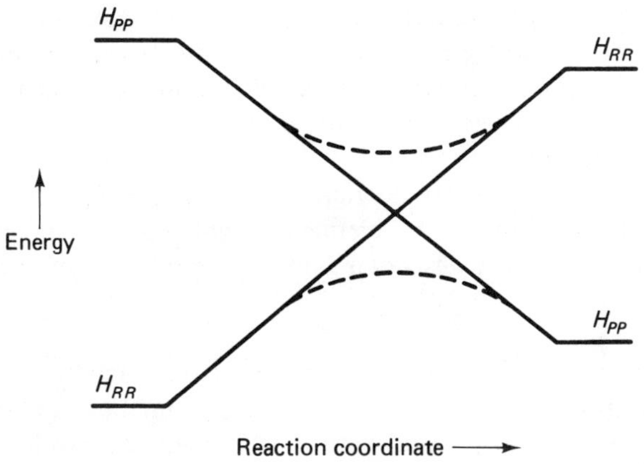

Fig. 13.1. Energy as a function of the reaction coordinate. Solid lines, $H_{RP} = S_{RP} = 0$; dashed lines, H_{RP} and/or $S_{RP} \neq 0$.

13.3 SYMMETRY CONSIDERATIONS

We will work from the reactant side. We will consider the point symmetry of the reacting system to be the point group of the system of reactants aligned in such a way as to give a least-motion transition to the products. Furthermore, we will consider a symmetry derived from a topology that contains only the bonds important to the reaction. For example, for the butadiene–cyclobutene type of conversion, the appropriate point group is the $\mathbf{C}_{2v}$ group of *cis*-butadiene (**1**); for

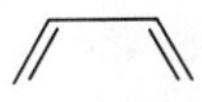

1

an S_N2 displacement at a tetrahedral carbon atom, the appropriate point group is the $\mathbf{C}_{3v}$ group of the system with the entering and leaving groups on the C_3 axis (**2**).

2

In either the molecular orbital or the valence bond scheme, the total electronic wave function of either the reactants or the products can be represented as a properly antisymmetrized product of one-electron spin orbitals. In the molecular orbital scheme, these can immediately be characterized with respect to symmetry. In the valence bond scheme, the total wave function is represented by a product of pair functions. Symmetry-adapted combinations of those pair functions may be required for the symmetry classifications; however, the predominant terms can ultimately be resolved into two-center one-electron spin orbitals and the total wave function can be expressed as antisymmetrized products of these (see Section 10.8). We will present our development within the molecular orbital formalism and then point out the generalization to the valence bond scheme and to even simpler bonding schemes.

The symmetry restrictions on S_{RP} and H_{RP} are the usual ones for overlap and Hamiltonian matrix elements involving determinantal functions. The overlap integral S_{RP} consists of a sum of permutations of terms of the form

$$\langle \phi_1^R(1)\bar{\phi}_2^R(2)\phi_3^R(3)\bar{\phi}_4^R(4)\ldots | \phi_1^P(1)\bar{\phi}_2^P(2)\phi_3^P(3)\bar{\phi}_4^P(4)\ldots\rangle \tag{13.5}$$

where the ϕ_i^R and ϕ_i^P are one-electron reactant and product molecular orbitals, respectively. A bar indicates a β spin function, and the absence of a bar an α spin function. As is usual with antisymmetrized product functions, permutations on only one side of the bracket are sufficient to yield all terms. Of these permutations, only those that do not interchange members of the α and β spin subsets lead to nonvanishing terms. Equation 13.5 can be rewritten in terms of a product of one-electron brackets:

$$\langle \phi_1^R(1)|\phi_1^P(1)\rangle\langle \phi_3^R(3)|\phi_3^P(3)\rangle \ldots \times \langle \bar{\phi}_2^R(2)|\bar{\phi}_2^P(2)\rangle\langle \bar{\phi}_4^R(4)|\bar{\phi}_4^P(4)\rangle \ldots \tag{13.6}$$

Each of the one-electron brackets has the usual symmetry restrictions associated with it; that is, $\langle \phi_i^R(i)|\phi_i^P(i)\rangle$ vanishes unless ϕ_i^R and ϕ_i^P belong to the same irreducible representation of the point group of the system. Thus, S_{RP} vanishes unless the same irreducible representations are spanned by the one-electron orbitals of the reactants and by the one-electron orbitals of the products. *The ordering of these orbitals with respect to energy is unimportant, as long as they are restricted to the occupied manifold.* If the same representations are spanned, there will be some permutation of Eq. 13.6 that is nonvanishing.

Let us now consider the off-diagonal term of the Hamiltonian, H_{RP}. We will consider this at an early stage along the reaction coordinate and assume that if the reaction starts off allowed, it will remain allowed throughout the reaction. If "concerted" is taken to apply only to a reaction that takes place during one normal vibration of the system, this must be the case, or else the motion would have to change symmetries in midcourse. This can happen only in restricted circumstances. The same conclusions result from consideration of the reverse reaction.

For small displacements from the starting geometry of the reactants, we can express the Hamiltonian as

$$\hat{H} = \hat{H}_R^0 + \hat{V} \tag{13.7}$$

where $\hat{H}_R^0$ is the Hamiltonian for the static reactants and $\hat{V}$ represents the perturbation caused by a small displacement along the reaction coordinate. This displacement can be expressed in terms of the normal vibrational modes of the system. $\hat{H}_R^0$ is a totally symmetric operator within the point group of the reactants; consequently, the selection rules for $\langle \Psi_R|\hat{H}_R^0|\Psi_P\rangle$ are the same as for S_{RP}. Any additional considerations must come from $\langle \Psi_R|\hat{V}|\Psi_P\rangle \equiv V_{RP}$. The potential-energy portion of the Hamiltonian contains the interaction of each of the electrons with each of the nuclei. Thus, $\hat{V}$ is a many-electron operator which, in the independent-particles approximation, can be expressed as a sum of one-electron operators, each term expressing the change in nuclear attraction experienced by a single electron. V_{RP} can be expressed as sums of permutations of terms of the type

$$\langle\phi_1^R(1)|\hat{V}(1)|\phi_1^P(1)\rangle\langle\phi_3^R(3)|\phi_3^P(3)\rangle \ldots \times \langle\bar{\phi}_2^R(2)|\bar{\phi}_2^P(2)\rangle\langle\bar{\phi}_4^R(4)|\bar{\phi}_4^P(4)\rangle \ldots \quad (13.8)$$

The α and β spin sets can again be considered separately since $\hat{V}$ is a spin-free operator. The requirement that these be nonvanishing is that there be a one-to-one correspondence between the irreducible representations of all but one of the ϕ_i^R and ϕ_i^P from each spin set, and that for the noncorrespondence the triple product $\Gamma_i^R\Gamma^V\Gamma_i^P$ must contain the totally symmetric irreducible representation of the point group (where Γ_i^R, Γ^V, and Γ_i^P are the irreducible representations corresponding to ϕ_i^R, $\hat{V}$, and ϕ_i^P, respectively). Thus, the overall selection rule for an allowed reaction is that there be at most one one-electron orbital from each spin set which differs in symmetry classification in the reactants and products. For closed-shell systems, only one spin set need be considered, since the spatial orbitals are the same for both spin sets. Furthermore, the product $\Gamma_i^R\Gamma_i^P$ for this mismatched orbital determines the symmetry of the allowed nuclear motion, since $\Gamma_i^R\Gamma^V\Gamma_i^P$ contains the totally symmetric irreducible representation only if Γ^V is contained in $\Gamma_i^R\Gamma_i^P$.

For applications using the valence bond description of the reactants and products, the appropriate functions to use for the ϕ_i^R and ϕ_i^P are localized two-center, one-electron bond orbitals. These must be the principal contributors to the valence bond structure of the system. Even Lewis dot structures can be used if these adequately describe the system, since Lewis dot structures are equivalent to simple valence bond structures (the σ and π nature of double bonds must, however, be recognized). The symmetry-related bonds in valence bond structures must be combined to correspond to the irreducible representations of the point group of the system. The irreducible representations thus spanned are completely equivalent to the representations spanned by the occupied molecular orbitals in a molecular orbital description of the system. Once these symmetry-adapted functions are constructed, the selection rules are the same as already outlined. The valence bond formalism has one distinct advantage in many cases in that it is frequently easier to find the proper symmetry-adapted combinations of these bond orbitals than it is to find the symmetries of the occupied molecular orbitals.

The justification of the orbital correlation schemes is obvious from this development. If there is a one-to-one correspondence between the ϕ_i^R and the ϕ_i^P, the $\hat{V}$ must transform as the totally symmetric irreducible representation for V_{RP} to be nonvanishing. In the orbital-following schemes, the point symmetry considered is that occurring well along the reaction coordinate. The reaction coordinate, and consequently $\hat{V}$, transforms as the totally symmetric representation in this point group. Thus, for an allowed reaction path, there must be a one-to-one correspondence of the occupied orbitals. In this case, S_{RP}, V_{RP}, and $\langle\Psi_R|\hat{H}_R^0|\Psi_P\rangle$ are all nonvanishing.

13.4 SELECTION RULES

There are three selection rules that would cause a reaction to be either forbidden or nonconcerted. These are:

1. There are two or more orbital mismatches between reactants and products. In this case H_{RP} vanishes and the reaction is forbidden. This does not preclude the possibility of there being a multistep mechanism to go from reactants to products.
2. There is only one mismatch, but Γ^V does not correspond to a normal mode of vibration of the system. This will be a relatively rare occurrence for systems having more than a very few atoms.
3. There is only one mismatch, but Γ^V does not correspond to a motion taking the reactants to the products. The reaction may or may not be allowed, but, if allowed, the mechanism will be nonconcerted.

13.5 EXAMPLES

Electrocyclic Reactions

The first application of the Woodward–Hoffmann rules was to electrocyclic reactions. This has become the classic test for any discussion of symmetry control of reactions. The classic examples are butadiene–cyclobutene isomerization and hexatriene–cyclohexadiene isomerization. The topological symmetry for the reactants or the products is $\mathbf{C}_{2v}$. The orbitals to be considered are the π orbitals of the acyclic polyolefin and the π orbitals and the new σ bond for the cyclic compound. Table 13.1 shows the molecular orbital scheme for the ground and first excited states for the first three members of the series. The symmetry labels for the orbitals are from the $\mathbf{C}_{2v}$ point group. For the butadiene–cyclobutene isomerization (A) in the ground state, there is orbital matching between the $b_2\ \pi_1$ orbital of butadiene and the $b_2\ \pi_1$ orbital of cyclobutene. There is a mismatching of the other orbitals. Thus, if the reaction occurs in a concerted fashion in the ground state (thermally), the nuclear motion must transform as $A_2 \times A_1 = A_2$. The conrotatory motion (i.e., both groups rotating in the same direction) of the two terminal CH_2 groups of *cis*-butadiene transforms as the A_2 irreducible representation within $\mathbf{C}_{2v}$. For the excited state, the two singly occupied orbitals match (providing the spins are matched properly), and the mismatch is between the $b_2\ \pi_1$ orbital of butadiene and the $a_1\ \sigma$ orbital of cyclobutene. The required nuclear motion for a concerted excited state (photochemical) reaction is $B_2 \times A_1 = B_2$. The disrotatory motion (opposite directions) of the two terminal CH_2 groups transforms as B_2. In reaction B we have a b_2, a_1 orbital mismatch for the thermal reaction, requiring a B_2 disrotatory motion, while the photochemical reaction has an a_2, a_1

Table 13.1. Molecular orbital schemes for some electrocyclic reactions.*

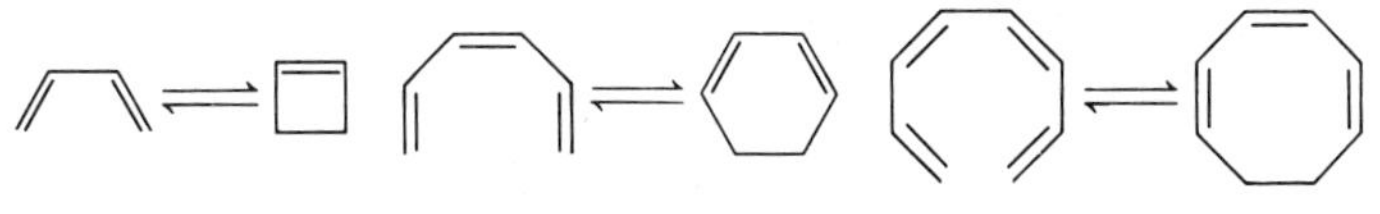

A		B		C	
Ground States					
$a_2(\pi_2)^2$	$b_2(\pi'_1)^2$	$b_2(\pi_3)^2$	$a_2(\pi'_2)^2$	$a_2(\pi_4)^2$	$b_2(\pi'_3)^2$
$b_2(\pi_1)^2$	$a_1(\sigma)^2$	$a_2(\pi_2)^2$	$b_2(\pi'_1)^2$	$b_2(\pi_3)^2$	$a_2(\pi'_2)^2$
		$b_2(\pi_1)^2$	$a_1(\sigma)^2$	$a_2(\pi_2)^2$	$b_2(\pi'_1)^2$
				$b_2(\pi_1)^2$	$a_1(\sigma)^2$
First Excited States					
$b_2(\pi_3)^1$	$a_2(\pi'_2)^1$	$a_2(\pi_4)^1$	$b_2(\pi'_3)^1$	$b_2(\pi_5)^1$	$a_2(\pi'_4)^1$
$a_2(\pi_2)^1$	$b_2(\pi'_1)^1$	$b_2(\pi_3)^1$	$a_2(\pi'_2)^1$	$a_2(\pi_4)^1$	$b_2(\pi'_3)^1$
$b_2(\pi_1)^2$	$a_1(\sigma)^2$	$a_2(\pi_2)^2$	$b_2(\pi'_1)^2$	$b_2(\pi_3)^2$	$a_2(\pi'_2)^2$
		$b_2(\pi_1)^2$	$a_1(\sigma)^2$	$a_2(\pi_2)^2$	$b_2(\pi_1)^2$
				$a_2(\pi_1)^2$	$a_1(\sigma)^2$

* A, Butadiene–cyclobutene; B, hexatriene–cyclohexadiene; C, octatetraene–cyclooctatriene. Symmetry labels are from the $\mathbf{C}_{2v}$ point group. Superscripts are the orbital occupancy.

mismatch, requiring an A_2 conrotatory motion. The motions of reaction C repeat those of reaction A. The same patterns will be followed for higher polyenes. The results are in complete agreement with the Woodward–Hoffmann rules and with experiment. It is interesting to note that, in all these reactions, the treatment requires the "promoted" electron to have opposite spins in the reactant and product if the photochemical reaction goes through an excited singlet state.

Cycloaddition Reactions

Table 13.2 shows the molecular orbital schemes for some cycloaddition reactions. In this figure, the ethylene dimerization is characterized within the $\mathbf{C}_s$ point group, even though the true point symmetry is $\mathbf{D}_{2h}$, to emphasize the continuity within the series. The orientation of the molecules is assumed to be such that the π orbitals on atoms A, B, C and D lie in the same plane. The localized σ orbitals in the cyclic structures are not symmetry orbitals; consequently, the indicated linear combinations must be used. The orbital $(\sigma^*_{\mathrm{AC}} + \sigma^*_{\mathrm{BD}})$ of cyclobutane has the MO form $(\chi_{\mathrm{A}} - \chi_{\mathrm{C}} + \chi_{\mathrm{B}} - \chi_{\mathrm{D}})$, where the χ's are the σ-type basis functions. From Table 13.2 it is seen that in the ground state of reaction *E* (the Diels–Alder reaction) and in the excited states of reactions D and F, there is complete matching of orbital symmetries. These reactions are allowed by a motion that is totally symmetric within $\mathbf{C}_s$. The direct symmetric approach of the A—B ethylene to the other

Table 13.2. Molecular orbital schemes for some cycloaddition reactions.*

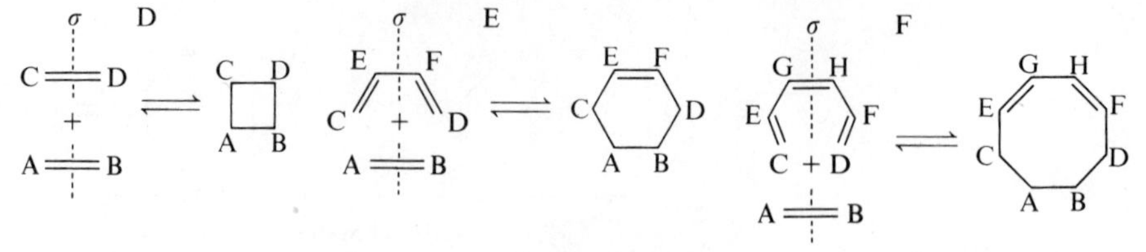

Ground States

$a'(\pi_{CD})^2$	$a''(\sigma_{AC}-\sigma_{BD})^2$	$a''(\pi_2)^2$	$a'(\pi)^2$	$a'(\pi_3)^2$	$a''(\pi_2)^2$
$a'(\pi_{AB})^2$ —	$a'(\sigma_{AC}+\sigma_{BD})^2$	$a'(\pi_1)^2$	$a''(\sigma_{AC}-\sigma_{BD})^2$	$a''(\pi_2)^2$	$a'(\pi_1)^2$
		$a'(\pi_{AB})^2$ —	$a'(\sigma_{AC}+\sigma_{BD})^2$	$a'(\pi_1)^2$	$a''(\sigma_{AC}-\sigma_{BD})^2$
				$a'(\pi_{AB})^2$ —	$a'(\sigma_{AC}+\sigma_{BD})^2$

Excited States

$a'(\pi^*_{CD})^1$	$a'(\sigma^*_{AC}+\sigma^*_{BD})^1$	$a'(\pi_3)^1$	$a''(\pi_2)^1$	$a''(\pi_4)^1$	$a'(\pi_3)^1$
$a'(\pi_{CD})^1$	$a''(\sigma_{AC}-\sigma_{BD})^1$	$a''(\pi_2)^1$	$a'(\pi_1)^1$	$a'(\pi_3)^1$	$a''(\pi_2)^1$
$a'(\pi_{AB})^2$ —	$a'(\sigma_{AC}+\sigma_{BD})^2$	$a'(\pi_1)^2$	$a''(\sigma_{AC}-\sigma_{BD})^2$	$a''(\pi_2)^2$	$a'(\pi_1)^2$
		$a'(\pi_{AB})^2$ —	$a'(\sigma_{AC}+\sigma_{BD})^2$	$a'(\pi_1)^2$	$a''(\sigma_{AC}-\sigma_{BD})^2$
				$a'(\pi_{AB})^2$ —	$a'(\sigma_{AC}+\sigma_{BD})^2$

* The molecules are all classified within the $\mathbf{C}_s$ point even though the true point symmetry for the ethylene dimerization is $\mathbf{D}_{2h}$.

molecule is such a motion. In the other cases there is a mismatch between an a' orbital in one structure and an a'' orbital in the other. For the reaction to be allowed, the motion would have to transform as $A' \times A'' = A''$ (i.e., it would correspond to a motion that is antisymmetric with respect to the plane of symmetry). There is no in-plane motion of this type that can yield the indicated products; consequently, the concerted in-plane reactions must be considered as forbidden. These results are in complete agreement with the Woodward–Hoffmann rules and with experiment for *suprafacial* cycloadditions. The *antarafacial* cycloadditions would require a different starting point group for the reactants. Further, the symmetry of the reactants and products would be different. However, an out-of-plane twisting motion transforms as A'' in $\mathbf{C}_s$. This would tend toward the postulated perpendicular transition state required for the *suprafacial–antarafacial* reactions to occur.

An interesting but complicated cycloreversion reaction is the isomerization of prismane to benzene, which is shown in Table 13.3. The arrows on the prismane structure indicate the motion that would carry out the indicated isomerization. The valence bond scheme is used to avoid having to determine the symmetries of the molecular orbitals of prismane. The symmetry labels are in terms of the $\mathbf{C}_{2v}$ point group, which is a common subgroup of the point symmetries of both molecules. The indicated canonical structures are symmetry-adapted linear combinations of pair functions for prismane, and of pair functions and the two Kékulé

Table 13.3. Valence bond scheme for the isomerization of prismane to benzene.*

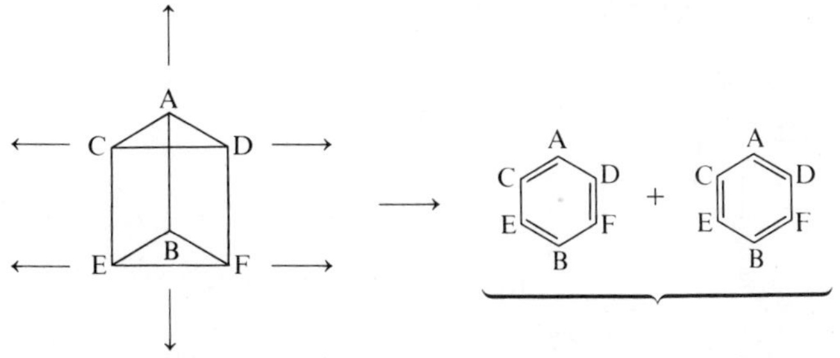

Bonds broken: $\sigma_{AB}, \sigma_{CD}, \sigma_{EF}$ Bonds formed: $\pi_{AC}, \pi_{BE}, \pi_{DF}$, and $\pi_{AD}, \pi_{BF}, \pi_{CE}$

$b_2(\sigma_{CD} - \sigma_{EF})^2$		$b_1(\pi_{AC} - \pi_{BE} + \pi_{AD} - \pi_{BF})^2$
$a_1(\sigma_{CD} + \sigma_{EE})^2$	————	$a_1(\pi_{AC} + \pi_{BE} + \pi_{AD} + \pi_{BF})^2$
$a_1(\sigma_{AB})^2$	————	$a_1(\pi_{CE} + \pi_{DF})^2$

* The symmetry labels are from the $\mathbf{C}_{2v}$ point group, which is a common subgroup to the point symmetries of both molecules. The C_2 axis is coincident with the C_6 axis of benzene and perpendicular to the A—B bond of prismane.

structures for benzene (see Section 10.8). Note that there is a b_2, b_1 mismatching. This means that the reaction would be thermally allowed by a $B_2 \times B_1 = A_2$ motion. The required motion transforms as A_1, however. Consequently, the thermal reaction must be considered to be forbidden or nonconcerted.

Group Transfers and Eliminations

Table 13.4 shows the MO schemes for some concerted transfers of two hydrogen atoms. The same schemes would be valid for the concerted transfer of any two σ-bonded groups. Here, the symmetrical concerted ground-state reaction is allowed for reactions G and I but not for reaction H. The exicted-state reactions are allowed for reactions G and H, but not I. The reason G is both thermally and photochemically allowed is that the reactants and products are identical and have identical orientation with respect to the symmetry elements.

Table 13.5 shows the molecular orbital schemes for two elimination reactions that give radical products. These are classified according to the $\mathbf{C}_{2v}$ point group. Here, because of the different number of occupied orbitals in the reactants and products, the α and β spin sets must be considered separately. In these, only one of a number of possible spin configurations is listed. In both ground electronic state reactions there is a mismatching of the α spin sets. (Interchange of the α and β spins in the product radicals would cause the mismatch to be in the β set.) The mismatch is a one-orbital a_1, b_1 mismatch. This would require that the nuclear

Table 13.4. Molecular orbital schemes for the concerted transfer of two H atoms.

G H I

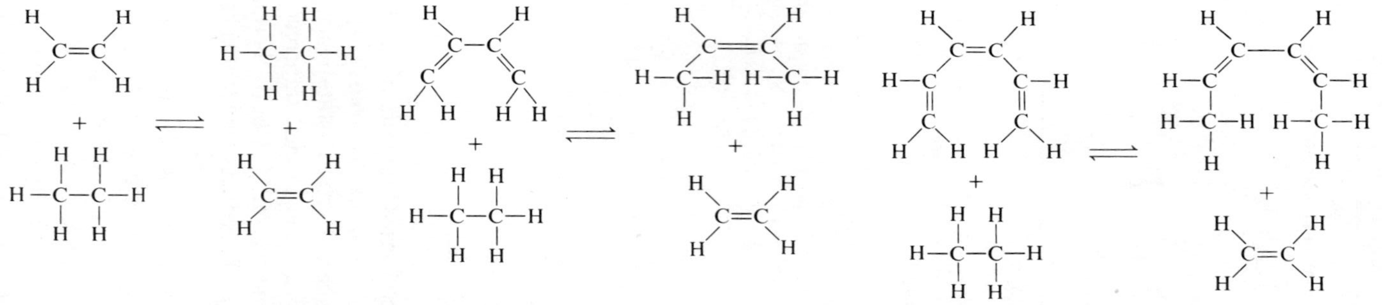

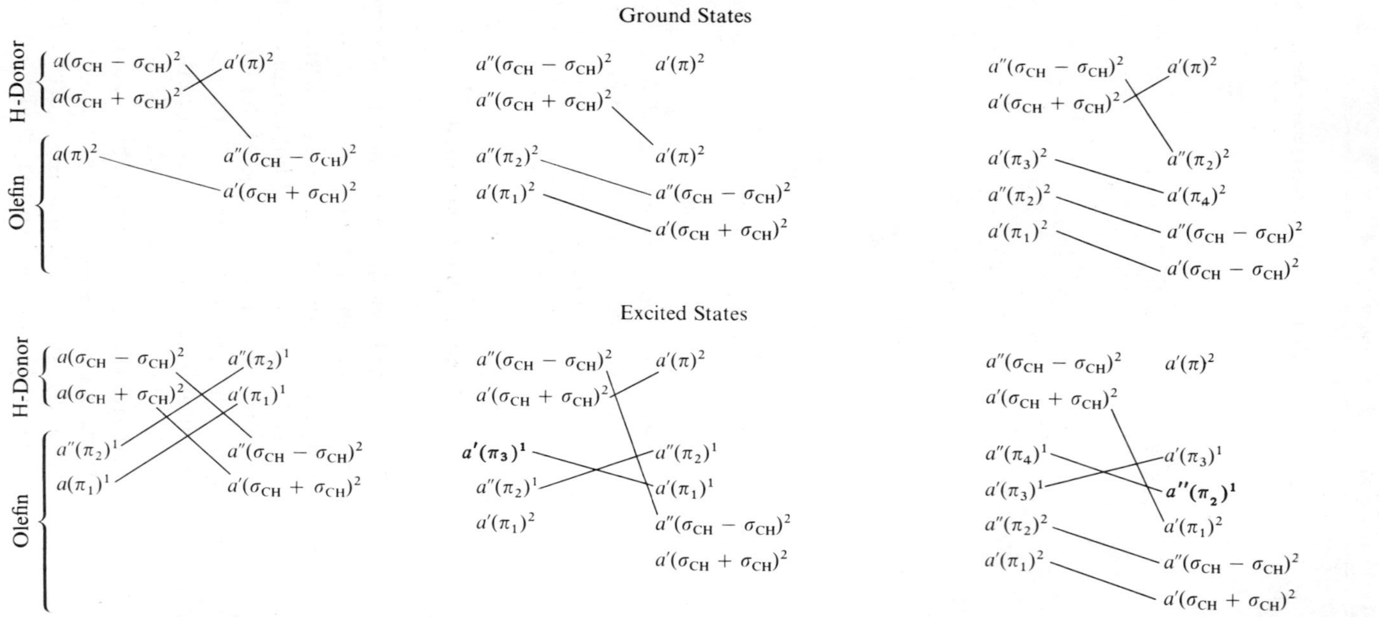

Table 13.5. Molecular orbital schemes for some elimination reactions that go to radical products (C_{2v} point group).*

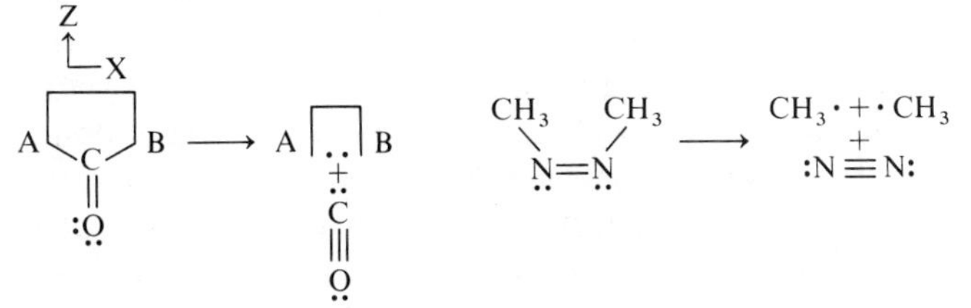

	Ground States		
$b_1\ n_O - n_O \uparrow\downarrow$	$b_1\ A\cdot - B\cdot \downarrow$	$b_1\ n_N - n_N \uparrow\downarrow$	$b_1\ C\cdot - C\cdot \downarrow$
$a_1\ n_O + n_O \uparrow\downarrow$	$a_1\ A\cdot + B\cdot \uparrow$	$a_1\ n_N + n_N \uparrow\downarrow$	$a_1\ C\cdot + C\cdot \uparrow$
$b_2\ \pi_{CO_y} \uparrow\downarrow$	$a_1\ n_C \uparrow\downarrow$	$b_2\ \pi_{NN_y} \uparrow\downarrow$	$b_1\ n_N - n_N \uparrow\downarrow$
$b_1\ \sigma_{CA} - \sigma_{CB} \uparrow\downarrow$	$a_1\ n_O \uparrow\downarrow$	$b_1\ \sigma_{NC} - \sigma_{NC} \uparrow\downarrow$	$a_1\ n_N + n_N \uparrow\downarrow$
$a_1\ \sigma_{CA} + \sigma_{CB} \uparrow\downarrow$	$b_1\ \pi_{CO_x} \uparrow\downarrow$	$a_1\ \sigma_{NC} + \sigma_{NC} \uparrow\downarrow$	$b_2\ \pi_{NN_y} \uparrow\downarrow$
	$b_2\ \pi_{CO_y} \uparrow\downarrow$		$a_1\ \pi_{NN_z} \uparrow\downarrow$
α: $2a_1, 2b_1, b_2$	α: $3a_1, b_1, b_2$	α: $2a_1, 2b_1, b_2$	α: $3a_1, b_1, b_2$
β: $2a_1, 2b_1, b_2$	β: $2a_1, 2b_1, b_2$	β: $2a_1, 2b_1, b_2$	β: $2a_1, 2b_1, b_2$
	Excited States		
$b_2\ \pi^*_{CO_y} \downarrow$	$b_1\ A\cdot - B\cdot \uparrow$	$a_2\ \pi^*_{NN_y} \downarrow$	$b_1\ C\cdot - C\cdot \uparrow$
$b_1\ n_O - n_O \uparrow$	$a_1\ A\cdot + B\cdot \downarrow$	$b_1\ n_N - n_N \uparrow$	$a_1\ C\cdot + C\cdot \downarrow$
$a_1\ n_O + n_O \uparrow\downarrow$	$b_2\ \pi^*_{CO_y} \downarrow$	$a_1\ n_N + n_N \uparrow\downarrow$	$a_2\ \pi^*_{NN_y} \downarrow$
$b_2\ \pi_{CO_y} \uparrow\downarrow$	$a_1\ n_C \uparrow$	$b_2\ \pi_{NN_y} \uparrow\downarrow$	$b_1\ n_N - n_N \uparrow\downarrow$
$b_1\ \sigma_{CA} - \sigma_{CB} \uparrow\downarrow$	$a_1\ n_O \uparrow\downarrow$	$b_1\ \sigma_{NC} - \sigma_{NC} \uparrow\downarrow$	$a_1\ n_N + n_N \uparrow$
$a_1\ \sigma_{CA} + \sigma_{CB} \uparrow\downarrow$	$b_1\ \pi_{CO_x} \uparrow\downarrow$	$a_1\ \sigma_{NC} + \sigma_{NC} \uparrow\downarrow$	$b_2\ \pi_{NN_y} \uparrow\downarrow$
	$b_2\ \pi_{CO_y} \uparrow\downarrow$		$a_1\ \pi_{NN_z} \uparrow\downarrow$
α: $2a_1, 2b_1, b_2$	α: $2a_1, 2b_1, b_2$	α: $2a_1, 2b_1, b_2$	α: $2a_1, 2b_1, b_2$
β: $2a_1, b_1, 2b_2$	β: $2a_1, b_1, 2b_2$	β: $2a_1, b_1, a_2, b_2$	β: $2a_1, b_1, a_2, b_2$

* The spins are indicated by arrows: $\uparrow \equiv \alpha$ spin, $\downarrow \equiv \beta$ spin.

motion accompanying the reaction be of B_1 symmetry. This corresponds to an unsymmetrical breaking of the bonds as shown in (**3**) and (**4**).

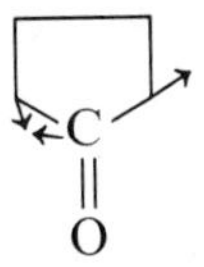

3

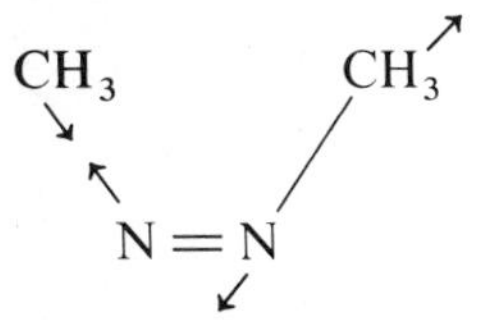

4

Thus, the thermal reaction is predicted not to be concerted. For the indicated spin configurations for the excited states, there is complete matching of the orbital symmetries for both spin sets for both reactions. (There are a number of other reasonable spin configurations possible, some of which give complete matching and some of which do not.) The reaction can go in a symmetrical manner (i.e., the leaving group leaving along the C_2 axis). These results are consistent with the experimental results for the decarbonylation of cyclopentanone. The vapor-phase photolysis of cyclopentanone yields a large amount of cyclobutane, while the pyrolysis yields only acyclic compounds. It is interesting to note that, if the scheme is applied to a direct one-step conversion of cyclopentanone to cyclobutane, both the excited-state and ground-state reactions are predicted to be nonconcerted.

Limitations

With the present development, the reactants and the products must have the same symmetry or a common subgroup of symmetry elements preserved in the reaction. In either case, this symmetry must be nontrivial. The bonds broken and formed must have different symmetries with respect to some symmetry element or elements of the group. In addition to the symmetry limitations, the wave functions of the reactant and product systems must each be adequately described by a single electronic configuration, or if configuration interaction is important, the important configurations must be known.

PROBLEMS

Deduce, by symmetry arguments, whether or not the following reactions are thermally or photochemically allowed.

1. 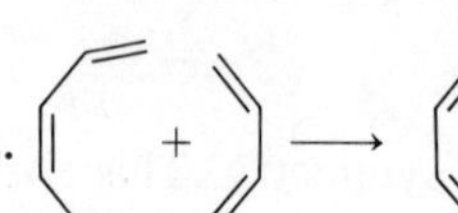

2. 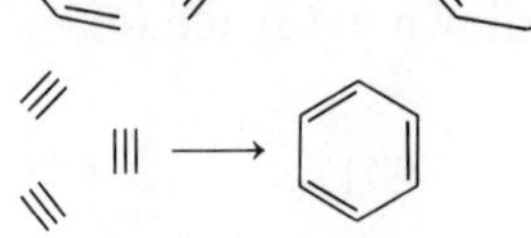

3. 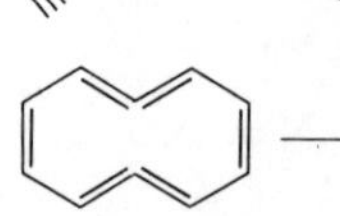

4. 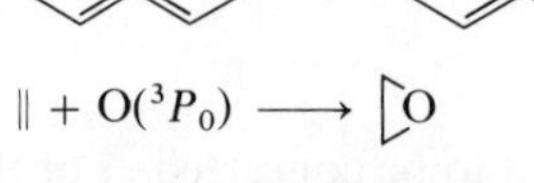

5. 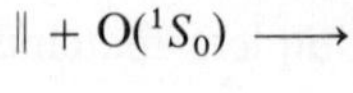

6.

BIBLIOGRAPHY

LONGUET-HIGGINS, H. C., AND E. W. ABRAHAMSON, *J. Am. Chem. Soc.*, **8**, 2045 (1967).

PEARSON, R. G., *Symmetry Rules for Chemical Reactions*, John Wiley & Sons, Inc., New York, 1976.

SIMMONS, H. E., AND J. F. BURNETT, EDS., *Orbital Symmetry Papers*, American Chemical Society, Washington, D.C., 1974.

WOODWARD, R. B., AND R. HOFFMANN, *The Conservation of Orbital Symmetry*, Academic Press, Inc., New York, 1970.

WOODWARD, R. B., AND R. HOFFMANN, *J. Am. Chem. Soc.*, **87**, 395 (1965).

Concluding Remarks

In this book I have tried to present enough material to give the reader some small idea of the power and the beauty (and the fun) of group theory as applied to molecular structure and other problems of interest to chemists. It is far from complete. No single book could be, and it is doubtful if the compiled works of a single author could be (certainly not this one). The choice of topics included throughout the book has been dictated partly by pedagogical value, partly by tradition ("everybody else includes it, so I should, too"), and largely by personal prejudice. The choice of topics excluded was dictated by the same considerations plus the additional fact that, in many cases, I did not feel competent (or ambitious enough) to tackle certain areas.

The group theory presented in this book, and in most books aimed toward applications of group theory to molecular structure or to molecular quantum mechanics, is really based upon applications of representation theory. The more fundamental (and often more powerful) algebraic structure of groups is largely ignored, as is any detailed discussion of unitary groups and Lie groups. Yet these are topics that are required for any adequate discussion of angular momentum of any form, be it spin, orbital, molecular, or any combination of the three.

Even the group theory that is included is not all illustrated in the last chapters. The most notable exclusions are space groups. The symmetry groups of nonrigid molecules are also slighted, with the only application occurring in Section 11.4. These were conscious choices. I felt that reasonable examples of the applications of space groups (other than those mentioned briefly in Chapters 4 and 7) would require too much background development for this book. The applications are available in books on solid-state theory, and I hope that the material in Chapters 4, 5, and 7 will aid readers in understanding such books. On the other hand, the concept of groups for nonrigid molecules is sufficiently new that there have been very few applications. Almost anything that I could come up with could be classified as original research and should more properly be published in the research literature, where its worth could be tested, before including it in a text.

One thing that I hope I have implied with the applications is that the answers provided by group theory are correct. If these answers do not agree with experiment, then either the theory was applied to an incorrect model or the experimental data were misinterpreted. Chemists do not find many theories with wide applicability for which such a statement can be made. In computational quantum mechanics, for example, our models must be incorporated into our theories. Thus, as a specific example, if a calculated electronic transition does not agree with experiment, we are not certain whether the error is due to the lack of electron correlation in our model, too small a basis set, a programming error in the computer program, or an error in the experimental value. On the other hand, the fact that we experimentally observe a band in the range of 256 nm in the spectrum of benzene, in spite of the fact that the symmetry of our electronic wave function says that we should not, *requires* us to recognize the fact that the transition is not purely electronic, and to consider vibrational–electronic interactions. The fact that the infrared spectrum of methane contains only two fundamentals *tells* us that the structure of methane must be tetrahedral. The fact that the oxygen molecule has a triplet spin state *forces* us to recognize that the spatial symmetry of this state is $\sum_g^-$. An almost endless list of examples could be cited.

As chemists, our theories, interpretations, and ideas concerning atoms and molecules are all based upon models. These models may be physical, mathematical, or conceptual. Group theory can be an invaluable aid in choosing a model and in interpreting the consequences of the model we have chosen. However, there is nothing in group theory to prevent us from reaching the wrong conclusions if we have chosen the wrong model. Our models may have more symmetry or less symmetry than the true system, or even a totally wrong symmetry. For example, simple Hückel molecular orbital theory predicts that there is only one excited state arising from the first $\pi^* \leftarrow \pi$ orbital transition in benzene. Adding the angular momentum of the molecular orbitals to the model increases the number to three, while adding the permutational symmetry of the electrons splits these into singlets and triplets. We must let the model fit the problem.

With these words of apology, praise, and caution, and with the hope that some of you who have read this will be interested enough to pursue the matter further, I would like to close.

Appendix 1

Notation and Nomenclature

An effort has been made to be reasonably consistent in the notation and nomenclature used throughout the text. The most common conventions employed are summarized here, along with some frequently used symbols. An effort has been made to point out the exceptions to these conventions when they are employed in the text.

A1.1 GENERAL

Vectors and matrices are denoted by boldface letters, lowercase for vectors and uppercase for matrices. The individual components of these are labeled by italics. When the array is given, closed parentheses or square brackets are used for vectors and matrices. The array for a determinant is enclosed by vertical straight lines. Covariant vectors and their components are labeled with subscripts, and contravariant vectors and their components are labeled with superscripts.

Symmetry operators are indicated by italics, while the matrices associated with them are boldface. Isodynamic operations for rotation and inversion are indicated in script letters. Names of point groups are also given in boldface. Irreducible representations are in italics.

Quantum mechanical operators are given in italics with a carat over the letter. The notation for orbitals involves lowercase symbols, while that for quantum mechanical states involves uppercase symbols.

A1.2 SPECIAL SYMBOLS

1. Matrices and vectors:

Cartesian unit vectors	**i, j, k**
Complex conjugate	*
Transpose	~
Conjugate transpose	†
Matrix or vector direct product	$\otimes$
Kronecker delta	$\delta_{ij}, \delta^i_j, \delta^{ij}$

2. Group theory:

Character of an operation (R)	$\chi(R)$
Contained in	$\subset$
Not contained in	$\not\subset$

SYMMETRY OPERATIONS

Identity	E
Proper rotation	C_n
Arbitrary rotation	$C(\phi)$
Improper rotation	S_n
Inversion	i
Reflection in a plane	σ
Space group operator involving point symmetry operator R and translation **t**	$\{R\|\mathbf{t}\}$
Product, general	$\times$
Direct	$\otimes$
Semidirect	$\wedge$
Projection operator	$\hat{P}$
Representation, general	Γ
One-dimensional, symmetrical with respect to principal axis	A
One-dimensional, antisymmetrical with respect to axis	B
Two-dimensional	E
Three-dimensional	T
Four-dimensional	G
Representations of three-dimensional rotation group	$D^{(j)}$

3. Quantum mechanics and spectroscopy:

Atomic-centered basis function	χ_μ
Dirac brackets	$\langle\ \|, \|\ \rangle$
Electromagnetic radiation:	
Electric field vector	**E**

Magnetic field vector	$\mathbf{H}$
Vector potential	$\mathbf{A}$
Frequency	ν
Angular frequency	ω
Wavelength	λ
Expectation value	$\langle\ \rangle$
Reduced mass	μ
Transition dipole	μ_{ij}

OPERATORS

Hamiltonian	$\hat{H}$
Kinetic energy	$\hat{T}$
Potential energy	$\hat{V}$
Perturbation	V
Laplacian	∇^2
Partial derivative	δ

QUANTUM NUMBERS

Principal	n
Angular momentum	l
Component of angular momentum	m
Spin	s
Component of spin	m_s
Total orbital angular momentum	L
Total spin	S
Total angular momentum, orbital plus total spin	J

Appendix **2**

Schur's Lemma and Wigner's Grand Orthogonality Theorem

In Section 5.5 we stated Wigner's grand orthogonality theorem without proof. The proof is presented in this appendix. Three other theorems are first required, however.

Theorem 1: Unitary Representations. Any matrix representation of a group may be transformed into unitary form (by a similarity transformation) if the matrices of the representation are nonsingular.

COMMENT: The use of this theorem simplifies the proof of the remaining theorems. They can be proven for unitary matrix representations, rather than for arbitrary forms. It should be noted that the matrix representations we have used for symmetry operations were all in unitary form. This is not neccessarily the case, however, from the general definition of representations.

PROOF: The proof involves the construction of a Hermitian matrix from the representation matrices, diagonalization of these Hermitian matrices, and then successive applications of similarity transformations on the original matrices to convert them into a unitary matrix.

Let R and S be elements of an arbitrary group $\mathbf{G}$. Let $\mathbf{D}(R)$ and $\mathbf{D}(S)$ be the matrices representing the elements. In the general case these will not be unitary. Define the Hermitian matrix $\mathbf{H}$ as

$$\mathbf{H} \equiv \sum_R \mathbf{D}(R)\mathbf{D}^\dagger(R) \tag{A2.1}$$

where the summation is over all the elements of the group. The matrix **H** will be positive definite, and, consequently, will have only real, positive eigenvalues. **H** can by diagonalized to give the diagonal matrix **H**′ (the matrix of eigenvalues) by some unitary transformation matrix **U**.

$$\mathbf{H}' = \mathbf{U}^{\dagger}\mathbf{H}\mathbf{U} \tag{A2.2}$$

H′ can also be constructed from the same unitary transformation applied to the original **D**(R) matrices:

$$\mathbf{H}' = \sum_R \mathbf{U}^{\dagger}\mathbf{D}(R)\mathbf{U}\mathbf{U}^{\dagger}\mathbf{D}^{\dagger}(R)\mathbf{U} = \sum_R \mathbf{D}'(R)\mathbf{D}'^{\dagger}(R) \tag{A2.3}$$

since $\mathbf{U}\mathbf{U}^{\dagger} = \mathbf{U}^{\dagger}\mathbf{U} = \mathbf{E}$, the identity matrix.

The matrix $\mathbf{H}'^{1/2}$ can be constructed. Consider the similarity transformation on **D**′(R):

$$\mathbf{D}''(R) = \mathbf{H}'^{1/2}\mathbf{D}'(R)\mathbf{H}'^{1/2} \tag{A2.4}$$

The matrix **D**″(R) can be shown to be unitary:

$$\mathbf{D}''(R)\mathbf{D}''^{\dagger}(R) = \mathbf{D}''(R)\mathbf{E}\mathbf{D}''^{\dagger}(R) = \mathbf{D}''(R)\mathbf{H}'^{-1/2}\mathbf{H}'\mathbf{H}'^{-1/2}\mathbf{D}''^{\dagger}(R) \tag{A2.5}$$

$$= [\mathbf{H}'^{1/2}\mathbf{D}'(R)\mathbf{H}'^{1/2}]\mathbf{H}'^{-1/2}\sum_S \mathbf{D}'(S)\mathbf{D}'^{\dagger}(S)\mathbf{H}'^{-1/2} \times [\mathbf{H}'^{1/2}\mathbf{D}'^{\dagger}(R)\mathbf{H}'^{-1/2}] \tag{A2.5a}$$

$$= \mathbf{H}'^{-1/2}\sum_S \mathbf{D}'(R)\mathbf{D}'(S)\mathbf{D}'^{\dagger}(S)\mathbf{D}'^{\dagger}(R)\mathbf{H}'^{-1/2} \tag{A2.5b}$$

where Eq. A2.3 was used to go from A2.5 to A2.5a. Now $\mathbf{D}'(R)\mathbf{D}'(S) = \mathbf{D}'(T)$, where R, S, and T are all elements of the group. Thus, the summation in A2.5b is equivalent to $\sum_T \mathbf{D}'(T)\mathbf{D}'^{\dagger}(T)$, where T is just a new label for the elements of the group. The summation is therefore equal to **H**′, and

$$\mathbf{D}''(R)\mathbf{D}''^{\dagger}(R) = \mathbf{H}'^{-1/2}\mathbf{H}'\mathbf{H}'^{-1/2} = \mathbf{E} \tag{A2.6}$$

The matrix **D**(R) has been converted to the unitary matrix **D**″(R) by a unitary transformation and a similarity transformation. This can be done for the matrices representing all elements of the group; consequently, the group can be represented by a unitary matrix representation and the proof is complete.

Theorem 2: Schur's Lemma. Any matrix that commutes with all the matrices of an irreducible representation must be a multiple of the unit matrix.

COMMENT: Schur's lemma provides a criterion for the reducibility or irreducibility of a matrix representation. If a matrix that is not a multiple of the unit matrix and that commutes with all the matrices of a representation can be found, then the representation is reducible.

PROOF: Let the set of **D**(R) be a set of unitary matrices that form an irreducible representation of the group **G**. Let **M** be a matrix that commutes with all the **D**(R):

$$\mathbf{D}(R)\mathbf{M} = \mathbf{M}\mathbf{D}(R) \tag{A2.7}$$

Then

$$\mathbf{M}^\dagger\mathbf{D}^\dagger(R) = \mathbf{D}^\dagger(R)\mathbf{M}^\dagger \tag{A2.8}$$

but since $\mathbf{D}(R)$ is unitary, pre- and postmultiplication by $\mathbf{D}(R)$ gives

$$\mathbf{D}(R)\mathbf{M}^\dagger = \mathbf{M}^\dagger\mathbf{D}(R) \tag{A2.9}$$

The Hermitian matrices $\mathbf{H}_1 = (\mathbf{M} + \mathbf{M}^\dagger)$ and $\mathbf{H}_2 = i(\mathbf{M} - \mathbf{M}^\dagger)$ also commute with the $\mathbf{D}(R)$:

$$\mathbf{D}(R)\mathbf{H}_1 = \mathbf{H}_1\mathbf{D}(R) \tag{A2.10a}$$

$$\mathbf{D}(R)\mathbf{H}_2 = \mathbf{H}_2\mathbf{D}(R) \tag{A2.10b}$$

A Hermitian matrix can be diagonalized by a unitary transformation $\mathbf{U}$.

$$\mathbf{H}'_1 = \mathbf{U}^\dagger\mathbf{H}_1\mathbf{U} \tag{A2.11}$$

Let

$$\mathbf{D}'(R) = \mathbf{U}^\dagger\mathbf{D}(R)\mathbf{U} \tag{A2.12}$$

Then

$$\mathbf{D}'(R)\mathbf{H}'_1 = \mathbf{H}'_1\mathbf{D}'(R) \tag{A2.13a}$$

and similarily for $\mathbf{H}_2$ and $\mathbf{H}'_2$.

Since $\mathbf{H}'_1$ is diagonal, A2.13a can be rewritten in terms of the components of the matrices as

$$D'_{ij}(R)\lambda_j\delta_{jk} = \lambda_i\delta_{ij}D'_{jk}(R) \tag{A2.13b}$$

where the λ_j are the diagonal elements of $\mathbf{H}'_1$ and δ_{jk} is the Kroeneker delta function. Rearranging A2.13b gives

$$D'_{ik}(R)(\lambda_k - \lambda_i) = 0 \tag{A2.14}$$

Thus, either $D'_{ik}(R) = 0$ or $\lambda_i = \lambda_k$. In the latter case, all the λ's are equal and $\mathbf{H}'_1$ is a multiple of the unit matrix. If any of the λ's are not equal, the matrices can be rearranged to give all equal λ's in sets. The corresponding rearrangement of $\mathbf{D}'(R)$ would lead to a block diagonal form. This would mean that the original set of $\mathbf{D}(R)$ could be factored into independent sets (i.e., that the original representation was reducible); but this is contrary to our original assumption that they formed an irreducible representation. Consequently, $\mathbf{H}'_1$ and $\mathbf{H}_1$, which is a unitary transform of $\mathbf{H}'_1$, are multiples of the unit matrix. The same holds for $\mathbf{H}_2$. The original matrix $\mathbf{M} = \frac{1}{2}(\mathbf{H}_1 - i\mathbf{H}_2)$ must also be a multiple of the unit matrix and the theorem is proven.

Theorem 3: Equivalence of Representations. If $\mathbf{D}^{(\mu)}$ and $\mathbf{D}^{(\nu)}$ are two irreducible representations of a group, having dimensions n_μ and n_ν, respectively, and if there exists a nonzero, nonsingular rectangular matrix $\mathbf{M}$ such that

$$\mathbf{M}\mathbf{D}^{(\mu)}(R) = \mathbf{D}^{(\nu)}(R)\mathbf{M} \qquad \text{for all } R \text{ in } \mathbf{G} \tag{A2.15}$$

then $\mathbf{D}^{(\mu)}$ and $\mathbf{D}^{(\nu)}$ are equivalent representations. If $n_\mu = n_\nu$ and $\mathbf{D}^{(\mu)}$ and $\mathbf{D}^{(\nu)}$ are not equivalent, $\mathbf{M}$ is the null matrix. If $n_\mu \neq n_\nu$, $\mathbf{M}$ is again the null matrix.

COMMENT: This theorem provides a tool for checking the equivalence of representations. It also provides the connection between Schur's lemma and Wigner's grand orthogonality theorem.

PROOF: Assume that the representations are unitary and that $n_\mu \leq n_\nu$. The conjugate transpose of A2.15 is

$$\mathbf{D}^{(\mu)\dagger}(R)\mathbf{M}^\dagger = \mathbf{M}^\dagger\mathbf{D}^{(\nu)\dagger}(R) \tag{A2.16}$$

But, the matrix representing the inverse of a given element is the conjugate transpose of the matrix representing that element; therefore,

$$\mathbf{D}^{(\mu)}(R^{-1})\mathbf{M}^\dagger = \mathbf{M}^\dagger\mathbf{D}^{(\nu)}(R^{-1}) \tag{A2.17}$$

Premultiplying both sides by $\mathbf{M}$ gives

$$\mathbf{M}\mathbf{D}^{(\mu)}(R^{-1})\mathbf{M}^\dagger = \mathbf{M}\mathbf{M}^\dagger\mathbf{D}^{(\nu)}(R^{-1}) \tag{A2.18}$$

Making use of A2.15 yields

$$\mathbf{D}^{(\nu)}(R^{-1})\mathbf{M}\mathbf{M}^\dagger = \mathbf{M}\mathbf{M}^\dagger\mathbf{D}^{\nu}(R^{-1}) \tag{A2.19}$$

This holds for all R; consequently, from Schur's lemma,

$$\mathbf{M}\mathbf{M}^\dagger = c\mathbf{E} \tag{A2.20}$$

where c is some constant.

Two cases must be considered: the case where $n_\mu = n_\nu$, and the case where $n_\mu \neq n_\nu$.

CASE 1: $n_\mu = n_\nu = n$

The matrix $\mathbf{M}$ must be square, and the determinant $|\mathbf{M}\mathbf{M}^\dagger|$ is

$$|\mathbf{M}\mathbf{M}^\dagger| = |\mathbf{M}||\mathbf{M}^\dagger| = c^n \tag{A2.21}$$

If $c \neq 0$, $|\mathbf{M}| \neq 0$ and from A2.15

$$\mathbf{D}^{(\mu)}(R) = \mathbf{M}^{-1}\mathbf{D}^{(\nu)}(R)\mathbf{M} \tag{A2.22}$$

That is, $\mathbf{D}^{(\mu)}$ and $\mathbf{D}^{(\nu)}$ are equivalent, being related by a similarity transformation.

If $c = 0$, then $\mathbf{M}\mathbf{M}^\dagger$ equals the null matrix. This means that

$$\sum_k M_{ik}M_{jk} = 0 \qquad \text{for all } i \text{ and } j \tag{A2.23a}$$

or for the particular case where i equals j,

$$\sum_k M_{ik}^2 = 0 \qquad \text{for all } i \tag{A2.23b}$$

Since the terms in the summation are all nonnegative, they must individually equal zero. Thus,

$$M_{ik} = 0 \qquad \text{for all } i \text{ and } k \tag{A2.24a}$$

or

$$\mathbf{M} = \mathbf{0} \tag{A2.24b}$$

CASE 2: $n_\mu < n_\nu$

In this case, the matrix **M** is no longer square. It has dimensions $n_\nu \times n_\mu$. Equations A2.19 to A2.21 are still valid. However, the determinant of a nonsquare matrix equals zero; consequently, from A2.21, c must equal zero. The remainder of the proof that **M** is the null matrix follows from A2.23 and A2.24, and the proof of the theorem is complete.

Theorem 4: Wigner's Grand Orthogonality Theorem. The inequivalent, irreducible unitary matrix representations $D^{(\mu)}$ of a group satisfy the relations

$$\sum_R [\mathbf{D}^{(\mu)}(R)]_{ij}^*[\mathbf{D}^{(\nu)}(R)]_{pq} = \frac{g}{n_\mu}\,\delta_{\mu\nu}\delta_{ip}\delta_{jq} \tag{A2.25}$$

where g is the order of the group, n_μ the dimensionality of the μth irreducible representation, and the summation runs over all elements of the group.

COMMENT: This is probably the singly most important theorem for practical applications of group theory. All the projection operator techniques (for reducing reducible representations, for constructing symmetry-adapted functions, etc.) are based upon this theorem. From a more abstract viewpoint, it shows that the number of irreducible representations of a finite group is finite and that the irreducible representations define complete sets of orthogonal vectors in a g-dimensional space.

PROOF: The proof involves the construction of a matrix **M** which satisfies A2.15, and then considering the results when $\mathbf{D}^{(\mu)}$ and $\mathbf{D}^{(\nu)}$ are first inequivalent, and then equivalent.

Let

$$\mathbf{M} = \sum_R \mathbf{D}^{(\nu)}(R)\,\mathbf{X}\mathbf{D}^{(\mu)}(R^{-1}) \tag{A2.26}$$

where **X** is an arbitrary $n_\nu \times n_\mu$ matrix, and the representation matrices are unitary. Multiplying by $\mathbf{D}^{(\nu)}(S)$, we have

$$\mathbf{D}^{(\nu)}(S)\mathbf{M} = \mathbf{D}^{(\nu)}(S)\sum_R \mathbf{D}^{(\nu)}(R)\mathbf{X}\mathbf{D}^{(\mu)}(R^{-1}) \tag{A2.27}$$

Multiplying from the right by $\mathbf{D}^{(\mu)}(S^{-1})\mathbf{D}^{(\mu)}(S) = \mathbf{E}$, we have

$$\mathbf{D}^{(\nu)}(S)\mathbf{M} = \mathbf{D}^{(\nu)}(S)\sum_R \mathbf{D}^{(\nu)}(R)\mathbf{X}\mathbf{D}^{(\mu)}(R^{-1})\mathbf{D}^{(\mu)}(S^{-1})\mathbf{D}^{(\mu)}(S) \tag{A2.28}$$

$$= \sum_R \mathbf{D}^{(\nu)}(SR)\mathbf{X}\mathbf{D}^{(\mu)}((SR)^{-1})\mathbf{D}^{(\mu)}(S) \tag{A2.28a}$$

But, $SR = T$, some other operation of the group; therefore,

$$\mathbf{D}^{(\nu)}(S)\mathbf{M} = \sum_T \mathbf{D}^{(\nu)}(T)\mathbf{X}\mathbf{D}^{(\mu)}(T^{-1})\mathbf{D}^{(\mu)}(S) \tag{A2.28b}$$

$$= \mathbf{M}\mathbf{D}^{(\mu)}(S) \tag{A2.28c}$$

satisfying A2.15.

CASE 1: $\mathbf{D}^{(\mu)}$ and $\mathbf{D}^{(\nu)}$ are not equivalent.

This means that **M** is the null matrix from Theorem 3; thus,

$$\sum_R \sum_q \sum_j [\mathbf{D}^{(\nu)}(\mathrm{R})]_{pq} \mathbf{X}_{qj} [\mathbf{D}^{(\mu)}(\mathrm{R}^{-1})]_{ji} = 0 \tag{A2.29}$$

Since **X** is completely arbitrary, it can be defined so that one component X_{QJ} equals 1 and all the rest are zero. Thus,

$$\sum_R [\mathbf{D}^{(\nu)}(R)]_{pQ} [\mathbf{D}^{(\mu)}(R^{-1})]_{Ji} = 0 \tag{A2.30}$$

Using the property that $\mathbf{D}^{(\mu)}(R^{-1}) = \mathbf{D}^{(\mu)\dagger}(R)$,

$$\sum_R [\mathbf{D}^{(\mu)}(R)]_{iJ}^* [\mathbf{D}^{(\nu)}(R)]_{pQ} = 0 \tag{A2.31}$$

But J and Q were arbitrarily chosen; thus, in general, for all j and q,

$$\sum_R [\mathbf{D}^{(\mu)}(R)]_{ij}^* [\mathbf{D}^{(\nu)}(R)]_{pq} = 0 \tag{A2.32}$$

CASE 2: $\mathbf{D}^{(\mu)}$ and $\mathbf{D}^{(\nu)}$ are equivalent.

From Schur's lemma, $\mathbf{M} = c\mathrm{E}$ in this case and

$$\sum_R \mathbf{D}^{(\mu)}(R)\mathbf{X}\mathbf{D}^{(\mu)}(R^{-1}) = \mathbf{M} = c\mathrm{E} \tag{A2.33a}$$

or

$$\sum_R \sum_q \sum_j [\mathbf{D}^{(\mu)}(R)]_{pq} \mathbf{X}_{qj} [\mathbf{D}^{(\mu)}(R^{-1})]_{ji} = c\delta_{ip} \tag{A2.33b}$$

Again letting X_{QJ} equal to 1 and all other components of **X** equal to zero

$$\sum_R [\mathbf{D}^{(\mu)}(R)]_{pQ} [\mathbf{D}^{(\mu)}(R^{-1})]_{Ji} = c_{JQ}\delta_{ip} \tag{A2.34}$$

In this case, c_{JQ} will depend explicitly on whichever component of **X** is nonzero, and consequently, it must be evaluated. To evaluate c_{JQ}, let $p = i$ and sum A2.34 over all i:

$$\sum_R \sum_i [\mathbf{D}^{(\mu)}(R^{-1})]_{Ji} [\mathbf{D}^{(\mu)}(R)]_{iQ} = c_{JQ} \sum_i \delta_{ii} \tag{A2.35}$$

But $\mathbf{D}^{(\mu)}(R^{-1})\mathbf{D}^{(\mu)}(R) = \mathbf{D}^{(\mu)}(E)$, where E is the identity element and A2.35 reduces to

$$\sum_R [\mathbf{D}^{(\mu)}(E)]_{JQ} = c_{JQ} \sum_i \delta_{ii} \tag{A2.36}$$

The summation over all R in **G** gives $g[\mathbf{D}^{(\mu)}(E)]_{JQ}$, while the element equals 1 if J equals Q, and zero otherwise. The summation over i runs over the dimension n_μ; then, A2.36 reduces to

$$g\delta_{JQ} = c_{JQ}n_\mu \tag{A2.37a}$$

or

$$c_{JQ} = \frac{g}{n_\mu}\delta_{JQ} \tag{A2.37b}$$

Substituting A2.37 into A2.34, using $\mathbf{D}^{(\mu)}(R^{-1}) = \mathbf{D}^{(\mu)\dagger}(R)$ and considering the general case, we have

$$\sum_R [\mathbf{D}^{(\mu)}(R)]^*_{ij}[\mathbf{D}^{(\mu)}(R)]_{pq} = \frac{g}{n_\mu}\delta_{ip}\delta_{jq} \tag{A2.38}$$

Finally, combining A2.38 with A2.32, we have

$$\sum_R [\mathbf{D}^{(\mu)}(R)]^*_{ij}[\mathbf{D}^{(\nu)}(R)]_{pq} = \frac{g}{n_\mu}\delta_{\mu\nu}\delta_{ip}\delta_{jq}$$

and the theorem is proven.

Appendix 3

Answers to Selected Exercises

CHAPTER 1

1.1. *Vector addition:*

$\mathbf{a} = (1, 2)$
$\mathbf{b} = (2, 1)$
$\mathbf{c} = \mathbf{a} + \mathbf{b}$

$$\begin{pmatrix}1\\2\end{pmatrix} + \begin{pmatrix}2\\1\end{pmatrix} = \begin{pmatrix}3\\3\end{pmatrix}$$

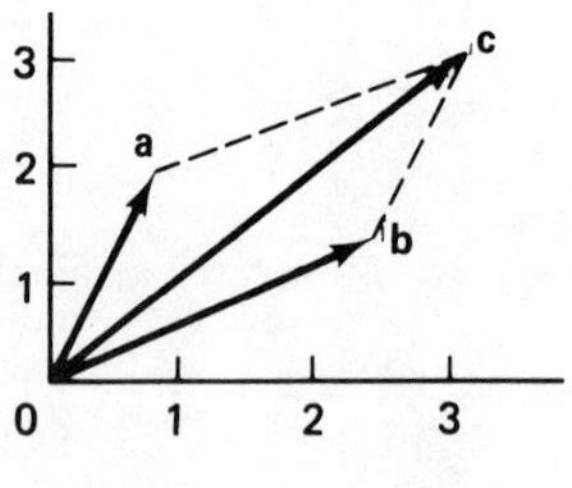

Vector subtraction:

$\mathbf{a} = (1, 2)$
$\mathbf{b} = (2, 1)$
$\mathbf{a} - \mathbf{b} = \mathbf{c}$
$\mathbf{c} = (-1, 1)$

$$\begin{pmatrix}1\\2\end{pmatrix} - \begin{pmatrix}2\\1\end{pmatrix} = \begin{pmatrix}-1\\1\end{pmatrix}$$

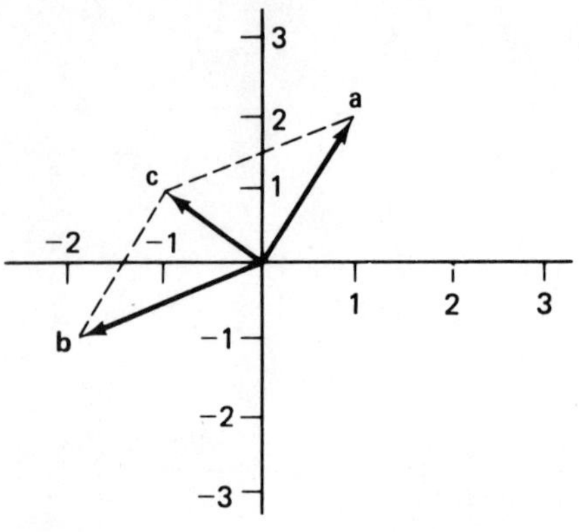

Dot product:

$\mathbf{a} \cdot \mathbf{b} = |\mathbf{a}||\mathbf{b}| \cos \theta$

$|\mathbf{a}| = \sqrt{2^2 + 2^2} = \sqrt{8} = 2\sqrt{2}$

$|\mathbf{b}| = \sqrt{2^2 + 0^2} = \sqrt{4} = 2$

$\theta = 45°$

$$2\sqrt{2} \times 2 \times \cos \theta = 4\sqrt{2} \cos 45° = 4\sqrt{2}\,\frac{1}{\sqrt{2}} = 4$$

$$(2, 2)\begin{pmatrix}2\\0\end{pmatrix} = 4 + 0 = 4$$

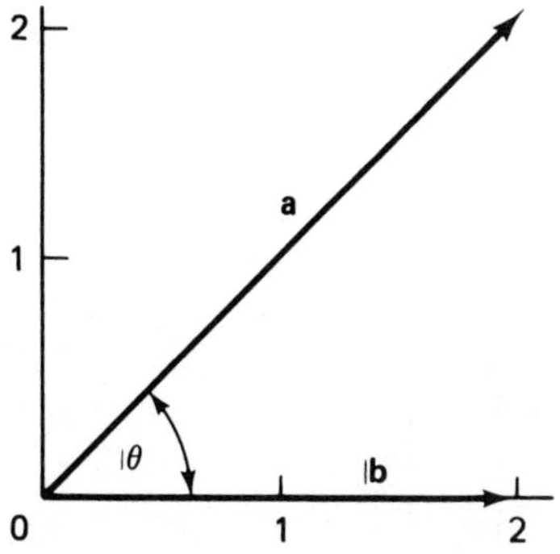

1.2. $\begin{pmatrix}1\\1\\1\end{pmatrix}$ and $\begin{pmatrix}-1\\1\\-1\end{pmatrix}$

$$|\mathbf{a}||\mathbf{b}| \cos \theta = (1 \quad 1 \quad 1)\begin{pmatrix}-1\\1\\-1\end{pmatrix}$$

$|\mathbf{a}| = \sqrt{1^2 + 1^2 + 1^2} = \sqrt{3}$

$|\mathbf{b}| = \sqrt{3}$

$$\cos \theta = \frac{-1 + 1 - 1}{\sqrt{3}\sqrt{3}} = \frac{-1}{3}$$

$\theta = 109°28'$

$\begin{pmatrix}-1\\1\\1\end{pmatrix}$ and $\begin{pmatrix}-1\\1\\-1\end{pmatrix}$

$|\mathbf{a}| = \sqrt{3}$

$|\mathbf{b}| = \sqrt{3}$

$$\cos \theta = \frac{1 + 1 - 1}{\sqrt{3}\sqrt{3}} = \tfrac{1}{3}$$

$\theta = 70°31'$

$\begin{pmatrix}1\\\sqrt{3}\\0\end{pmatrix}$ and $\begin{pmatrix}1\\-\sqrt{3}\\0\end{pmatrix}$

$|\mathbf{a}| = \sqrt{1^2 + \sqrt{3}^2 + 0} = 2$

$|\mathbf{b}| = \sqrt{1^2 + \sqrt{3}^2 + 0} = 2$

$$\cos \theta = \frac{1 - 3 + 0}{4} = -\frac{1}{2}$$

$\theta = 120°$

$\begin{pmatrix}1\\-1\\1\end{pmatrix}$ and $\begin{pmatrix}-1\\1\\-1\end{pmatrix}$

$$|\mathbf{a}||\mathbf{b}| \cos \theta = (1 \quad -1 \quad 1)\begin{pmatrix}-1\\1\\-1\end{pmatrix}$$

$$\cos \theta = \frac{-1 - 1 - 1}{\sqrt{3}\sqrt{3}} = \frac{-3}{3} = -1$$

$\theta = 180°$

$\begin{pmatrix}1/2\\1/\sqrt{2}\\1/2\end{pmatrix}$ and $\begin{pmatrix}1/2\\-1/\sqrt{2}\\1/2\end{pmatrix}$

$|\mathbf{a}| = \sqrt{\tfrac{1}{4} + \tfrac{1}{2} + \tfrac{1}{4}} = 1$

$|\mathbf{b}| = \sqrt{\tfrac{1}{4} + \tfrac{1}{2} + \tfrac{1}{4}} = 1$

$$\cos \theta = \frac{1}{4} - \frac{1}{\sqrt{2}\sqrt{2}} + \frac{1}{4} = 0$$

$\theta = 90°$

1.6.

$$A = \begin{bmatrix} 1 & 2 & 3 \\ 2 & 3 & 1 \\ 3 & 1 & 2 \end{bmatrix}$$

$$A^{-1} = \tfrac{1}{18}\begin{bmatrix} -5 & 1 & 7 \\ 1 & 7 & -5 \\ 7 & -5 & 1 \end{bmatrix}$$

$$B = \begin{bmatrix} 1/2 & 1/\sqrt{2} & 1/2 \\ 1/\sqrt{2} & 0 & -1/\sqrt{2} \\ 1/2 & -1/\sqrt{2} & 1/2 \end{bmatrix}$$

$$B^{-1} = \begin{bmatrix} 1/2 & 1/\sqrt{2} & 1/2 \\ 1/\sqrt{2} & 0 & -1/\sqrt{2} \\ 1/2 & -1/\sqrt{2} & 1/2 \end{bmatrix}$$

1.7. (a)

$$\mathbf{T}\begin{pmatrix} 1 \\ 1 \\ 1 \end{pmatrix} = \begin{pmatrix} 0 \\ 0 \\ \sqrt{3} \end{pmatrix}$$

$$\mathbf{T}\begin{pmatrix} 1 \\ -1 \\ 0 \end{pmatrix} = \begin{pmatrix} 1 \\ -1 \\ 0 \end{pmatrix}$$

$$\mathbf{T}^{\dagger}\mathbf{T} = \begin{bmatrix} 1 & 0 & 0 \\ 0 & 1 & 0 \\ 0 & 0 & 1 \end{bmatrix}; \ \mathbf{T}^{\dagger} = \mathbf{T}^{-1}$$

$$\mathbf{T} = \begin{bmatrix} 1/2 \mp \sqrt{3}/6 & -1/2 \mp \sqrt{3}/6 & \pm 1/\sqrt{3} \\ -1/2 \mp \sqrt{3}/6 & 1/2 \mp \sqrt{3}/6 & \pm 1/\sqrt{3} \\ 1/\sqrt{3} & 1/\sqrt{3} & 1/\sqrt{3} \end{bmatrix} \quad \text{allow for either + or −}$$

(b)

$$\mathbf{T}\begin{pmatrix} 1 \\ -1 \\ 1 \end{pmatrix} = \begin{pmatrix} 1 \mp \sqrt{3}/3 \\ -1 \mp \sqrt{3}/3 \\ -1/\sqrt{3} \end{pmatrix} \quad \text{allow for + or − signs}$$

(c)

$$\left(1 \mp \frac{\sqrt{3}}{3}, -1 \mp \frac{\sqrt{3}}{3}, -\frac{1}{\sqrt{3}}\right)\begin{pmatrix} 0 \\ 0 \\ \sqrt{3} \end{pmatrix} = |\mathbf{a}|\,|\mathbf{b}|\cos\theta$$

$$|\mathbf{a}| = \sqrt{3}$$

$$|\mathbf{b}| = \sqrt{3}$$

$$\cos\theta = -\tfrac{1}{3}$$

$$\theta = 109°28'$$

CHAPTER 2

2.1. (b) $\{1, -1\}$ *Multiplication*

$1 \times -1 = -1$

$1 \times 1 = 1$ Closure satisfied

$-1 \times -1 = 1$

$-1 \times (1 \times 1) = (-1 \times 1) \times 1$ Associative law satisfied

$-1 \times 1 = -1$

$1 \times 1 = 1$ Identity element

reciprocal of $-1 = -1$

$1 = 1$

(c) $\{1, -1, i, -i\}$ *Multiplication*

$1 \times i = i$

$-1 \times i = -i$

$-i \times i = 1$ Closure

$i \times i = -1$

$-i \times -i = -1$

$(1 \times i) \times i = 1 \times (i \times i)$ Associativity

$1 \times i = i$, etc. Identity

$1 \times 1 = 1$

$-1 \times -1 = 1$, etc. Reciprocal

(d) {*All positive and negative integers including zero*} *Addition*

$1 + 2 = 3$

Closure

integer + integer = integer

−integer + −integer = −integer

−integer + integer = ±integer

Associativity $1 + (2 + 3) = (1 + 2) + 3$

Identity $1 + 0 = 1$

Zero

$1 - 1 = 0$

Reciprocal $2 - 2 = 0$, etc.

(e) {*All rational numbers* > 0} *Multiplication*

Closure $\frac{1}{2} \times \frac{3}{2} = \frac{4}{2}$

fraction × fraction = fraction or whole number

Associativity $\frac{1}{2} \times \left(\frac{3}{2} \times \frac{1}{2}\right) = \left(\frac{1}{2} \times \frac{3}{2}\right) \times \frac{1}{2}$

Identity $\frac{1}{2} \times 1 = \frac{1}{2}$

Reciprocal $\frac{1}{2} \times \frac{2}{1} = 1$

$\frac{3}{4} \times \frac{4}{3} = 1$, etc.

2.2. *Symmetry Elements*

(a) CH_2Cl_2 $\{E, C_2, \sigma_v, \sigma_v'\}$

(b) BF_3 $\{E, C_3, C_3^2, \sigma_h, \sigma_v, \sigma_v', \sigma_v'', C_2, C_2', C_2'', S_3, S_3^5\}$

(c) Cyclohexane $\{E, C_3, C_3^2, \sigma_d, \sigma_d', \sigma_d'', C_2, C_2', C_2'', i, S_6, S_6^5\}$

2.5. *Subgroups of:*

CH_2Cl_2

$\{E\}, \{E, C_2\}, \{E, \sigma_v\}, \{E, \sigma_v'\}$ $\mathbf{G} = \{E, C_2\} \times \{E, \sigma_v\}$

BF_3

$\{E, C_3, C_3^2\}$ $\{E, \sigma_h\}$
$\{E, \sigma_v\}$ $\{E, \sigma_v'\}$
$\{E, \sigma_v''\}$ $\{E, C_2\}$
$\{E, C_2'\}$ $\{E, C_2''\}$
$\{E, C_2, \sigma_v, \sigma_v'\}$ $\{E, S_3, S_3^5, \sigma_h, C_3, C_3^2\}$
$\{E, C_3, C_3^2, \sigma_v', \sigma_v'', \sigma_v\}$
$\{E, C_3, C_3^2, C_2', C_2'', C_2\}$ $\mathbf{G} = \{E, C_3, C_3^2\} \wedge \{E, C_2\} \times \{E, \sigma_h\}$

Cyclohexane

$\{E, i\}$ $\{E, C_3, C_3^2\}$ $\{E, C_2\}$ $\{E, C_2'\}$ $\{E, C_2''\}$ $\{E, \sigma_d\}$ $\{E, \sigma_d'\}$ $\{E, \sigma_d''\}$
$\{E, C_3, C_3^2, i, S_6, S_6^5\}$ $\{E, C_3, C_3^2, \sigma_d, \sigma_d', \sigma_d''\}$ $\{E, C_3, C_3^2, C_2, C_2', C_2''\}$ $\{E, C_2, i, \sigma_d\}$
$\mathbf{G} = \{E, C_3, C_3^2\} \wedge \{E, C_2\} \times \{E, i\}$

2.7.

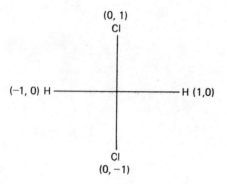

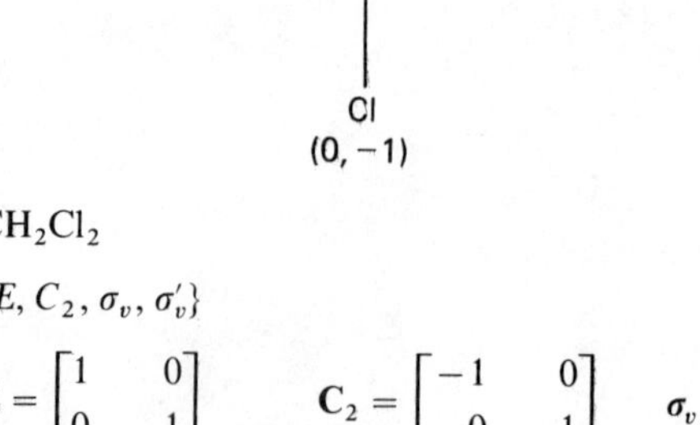

CH_2Cl_2

$\{E, C_2, \sigma_v, \sigma_v'\}$

$$\mathbf{E} = \begin{bmatrix} 1 & 0 \\ 0 & 1 \end{bmatrix} \quad \mathbf{C}_2 = \begin{bmatrix} -1 & 0 \\ 0 & -1 \end{bmatrix} \quad \sigma_v = \begin{bmatrix} -1 & 0 \\ 0 & 1 \end{bmatrix} \quad \sigma_v' = \begin{bmatrix} 1 & 0 \\ 0 & -1 \end{bmatrix}$$

CHAPTER 3

3.2. T *Point Group*

(a)

$$\mathbf{C}_3^{xyz} = \begin{bmatrix} 0 & 0 & 1 \\ 1 & 0 & 0 \\ 0 & 1 & 0 \end{bmatrix} \qquad \mathbf{C}_3^2 = \begin{bmatrix} 0 & 1 & 0 \\ 0 & 0 & 1 \\ 1 & 0 & 0 \end{bmatrix}$$

$$\mathbf{C}_3' = \begin{bmatrix} 0 & 0 & -1 \\ 1 & 0 & 0 \\ 0 & -1 & 0 \end{bmatrix} \qquad \mathbf{C}_3'^2 = \begin{bmatrix} 0 & 1 & 0 \\ 0 & 0 & -1 \\ -1 & 0 & 0 \end{bmatrix}$$

$$\mathbf{C}_3'' = \begin{bmatrix} 0 & 0 & 1 \\ -1 & 0 & 0 \\ 0 & -1 & 0 \end{bmatrix} \qquad \mathbf{C}_3''^2 = \begin{bmatrix} 0 & -1 & 0 \\ 0 & 0 & -1 \\ 1 & 0 & 0 \end{bmatrix}$$

$$\mathbf{C}_3''' = \begin{bmatrix} 0 & 0 & -1 \\ -1 & 0 & 0 \\ 0 & 1 & 0 \end{bmatrix} \qquad \mathbf{C}_3'''^2 = \begin{bmatrix} 0 & -1 & 0 \\ 0 & 0 & 1 \\ -1 & 0 & 0 \end{bmatrix}$$

$$\mathbf{C}_2 = \begin{bmatrix} 1 & 0 & 0 \\ 0 & -1 & 0 \\ 0 & 0 & -1 \end{bmatrix} \qquad \mathbf{E} = \begin{bmatrix} 1 & 0 & 0 \\ 0 & 1 & 0 \\ 0 & 0 & 1 \end{bmatrix}$$

$$\mathbf{C}_2' = \begin{bmatrix} -1 & 0 & 0 \\ 0 & -1 & 0 \\ 0 & 0 & 1 \end{bmatrix} \qquad \mathbf{C}_2'' = \begin{bmatrix} -1 & 0 & 0 \\ 0 & 1 & 0 \\ 0 & 0 & -1 \end{bmatrix}$$

(b) *Operating on Vector* (1 1 1)

$$\mathbf{C}_3\begin{pmatrix}1\\1\\1\end{pmatrix} = \begin{pmatrix}1\\1\\1\end{pmatrix} \qquad \mathbf{C}_3'\begin{pmatrix}1\\1\\1\end{pmatrix} = \begin{pmatrix}-1\\1\\-1\end{pmatrix}$$

$$\mathbf{C}_3^2\begin{pmatrix}1\\1\\1\end{pmatrix} = \begin{pmatrix}1\\1\\1\end{pmatrix} \qquad \mathbf{C}_3'^2\begin{pmatrix}1\\1\\1\end{pmatrix} = \begin{pmatrix}1\\-1\\-1\end{pmatrix}$$

$$\mathbf{C}_3''\begin{pmatrix}1\\1\\1\end{pmatrix} = \begin{pmatrix}1\\-1\\-1\end{pmatrix} \qquad \mathbf{C}_3'''\begin{pmatrix}1\\1\\1\end{pmatrix} = \begin{pmatrix}-1\\-1\\1\end{pmatrix}$$

$$\mathbf{C}_3''^2\begin{pmatrix}1\\1\\1\end{pmatrix} = \begin{pmatrix}-1\\-1\\1\end{pmatrix} \qquad \mathbf{C}_3'''^2\begin{pmatrix}1\\1\\1\end{pmatrix} = \begin{pmatrix}-1\\1\\-1\end{pmatrix}$$

$$\mathbf{C}_2\begin{pmatrix}1\\1\\1\end{pmatrix} = \begin{pmatrix}1\\-1\\-1\end{pmatrix} \qquad \mathbf{E}\begin{pmatrix}1\\1\\1\end{pmatrix} = \begin{pmatrix}1\\1\\1\end{pmatrix}$$

$$\mathbf{C}_2'\begin{pmatrix}1\\1\\1\end{pmatrix} = \begin{pmatrix}-1\\-1\\1\end{pmatrix} \qquad \mathbf{C}_2''\begin{pmatrix}1\\1\\1\end{pmatrix} = \begin{pmatrix}-1\\1\\-1\end{pmatrix}$$

CHAPTER 4

4.1. (a) *A C_2 operation*

$$\mathbf{M} = \begin{bmatrix} M_{11} & M_{12} & M_{13} \\ M_{21} & M_{22} & M_{23} \\ M_{31} & M_{32} & M_{33} \end{bmatrix}$$

$$\mathbf{R}(C_2)\mathbf{M}\tilde{\mathbf{R}}(C_2) = \begin{bmatrix} -1 & 0 & 0 \\ 0 & -1 & 0 \\ 0 & 0 & 1 \end{bmatrix}\begin{bmatrix} M_{11} & M_{12} & M_{13} \\ M_{21} & M_{22} & M_{23} \\ M_{31} & M_{32} & M_{33} \end{bmatrix}\begin{bmatrix} -1 & 0 & 0 \\ 0 & -1 & 0 \\ 0 & 0 & 1 \end{bmatrix}$$

$$= \begin{bmatrix} M_{11} & M_{12} & -M_{13} \\ M_{21} & M_{22} & -M_{23} \\ -M_{31} & -M_{32} & M_{33} \end{bmatrix}$$

For this to be equal to the original matrix,

$$M_{13} = -M_{13} \qquad -M_{31} = M_{31}$$
$$M_{23} = -M_{23} \qquad M_{32} = -M_{32}$$

This can be possible only if these elements are zero; thus,

$$\mathbf{M} = \begin{bmatrix} M_{11} & M_{12} & 0 \\ M_{21} & M_{22} & 0 \\ 0 & 0 & M_{33} \end{bmatrix} \qquad \begin{matrix} \theta_{13} = \theta_{23} = 90^\circ \\ \theta_{12} \neq 90^\circ \end{matrix}$$

There are no restrictions on translations.

(b) *Restriction by C_3^{xyz}*

$$\mathbf{R}(C_3^{xyz}) = \begin{bmatrix} 0 & 0 & 1 \\ 1 & 0 & 0 \\ 0 & 1 & 0 \end{bmatrix}$$

Therefore,

$$\tilde{\mathbf{R}}(C_3^{xyz}) = \begin{bmatrix} 0 & 1 & 0 \\ 0 & 0 & 1 \\ 1 & 0 & 0 \end{bmatrix}$$

$$\mathbf{R}(C_3)\mathbf{M}\tilde{\mathbf{R}}(C_3) = \begin{bmatrix} 0 & 0 & 1 \\ 1 & 0 & 0 \\ 0 & 1 & 0 \end{bmatrix}\begin{bmatrix} M_{11} & M_{12} & M_{13} \\ M_{21} & M_{22} & M_{23} \\ M_{33} & M_{31} & M_{32} \end{bmatrix}\begin{bmatrix} 0 & 1 & 0 \\ 0 & 0 & 1 \\ 1 & 0 & 0 \end{bmatrix}$$

$$= \begin{bmatrix} M_{33} & M_{31} & M_{32} \\ M_{13} & M_{11} & M_{12} \\ M_{23} & M_{21} & M_{22} \end{bmatrix}$$

Therefore, the restrictions are $M_{33} = M_{11}$; $M_{11} = M_{22}$; $M_{33} = M_{22}$ or $a_1 = a_2 = a_3$. Also, no term is zero; therefore, $\theta_{12} = \theta_{13} = \theta_{23} \neq 90^\circ$ since

$$M_{31} = M_{12} \qquad M_{12} = M_{23} \qquad M_{23} = M_{31}$$
$$M_{13} = M_{21} \qquad M_{21} = M_{32} \qquad M_{32} = M_{13}$$

4.2. (a) The full holohedral symmetry of the cubic system is $\mathbf{O}_h$ (order of 48). Hemihedral symmetry (site symmetry) of the point under consideration is $\mathbf{C}_{4v}$ (order of 8). The number of such points is $48/8 = 6$.

(c) The full symmetry of the trigonal system is $\mathbf{D}_{3d}$ (order of 12). The hemihedral symmetry of the point is $\mathbf{C}_s$ (order of 2). The number of such points is $12/2 = 6$.

CHAPTER 5

5.3. (a) $A_1 + A_2 + E$

(b) $A_2' + E' + E''$

(c) $A_2 + E + T_1$

CHAPTER 6

6.3. $D_g^{(2)} \times D_g^{(2)} = D_g^{(0)} + D_g^{(1)} + D_g^{(2)} + D_g^{(3)} + D_g^{(4)}$

$D_g^{(2)} \times D_u^{(1/2)} = D_u^{(3/2)} + D_u^{(5/2)}$

6.4.

$\mathbf{R}_h(3)$	$\mathbf{O}_h$	$\mathbf{D}_{4h}$	$\mathbf{C}_{3v}$
$D_g^{(1)}$	T_{1g}	$A_{2g} + E_g$	$A_2 + E$
$D_u^{(2)}$	$E_u + T_{2u}$	$A_{1u} + B_{1u} + B_{2u} + E_u$	$A_2 + 2E$
$D_u^{(3/2)}$	$G_{3/2u}$	$E_{1/2u} + E_{3/2u}$	$E_{1/2} + E_{3/2}$

6.12. (a) CH_3BF_2:

$\mathbf{C}_s$ conformation:

$\mathbf{I} = \mathscr{C}_3 \times \mathscr{C}_2$

$\mathbf{G} = \mathbf{C}_s$

$\mathbf{S} = \mathbf{I} \wedge \mathbf{G} = (\mathscr{C}_3 \times \mathscr{C}_2) \wedge \mathbf{C}_s = (\mathscr{C}_3 \wedge \mathbf{C}_s) \times \mathscr{C}_2$ isomorphic to $\mathbf{D}_{3d}$

$\mathbf{C}_1$ conformation:

$\mathbf{I} = \mathscr{C}_3 \times \mathscr{C}_2 \wedge \mathbf{U} = (\mathscr{C}_3 \wedge \mathbf{U}) \times \mathscr{C}_2$ isomorphic to $\mathbf{D}_{3d}$

CHAPTER 7

7.1. The eigenvalues are $\alpha + \sqrt{2}\beta$, α, and $\alpha - \sqrt{2}\beta$.

7.2. (a) $\nu_1 \sim a_1$; $\nu_2 \sim a_1$; $\nu_3 \sim b_1$

(b) $\nu_1 \sim a_1'$; $\nu_2 \pm \nu_3 \sim e'$

(c) $\nu_1 \sim a_g$; $\nu_2 \sim a_g$; $\nu_3 \sim a_g$; $\nu_4 \sim b_g$; $\nu_5 \sim b_g$; $\nu_6 \sim a_u$

CHAPTER 8

8.1. (a) $x \sim B_1$; $y \sim B_2$; $z \sim A_1$

(b) ν_1 and ν_2 are allowed by μ^z; ν_3 by μ^x

CHAPTER 9

9.1.

From	Forbidden States	Forbidden by
${}^1S_0$	${}^3S_1$	S, L
	${}^1P_0$	J
	${}^1D_2$	L, J
	${}^3P_1$	S
${}^2D_{3/2}$	${}^2S_{1/2}$	L
	${}^2F_{7/2}$	J
	${}^4P_{5/2}$	S
${}^4S_{3/2}$	${}^2S_{1/2}$	S, L
	${}^4D_{1/2}$	L
	${}^2P_{3/2}$	S
${}^4P_{1/2}$	${}^4P_{5/2}$	J
	${}^4D_{7/2}$	J
	${}^2P_{3/2}$	S
	${}^2S_{1/2}$	S

9.2. $a_{1g} < e_g < b_{2g} < b_{1g}$ (if the ligands lie along x and y)

CHAPTER 10

10.1. (a) $2a_1$ and $2t_2$

(b) $3a_{1g}$, $2e_g$, $3a_{2u}$, and $2e_u$

(c) $3a_{1g}$, $3e_g$, $2t_{1g}$, t_{2g}, $2a_{1u}$, $2e_u$, $2t_{1u}$, and t_{2u} (assuming s, p, and d orbitals on Co and s and p on Cl)

10.3. $(1a_1)^2(2a_1)^2(3a_1)^2(b_1)^2(b_2)^2$

10.5. Forty-two

CHAPTER 11

11.1. (a) $2\Sigma^+$ and Π

(b) $3A_1$, B_1, and $2B_2$ (assuming the yz plane is the molecular plane)

(c) $2\Sigma_g^+$, Σ_u^+, Π_g, and Π_u

11.5. (a) A_2

(b) No

(c) $3A_1$, B_1, and $2B_2$

(d) It is made allowed by vibronic interaction with the b_2 vibrations.

11.7. (a) $A_1 + E$

(b) $A_1 + E + T_2$

(c) $A_1 + A_2 + E$

CHAPTER 12

12.1.

J	K	Rotational States in $\mathbf{C}_{3v}$
0	0	A_1
1	0	$A_1 + E$
1	1	$A_1 + A_2 + 2E$
2	0	$A_1 + 2E$
2	1	$2A_1 + 2A_2 + 3E$
2	2	$2A_1 + 2A_2 + 3E$
3	0	$2A_1 + A_2 + 2E$
3	1	$2A_1 + 2A_2 + 5E$
3	2	$2A_1 + 2A_2 + 5E$
3	3	$3A_1 + 3A_2 + 4E$
4	0	$2A_1 + A_2 + 3E$
4	1	$3A_1 + 3A_2 + 6E$
4	2	$3A_1 + 3A_2 + 6E$
4	3	$3A_1 + 3A_2 + 6E$
4	4	$3A_1 + 3A_2 + 6E$

12.2. The electron EPR signal in the CH_3 radical is split into the same pattern as the fluorine NMR signal in CH_3F.

Appendix **4**

Correlation Tables

These tables give the representations that a given representation in a given group becomes when the symmetry is reduced to a subgroup of the given group. No redundancy is given in the tables. A given group is reduced only to the level of subgroups which themselves have already been reduced. For example, if the reduction of $\mathbf{T}_d$ to $\mathbf{C}_{2v}$ were desired, the reduction to $\mathbf{D}_{2d}$ could be found in the $\mathbf{T}_d$ table and the further reduction to $\mathbf{C}_{2v}$ would come from the $\mathbf{D}_{2d}$ table. Care should be taken when using these, or any other, correlation tables to make sure that the axes of the subgroups are properly aligned with respect to the parent group.

$\mathbf{C}_4$	$\mathbf{C}_2$
A	A
B	A
E	$2B$

$\mathbf{C}_6$	$\mathbf{C}_3$	$\mathbf{C}_2$
A	A	A
B	A	B
E_1	E	$2B$
E_2	E	$2A$

$\mathbf{S}_4$	$\mathbf{C}_2$
A	A
B	A
E	$2B$

$\mathbf{S}_6$	$\mathbf{C}_3$	$\mathbf{C}_i$
A_g	A	A_g
E_g	E	$2A_g$
A_u	A	A_u
E_u	E	$2A_u$

$\mathbf{S}_8$	$\mathbf{C}_4$
A	A
B	A
E_1	E
E_2	$2B$
E_3	E

$\mathbf{C}_{2h}$	$\mathbf{C}_2$	$\mathbf{C}_s$	$\mathbf{C}_i$
A_g	A	A'	A_g
B_g	B	A''	A_g
A_u	A	A''	A_u
B_u	B	A'	A_u

$\mathbf{C}_{3h}$	$\mathbf{C}_3$	$\mathbf{C}_s$
A'	A	A'
E'	E	$2A'$
A''	A	A''
E''	E	$2A''$

$\mathbf{C}_{4h}$	$\mathbf{C}_4$	$\mathbf{S}_4$	$\mathbf{C}_{2h}$
A_g	A	A	A_g
B_g	B	B	A_g
E_g	E	E	$2B_g$
A_u	A	B	A_u
B_u	B	A	A_u
E_u	E	E	$2B_u$

$\mathbf{C}_{5h}$	$\mathbf{C}_5$	$\mathbf{C}_s$
A'	A	A'
E'_1	E_1	$2A'$
E'_2	E_2	$2A'$
A''	A	A''
E''_1	E_1	$2A''$
E''_2	E_2	$2A''$

$\mathbf{C}_{6h}$	$\mathbf{C}_6$	$\mathbf{C}_{3h}$	$\mathbf{S}_6$	$\mathbf{C}_{2h}$
A_g	A	A'	A_g	A_g
B_g	B	A''	A_g	B_g
E_{1g}	E_1	E''	E_g	$2B_g$
E_{2g}	E_2	E'	E_g	$2A_g$
A_u	A	A''	A_u	A_u
B_u	B	A'	A_u	B_u
E_{1u}	E_1	E'	E_u	$2B_u$
E_{2u}	E_2	E''	E_u	$2A_u$

$\mathbf{C}_{2v}$	$\mathbf{C}_2$	(zx) $\mathbf{C}_s$	(yz) $\mathbf{C}_s$
A_1	A	A'	A'
A_2	A	A''	A''
B_1	B	A'	A''
B_2	B	A''	A'

$\mathbf{C}_{3v}$	$\mathbf{C}_3$	$\mathbf{C}_s$
A_1	A	A'
A_2	A	A''
E	E	$A' + A''$

$\mathbf{C}_{4v}$	$\mathbf{C}_4$	σ_v $\mathbf{C}_{2v}$	σ_d $\mathbf{C}_{2v}$
A_1	A	A_1	A_1
A_2	A	A_2	A_2
B_1	B	A_1	A_2
B_2	B	A_2	A_1
E	E	$B_1 + B_2$	$B_1 + B_2$

$\mathbf{C}_{5v}$	$\mathbf{C}_5$	$\mathbf{C}_s$
A_1	A	A'
A_2	A	A''
E_1	E_1	$A' + A''$
E_2	E_2	$A' + A''$

$\mathbf{C}_{6v}$	$\mathbf{C}_6$	σ_v $\mathbf{C}_{3v}$	σ_d $\mathbf{C}_{3v}$	$\sigma_v \rightarrow \sigma(zx)$ $\mathbf{C}_{2v}$
A_1	A	A_1	A_1	A_1
A_2	A	A_2	A_2	A_2
B_1	B	A_1	A_2	B_1
B_2	B	A_2	A_1	B_2
E_1	E_1	E	E	$B_1 + B_2$
E_2	E_2	E	E	$A_1 + A_2$

$\mathbf{D}_2$	$\mathbf{C}_{2(z)}$	$\mathbf{C}_{2(y)}$	$\mathbf{C}_{2(x)}$
A	A	A	A
B_1	A	B	B
B_2	B	A	B
B_3	B	B	A

$\mathbf{D}_3$	$\mathbf{C}_3$	$\mathbf{C}_2$
A_1	A	A
A_2	A	B
E	E	$A + B$

$\mathbf{D}_4$	$\mathbf{C}_4$	$\mathbf{C}_2$	C'_2 $\mathbf{C}_2$	C''_2 $\mathbf{C}_2$
A_1	A	A	A	A
A_2	A	A	B	B
B_1	B	A	A	B
B_2	B	A	B	A
E	E	$2B$	$A + B$	$A + B$

$\mathbf{D}_6$	$\mathbf{C}_6$	C'_2 $\mathbf{D}_3$	C''_2 $\mathbf{D}_3$	$\mathbf{D}_2$
A_1	A	A_1	A_1	A
A_2	A	A_2	A_2	B_1
B_1	B	A_1	A_2	B_2
B_2	B	A_2	A_1	B_3
E_1	E_1	E	E	$B_2 + B_3$
E_2	E_2	E	E	$A + B_1$

$\mathbf{D}_{2h}$	$\mathbf{D}_2$	$C_2(z)$ $\mathbf{C}_{2v}$	$C_2(y)$ $\mathbf{C}_{2v}$	$C_2(x)$ $\mathbf{C}_{2v}$	$C_2(z)$ $\mathbf{C}_{2h}$	$C_2(y)$ $\mathbf{C}_{2h}$	$C_2(x)$ $\mathbf{C}_{2h}$
A_g	A	A_1	A_1	A_1	A_g	A_g	A_g
B_{1g}	B_1	A_2	B_2	B_1	A_g	B_g	B_g
B_{2g}	B_2	B_1	A_2	B_2	B_g	A_g	B_g
B_{3g}	B_3	B_2	B_1	A_2	B_g	B_g	A_g
A_u	A	A_2	A_2	A_2	A_u	A_u	A_u
B_{1u}	B_1	A_1	B_1	B_2	A_u	B_u	B_u
B_{2u}	B_2	B_2	A_1	B_1	B_u	B_u	B_u
B_{3u}	B_3	B_1	B_2	A_1	B_u	B_u	A_u

$\mathbf{D}_{3h}$	$\mathbf{C}_{3h}$	$\mathbf{D}_3$	$\mathbf{C}_{3v}$	$\sigma_h \to \sigma_v(zy)$ $\mathbf{C}_{2v}$
A'_1	A'	A_1	A_1	A_1
A'_2	A'	A_2	A_2	B_2
E'	E'	E	E	$A_1 + B_2$
A''_1	A''	A_1	A_2	A_2
A''_2	A''	A_2	A_1	B_1
E''	E''	E	E	$A_2 + B_1$

$\mathbf{D}_{4h}$	$\mathbf{D}_4$	$C'_2 \to C'_2$ $\mathbf{D}_{2d}$	$C''_2 \to C'_2$ $\mathbf{D}_{2d}$	$\mathbf{C}_{4v}$	$\mathbf{C}_{4h}$	C'_2 $\mathbf{D}_{2h}$	C''_2 $\mathbf{D}_{2h}$
A_{1g}	A_1	A_1	A_1	A_1	A_g	A_g	A_g
A_{2g}	A_2	A_2	A_2	A_2	A_g	B_{1g}	B_{1g}
B_{1g}	B_1	B_1	B_2	B_1	B_g	A_g	B_{1g}
B_{2g}	B_2	B_2	B_1	B_2	B_g	B_{1g}	A_g
E_g	E	E	E	E	E_g	$B_{2g} + B_{3g}$	$B_{2g} + B_{3g}$
A_{1u}	A_1	B_1	B_1	A_2	A_u	A_u	A_u
A_{2u}	A_2	B_2	B_2	A_1	A_u	B_{1u}	B_{1u}
B_{1u}	B_1	A_1	A_2	B_2	B_u	A_u	B_{1u}
B_{2u}	B_2	A_2	A_1	B_1	B_u	B_{1u}	A_u
E_u	E	E	E	E	E_u	$B_{2u} + B_{3u}$	$B_{2u} + B_{3u}$

$\mathbf{D}_{5h}$	$\mathbf{D}_5$	$\mathbf{C}_{5v}$	$\mathbf{C}_{5h}$	$\mathbf{C}_5$	$\sigma_h \to \sigma(xz)$ $\mathbf{C}_{2v}$
A'_1	A_1	A_1	A'	A	A_1
A'_2	A_2	A_2	A'	A	B_1
E'_1	E_1	E_1	E'_1	E_1	$A_1 + B_1$
E'_2	E_2	E_2	E'_2	E_2	$A_1 + B_1$
A''_1	A_1	A_2	A''	A	A_2
A''_2	A_2	A_1	A''	A	B_2
E''_1	E_1	E_1	E''_1	E_1	$A_2 + B_2$
E''_2	E_2	E_2	E''_2	E_2	$A_2 + B_2$

$\mathbf{D}_{6h}$	$\mathbf{D}_6$	C'_2 $\mathbf{D}_{3h}$	C''_2 $\mathbf{D}_{3h}$	$\mathbf{C}_{6v}$	$\mathbf{C}_{6h}$	C''_2 $\mathbf{D}_{3d}$	C'_2 $\mathbf{D}_{3d}$	$\sigma_h \to \sigma(xy)$ $\sigma_v \to \sigma(yz)$ $\mathbf{D}_{2h}$	$\sigma'_v = \sigma_v$ $\sigma_v = \sigma_h$ $C_2 = C'_2$ $\mathbf{C}_{2v}$
A_{1g}	A_1	A'_1	A'_1	A_1	A_g	A_{1g}	A_{1g}	A_g	A_1
A_{2g}	A_2	A'_2	A'_2	A_2	A_g	A_{2g}	A_{2g}	B_{1g}	B_1
B_{1g}	B_1	A''_1	A''_2	B_2	B_g	A_{2g}	A_{1g}	B_{2g}	A_2
B_{2g}	B_2	A''_2	A''_1	B_1	B_g	A_{1g}	A_{2g}	B_{3g}	B_2
E_{1g}	E_1	E''	E''	E_1	E_{1g}	E_g	E_g	$B_{2g} + B_{3g}$	$A_2 + B_2$
E_{2g}	E_2	E'	E'	E_2	E_{2g}	E_g	E_g	$A_g + B_{1g}$	$A_1 + B_1$
A_{1u}	A_1	A''_1	A''_1	A_2	A_u	A_{1u}	A_{1u}	A_u	A_2
A_{2u}	A_2	A''_2	A''_2	A_1	A_u	A_{2u}	A_{2u}	B_{1u}	B_2
B_{1u}	B_1	A'_1	A'_2	B_1	B_u	A_{2u}	A_{1u}	B_{2u}	A_1
B_{2u}	B_2	A'_2	A'_1	B_2	B_u	A_{1u}	A_{2u}	B_{3u}	B_1
E_{1u}	E_1	E'	E'	E_1	E_{1u}	E_u	E_u	$B_{2u} + B_{3u}$	$A_1 + B_1$
E_{2u}	E_2	E''	E''	E_2	E_{2u}	E_u	E_u	$A_u + B_{1u}$	$A_2 + B_2$

$\mathbf{D}_{2d}$	$\mathbf{S}_4$	$\mathbf{D}_2$ ($C_2 \rightarrow C_2(z)$)	$\mathbf{C}_{2v}$
A_1	A	A	A_1
A_2	A	B_1	A_2
B_1	B	A	A_2
B_2	B	B_1	A_1
E	E	$B_2 + B_3$	$B_1 + B_2$

$\mathbf{D}_{3d}$	$\mathbf{D}_3$	$\mathbf{C}_{3v}$	$\mathbf{S}_6$	$\mathbf{C}_3$	$\mathbf{C}_{2h}$
A_{1g}	A_1	A_1	A_g	A	A_g
A_{2g}	A_2	A_2	A_g	A	B_g
E_g	E	E	E_g	E	$A_g + B_g$
A_{1u}	A_1	A_2	A_u	A	A_u
A_{2u}	A_2	A_1	A_u	A	B_u
E_u	E	E	E_u	E	$A_u + B_u$

$\mathbf{D}_{4d}$	$\mathbf{D}_4$	$\mathbf{C}_{4v}$	$\mathbf{S}_8$
A_1	A_1	A_1	A
A_2	A_2	A_2	A
B_1	A_1	A_2	B
B_2	A_2	A_1	B
E_1	E	E	E_1
E_2	$B_1 + B_2$	$B_1 + B_2$	E_2
E_3	E	E	E_3

$\mathbf{D}_{5d}$	$\mathbf{D}_5$	$\mathbf{C}_{5v}$
A_{1g}	A_1	A_1
A_{2g}	A_2	A_2
E_{1g}	E_1	E_1
E_{2g}	E_2	E_2
A_{1u}	A_1	A_2
A_{2u}	A_2	A_1
E_{1u}	E_1	E_1
E_{2u}	E_2	E_2

$\mathbf{D}_{6d}$	$\mathbf{D}_6$	$\mathbf{C}_{6v}$	$\mathbf{D}_{2d}$
A_1	A_1	A_1	A_1
A_2	A_2	A_2	A_2
B_1	A_1	A_2	B_1
B_2	A_2	A_1	B_2
E_1	E_1	E_1	E
E_2	E_2	E_2	$B_1 + B_2$
E_3	$B_1 + B_2$	$B_1 + B_2$	E
E_4	E_2	E_2	$A_1 + A_2$
E_5	E_1	E_1	E

$\mathbf{T}$	$\mathbf{D}_2$	$\mathbf{C}_3$
A	A	A
E	$2A$	E
T	$B_1 + B_2 + B_3$	$A + E$

$\mathbf{T}_h$	$\mathbf{T}$	$\mathbf{D}_{2h}$	$\mathbf{S}_6$
A_g	A	A_g	A_g
E_g	E	$2A_g$	E_g
T_g	T	$B_{1g} + B_{2g} + B_{3g}$	$A_g + E_g$
A_u	A	A_u	A_u
E_u	E	$2A_u$	E_u
T_u	T	$B_{1u} + B_{2u} + B_{3u}$	$A_u + E_u$

$\mathbf{T}_d$	$\mathbf{T}$	$\mathbf{D}_{2d}$	$\mathbf{C}_{3v}$	$\mathbf{S}_4$
A_1	A	A_1	A_1	A
A_2	A	B_1	A_2	B
E	E	$A_1 + B_1$	E	$A + B$
T_1	T	$A_2 + E$	$A_2 + E$	$A + E$
T_2	T	$B_2 + E$	$A_1 + E$	$B + E$

$\mathbf{O}$	$\mathbf{T}$	$\mathbf{D}_4$	$\mathbf{D}_3$
A_1	A	A_1	A_1
A_2	A	B_1	A_2
E	E	$A_1 + B_1$	E
T_1	T	$A_2 + E$	$A_2 + E$
T_2	T	$B_2 + E$	$A_1 + E$

$\mathbf{O}_h$	$\mathbf{O}$	$\mathbf{T}_d$	$\mathbf{T}_h$	$\mathbf{D}_{4h}$	$\mathbf{D}_{3d}$
A_{1g}	A_1	A_1	A_g	A_{1g}	A_{1g}
A_{2g}	A_2	A_2	A_g	B_{1g}	A_{2g}
E_g	E	E	E_g	$A_{1g} + B_{1g}$	E_g
T_{1g}	T_1	T_1	T_g	$A_{2g} + E_g$	$A_{2g} + E_g$
T_{2g}	T_2	T_2	T_g	$B_{2g} + E_g$	$A_{1g} + E_g$
A_{1u}	A_1	A_2	A_u	A_{1u}	A_{1u}
A_{2u}	A_2	A_1	A_u	B_{1u}	A_{2u}
E_u	E	E	E_u	$A_{1u} + B_{1u}$	E_u
T_{1u}	T_1	T_2	T_u	$A_{2u} + E_u$	$A_{2u} + E_u$
T_{2u}	T_2	T_1	T_u	$B_{2u} + E_u$	$A_{1u} + E_u$

Appendix **5**

Character Tables

These tables include the discrete axial point groups up to a rotation axis of order 6; the cubic point groups; the linear and spherical continuous rotation groups; and the symmetric permutation group up to degree 7. The point groups contain both the single-valued and the double-valued representations. The point-group tables also contain the transformation properties of the Cartesian coordinates, rotations about the Cartesian coordinates, and quadratic terms in the Cartesian coordinates. The transformation properties of higher polynomials can be generated by multiplication of these representations.

The product structure for constructing the group from its most common generators is given for the point groups. This, coupled with the fact that the cyclic groups having orders that are not prime numbers have cyclic subgroups whose orders are the integer divisors of the order of the parent group, allows one to immediately find all the subgroups of a given group. For example, $\mathbf{D}_{6h}$ has the product structure $\mathbf{C}_6 \wedge \mathbf{C}_2' \times \mathbf{C}_s$. Each of the groups $\mathbf{C}_6$, $\mathbf{C}_3$, $\mathbf{C}_2$, $\mathbf{C}_2'$, and $\mathbf{C}_s$, as well as their products, are subgroups of $\mathbf{D}_{6h}$.

The final bit of information given with the point-group tables has to do with their relation to space groups. The crystal system in which each occurs, the non-primitive translations with which each is compatible, and the total number of space groups having the given symmetry are listed.

The organization of the tables is as follows:

Group = Product structure (Crystal system; Nonprimitive translations; Total number of space groups)

Group	*Classes*	*Double-group Classes*		
Single-valued Representations	Characters of single-valued representations	Characters of single-valued representations	Cartesian coordinates and rotations	Quadratic terms
Double-valued Representations	Characters of double-valued representations	Characters of double-valued representations		

Important note: For the construction used in these tables, the double groups require that if a C_n^m and its inverse appear in a class, the inverse *must* be interpreted as C_n^{-m} rather that as $C_n^{(n-m)}$.

1. The Cyclic Groups, $\mathbf{C}_n$

$\mathbf{C}_1 = \mathbf{C}_1$ (triclinic; none; 1)

$\mathbf{C}_1$	E	$\bar{E}$		
A	1	1	All coordinates and rotations	All
$B_{1/2}$	1	-1		

$\mathbf{C}_2 = \mathbf{C}_2$ (monoclinic; twofold screw; 3)

$\mathbf{C}_2$	E	C_2	$\bar{E}$	$\bar{C}_2$		
A	1	1	1	1	z, R_z	x^2, y^2, z^2, xy
B	1	-1	1	-1	x, y, R_x, R_y	yz, xz
$E_{1/2}$	1	i	-1	$-i$		
	1	$-i$	-1	i		

$\mathbf{C}_3 = C_3$ (trigonal; threefold screw; 4)

$\mathbf{C}_3$	E	C_3	C_3^2	$\bar{E}$	$\bar{C}_3$	$\bar{C}_3^2$	$\varepsilon = \exp(2\pi i/3)$	
A	1	1	1	1	1	1	z, R_z	$x^2 + y^2, z^2$
E	1	ε	ε^*	1	ε	ε^*	(x, y)	$(x^2 - y^2, xy)$
	1	ε^*	ε	1	ε^*	ε	(R_x, R_y)	(xz, yz)
$E_{1/2}$	1	$-\varepsilon^*$	ε	-1	ε^*	$-\varepsilon$		
	1	$-\varepsilon$	ε^*	-1	ε	$-\varepsilon^*$		
$B_{3/2}$	1	-1	1	-1	1	-1		

$\mathbf{C}_4 = C_4$ (tetragonal; fourfold and twofold screw; 6)

$\mathbf{C}_4$	E	C_4	C_2	C_4^3	$\bar{E}$	$\bar{C}_4$	$\bar{C}_2$	$\bar{C}_4^3$	$\omega = \exp(\pi i/4)$	
A	1	1	1	1	1	1	1	1	z, R_z	$x^2 + y^2, z^2$
B	1	-1	1	-1	1	-1	1	-1		$x^2 - y^2, xy$
E	1	i	-1	$-i$	1	i	-1	$-i$	(x, y)	(yz, xz)
	1	$-i$	-1	i	1	$-i$	-1	i	(R_x, R_y)	
$E_{1/2}$	1	ω	i	$-\omega^*$	-1	$-\omega$	$-i$	ω^*		
	1	ω^*	$-i$	$-\omega$	-1	$-\omega^*$	i	ω		
$E_{3/2}$	1	$-\omega^*$	$-i$	ω	-1	ω^*	i	$-\omega$		
	1	$-\omega$	i	ω^*	-1	ω	$-i$	$-\omega^*$		

$\mathbf{C}_5 = C_5$ (none; – ; –)

$\mathbf{C}_5$	E	C_5	C_5^2	C_5^3	C_5^4	$\bar{E}$	$\bar{C}_5$	$\bar{C}_5^2$	$\bar{C}_5^3$	$\bar{C}_5^4$	$\varepsilon = \exp(2\pi i/5)$; $\omega = \exp(\pi i/5)$	
A	1	1	1	1	1	1	1	1	1	1	z, R_z	$x^2 + y^2, z^2$
E_1	1	ε	$-\omega^*$	$-\omega$	ε^*	1	ε	$-\omega^*$	$-\omega$	ε^*	(x, y)	(yz, xz)
	1	ε^*	$-\omega$	$-\omega^*$	ε	1	ε^*	$-\omega$	$-\omega^*$	ε	(R_x, R_y)	
E_2	1	$-\omega^*$	ε^*	ε	$-\omega$	1	$-\omega^*$	ε^*	ε	$-\omega$		$(x^2 - y^2, xy)$
	1	$-\omega$	ε	ε^*	$-\omega^*$	1	$-\omega$	ε	ε^*	$-\omega^*$		
$E_{1/2}$	1	ω	ε	$-\varepsilon^*$	$-\omega^*$	-1	$-\omega$	$-\varepsilon$	ε^*	ω^*		
	1	ω^*	ε^*	$-\varepsilon$	$-\omega$	-1	$-\omega^*$	$-\varepsilon^*$	ε	ω		
$E_{3/2}$	1	$-\varepsilon^*$	$-\omega$	ω^*	ε	-1	ε^*	ω	$-\omega^*$	$-\varepsilon$		
	1	$-\varepsilon$	$-\omega^*$	ω	ε^*	-1	ε	ω^*	$-\omega$	$-\varepsilon^*$		
$B_{5/2}$	1	-1	1	-1	1	-1	1	-1	1	-1		

$C_6 = \mathbf{C_3 \times C_2}$ (hexagonal; sixfold, threefold, and twofold screws; 6)

6	E	C_6	C_3	C_2	C_3^2	C_6^5	$\bar{E}$	$\bar{C}_6$	$\bar{C}_3$	$\bar{C}_2$	$\bar{C}_3^2$	$\bar{C}_6^5$	$\varepsilon = \exp(2\pi i/6)$; $\omega = \exp(\pi i/6)$	
	1	1	1	1	1	1	1	1	1	1	1	1	z, R_z	$x^2 + y^2, z^2$
	1	−1	1	−1	1	−1	1	−1	1	−1	1	−1		
1	1	ε	$-\varepsilon^*$	−1	$-\varepsilon$	ε^*	1	ε	$-\varepsilon^*$	−1	$-\varepsilon$	ε^*	(x, y) (R_x, R_y)	(xz, yz)
	1	ε^*	$-\varepsilon$	−1	$-\varepsilon^*$	ε	1	ε^*	$-\varepsilon$	−1	$-\varepsilon^*$	ε		
2	1	$-\varepsilon^*$	$-\varepsilon$	1	$-\varepsilon^*$	$-\varepsilon$	1	$-\varepsilon^*$	$-\varepsilon$	1	$-\varepsilon^*$	$-\varepsilon$		$(x^2 - y^2, xy)$
	1	$-\varepsilon$	$-\varepsilon^*$	1	$-\varepsilon$	$-\varepsilon^*$	1	$-\varepsilon$	$-\varepsilon^*$	1	$-\varepsilon$	$-\varepsilon^*$		
1/2	1	ω	ε	i	$-\varepsilon^*$	$-\omega^*$	−1	$-\omega$	$-\varepsilon$	$-i$	ε^*	ω^*		
	1	ω^*	ε^*	$-i$	$-\varepsilon$	$-\omega$	−1	$-\omega^*$	$-\varepsilon^*$	i	ε	ω		
3/2	1	i	−1	$-i$	1	i	−1	$-i$	1	i	−1	$-i$		
	1	$-i$	−1	i	1	$-i$	−1	i	1	$-i$	−1	i		
5/2	1	$-\omega^*$	ε^*	i	$-\varepsilon$	ω	−1	ω^*	$-\varepsilon^*$	$-i$	ε	$-\omega$		
	1	$-\omega$	ε	$-i$	$-\varepsilon^*$	ω^*	−1	ω	$-\varepsilon$	i	ε^*	$-\omega^*$		

C_n (general)

The elements, irreducible representations, and characters for any cyclic point group of order n can be generated as follows:

Elements: C_n^j, with j going from 0 to $n - 1$ (note that $C_n^0 = E$);
$\bar{C}_n^j$, with same limits for double-group elements

Irreducible representations:

a. Single-valued:
   1. n odd: A and E_k, k going from 1 to $(n - 1)/2$
   2. n even: A, B and E_k, k going from 1 to $(n/2 - 1)$

b. Double-valued:
   1. n odd: $B_{n/2}$ and E_l, half-integer l going from 1/2 to $(n/2 - 1)$
   2. n even: E_l, half-integer l going from 1/2 to $(n - 1)/2$

Characters:

a. Single-valued representations:
   1. A: all +1
   2. B: alternating +1 and −1
   3. E_k: $\begin{cases} \varepsilon^{kj} \\ \varepsilon^{-kj} \end{cases}$ j going from 0 to $(n - 1)$, $\varepsilon = \exp(2\pi i/n)$

   (Note: $\varepsilon^0 = 1$; double-group characters are the same as corresponding "normal" characters)

b. Double-valued representations:

1. $B_{n/2}$: alternating +1 and −1

2. E_l: $\begin{cases}\varepsilon^{lj} \\ \varepsilon^{-lj}\end{cases}$ j going from 0 to $(2n - 1)$, $\varepsilon = \exp(2\pi i/n)$

[*Note*: $\varepsilon^0 = 1$, $\varepsilon^{1/2} = \omega = \exp(\pi i/n)$; double-group characters are the negative of the corresponding "normal" characters]

2. The groups $\mathbf{S}_n$

$\mathbf{S}_2 = \mathbf{C}_i$ (triclinic; none; 1)

$\mathbf{C}_i$	E	i	$\bar{E}$	$\bar{i}$		
A_g	1	1	1	1	R_x, R_y, R_z	All
A_u	1	−1	1	−1	x, y, z	
$B_{1/2g}$	1	1	−1	−1		
$B_{1/2u}$	1	−1	−1	1		

$\mathbf{S}_4 = \mathbf{S}_4$ (tetragonal; none; 2)

$\mathbf{S}_4$	E	S_4	C_2	S_4^3	$\bar{E}$	$\bar{S}_4$	$\bar{C}_2$	$\bar{S}_4^3$	$\omega = \exp(\pi i/4)$	
A	1	1	1	1	1	1	1	1	R_z	$x^2 + y^2, z^2$
B	1	−1	1	−1	1	−1	1	−1	z	$x^2 - y^2, xy$
E	1	i	−1	$-i$	1	i	−1	$-i$	(x, y)	(xz, yz)
	1	$-i$	−1	i	1	$-i$	−1	i	(R_x, R_y)	
$E_{1/2}$	1	ω	i	$-\omega^*$	−1	$-\omega$	$-i$	ω^*		
	1	ω^*	$-i$	$-\omega$	−1	$-\omega^*$	i	ω		
$E_{3/2}$	1	$-\omega^*$	$-i$	ω	−1	ω^*	i	$-\omega$		
	1	$-\omega$	i	ω^*	−1	ω	$-i$	$-\omega^*$		

$\mathbf{S}_6 = \mathbf{C}_3 \times \mathbf{C}_i = \mathbf{C}_{3i}$ (trigonal; none; 2)

$\mathbf{S}_6$	E	C_3	C_3^2	i	S_6^5	S_6	$\bar{E}$	$\bar{C}_3$	$\bar{C}_3^2$	$\bar{i}$	$\bar{S}_6^5$	$\bar{S}_6$	$\varepsilon = \exp(2\pi i/3)$	
A_g	1	1	1	1	1	1	1	1	1	1	1	1	R_z	$x^2 + y^2, z^2$
E_g	1	ε	ε^*	1	ε	ε^*	1	ε	ε^*	1	ε	ε^*	(R_x, R_y)	$(x^2 - y^2, xy)$
	1	ε^*	ε	1	ε^*	ε	1	ε^*	ε	1	ε^*	ε		(xz, yz)
A_u	1	1	1	−1	−1	−1	1	1	1	−1	−1	−1	z	
E_u	1	ε	ε^*	−1	$-\varepsilon$	$-\varepsilon^*$	1	ε	ε^*	−1	$-\varepsilon$	$-\varepsilon^*$	(x, y)	
	1	ε^*	ε	−1	$-\varepsilon^*$	$-\varepsilon$	1	ε^*	ε	−1	$-\varepsilon^*$	$-\varepsilon$		
$E_{1/2g}$	1	$-\varepsilon^*$	ε	1	$-\varepsilon^*$	ε	−1	ε^*	$-\varepsilon$	−1	ε^*	$-\varepsilon$		
	1	$-\varepsilon$	ε^*	1	$-\varepsilon$	ε^*	−1	ε	$-\varepsilon^*$	−1	ε	$-\varepsilon^*$		
$B_{3/2g}$	1	−1	1	1	−1	1	−1	1	−1	−1	1	−1		
$E_{1/2u}$	1	$-\varepsilon^*$	ε	−1	ε^*	$-\varepsilon$	−1	ε^*	$-\varepsilon$	1	$-\varepsilon^*$	ε		
	1	$-\varepsilon$	ε^*	−1	ε	$-\varepsilon^*$	−1	ε	$-\varepsilon^*$	1	$-\varepsilon$	ε^*		
$B_{3/2u}$	1	−1	1	−1	1	−1	−1	1	−1	1	−1	1		

3. The Groups $\mathbf{C}_{nh}$(*Note*: The $\mathbf{C}_s$ represents a horizontal plane)

$\mathbf{C}_{1h} = \mathbf{C}_s$ (monoclinic; glide plane; 4)

$\mathbf{C}_s$	E	σ_h	$\bar{E}$	$\bar{\sigma}_h$		
A'	1	1	1	1	x, y, R_z	x^2, y^2, z^2, xy
A''	1	-1	1	-1	z, R_x, R_y	yz, xz
$E_{1/2}$	1	i	-1	$-i$		
	1	$-i$	-1	i		

$\mathbf{C}_{2h} = \mathbf{C}_2 \times \mathbf{C}_s$ (monoclinic; twofold screw, glide; 6)

$\mathbf{C}_{2h}$	E	C_2	i	σ_h	$\bar{E}$	$\bar{C}_2$	$\bar{i}$	$\bar{\sigma}_h$		
A_g	1	1	1	1	1	1	1	1	R_z	x^2, y^2, z^2, xy
B_g	1	-1	1	-1	1	-1	1	-1	R_y, R_y	xz, yz
A_u	1	1	-1	-1	1	1	-1	-1	z	
B_u	1	-1	-1	1	1	-1	-1	1	x, y	
$E_{1/2g}$	1	i	1	i	-1	$-i$	-1	$-i$		
	1	$-i$	1	$-i$	-1	i	-1	i		
$E_{1/2u}$	1	i	-1	$-i$	-1	$-i$	1	i		
	1	$-i$	-1	i	-1	i	1	$-i$		

$\mathbf{C}_{3h} = \mathbf{C}_3 \times \mathbf{C}_s$ (hexagonal; none; 1)

$\mathbf{C}_{3h}$	E	C_3	C_3^2	σ_h	S_3	S_3^5	$\bar{E}$	$\bar{C}_3$	$\bar{C}_3^2$	$\bar{\sigma}_h$	$\bar{S}_3$	$\bar{S}_3^5$	$\varepsilon = \exp(2\pi i/3)$	
A'	1	1	1	1	1	1	1	1	1	1	1	1	R_z	$x^2 + y^2, z^2$
E'	1	ε	ε^*	1	ε	ε^*	1	ε	ε^*	1	ε	ε^*	(x, y)	$(x^2 - y^2, xy)$
	1	ε^*	ε	1	ε^*	ε	1	ε^*	ε	1	ε^*	ε		
A''	1	1	1	-1	-1	-1	1	1	1	-1	-1	-1	z	
E''	1	ε	ε^*	-1	$-\varepsilon$	$-\varepsilon^*$	1	ε	ε^*	-1	$-\varepsilon$	$-\varepsilon^*$	(R_x, R_y)	(xz, yz)
	1	ε^*	ε	-1	$-\varepsilon^*$	$-\varepsilon$	1	ε^*	ε	-1	$-\varepsilon^*$	$-\varepsilon$		
$E'_{1/2}$	1	$-\varepsilon^*$	ε	1	$-\varepsilon^*$	ε	-1	ε^*	$-\varepsilon$	-1	ε^*	$-\varepsilon$		
	1	$-\varepsilon$	ε^*	1	$-\varepsilon$	ε^*	-1	ε	$-\varepsilon^*$	-1	ε	$-\varepsilon^*$		
$B'_{3/2}$	1	-1	1	1	-1	1	-1	1	-1	-1	1	-1		
$E''_{1/2}$	1	$-\varepsilon^*$	ε	-1	ε^*	$-\varepsilon$	-1	ε^*	$-\varepsilon$	1	$-\varepsilon^*$	ε		
	1	$-\varepsilon$	ε^*	-1	ε	$-\varepsilon^*$	-1	ε	$-\varepsilon^*$	1	$-\varepsilon$	ε^*		
$B''_{3/2}$	1	-1	1	-1	1	-1	-1	1	-1	1	-1	1		

$\mathbf{C}_{4h} = \mathbf{C}_4 \times \mathbf{C}_s$ (tetragonal; fourfold and twofold screw, glide; 6)

$\mathbf{C}_{4h}$	E	C_4	C_2	C_4^3	i	S_4^3	σ_h	S_4	$\bar{E}$	$\bar{C}_4$	$\bar{C}_2$	$\bar{C}_4^3$	$\bar{i}$	$\bar{S}_4^3$	$\bar{\sigma}_h$	$\bar{S}_4$	$\omega = \exp(\pi i/4)$	
A_g	1	1	1	1	1	1	1	1	1	1	1	1	1	1	1	1	R_z	$x^2 + y^2, z^2$
B_g	1	-1	1	-1	1	-1	1	-1	1	-1	1	-1	1	-1	1	-1		$x^2 - y^2, xy$
E_g	1	i	-1	$-i$	1	i	-1	$-i$	1	i	-1	$-i$	1	i	-1	$-i$	(R_x, R_y)	(yz, xz)
	1	$-i$	-1	i	1	$-i$	-1	i	1	$-i$	-1	i	1	$-i$	-1	i		
A_u	1	1	1	1	-1	-1	-1	-1	1	1	1	1	-1	-1	-1	-1	z	
B_u	1	-1	1	-1	-1	1	-1	1	1	-1	1	-1	-1	1	-1	1		
E_u	1	i	-1	$-i$	-1	$-i$	1	i	1	i	-1	$-i$	-1	$-i$	1	i	x, y	
	1	$-i$	-1	i	-1	i	1	$-i$	1	$-i$	-1	i	-1	i	1	$-i$		
$E_{1/2g}$	1	ω	i	$-\omega^*$	1	ω	i	$-\omega^*$	-1	$-\omega$	$-i$	ω^*	-1	$-\omega$	$-i$	ω^*		
	1	ω^*	$-i$	$-\omega$	1	ω^*	$-i$	$-\omega$	-1	$-\omega^*$	i	ω	-1	$-\omega^*$	i	ω		
$E_{3/2g}$	1	$-\omega^*$	$-i$	ω	1	$-\omega^*$	$-i$	ω	-1	ω^*	i	$-\omega$	-1	ω^*	i	$-\omega$		
	1	$-\omega$	i	ω^*	1	$-\omega$	i	ω^*	-1	ω	$-i$	$-\omega^*$	-1	ω	$-i$	$-\omega^*$		
$E_{1/2u}$	1	ω	i	$-\omega^*$	-1	$-\omega$	$-i$	ω^*	-1	$-\omega$	$-i$	ω^*	1	ω	i	$-\omega^*$		
	1	ω^*	$-i$	$-\omega$	-1	$-\omega^*$	i	ω	-1	$-\omega^*$	i	ω	1	ω^*	$-i$	$-\omega$		
$E_{3/2u}$	1	$-\omega^*$	$-i$	ω	-1	ω^*	i	$-\omega$	-1	ω^*	i	$-\omega$	1	$-\omega^*$	$-i$	ω		
	1	$-\omega$	i	ω^*	-1	ω	$-i$	$-\omega^*$	-1	ω	$-i$	$-\omega^*$	1	$-\omega$	i	ω^*		

$\mathbf{C_{5h} = C_5 \times C_s}$ (none; – ; –)

$\varepsilon = \exp(2\pi i/5)$; $\omega = \exp(\pi i/5)$

C_{5h}	E	C_5	C_5^2	C_5^3	C_5^4	σ_h	S_5	S_5^7	S_5^3	S_5^9	$\bar{E}$	$\bar{C}_5$	$\bar{C}_5^2$	$\bar{C}_5^3$	$\bar{C}_5^4$	$\bar{\sigma}_h$	$\bar{S}_5$	$\bar{S}_5^7$	$\bar{S}_5^3$	$\bar{S}_5^9$		
A'	1	1	1	1	1	1	1	1	1	1	1	1	1	1	1	1	1	1	1	1	R_z	x^2+y^2, z^2
E_1'	1	ε	$-\omega^*$	$-\omega$	ε^*	1	ε	$-\omega^*$	$-\omega$	ε^*	1	ε	$-\omega^*$	$-\omega$	ε^*	1	ε	$-\omega^*$	$-\omega$	ε^*	(x, y)	
	1	ε^*	$-\omega$	$-\omega^*$	ε	1	ε^*	$-\omega$	$-\omega^*$	ε	1	ε^*	$-\omega$	$-\omega^*$	ε	1	ε^*	$-\omega$	$-\omega^*$	ε		
E_2'	1	$-\omega^*$	ε^*	ε	$-\omega$	1	$-\omega^*$	ε^*	ε	$-\omega$	1	$-\omega^*$	ε^*	ε	$-\omega$	1	$-\omega^*$	ε^*	ε	$-\omega$		(x^2-y^2, xy)
	1	$-\omega$	ε	ε^*	$-\omega^*$	1	$-\omega$	ε	ε^*	$-\omega^*$	1	$-\omega$	ε	ε^*	$-\omega^*$	1	$-\omega$	ε	ε^*	$-\omega^*$		
A''	1	1	1	1	1	−1	−1	−1	−1	−1	1	1	1	1	1	−1	−1	−1	−1	−1	z	
E_1''	1	ε	$-\omega^*$	$-\omega$	ε^*	−1	$-\varepsilon$	ω^*	ω	$-\varepsilon^*$	1	ε	$-\omega^*$	$-\omega$	ε^*	−1	$-\varepsilon$	ω^*	ω	$-\varepsilon^*$	(R_x, R_y)	(xz, yz)
	1	ε^*	$-\omega$	$-\omega^*$	ε	−1	$-\varepsilon^*$	ω	ω^*	$-\varepsilon$	1	ε^*	$-\omega$	$-\omega^*$	ε	−1	$-\varepsilon^*$	ω	ω^*	$-\varepsilon$		
E_2''	1	$-\omega^*$	ε^*	ε	$-\omega$	−1	ω^*	$-\varepsilon^*$	$-\varepsilon$	ω	1	$-\omega^*$	ε^*	ε	$-\omega$	−1	ω^*	$-\varepsilon^*$	$-\varepsilon$	ω		
	1	$-\omega$	ε	ε^*	$-\omega^*$	−1	ω	$-\varepsilon$	$-\varepsilon^*$	ω^*	1	$-\omega$	ε	ε^*	$-\omega^*$	−1	ω	$-\varepsilon$	$-\varepsilon^*$	ω^*		
$E_{1/2}'$	1	ω	ε	$-\varepsilon^*$	$-\omega^*$	1	ω	ε	$-\varepsilon^*$	$-\omega^*$	−1	$-\omega$	$-\varepsilon$	ε^*	ω^*	−1	$-\omega$	$-\varepsilon$	ε^*	ω^*		
	1	ω^*	ε^*	$-\varepsilon$	$-\omega$	1	ω^*	ε^*	$-\varepsilon$	$-\omega$	−1	$-\omega^*$	$-\varepsilon^*$	ε	ω	−1	$-\omega^*$	$-\varepsilon^*$	ε	ω		
$E_{3/2}'$	1	$-\varepsilon^*$	$-\omega$	ω^*	ε	1	$-\varepsilon^*$	$-\omega$	ω^*	ε	−1	ε^*	ω	$-\omega^*$	$-\varepsilon$	−1	ε^*	ω	$-\omega^*$	$-\varepsilon$		
	1	$-\varepsilon$	$-\omega^*$	ω	ε^*	1	$-\varepsilon$	$-\omega^*$	ω	ε^*	−1	ε	ω^*	$-\omega$	$-\varepsilon^*$	−1	ε	ω^*	$-\omega$	$-\varepsilon^*$		
$B_{5/2}'$	1	−1	1	−1	1	1	−1	1	−1	1	−1	1	−1	1	−1	−1	1	−1	1	−1		
$E_{1/2}''$	1	ω	ε	$-\varepsilon^*$	$-\omega^*$	−1	$-\omega$	$-\varepsilon$	ε^*	ω^*	−1	$-\omega$	$-\varepsilon$	ε^*	ω^*	1	ω	ε	$-\varepsilon^*$	$-\omega^*$		
	1	ω^*	ε^*	$-\varepsilon$	$-\omega$	−1	$-\omega^*$	$-\varepsilon^*$	ε	ω	−1	$-\omega^*$	$-\varepsilon^*$	ε	ω	1	ω^*	ε^*	$-\varepsilon$	$-\omega$		
$E_{3/2}''$	1	$-\varepsilon^*$	$-\omega$	ω^*	ε	−1	ε^*	ω	$-\omega^*$	$-\varepsilon$	−1	ε^*	ω	$-\omega^*$	$-\varepsilon$	1	$-\varepsilon^*$	$-\omega$	ω^*	ε		
	1	$-\varepsilon$	$-\omega^*$	ω	ε^*	−1	ε	ω^*	$-\omega$	$-\varepsilon^*$	−1	ε	ω^*	$-\omega$	$-\varepsilon^*$	1	$-\varepsilon$	$-\omega^*$	ω	ε^*		
$B_{5/2}''$	1	−1	1	−1	1	−1	1	−1	1	−1	−1	1	−1	1	−1	1	−1	1	−1	1		

$C_{6h} = C_6 \times C_s$ (hexagonal; twofold screw; 2)

$\varepsilon = \exp(2\pi i/6); \ \omega = \exp(\pi i/6)$

C_{6h}	E	C_6	C_3	C_2	C_3^2	C_6^5	i	S_3^5	S_6^5	σ_h	S_6	S_3	$\bar{E}$	$\bar{C}_6$	$\bar{C}_3$	$\bar{C}_2$	$\bar{C}_3^2$	$\bar{C}_6^5$	$\bar{\imath}$	$\bar{S}_3^5$	$\bar{S}_6^5$	$\bar{\sigma}_h$	$\bar{S}_6$	$\bar{S}_3$		
A_g	1	1	1	1	1	1	1	1	1	1	1	1	1	1	1	1	1	1	1	1	1	1	1	1	R_z	$x^2+y^2,\ z^2$
B_g	1	-1	1	-1	1	-1	1	-1	1	-1	1	-1	1	-1	1	-1	1	-1	1	-1	1	-1	1	-1		
E_{1g}	1	ε	$-\varepsilon^*$	-1	$-\varepsilon$	ε^*	1	ε	$-\varepsilon^*$	-1	$-\varepsilon$	ε^*	1	ε	$-\varepsilon^*$	-1	$-\varepsilon$	ε^*	1	ε	$-\varepsilon^*$	-1	$-\varepsilon$	ε^*	(R_x, R_y)	(xz, yz)
	1	ε^*	$-\varepsilon$	-1	$-\varepsilon^*$	ε	1	ε^*	$-\varepsilon$	-1	$-\varepsilon^*$	ε	1	ε^*	$-\varepsilon$	-1	$-\varepsilon^*$	ε	1	ε^*	$-\varepsilon$	-1	$-\varepsilon^*$	ε		
E_{2g}	1	$-\varepsilon^*$	$-\varepsilon$	1	$-\varepsilon^*$	$-\varepsilon$	1	$-\varepsilon^*$	$-\varepsilon$	1	$-\varepsilon^*$	$-\varepsilon$	1	$-\varepsilon^*$	$-\varepsilon$	1	$-\varepsilon^*$	$-\varepsilon$	1	$-\varepsilon^*$	$-\varepsilon$	1	$-\varepsilon^*$	$-\varepsilon$		(x^2-y^2, xy)
	1	$-\varepsilon$	$-\varepsilon^*$	1	$-\varepsilon$	$-\varepsilon^*$	1	$-\varepsilon$	$-\varepsilon^*$	1	$-\varepsilon$	$-\varepsilon^*$	1	$-\varepsilon$	$-\varepsilon^*$	1	$-\varepsilon$	$-\varepsilon^*$	1	$-\varepsilon$	$-\varepsilon^*$	1	$-\varepsilon$	$-\varepsilon^*$		
A_u	1	1	1	1	1	1	-1	-1	-1	-1	-1	-1	1	1	1	1	1	1	-1	-1	-1	-1	-1	-1	z	
B_u	1	-1	1	-1	1	-1	-1	1	-1	1	-1	1	1	-1	1	-1	1	-1	-1	1	-1	1	-1	1		
E_{1u}	1	ε	$-\varepsilon^*$	-1	$-\varepsilon$	ε^*	-1	$-\varepsilon$	ε^*	1	ε	$-\varepsilon^*$	1	ε	$-\varepsilon^*$	-1	$-\varepsilon$	ε^*	-1	$-\varepsilon$	ε^*	1	ε	$-\varepsilon^*$	(x, y)	
	1	ε^*	$-\varepsilon$	-1	$-\varepsilon^*$	ε	-1	$-\varepsilon^*$	ε	1	ε^*	$-\varepsilon$	1	ε^*	$-\varepsilon$	-1	$-\varepsilon^*$	ε	-1	$-\varepsilon^*$	ε	1	ε^*	$-\varepsilon$		
E_{2u}	1	$-\varepsilon^*$	$-\varepsilon$	1	$-\varepsilon^*$	$-\varepsilon$	-1	ε^*	ε	-1	ε^*	ε	1	$-\varepsilon^*$	$-\varepsilon$	1	$-\varepsilon^*$	$-\varepsilon$	-1	ε^*	ε	-1	ε^*	ε		
	1	$-\varepsilon$	$-\varepsilon^*$	1	$-\varepsilon$	$-\varepsilon^*$	-1	ε	ε^*	-1	ε	ε^*	1	$-\varepsilon$	$-\varepsilon^*$	1	$-\varepsilon$	$-\varepsilon^*$	-1	ε	ε^*	-1	ε	ε^*		
$E_{1/2g}$	1	ω	ε	i	$-\varepsilon^*$	$-\omega^*$	1	ω	ε	i	$-\varepsilon^*$	$-\omega^*$	-1	$-\omega$	$-\varepsilon$	$-i$	ε^*	ω^*	-1	$-\omega$	$-\varepsilon$	$-i$	ε^*	ω^*		
	1	ω^*	ε^*	$-i$	$-\varepsilon$	$-\omega$	1	ω^*	ε^*	$-i$	$-\varepsilon$	$-\omega$	-1	$-\omega^*$	$-\varepsilon^*$	i	ε	ω	-1	$-\omega^*$	$-\varepsilon^*$	i	ε	ω		
$E_{3/2g}$	1	i	-1	$-i$	1	i	1	i	-1	$-i$	1	i	-1	$-i$	1	i	-1	$-i$	-1	$-i$	1	i	-1	$-i$		
	1	$-i$	-1	i	1	$-i$	1	$-i$	-1	i	1	$-i$	-1	i	1	$-i$	-1	i	-1	i	1	$-i$	-1	i		
$E_{5/2g}$	1	$-\omega^*$	ε^*	i	$-\varepsilon$	ω	1	$-\omega^*$	ε^*	i	$-\varepsilon$	ω	-1	ω^*	$-\varepsilon^*$	$-i$	ε	$-\omega$	-1	ω^*	$-\varepsilon^*$	$-i$	ε	$-\omega$		
	1	$-\omega$	ε	$-i$	$-\varepsilon^*$	ω^*	1	$-\omega$	ε	$-i$	$-\varepsilon^*$	ω^*	-1	ω	$-\varepsilon$	i	ε^*	$-\omega^*$	-1	ω	$-\varepsilon$	i	ε^*	$-\omega^*$		
$E_{1/2u}$	1	ω	ε	i	$-\varepsilon^*$	$-\omega^*$	-1	$-\omega$	$-\varepsilon$	$-i$	ε^*	ω^*	-1	$-\omega$	$-\varepsilon$	$-i$	ε^*	ω^*	1	ω	ε	i	$-\varepsilon^*$	$-\omega^*$		
	1	ω^*	ε^*	$-i$	$-\varepsilon$	$-\omega$	-1	$-\omega^*$	$-\varepsilon^*$	i	ε	ω	-1	$-\omega^*$	$-\varepsilon^*$	i	ε	ω	1	ω^*	ε^*	$-i$	$-\varepsilon$	$-\omega$		
$E_{3/2u}$	1	i	-1	$-i$	1	i	-1	$-i$	1	i	-1	$-i$	-1	$-i$	1	i	-1	$-i$	1	i	-1	$-i$	1	i		
	1	$-i$	-1	i	1	$-i$	-1	i	1	$-i$	-1	i	-1	i	1	$-i$	-1	i	1	$-i$	-1	i	1	$-i$		
$E_{5/2u}$	1	$-\omega^*$	ε^*	i	$-\varepsilon$	ω	-1	ω^*	$-\varepsilon^*$	$-i$	ε	$-\omega$	-1	ω^*	$-\varepsilon^*$	$-i$	ε	$-\omega$	1	$-\omega^*$	ε^*	i	$-\varepsilon$	ω		
	1	$-\omega$	ε	$-i$	$-\varepsilon^*$	ω^*	-1	ω	$-\varepsilon$	i	ε^*	$-\omega^*$	-1	ω	$-\varepsilon$	i	ε^*	$-\omega^*$	1	$-\omega$	ε	$-i$	$-\varepsilon^*$	ω^*		

4. The Groups $\mathbf{C}_{nv}$ (*Note*: The $\mathbf{C}_s$ represents a vertical plane)

$\mathbf{C}_{2v} = \mathbf{C}_2 \wedge \mathbf{C}_s = \mathbf{C}_2 \times \mathbf{C}_s$ (orthorhombic; twofold screw, glide; 22)

		$\bar{C}_2$	$\bar{\sigma}_v(xz)$	$\bar{\sigma}'_v(yz)$	$\bar{E}$		
$\mathbf{C}_{2v}$	E	C_2	$\sigma_v(xz)$	$\sigma'_v(yz)$			
A_1	1	1	1	1	1	z	x^2, y^2, z^2
A_2	1	1	−1	−1	1	R_z	xy
B_1	1	−1	1	−1	1	x, R_y	xz
B_2	1	−1	−1	1	1	y, R_x	yz
$E_{1/2}$	2	0	0	0	−2		

$\mathbf{C}_{3v} = \mathbf{C}_3 \wedge \mathbf{C}_s$ (trigonal; glide; 6)

$\mathbf{C}_{3v}$	E	$2C_3$	$3\sigma_v$	$\bar{E}$	$2\bar{C}_3$	$3\bar{\sigma}_v$		
A_1	1	1	1	1	1	1	z	$x^2 + y^2, z^2$
A_2	1	1	−1	1	1	−1	R_z	
E	2	−1	0	2	−1	0	$(x, y)(R_x, R_y)$	$(x^2 - y^2, xy)(xz, yz)$
$E_{1/2}$	2	1	0	−2	−1	0		
$E_{3/2}$ {	1	−1	i	−1	1	$-i$		
	1	−1	$-i$	−1	1	i		

$\mathbf{C}_{4v} = \mathbf{C}_4 \wedge \mathbf{C}_s$ (tetragonal; fourfold and twofold screw, glide; 12)

			$\bar{C}_2$	$2\bar{\sigma}_v$	$2\bar{\sigma}_d$	$\bar{E}$	$2\bar{C}_4$		
$\mathbf{C}_{4v}$	E	$2C_4$	C_2	$2\sigma_v$	$2\sigma_d$				
A_1	1	1	1	1	1	1	1	z	$x^2 + y^2, z^2$
A_2	1	1	1	−1	−1	1	1	R_z	
B_1	1	−1	1	1	−1	1	−1		$x^2 - y^2$
B_2	1	−1	1	−1	1	1	−1		xy
E	2	0	−2	0	0	2	0	$(x, y)(R_x, R_y)$	(xz, yz)
$E_{1/2}$	2	$\sqrt{2}$	0	0	0	−2	$-\sqrt{2}$		
$E_{3/2}$	2	$-\sqrt{2}$	0	0	0	−2	$\sqrt{2}$		

$\mathbf{C}_{5v} = \mathbf{C}_5 \wedge \mathbf{C}_s$ (none; – ; –)

$\mathbf{C}_{5v}$	E	$2C_5$	$2C_5^2$	$5\sigma_v$	$\bar{E}$	$2\bar{C}_5^2$	$2\bar{C}_5$	$5\bar{\sigma}_v$		
A_1	1	1	1	1	1	1	1	1	z	$x^2 + y^2, z^2$
A_2	1	1	1	−1	1	1	1	−1	R_z	
E_1	2	2 cos 72°	2 cos 144°	0	2	2 cos 72°	2 cos 144°	0	$(x, y)(R_x, R_y)$	(xy, yz)
E_2	2	2 cos 144°	2 cos 72°	0	2	2 cos 144°	2 cos 72°	0		$(x^2 - y^2, x$
$E_{1/2}$	2	−2 cos 144°	2 cos 72°	0	−2	2 cos 144°	−2 cos 72°	0		
$E_{3/2}$	2	−2 cos 72°	2 cos 144°	0	−2	2 cos 72°	−2 cos 144°	0		
$E_{5/2}$	1	−1	1	i	−1	1	−1	$-i$		
	1	−1	1	$-i$	−1	1	−1	i		

$\mathbf{C}_{6v} = \mathbf{C}_6 \wedge \mathbf{C}_s$ (hexagonal; twofold screw, glide; 4)

				$\bar{C}_2$	$3\bar{\sigma}_v$	$3\bar{\sigma}_d$	$\bar{E}$	$2\bar{C}_6$	$2\bar{C}_3$		
$\mathbf{C}_{6v}$	E	$2C_6$	$2C_3$	C_2	$3\sigma_v$	$3\sigma_d$					
A_1	1	1	1	1	1	1	1	1	1	z	$x^2 + y^2, z^2$
A_2	1	1	1	1	−1	−1	1	1	1	R_z	
B_1	1	−1	1	−1	1	−1	1	−1	1		
B_2	1	−1	1	−1	−1	1	1	−1	1		
E_1	2	1	−1	−2	0	0	2	1	−1	$(x, y)(R_x, R_y)$	(xz, yz)
E_2	2	−1	−1	2	0	0	2	−1	−1		$(x^2 - y^2, xy)$
$E_{1/2}$	2	$\sqrt{3}$	1	0	0	0	−2	$-\sqrt{3}$	−1		
$E_{3/2}$	2	0	−2	0	0	0	−2	0	2		
$E_{5/2}$	2	$-\sqrt{3}$	1	0	0	0	−2	$\sqrt{3}$	−1		

5. The groups $\mathbf{D}_n$ (*Note*: the $\mathbf{C}_2$ axis is perpendicular to the $\mathbf{C}_n$)

$\mathbf{D}_2 = \mathbf{C}_2 \wedge \mathbf{C}_2' = \mathbf{C}_2 \times \mathbf{C}_2'$ (orthorhombic; twofold screw; 9)

		$\bar{C}_2(z)$	$\bar{C}_2(y)$	$\bar{C}_2(x)$	$\bar{E}$		
$\mathbf{D}_2$	E	$C_2(z)$	$C_2(y)$	$C_2(x)$			
A_1	1	1	1	1	1		x^2, y^2, z^2
B_1	1	1	−1	−1	1	z, R_z	xy
B_2	1	−1	1	−1	1	y, R_y	xz
B_3	1	−1	−1	1	1	x, R_x	yz
$E_{1/2}$	2	0	0	0	−2		

$\mathbf{D}_3 = \mathbf{C}_3 \wedge \mathbf{C}_2$ (trigonal; threefold screw; 7)

$\mathbf{D}_3$	E	$2C_3$	$3C_2$	$\bar{E}$	$2\bar{C}_3$	$3\bar{C}_2$		
A_1	1	1	1	1	1	1		x^2+y^2, z^2
A_2	1	1	-1	1	1	-1	z, R_z	
E	2	-1	0	2	-1	0	$(x, y)(R_x, R_y)$	$(x^2-y^2, xy)(xz, yz)$
$E_{1/2}$	2	1	0	-2	-1	0		
$E_{3/2}$	1	-1	i	-1	1	$-i$		
	1	-1	$-i$	-1	1	i		

$\mathbf{D}_4 = \mathbf{C}_4 \wedge \mathbf{C}_2$ (tetragonal; fourfold and twofold screws; 10)

			$\bar{C}_2$	$2\bar{C}_2'$	$2\bar{C}_2''$	$\bar{E}$	$2\bar{C}_4$		
$\mathbf{D}_4$	E	$2C_4$	C_2	$2C_2'$	$2C_2''$				
A_1	1	1	1	1	1	1	1		x^2+y^2, z^2
A_2	1	1	1	-1	-1	1	1	z, R_z	
B_1	1	-1	1	1	-1	1	-1		x^2-y^2
B_2	1	-1	1	-1	1	1	-1		xy
E	2	0	-2	0	0	2	0	$(x, y)(R_x, R_y)$	(xz, yz)
$E_{1/2}$	2	$\sqrt{2}$	0	0	0	-2	$-\sqrt{2}$		
$E_{3/2}$	2	$-\sqrt{2}$	0	0	0	-2	$\sqrt{2}$		

$\mathbf{D}_5 = \mathbf{C}_5 \wedge \mathbf{C}_2$ (none; –; –)

$\mathbf{D}_5$	E	$2C_5$	$2C_5^2$	$5C_2$	$\bar{E}$	$2\bar{C}_5$	$2\bar{C}_5^2$	$5\bar{C}_2$		
A_1	1	1	1	1	1	1	1	1		x^2+y^2, z^2
A_2	1	1	1	-1	1	1	1	-1	z, R_z	
E_1	2	$2\cos 72^\circ$	$2\cos 144^\circ$	0	2	$2\cos 72^\circ$	$2\cos 144^\circ$	0	(x, y) (R_x, R_y)	(xz, yz)
E_2	2	$2\cos 144^\circ$	$2\cos 72^\circ$	0	2	$2\cos 144^\circ$	$2\cos 72^\circ$	0		(x^2-y^2, xy)
$E_{1/2}$	2	$-2\cos 144^\circ$	$2\cos 72^\circ$	0	-2	$2\cos 144^\circ$	$-2\cos 72^\circ$	0		
$E_{3/2}$	2	$-2\cos 72^\circ$	$2\cos 144^\circ$	0	-2	$2\cos 72^\circ$	$-2\cos 144^\circ$	0		
$E_{5/2}$	1	-1	1	i	-1	1	-1	$-i$		
	1	-1	1	$-i$	-1	1	-1	i		

$\mathbf{D}_6 = \mathbf{C}_6 \wedge \mathbf{C}_2$ (hexagonal; sixfold, threefold, and twofold screws; 6)

				$\bar{C}_2$	$3\bar{C}'_2$	$3\bar{C}''_2$	$\bar{E}$	$2\bar{C}_6$	$2\bar{C}_3$		
$\mathbf{D}_6$	E	$2C_6$	$2C_3$	C_2	$3C'_2$	$3C''_2$					
A_1	1	1	1	1	1	1	1	1	1		$x^2 + y^2, z^2$
A_2	1	1	1	1	−1	−1	1	1	1	z, R_z	
B_1	1	−1	1	−1	1	−1	1	−1	1		
B_2	1	−1	1	−1	−1	1	1	−1	1		
E_1	2	1	−1	−2	0	0	2	1	−1	$(x, y)(R_x, R_y)$	(xz, yz)
E_2	2	−1	−1	2	0	0	2	−1	−1		$(x^2 - y^2, xy)$
$E_{1/2}$	2	$\sqrt{3}$	1	0	0	0	−2	$-\sqrt{3}$	−1		
$E_{3/2}$	2	0	−2	0	0	0	−2	0	2		
$E_{5/2}$	2	$-\sqrt{3}$	1	0	0	0	−2	$\sqrt{3}$	−1		

6. The Groups $\mathbf{D}_{nh}$ (*Note*: The $\mathbf{C}_s$ is perpendicular to the principal axis)

$\mathbf{D}_{2h} = \mathbf{D}_2 \times \mathbf{C}_s$ (orthorhombic; up to three twofold screws and/or glides; 28)

		$\bar{C}_2(z)$	$\bar{C}_2(y)$	$\bar{C}_2(x)$		$\bar{\sigma}(xy)$	$\bar{\sigma}(xz)$	$\bar{\sigma}(yz)$	$\bar{E}$	$\bar{i}$		
$\mathbf{D}_{2h}$	E	$C_2(z)$	$C_2(y)$	$C_2(x)$	i	$\sigma(xy)$	$\sigma(xz)$	$\sigma(yz)$				
A_g	1	1	1	1	1	1	1	1	1	1		x^2, y^2, z^2
B_{1g}	1	1	−1	−1	1	1	−1	−1	1	1	R_z	xy
B_{2g}	1	−1	1	−1	1	−1	1	−1	1	1	R_y	xz
B_{3g}	1	−1	−1	1	1	−1	−1	1	1	1	R_x	yz
A_u	1	1	1	1	−1	−1	−1	−1	1	−1		
B_{1u}	1	1	−1	−1	−1	−1	1	1	1	−1	z	
B_{2u}	1	−1	1	−1	−1	1	−1	1	1	−1	y	
B_{3u}	1	−1	−1	1	−1	1	1	−1	1	−1	x	
$E_{1/2g}$	2	0	0	0	2	0	0	0	−2	−2		
$E_{1/2u}$	2	0	0	0	−2	0	0	0	−2	2		

$\mathbf{D}_{3h} = \mathbf{D}_3 \times \mathbf{C}_s$ (hexagonal; glide; 4)

$\mathbf{D}_{3h}$	E	$2C_3$	$3C_2$	σ_h	$2S_3$	$3\sigma_v$	$\bar{E}$	$2\bar{C}_3$	$3\bar{C}_2$	$\bar{\sigma}_h$	$2\bar{S}_3$	$3\bar{\sigma}_v$		
A'_1	1	1	1	1	1	1	1	1	1	1	1	1		x^2+y^2, z^2
A'_2	1	1	−1	1	1	−1	1	1	−1	1	1	−1	R_z	
E'	2	−1	0	2	−1	0	2	−1	0	2	−1	0	(x, y)	(x^2-y^2, xy)
A''_1	1	1	1	−1	−1	−1	1	1	1	−1	−1	−1		
A''_2	1	1	−1	−1	−1	1	1	1	−1	−1	−1	1	z	
E''	2	−1	0	−2	1	0	2	−1	0	−2	1	0	(R_x, R_y)	
$E'_{1/2}$	2	1	0	2	1	0	−2	−1	0	−2	−1	0		
$E'_{3/2}$	1	−1	i	1	−1	i	−1	1	$-i$	−1	1	$-i$		
	1	−1	$-i$	1	−1	$-i$	−1	1	i	−1	1	i		
$E''_{1/2}$	2	1	0	−2	−1	0	−2	−1	0	2	1	0		
$E''_{3/2}$	1	−1	i	−1	1	$-i$	−1	1	$-i$	1	−1	i		
	1	−1	$-i$	−1	1	i	−1	1	i	1	−1	$-i$		

$_{4h} = \mathbf{D}_4 \times \mathbf{C}_s$ (tetragonal; fourfold and twofold screws, glide; 20)

			$\bar{C}_2$	$2\bar{C}'_2$	$2\bar{C}''_2$			$\bar{\sigma}_h$	$2\bar{\sigma}_v$	$2\bar{\sigma}_d$	$\bar{E}$	$2\bar{C}_4$	$\bar{i}$	$2\bar{S}_4$		
$_h$	E	$2C_4$	C_2	$2C'_2$	$2C''_2$	i	$2S_4$	σ_h	$2\sigma_v$	$2\sigma_d$						
$_g$	1	1	1	1	1	1	1	1	1	1	1	1	1	1		x^2+y^2, z^2
$_g$	1	1	1	−1	−1	1	1	1	−1	−1	1	1	1	1	R_z	
$_g$	1	−1	1	1	−1	1	−1	1	1	−1	1	−1	1	−1		x^2-y^2
$_g$	1	−1	1	−1	1	1	−1	1	−1	1	1	−1	1	−1		xy
	2	0	−2	0	0	2	0	−2	0	0	2	0	2	0	(R_x, R_y)	(xz, yz)
	1	1	1	1	1	−1	−1	−1	−1	−1	1	1	−1	−1		
	1	1	1	−1	−1	−1	−1	−1	1	1	1	1	−1	−1	z	
	1	−1	1	1	−1	−1	1	−1	−1	1	1	−1	−1	1		
	1	−1	1	−1	1	−1	1	−1	1	−1	1	−1	−1	1		
	2	0	−2	0	0	−2	0	2	0	0	2	0	−2	0	(x, y)	
$_{2g}$	2	$\sqrt{2}$	0	0	0	2	$\sqrt{2}$	0	0	0	−2	$-\sqrt{2}$	−2	$-\sqrt{2}$		
$_{2g}$	2	$-\sqrt{2}$	0	0	0	2	$-\sqrt{2}$	0	0	0	−2	$\sqrt{2}$	−2	$\sqrt{2}$		
$_{2u}$	2	$\sqrt{2}$	0	0	0	−2	$-\sqrt{2}$	0	0	0	−2	$-\sqrt{2}$	2	$\sqrt{2}$		
$_{2u}$	2	$-\sqrt{2}$	0	0	0	−2	$\sqrt{2}$	0	0	0	−2	$\sqrt{2}$	2	$-\sqrt{2}$		

$\mathbf{D}_{5h} = \mathbf{D}_5 \times \mathbf{C}_s$ (none; −; −)

$\mathbf{D}_{5h}$	E	$2C_5$	$2C_5^2$	$5C_2$	σ_h	$2S_5$	$2S_5^3$	$5\sigma_v$	$\bar{E}$	$2\bar{C}_5$	$2\bar{C}_5^2$	$5\bar{C}_2$	$\bar{\sigma}_h$	$2\bar{S}_5$	$2\bar{S}_5^3$	$5\bar{\sigma}_v$		
A_1'	1	1	1	1	1	1	1	1	1	1	1	1	1	1	1	1		$x^2 + y^2, z^2$
A_2'	1	1	1	−1	1	1	1	−1	1	1	1	−1	1	1	1	−1	R_z	
E_1'	2	2 cos 72	2 cos 144°	0	2	2 cos 72°	2 cos 144°	0	2	2 cos 72°	2 cos 144°	0	2	2 cos 72°	2 cos 144°	0	(x, y)	
E_2'	2	2 cos 144°	2 cos 72°	0	2	2 cos 144°	2 cos 72°	0	2	2 cos 144°	2 cos 72°	0	2	2 cos 144°	2 cos 72°	0		$(x^2 - y^2, xy)$
A_1''	1	1	1	1	−1	−1	−1	−1	1	1	1	1	−1	−1	−1	−1		
A_2''	1	1	1	−1	−1	−1	−1	1	1	1	1	−1	−1	−1	−1	1	z	
E_1''	2	2 cos 72°	2 cos 144°	0	−2	−2 cos 72°	−2 cos 144°	0	2	2 cos 72°	2 cos 144°	0	−2	−2 cos 72°	−2 cos 144°	0	(R_x, R_y)	(xz, yz)
E_2''	2	2 cos 144°	2 cos 72°	0	−2	−2 cos 144°	−2 cos 77°	0	2	2 cos 144°	2 cos 72°	0	−2	−2 cos 144°	−2 cos 72°	0		
$E_{1/2}'$	2	−2 cos 144°	2 cos 72°	0	2	−2 cos 144°	2 cos 72°	0	−2	2 cos 144°	−2 cos 72°	0	−2	2 cos 144°	−2 cos 72°	0		
$E_{3/2}'$	2	−2cos 72°	2 cos 144°	0	2	−2 cos 72°	2 cos 144°	0	−2	2 cos 72°	−2 cos 144°	0	−2	2 cos 72°	−2 cos 144°	0		
$E_{5/2}'$	1	−1	1	i	1	−1	1	i	−1	1	−1	$-i$	−1	1	−1	$-i$		
	1	−1	1	$-i$	1	−1	1	$-i$	−1	1	−1	i	−1	1	−1	i		
$E_{1/2}''$	2	−2 cos 144°	**2 cos 72°**	0	−2	2 cos 144°	−2 cos 72°	0	−2	2 cos 144°	−2 cos 72°	0	2	−2 cos 144°	2 cos 72°	0		
$E_{3/2}''$	2	−2 cos 72°	2 cos 144°	0	−2	2 cos 72°	−2 cos 144	0	−2	2 cos 72°	−2 cos 144°	0	2	−2 cos 72°	2 cos 144°	0		
$E_{5/2}''$	1	−1	1	i	−1	1	−1	$-i$	−1	1	−1	$-i$	1	−1	1	i		
	1	−1	1	$-i$	−1	1	−1	i	−1	1	−1	i	1	−1	1	$-i$		

$\mathbf{D}_{6h} = \mathbf{C}_6 \times \mathbf{C}_s$ (hexagonal; twofold screw, glide; 4)

				$\bar{C}_2$	$3\bar{C}_2'$	$3\bar{C}_2''$				$\bar{\sigma}_h$	$3\bar{\sigma}_d$	$3\bar{\sigma}_v$	$\bar{E}$	$2\bar{C}_6$	$2\bar{C}_3$	$\bar{i}$	$2\bar{S}_3$	$2\bar{S}_6$		
$\mathbf{D}_{6h}$	E	$2C_6$	$2C_3$	C_2	$3C_2'$	$3C_2''$	i	$2S_3$	$2S_6$	σ_h	$3\sigma_d$	$3\sigma_v$								
A_{1g}	1	1	1	1	1	1	1	1	1	1	1	1	1	1	1	1	1	1		$x^2 + y^2, z$
A_{2g}	1	1	1	1	−1	−1	1	1	1	1	−1	−1	1	1	1	1	1	1	R_z	
B_{1g}	1	−1	1	−1	1	−1	1	−1	1	−1	1	−1	1	−1	1	1	−1	1		
B_{2g}	1	−1	1	−1	−1	1	1	−1	1	−1	−1	1	1	−1	1	1	−1	1		
E_{1g}	2	1	−1	−2	0	0	2	1	−1	−2	0	0	2	1	−1	2	1	−1	(R_x, R_y)	(xz, yz)
E_{2g}	2	−1	−1	2	0	0	2	−1	−1	2	0	0	2	−1	−1	2	−1	−1		$(x^2 - y^2, xy)$
A_{1u}	1	1	1	1	1	1	−1	−1	−1	−1	−1	−1	1	1	1	−1	−1	−1		
A_{2u}	1	1	1	1	−1	−1	−1	−1	−1	−1	1	1	1	1	1	−1	−1	−1	z	
B_{1u}	1	−1	1	−1	1	−1	−1	1	−1	1	−1	1	1	−1	1	−1	1	−1		
B_{2u}	1	−1	1	−1	−1	1	−1	1	−1	1	1	−1	1	−1	1	−1	1	−1		
E_{1u}	2	1	−1	−2	0	0	−2	−1	1	2	0	0	2	1	−1	−2	−1	1	(x, y)	
E_{2u}	2	−1	−1	2	0	0	−2	1	1	−2	0	0	2	−1	−1	−2	1	1		
$E_{1/2g}$	2	$\sqrt{3}$	1	0	0	0	2	$\sqrt{3}$	1	0	0	0	−2	$-\sqrt{3}$	−1	−2	$-\sqrt{3}$	−1		
$E_{3/2g}$	2	0	−2	0	0	0	2	0	−2	0	0	0	−2	0	2	−2	0	2		
$E_{5/2g}$	2	$-\sqrt{3}$	1	0	0	0	2	$-\sqrt{3}$	1	0	0	0	−2	$\sqrt{3}$	−1	−2	$\sqrt{3}$	−1		
$E_{1/2u}$	2	$\sqrt{3}$	1	0	0	0	−2	$-\sqrt{3}$	−1	0	0	0	−2	$-\sqrt{3}$	−1	2	$\sqrt{3}$	1		
$E_{3/2u}$	2	0	−2	0	0	0	−2	0	2	0	0	0	−2	0	2	2	0	−2		
[illegible]	[illegible]	[illegible]	[illegible]	0	0	0	[illegible]	$\sqrt{3}$	1	0	0	0	−2	$\sqrt{3}$	−1	2	$-\sqrt{3}$	1		

7. The Groups $\mathbf{D}_{nd}$ (*Note*: The $\mathbf{C}_s$ refers to a dihedral plane of symmetry, bisecting pairs of twofold axes)

$\mathbf{D}_{2d} = \mathbf{D}_2 \wedge \mathbf{C}_s = \mathbf{S}_4 \wedge \mathbf{C}_2$ (tetragonal; twofold screw, glide; 12)

			$\bar{C}_2$	$2\bar{C}'_2$	$2\bar{\sigma}_d$	$\bar{E}$	$2\bar{S}_4$		
$\mathbf{D}_{2d}$	E	$2S_4$	C_2	$2C'_2$	$2\sigma_d$				
A_1	1	1	1	1	1	1	1		$x^2 + y^2, z^2$
A_2	1	1	1	-1	-1	1	1	R_z	
B_1	1	-1	1	1	-1	1	-1		$x^2 - y^2$
B_2	1	-1	1	-1	1	1	-1	z	xy
E	2	0	-2	0	0	2	0	$(x, y)(R_x, R_y)$	(xz, yz)
$E_{1/2}$	2	$\sqrt{2}$	0	0	0	-2	$-\sqrt{2}$		
$E_{3/2}$	2	$-\sqrt{2}$	0	0	0	-2	$\sqrt{2}$		

$\mathbf{D}_{3d} = \mathbf{D}_3 \times \mathbf{C}_i$ (trigonal; glide; 6)

$\mathbf{D}_{3d}$	E	$2C_3$	$3C_2$	i	$2S_6$	$3\sigma_d$	$\bar{E}$	$2\bar{C}_3$	$3\bar{C}_2$	$\bar{i}$	$2\bar{S}_6$	$3\bar{\sigma}_d$		
A_{1g}	1	1	1	1	1	1	1	1	1	1	1	1		$x^2 + y^2, z^2$
A_{2g}	1	1	-1	1	1	-1	1	1	-1	1	1	-1	R_z	
E_g	2	-1	0	2	-1	0	2	-1	0	2	-1	0	(R_x, R_y)	$(x^2 - y^2, xy)(xz, yz)$
A_{1u}	1	1	1	-1	-1	-1	1	1	1	-1	-1	-1		
A_{2u}	1	1	-1	-1	-1	1	1	1	-1	-1	-1	1	z	
E_u	2	-1	0	-2	1	0	2	-1	0	-2	1	0	(x, y)	
$E_{1/2g}$	2	1	0	2	1	0	-2	-1	0	-2	-1	0		
$E_{3/2g}$	1	-1	i	1	-1	i	-1	1	$-i$	-1	1	$-i$		
	1	-1	$-i$	1	-1	$-i$	-1	1	i	-1	1	i		
$E_{1/2u}$	2	1	0	-2	-1	0	-2	-1	0	2	1	0		
$E_{3/2u}$	1	-1	i	-1	1	$-i$	-1	1	$-i$	1	-1	i		
	1	-1	$-i$	-1	1	i	-1	1	i	1	-1	$-i$		

$\mathbf{D}_{4d} = \mathbf{D}_4 \wedge \mathbf{C}_s = \mathbf{S}_8 \wedge C_2$ (none; – ; –)

					$\bar{C}_2$	$4\bar{C}'_2$	$4\bar{\sigma}_d$	$\bar{E}$	$2\bar{S}_8$	$2\bar{C}_4$	$2\bar{S}_8^3$		
$\mathbf{D}_{4d}$	E	$2S_8$	$2C_4$	$2S_8^3$	C_2	$4C'_2$	$4\sigma_d$						
A_1	1	1	1	1	1	1	1	1	1	1	1		$x^2 + y^2, z^2$
A_2	1	1	1	1	1	−1	−1	1	1	1	1	R_z	
B_1	1	−1	1	−1	1	1	−1	1	−1	1	−1		
B_2	1	−1	1	−1	1	−1	1	1	−1	1	−1	z	
E_1	2	$\sqrt{2}$	0	$-\sqrt{2}$	−2	0	0	2	$\sqrt{2}$	0	$-\sqrt{2}$	(x, y)	
E_2	2	0	−2	0	2	0	0	2	0	−2	0		$(x^2 - y^2, xy)$
E_3	2	$-\sqrt{2}$	0	$\sqrt{2}$	−2	0	0	2	$-\sqrt{2}$	0	$\sqrt{2}$	(R_x, R_y)	(xz, yz)
$E_{1/2}$	2	$(2+\sqrt{2})^{1/2}$	$\sqrt{2}$	$(2-\sqrt{2})^{1/2}$	0	0	0	−2	$-(2+\sqrt{2})^{1/2}$	$-\sqrt{2}$	$-(2-\sqrt{2})^{1/2}$		
$E_{3/2}$	2	$(2-\sqrt{2})^{1/2}$	$-\sqrt{2}$	$-(2+\sqrt{2})^{1/2}$	0	0	0	−2	$-(2-\sqrt{2})^{1/2}$	$\sqrt{2}$	$(2+\sqrt{2})^{1/2}$		
$E_{5/2}$	2	$-(2-\sqrt{2})^{1/2}$	$-\sqrt{2}$	$(2+\sqrt{2})^{1/2}$	0	0	0	−2	$(2-\sqrt{2})^{1/2}$	$\sqrt{2}$	$-(2+\sqrt{2})^{1/2}$		
$E_{7/2}$	2	$-2(+\sqrt{2})^{1/2}$	$\sqrt{2}$	$-(2-\sqrt{2})^{1/2}$	0	0	0	−2	$(2+\sqrt{2})^{1/2}$	$-\sqrt{2}$	$(2-\sqrt{2})^{1/2}$		

$\mathbf{D}_{5d} = \mathbf{D}_5 \times \mathbf{C}_i$ (none; – ; –)

$\mathbf{D}_{5d}$	E	$2C_5$	$2C_5^2$	$5C_2$	i	$2S_{10}^3$	$2S_{10}$	$5\sigma_d$	$\bar{E}$	$2\bar{C}_5$	$2\bar{C}_5^2$	$5C_2$	$\bar{i}$	$2\bar{S}_{10}^3$	$2\bar{S}_{10}$	$5\bar{\sigma}_d$		
A_{1g}	1	1	1	1	1	1	1	1	1	1	1	1	1	1	1	1		$x^2 + y^2, z^2$
A_{2g}	1	1	1	−1	1	1	1	−1	1	1	1	−1	1	1	1	−1	R_z	
E_{1g}	2	2 cos 72°	2 cos 144°	0	2	2 cos 72°	2 cos 144°	0	2	2 cos 72°	2 cos 144°	0	2	2 cos 72°	2 cos 144°	0	(R_x, R_y)	(xz, yz)
E_{2g}	2	2 cos 144°	2 cos 72°	0	2	2 cos 144°	2 cos 72°	0	2	2 cos 144°	2 cos 72°	0	2	2 cos 144°	2 cos 72°	0		$(x^2 - y^2, xy)$
A_{1u}	1	1	1	1	−1	−1	−1	−1	1	1	1	1	−1	−1	−1	−1		
A_{2u}	1	1	1	−1	−1	−1	−1	1	1	1	1	−1	−1	−1	−1	1	z	
E_{1u}	2	2 cos 72°	2 cos 144°	0	−2	−2 cos 72°	−2 cos 144°	0	2	2 cos 72°	2 cos 144°	0	−2	−2 cos 72°	−2 cos 144°	0	(x, y)	
E_{2u}	2	2 cos 144°	2 cos 72°	0	−2	−2 cos 144°	−2 cos 72°	0	2	2 cos 144°	2 cos 72°	0	−2	−2 cos 144°	−2 cos 72°	0		
$E_{1/2g}$	2	−2 cos 144°	2 cos 72°	0	2	−2 cos 144°	2 cos 72°	0	−2	2 cos 144°	−2 cos 72°	0	−2	2 cos 144°	−2 cos 72°	0		
$E_{3/2g}$	2	−2 cos 72°	2 cos 144°	0	2	−2 cos 72°	2 cos 144°	0	−2	2 cos 72°	−2 cos 144°	0	−2	2 cos 72°	−2 cos 144°	0		
$E_{5/2g}$ {	1	−1	1	i	1	−1	1	i	−1	1	−1	$-i$	−1	1	−1	$-i$		
	1	−1	1	$-i$	1	−1	1	$-i$	−1	1	−1	i	−1	1	−1	i		
$E_{1/2u}$	2	−2 cos 144°	2 cos 72°	0	−2	2 cos 144°	−2 cos 72°	0	−2	2 cos 144°	−2 cos 72°	0	2	−2 cos 144°	2 cos 72°	0		
$E_{3/2u}$	2	−2 cos 72°	2 cos 144°	0	−2	2 cos 72°	−2 cos 144°	0	−2	2 cos 72°	−2 cos 144°	0	2	−2 cos 72°	2 cos 144°	0		
$E_{5/2u}$ {	1	−1	1	i	−1	1	−1	$-i$	−1	1	−1	$-i$	1	−1	1	i		
	1	−1	1	$-i$	−1	1	−1	i	−1	1	−1	i	1	−1	1	$-i$		

$\mathbf{D}_{6d} = \mathbf{D}_6 \wedge \mathbf{C}_s = \mathbf{S}_{12} \wedge \mathbf{C}_2$ (none; – ; –)

							$\bar{C}_2$	$6\bar{C}'_2$	$6\bar{\sigma}_d$	$\bar{E}$	$2\bar{S}_{12}$	$2\bar{C}_6$	$2\bar{S}_4$	$2\bar{C}_3$	$2\bar{S}_{12}^5$		
$\mathbf{D}_{6d}$	E	$2S_{12}$	$2C_6$	$2S_4$	$2C_3$	$2S_{12}^5$	C_2	$6C'_2$	$6\sigma_d$								
A_1	1	1	1	1	1	1	1	1	1	1	1	1	1	1	1		x^2+y^2, z^2
A_2	1	1	1	1	1	1	1	−1	−1	1	1	1	1	1	1	R_z	
B_1	1	−1	1	−1	1	−1	1	1	−1	1	−1	1	−1	1	−1		
B_2	1	−1	1	−1	1	−1	1	−1	1	1	−1	1	−1	1	−1	z	
E_1	2	$\sqrt{3}$	1	0	−1	$-\sqrt{3}$	−2	0	0	2	$\sqrt{3}$	1	0	−1	$-\sqrt{3}$	(x, y)	
E_2	2	1	−1	−2	−1	1	2	0	0	2	1	−1	−2	−1	1		(x^2-y^2, xy)
E_3	2	0	−2	0	2	0	−2	0	0	2	0	−2	0	2	0		
E_4	2	−1	−1	2	−1	−1	2	0	0	2	−1	−1	2	−1	−1		
E_5	2	$-\sqrt{3}$	1	0	−1	$\sqrt{3}$	−2	0	0	2	$-\sqrt{3}$	1	0	−1	$\sqrt{3}$	(R_x, R_y)	(xz, yz)
$E_{1/2}$	2	$(2+\sqrt{3})^{1/2}$	$\sqrt{3}$	$\sqrt{2}$	−1	$(2-\sqrt{3})^{1/2}$	0	0	0	−2	$-(2+\sqrt{3})^{1/2}$	$-\sqrt{3}$	$-\sqrt{2}$	1	$-(2-\sqrt{3})^{1/2}$		
$E_{3/2}$	2	$\sqrt{2}$	0	$-\sqrt{2}$	−2	$-\sqrt{2}$	0	0	0	−2	$-\sqrt{2}$	0	$\sqrt{2}$	2	$\sqrt{2}$		
$E_{5/2}$	2	$(2-\sqrt{3})^{1/2}$	$-\sqrt{3}$	$-\sqrt{2}$	1	$(2+\sqrt{3})^{1/2}$	0	0	0	−2	$-(2-\sqrt{3})^{1/2}$	$\sqrt{3}$	$\sqrt{2}$	−1	$-(2+\sqrt{3})^{1/2}$		
$E_{7/2}$	2	$-(2-\sqrt{3})^{1/2}$	$-\sqrt{3}$	$\sqrt{2}$	1	$-(2+\sqrt{3})^{1/2}$	0	0	0	−2	$(2-\sqrt{3})^{1/2}$	$\sqrt{3}$	$-\sqrt{2}$	−1	$(2+\sqrt{3})^{1/2}$		
$E_{9/2}$	2	$-\sqrt{2}$	0	$\sqrt{2}$	−2	$\sqrt{2}$	0	0	0	−2	$\sqrt{2}$	0	$-\sqrt{2}$	2	$-\sqrt{2}$		
$E_{11/2}$	2	$-(2+\sqrt{3})^{1/2}$	$\sqrt{3}$	$-\sqrt{2}$	1	$-(2-\sqrt{3})^{1/2}$	0	0	0	−2	$(2+\sqrt{3})^{1/2}$	$-\sqrt{3}$	$\sqrt{2}$	−1	$(2-\sqrt{3})^{1/2}$		

8. The Cubic Groups (*Note*: The $\mathbf{C}_3$ is along the xyz diagonal if the $\mathbf{C}_2$'s are along x, y, and z)

$\mathbf{T} = \mathbf{D}_2 \wedge \mathbf{C}_3$ (cubic; twofold screw; 5)

T	E	$4C_3$	$4C_3^2$	$3C_2$ / $3\bar{C}_2$	$\bar{E}$	$4\bar{C}_3$	$4\bar{C}_3^2$		$\varepsilon = \exp(2\pi i/3)$
A	1	1	1	1	1	1	1		$x^2 + y^2 + z^2$
E {	1	ε	ε^*	1	1	ε	ε^*	}	$(x^2 - y^2, 2z^2 - x^2 - y^2)$
	1	ε^*	ε	1	1	ε^*	ε		
T	3	0	0	-1	3	0	0	$(x, y, z)(R_x, R_y, R_z)$	(xy, xz, yz)
$E_{1/2}$	2	1	1	0	-2	-1	-1		
$G_{3/2}$ {	2	ε	ε^*	0	-2	$-\varepsilon$	$-\varepsilon^*$		
	2	ε^*	ε	0	-2	$-\varepsilon^*$	$-\varepsilon$		

$\mathbf{T}_d = \mathbf{D}_2 \wedge \mathbf{C}_{3v}$ (cubic; glide; 6)

$\mathbf{T}_d$	E	$8C_3$	$3C_2$ / $3\bar{C}_2$	$6S_4$	$6\sigma_d$ / $6\bar{\sigma}_d$	$\bar{E}$	$8\bar{C}_3$	$6\bar{S}_4$		
A_1	1	1	1	1	1	1	1	1		$x^2 + y^2 + z^2$
A_2	1	1	1	-1	-1	1	1	-1		
E	2	-1	2	0	0	2	-1	0		$(x^2 - y^2, 2z^2 - x^2 - y^2)$
T_1	3	0	-1	1	-1	3	0	1	(R_x, R_y, R_z)	
T_2	3	0	-1	-1	1	3	0	-1	(x, y, z)	(xy, xz, yz)
$E_{1/2}$	2	1	0	$\sqrt{2}$	0	-2	-1	$-\sqrt{2}$		
$E_{5/2}$	2	1	0	$-\sqrt{2}$	0	-2	-1	$\sqrt{2}$		
$G_{3/2}$	4	-1	0	0	0	-4	1	0		

$\mathbf{T}_h = \mathbf{T} \times \mathbf{C}_i$ (cubic; glide; 7)

				$3\bar{C}_2$				$3\bar{\sigma}_h$	$\bar{E}$	$4\bar{C}_3$	$4\bar{C}_3^2$	$\bar{i}$	$4\bar{S}_6^5$	$4\bar{S}_4$		
h	E	$4C_3$	$4C_3^2$	$3C_2$	i	$4S_6^5$	$4S_6$	$3\sigma_h$								$\varepsilon = \exp(2\pi i/3)$
g	1	1	1	1	1	1	1	1	1	1	1	1	1	1		$(x^2 + y^2 + z^2)$
g {	1	ε	ε^*	1	1	ε	ε^*	1	1	ε	ε^*	1	ε	ε^*	}	$(x^2 - y^2, 2z^2 - x^2 - z^2)$
	1	ε^*	ε	1	1	ε^*	ε	1	1	ε^*	ε	1	ε^*	ε		
	3	0	0	−1	3	0	0	−1	3	0	0	3	0	0	(R_x, R_y, R_z)	(xy, xz, yz)
u	1	1	1	1	−1	−1	−1	−1	1	1	1	−1	−1	−1		
u {	1	ε	ε^*	1	−1	$-\varepsilon$	$-\varepsilon^*$	−1	1	ε	ε^*	−1	$-\varepsilon$	$-\varepsilon^*$		
	1	ε^*	ε	1	−1	$-\varepsilon^*$	$-\varepsilon$	−1	1	ε^*	ε	−1	$-\varepsilon^*$	$-\varepsilon$		
	3	0	0	−1	−3	0	0	1	3	0	0	−3	0	0	(x, y, z)	
/2g	2	1	1	0	2	1	1	0	−2	−1	−1	−2	−1	−1		
{	2	ε	ε^*	0	2	ε	ε^*	0	−2	$-\varepsilon$	$-\varepsilon^*$	−2	$-\varepsilon$	$-\varepsilon^*$		
3/2g	2	ε^*	ε	0	2	ε^*	ε	0	−2	$-\varepsilon^*$	$-\varepsilon$	−2	$-\varepsilon^*$	$-\varepsilon$		
/2u	2	1	1	0	−2	−1	−1	0	−2	−1	−1	2	1	1		
{	2	ε	ε^*	0	−2	$-\varepsilon$	$-\varepsilon^*$	0	−2	$-\varepsilon$	$-\varepsilon^*$	2	ε	ε^*		
3/2u	2	ε^*	ε	0	−2	$-\varepsilon^*$	$-\varepsilon$	0	−2	$-\varepsilon^*$	$-\varepsilon$	2	ε^*	ε		

$\mathbf{O} = \mathbf{D}_2 \wedge \mathbf{D}_3$ (cubic; fourfold and twofold screws; 8)

			$3\bar{C}_2$		$6\bar{C}_2'$	$\bar{E}$	$8\bar{C}_3$	$6\bar{C}_4$		
O	E	$8C_3$	$3C_2$	$6C_4$	$6C_2'$					
A_1	1	1	1	1	1	1	1	1		$x^2 + y^2 + z^2$
A_2	1	1	1	−1	−1	1	1	−1		
E	2	−1	2	0	0	2	−1	0		$(x^2 - y^2, 2z^2 - x^2 - y^2)$
T_1	3	0	−1	1	−1	3	0	1	$(x, y, z)(R_x, R_y, R_z)$	
T_2	3	0	−1	−1	1	3	0	−1		(xy, xz, yz)
$E_{1/2}$	2	1	0	$\sqrt{2}$	0	−2	−1	$-\sqrt{2}$		
$E_{5/2}$	2	1	0	$-\sqrt{2}$	0	−2	−1	$\sqrt{2}$		
$G_{3/2}$	4	−1	0	0	0	−4	1	0		

$\mathbf{O}_h = \mathbf{O} \times \mathbf{C}_i$ (cubic; fourfold and twofold screws, glide; 10)

			$3\bar{C}_2$		$6\bar{C}_2'$			$3\bar{\sigma}_h$		$6\bar{\sigma}_d$	$\bar{E}$	$8\bar{C}_3$	$6\bar{C}_4$	$\bar{i}$	$8\bar{S}_6$	$6\bar{S}_4$		
$\mathbf{O}_h$	E	$8C_3$	$3C_2$	$6C_4$	$6C_2'$	i	$8S_6$	$3\sigma_h$	$6S_4$	$6\sigma_d$								
A_{1g}	1	1	1	1	1	1	1	1	1	1	1	1	1	1	1	1		$x^2 + y^2 + z^2$
A_{2g}	1	1	1	−1	−1	1	1	1	−1	−1	1	1	−1	1	1	−1		
E_g	2	−1	2	0	0	2	−1	2	0	0	2	−1	0	2	−1	0		$(x^2 - y^2, 2z^2 - x^2 - y^2)$
T_{1g}	3	0	−1	1	−1	3	0	−1	1	−1	3	0	1	3	0	1	(R_x, R_y, R_z)	
T_{2g}	3	0	−1	−1	1	3	0	−1	−1	1	3	0	−1	3	0	−1		(xy, xz, yz)
A_{1u}	1	1	1	1	1	−1	−1	−1	−1	−1	1	1	1	−1	−1	−1		
A_{2u}	1	1	1	−1	−1	−1	−1	−1	1	1	1	1	−1	−1	−1	1		
E_u	2	−1	2	0	0	−2	1	−2	0	0	2	−1	0	−2	1	0		
T_{1u}	3	0	−1	1	−1	−3	0	1	−1	1	3	0	1	−3	0	−1	(x, y, z)	
T_{2u}	3	0	−1	−1	1	−3	0	1	1	−1	3	0	−1	−3	0	1		
$E_{1/2g}$	2	1	0	$\sqrt{2}$	0	2	1	0	$\sqrt{2}$	0	−2	−1	$-\sqrt{2}$	−2	−1	$-\sqrt{2}$		
$E_{5/2g}$	2	1	0	$-\sqrt{2}$	0	2	1	0	$-\sqrt{2}$	0	−2	−1	$\sqrt{2}$	−2	−1	$\sqrt{2}$		
$G_{3/2g}$	4	−1	0	0	0	4	−1	0	0	0	−4	1	0	−4	1	0		
$E_{1/2u}$	2	1	0	$\sqrt{2}$	0	−2	−1	0	$-\sqrt{2}$	0	−2	−1	$-\sqrt{2}$	2	1	$\sqrt{2}$		
$E_{5/2u}$	2	1	0	$-\sqrt{2}$	0	−2	−1	0	$\sqrt{2}$	0	−2	−1	$\sqrt{2}$	2	1	$-\sqrt{2}$		
$G_{3/2u}$	4	−1	0	0	0	−4	1	0	0	0	−4	1	0	4	−1	0		

9. Continuous Rotation Groups (*Note*: No space groups are associated with these)

In all cases there are an infinite number of classes of the form $2C(\phi)$, $2C(2\phi)$, ...

$\mathbf{C}_\infty = \mathbf{C}_\infty$

$\mathbf{C}_\infty$	E	$2C(\phi)$	$\bar{E}$	$2\bar{C}(\phi)$	*Note:* The two-dimensional representations of $\mathbf{C}_\infty$ are all separable.	
Σ	1	1	1	1	z	x^2+y^2, z^2
Π	2	$2\cos\phi$	2	2	$(x, y)(R_x, R_y)$	(xz, yz)
Δ	2	$2\cos 2\phi$	2	$2\cos 2\phi$		(x^2-y^2, xy)
Φ	2	$2\cos 3\phi$	2	$2\cos 3\phi$		
⋮	⋮	⋮	⋮	⋮		
Γ_j	2	$2\cos j\phi$	2	$2\cos j\phi$		
$E_{1/2}$	2	$2\cos 1/2\phi$	-2	$-2\cos 1/2\phi$		
$E_{3/2}$	2	$2\cos 3/2\phi$	-2	$-2\cos 3/2\phi$		
$E_{5/2}$	2	$2\cos 5/2\phi$	-2	$-2\cos 5/2\phi$		
⋮	⋮	⋮	⋮	⋮		
E_j	2	$2\cos j\phi$	-2	$-2\cos j\phi$		

$\mathbf{C}_{\infty v} = \mathbf{C}_\infty \wedge \mathbf{C}_s$

			$\infty\bar{\sigma}_v$	$\bar{E}$	$2\bar{C}(\phi)$		
$\mathbf{C}_{\infty v}$	E	$2C(\phi)$	$\infty\sigma_v$				
Σ^+	1	1	1	1	1	z	x^2+y^2, z^2
Σ^-	1	1	-1	1	1	R_z	
Π	2	$2\cos\phi$	0	2	$2\cos\phi$	$(x, y)(R_x, R_y)$	(xz, yz)
Δ	2	$2\cos 2\phi$	0	2	$2\cos 2\phi$		(x^2-y^2, xy)
Φ	2	$2\cos 3\phi$	0	2	$2\cos 3\phi$		
⋮	⋮	⋮	⋮	⋮	⋮		
Γ_j	2	$2\cos j\phi$	0	2	$2\cos j\phi$		
$E_{1/2}$	2	$2\cos 1/2\phi$	0	-2	$-2\cos 1/2\phi$		
$E_{3/2}$	2	$2\cos 3/2\phi$	0	-2	$-2\cos 3/2\phi$		
$E_{5/2}$	2	$2\cos 5/2\phi$	0	-2	$-2\cos 5/2\phi$		
⋮	⋮	⋮	⋮	⋮	⋮		
E_j	2	$2\cos j\phi$	0	-2	$-2\cos j\phi$		

$\mathbf{D}_\infty = \mathbf{C}_\infty \wedge \mathbf{C}_2$

			$\infty \bar{C}_2$	$\bar{E}$	$2\bar{C}(\phi)$		
$\mathbf{D}_\infty$	E	$2C(\phi)$	∞C_2				
Σ^+	1	1	1	1	1	z	$x^2 + y^2, z^2$
Σ^-	1	1	-1	1	1	R_z	
Π	2	$2 \cos \phi$	0	2	$2 \cos \phi$	$(x, y)(R_x, R_y)$	(xz, yz)
Δ	2	$2 \cos 2\phi$	0	2	$2 \cos 2\phi$		$(x^2 - y^2, xy)$
Φ	2	$2 \cos 3\phi$	0	2	$2 \cos 3\phi$		
$\vdots$	$\vdots$	$\vdots$	$\vdots$	$\vdots$	$\vdots$		
Γ_j	2	$2 \cos j\phi$	0	2	$2 \cos j\phi$		
$E_{1/2}$	2	$2 \cos 1/2\phi$	0	-2	$-2 \cos 1/2\phi$		
$E_{3/2}$	2	$2 \cos 3/2\phi$	0	-2	$-2 \cos 3/2\phi$		
$E_{5/2}$	2	$2 \cos 5/2\phi$	0	-2	$-2 \cos 5/2\phi$		
$\vdots$	$\vdots$	$\vdots$	$\vdots$	$\vdots$	$\vdots$		
E_j	2	$2 \cos j\phi$	0	-2	$-2 \cos j\phi$		

$\mathbf{D}_{\infty h} = \mathbf{D}_{\infty} \times \mathbf{C}_i$

			$\infty\bar{C}_2$			$\infty\bar{\sigma}_v$	$\bar{E}$	$2\bar{C}(\phi)$	$\bar{i}$	$2\bar{S}(-\phi)$		
$\mathbf{D}_{\infty h}$	E	$2C(\phi)$	∞C_2	i	$2S(-\phi)$	$\infty\sigma_v$						
Σ_g^+	1	1	1	1	1	1	1	1	1	1		$x^2 + y^2, z^2$
Σ_g^-	1	1	−1	1	1	−1	1	1	1	1	R_z	
Π_g	2	$2 \cos \phi$	0	2	$-2 \cos \phi$	0	2	$2 \cos \phi$	2	$-2 \cos \phi$	(R_x, R_y)	(xz, yz)
Δ_g	2	$2 \cos 2\phi$	0	2	$2 \cos 2\phi$	0	2	$2 \cos 2\phi$	2	$2 \cos 2\phi$		$(x^2 - y^2, xy)$
⋮	⋮	⋮	⋮	⋮	⋮	⋮	⋮	⋮	⋮	⋮		
Γ_{jg}	2	$2 \cos j\phi$	0	2	$(-1)^j 2 \cos j\phi$	0	2	$2 \cos j\phi$	2	$(-1)^j 2 \cos j\phi$		
Σ_u^+	1	1	1	−1	−1	−1	1	1	−1	−1	z	
Σ_u^-	1	1	−1	−1	−1	1	1	1	−1	−1		
Π_u	2	$2 \cos \phi$	0	−2	$2 \cos \phi$	0	2	$2 \cos \phi$	−2	$2 \cos \phi$	(x, y)	
Δ_u	2	$2 \cos 2\phi$	0	−2	$-2 \cos \phi$	0	2	$2 \cos 2\phi$	−2	$-2 \cos 2\phi$		
⋮	⋮	⋮	⋮	⋮	⋮	⋮	⋮	⋮	⋮	⋮		
Γ_{ju}	2	$2 \cos j\phi$	0	−2	$-(-1)^j 2 \cos j\phi$	0	2	$2 \cos j\phi$	−2	$-(-1)^j 2 \cos j\phi$		
$E_{1/2g}$	2	$2 \cos 1/2\phi$	0	2	$2 \sin 1/2\phi$	0	−2	$-2 \cos 1/2\phi$	−2	$-2 \sin 1/2\phi$		
$E_{3/2g}$	2	$2 \cos 3/2\phi$	0	2	$-2 \sin 3/2\phi$	0	−2	$-2 \cos 3/2\phi$	−2	$2 \sin 3/2\phi$		
⋮	⋮	⋮	⋮	⋮	⋮	⋮	⋮	⋮	⋮	⋮		
E_{jg}	2	$2 \cos j\phi$	0	2	$(-1)^{(j-1/2)} 2 \sin j\phi$	0	−2	$-2 \cos j\phi$	−2	$(-1)^{(j+1/2)} 2 \sin j\phi$		
$E_{1/2u}$	2	$2 \cos 1/2\phi$	0	−2	$-2 \sin 1/2\phi$	0	−2	$-2 \cos i/2\phi$	2	$2 \sin 1/2\phi$		
$E_{3/2u}$	2	$2 \cos 3/2\phi$	0	−2	$2 \sin 3/2\phi$	0	−2	$-2 \cos 3/2\phi$	2	$-2 \sin 1/2\phi$		
⋮	⋮	⋮	⋮	⋮	⋮	⋮	⋮	⋮	⋮	⋮		
E_{ju}	2	$2 \cos j\phi$	0	−2	$(-1)^{(j+1/2)} 2 \cos j\phi)$	0	−2	$-2 \cos j\phi$	2	$(-1)^{(j-1/2)} 2 \cos j\phi$		

$\mathbf{R}(3) = \mathbf{R}(3)$

$\mathbf{R}(3)$	E	$C(\phi, x, y, z)$	$\bar{E}$	$\bar{C}(\phi, x, y, z)$		
$D^{(0)}$	1	1	1	1		$x^2 + y^2 + z^2$
$D^{(1)}$	3	$1 + 2\cos\phi$	3	$1 + 2\cos\phi$	(x, y, z) (R_x, R_y, R_z)	
$D^{(2)}$	5	$1 + 2\cos\phi + 2\cos 2\phi$	5	$1 + 2\cos\phi + 2\cos 2\phi$		All independent combinations
$D^{(3)}$	7	$1 + 2\cos\phi + 2\cos 2\phi + 2\cos 3\phi$	7	$1 + 2\cos\phi + 2\cos 2\phi + 2\cos 3\phi$		
⋮	⋮	⋮	⋮	⋮		
$D^{(j)}$	$2j + 1$	$1 + \sum_{l=1}^{j} 2\cos l\phi$	$2j + 1$	$1 + \sum_{l=1}^{j} 2\cos l\phi$		
$D^{1/2}$	2	$2\cos 1/2\phi$	-2	$-2\cos 1/2\phi$		
$D^{3/2}$	4	$2\cos 1/2\phi + 2\cos 3/2\phi$	-4	$-2\cos 1/2\phi - 2\cos 3/2\phi$		
$D^{5/2}$	6	$2\cos 1/2\phi + 2\cos 3/2\phi + 2\cos 5/2\phi$	-6	$-2\cos 1/2\phi - 2\cos 3/2\phi - 2\cos 5/2\phi$		
⋮	⋮	⋮	⋮	⋮		
$D^{(j)}$	$2j + 1$	$\sum_{l=1/2}^{j} 2\cos l\phi$	$-(2j + 1)$	$-\sum_{l=1/2}^{j} 2\cos l\phi$		

$\mathbf{R}_h(3) = \mathbf{R}(3) \times \mathbf{C}_i$ (*Note*: Only the unique classes for the *single-valued* representations are given. For integer j values the characters for the double-group classes are the same as those listed. For half-integer j the sign is changed)

$\mathbf{R}_h(3)$	E	$C(\phi, x, y, z)$	i	$S(-\phi, x, y, z)$	σ		
$D_g^{(0)}$	1	1	1	1	1		$x^2 + y^2 + z^2$
$D_g^{(1)}$	3	$1 + 2\cos\phi$	3	$1 - 2\cos\phi$	-1	(R_x, R_y, R_z)	
$D_g^{(2)}$	5	$1 + 2\cos\phi + 2\cos 2\phi$	5	$1 - 2\cos\phi + 2\cos 2\phi$	1		All independent combinations
$\vdots$	$\vdots$	$\vdots$	$\vdots$	$\vdots$	$\vdots$		
$D_g^{(j)}$	$2j + 1$	$1 + \sum_{l=1}^{j} 2\cos l\phi$	$2j + 1$	$1 + \sum_{l=1}^{j} (-1)^l \cos l\phi$	$(-1)^j$		
$D_u^{(0)}$	1	1	-1	-1	-1		
$D_u^{(1)}$	3	$1 + 2\cos\phi$	-3	$-1 + 2\cos\phi$	1	(x, y, z)	
$D_u^{(2)}$	5	$1 + 2\cos\phi + 2\cos 2\phi$	-5	$-1 + 2\cos\phi - 2\cos 2\phi$	-1		
$\vdots$	$\vdots$	$\vdots$	$\vdots$	$\vdots$	$\vdots$		
$D_u^{(j)}$	$2j + 1$	$1 + \sum_{l=1}^{j} 2\cos l\phi$	$-(2j + 1)$	$-1 - \sum_{l=1}^{j} (-1)^l 2\cos l\phi$	$-(-1)^j$		
$D_g^{(1/2)}$	2	$2\cos 1/2\phi$	2	$2\sin 1/2\phi$	0		
$D_g^{(3/2)}$	4	$2\cos 1/2\phi + 2\cos 3/2\phi$	4	$2\sin 1/2\phi - 2\sin 3/2\phi$	0		
$D_g^{(5/2)}$	6	$2\cos 1/2\phi + 2\cos 3/2\phi + 2\cos 5/2\phi$	6	$2\sin 1/2\phi - 2\sin 3/2\phi + 2\sin 5/2\phi$	0		
$\vdots$	$\vdots$	$\vdots$	$\vdots$	$\vdots$	$\vdots$		
$D_g^{(j)}$	$2j + 1$	$\sum_{l=1/2}^{j} 2\cos l\phi$	$2j + 1$	$\sum_{l=1/2}^{j} (-1)^{(l-1/2)} 2\sin l\phi$	0		
$D_u^{(1/2)}$	2	$2\cos 1/2\phi$	-2	$-2\sin 1/2\phi$	0		
$D_u^{(3/2)}$	4	$2\cos 1/2\phi + 2\cos 3/2\phi$	-4	$-2\sin 1/2\phi + 2\sin 3/2\phi$	0		
$D_u^{(5/2)}$	6	$2\cos 1/2\phi + 2\cos 3/2\phi + 2\cos 5/2\phi$	-6	$-2\sin 1/2\phi + 2\sin 3/2\phi - 2\sin 5/2\phi$	0		
$\vdots$	$\vdots$	$\vdots$	$\vdots$	$\vdots$	$\vdots$		
$D_u^{(j)}$	$2j + 1$	$\sum_{l=1/2}^{j} 2\cos l\phi$	$-(2j + 1)$	$\sum_{l=1/2}^{j} (-1)^{(l+1/2)} 2\sin l\phi$	0		

10. Symmetric Permutation Groups

Degree 2:

S(2)	(1^2)	(2)
[2]	1	1
$[1^2]$	1	−1

Degree 3:

S(3)	(1^3)	2(3)	3(2, 1)
[3]	1	1	1
$[1^3]$	1	1	−1
[2, 1]	2	−1	0

Degree 4:

S(4)	(1^4)	$6(2, 1^2)$	$3(2^2)$	8(3, 1)	6(4)
[4]	1	1	1	1	1
[3, 1]	3	1	−1	0	−1
$[2^2]$	2	0	2	−1	0
$[2, 1^2]$	3	−1	−1	0	1
$[1^4]$	1	−1	1	1	−1

Degree 5:

S(5)	(1^5)	30(4, 1)	20(3, 2)	$20(3, 1^2)$	$15(2^2, 1)$	$10(2, 1^3)$	24(5)
[5]	1	1	1	1	1	1	1
[4, 1]	4	0	−1	1	0	2	−1
[3, 2]	5	−1	1	−1	1	1	0
$[3, 1^2]$	6	0	0	0	−2	0	1
$[2^2, 1]$	5	1	−1	−1	1	−1	0
$[2, 1^3]$	4	0	1	1	0	−2	−1
$[1^5]$	1	−1	−1	1	1	−1	1

Degree 6:

S(6)	(1^6)	$144(5, 1)$	$90(4, 2)$	$90(4, 1^2)$	$40(3^2)$	$120(3, 2, 1)$	$40(3, 1^3)$	$15(2^3)$	$45(2^2, 1^2)$	$15(2, 1^4)$	$120(6)$
[6]	1	1	1	1	1	1	1	1	1	1	1
[5, 1]	5	0	−1	1	−1	0	2	−1	1	3	−1
[4, 2]	9	−1	1	−1	0	0	0	3	1	3	0
$[4, 1^2]$	10	0	0	0	1	−1	1	−2	−2	2	1
$[3^2]$	5	0	−1	−1	2	1	−1	−3	1	1	0
[3, 2, 1]	16	1	0	0	−2	0	−2	0	0	0	0
$[2^3]$	5	0	−1	1	2	−1	−1	3	1	−1	0
$[3, 1^3]$	10	0	0	0	1	1	1	2	−2	−2	−1
$[2^2, 1^2]$	9	−1	1	1	0	0	0	−3	1	−3	0
$[2, 1^4]$	5	0	−1	−1	−1	0	2	1	1	−3	1
$[1^6]$	1	1	1	−1	1	−1	1	−1	1	−1	−1

Degree 7:

S(7)	(1^7)	$840(6, 1)$	$504(5, 2)$	$504(5, 1^2)$	$420(4, 3)$	$630(4, 2, 1)$	$210(4, 1^3)$	$280(3^2, 1)$	$210(3, 2^2)$	$420(3, 2, 1^3)$	$70(3, 1^4)$	$105(2^3, 1)$	$105(2^2, 1^3)$	$21(2, 1^5)$	$720(7)$
[7]	1	1	1	1	1	1	1	1	1	1	1	1	1	1	1
[6, 1]	6	0	−1	1	−1	0	2	0	−1	1	3	0	2	4	−1
[5, 2]	14	−1	1	−1	0	0	0	−1	2	0	2	2	2	6	0
$[5, 1^2]$	15	0	0	0	1	−1	1	0	−1	−1	3	−3	−1	5	1
[4, 3]	14	0	−1	−1	1	0	−2	2	−1	1	−1	0	2	4	0
[4, 2, 1]	35	1	0	0	−1	1	−1	−1	−1	−1	−1	1	−1	5	0
$[3^2, 1]$	21	0	1	1	−1	−1	−1	0	1	1	−3	−3	1	1	0
$[4, 1^3]$	20	0	0	0	0	0	0	2	2	0	2	0	−4	0	−1
$[3, 2^2]$	21	0	−1	1	1	−1	1	0	1	−1	−3	3	1	−1	0
$[3, 2, 1^2]$	35	−1	0	0	1	1	1	−1	−1	1	−1	−1	−1	−5	0
$[2^3, 1]$	14	0	1	−1	−1	0	2	2	−1	−1	−1	0	2	−4	0
$[3, 1^4]$	15	0	0	0	−1	−1	−1	0	−1	1	3	3	−1	−5	1
$[2^2, 1^3]$	14	1	−1	−1	0	0	0	−1	2	0	2	−2	2	−6	0
$[2, 1^5]$	6	0	1	1	1	0	−2	0	−1	−1	3	0	2	−4	−1
$[1^7]$	1	−1	−1	1	−1	1	−1	1	1	−1	1	−1	1	−1	1

Appendix 6

Glossary

Abelian group. A group whose elements all commute with each other and whose representations are all one-dimensional.

Associative law of combination. The law that is obeyed if the grouping in a chain of operations is immaterial, that is, if

$$ABCD = (AB)(CD) = A(BC)D, \qquad \text{etc.}$$

Basis functions. A set of functions from which any other function in the same function space can be constructed.

Basis vectors. A set of vectors from which any other vector in the same vector space can be constructed.

Character. The trace of a matrix representation of a group operation.

Character table. A table displaying the characters of the various operations, corresponding to the various irreducible representations of a group.

Commutative law of combination. The law that is obeyed if the order of performing two operations is immaterial, that is, if

$$AB = BA$$

Contravariant vectors. Vectors for which the matrix and operator equivalents of an operation occur in reversed order; that is, if R and S are operations, $\mathbf{R}$ and $\mathbf{S}$ their matrix representations, and $\mathbf{a}$ is a vector, then

$$R\mathbf{a} = \mathbf{aR}$$
$$RS\mathbf{a} = \mathbf{aSR}, \qquad \text{etc.}$$

Covariant vectors. Vectors for which the matrix and operator equivalents of an operation occur in like order; that is, if R and S are operators, **R** and **S** their matrix representations and **a** is a vector, then

$$R\mathbf{a} = \mathbf{Ra}$$
$$RS\mathbf{a} = \mathbf{RSa}, \qquad \text{etc.}$$

Degenerate states. Independent states having the same value of the state-defining property (such as energy). The number of such states is the degeneracy of the value of the defining property (said to be the degeneracy of the state).

Double groups. Groups containing operations and representations suitable for handling systems of half-integer angular momentum.

Eigenfunction. A function that satisfies an eigenvalue equation.

Eigenstate. The state resulting when the operator corresponding to a state-defining quantity (such as energy) operates on a function or vector describing the state of the system.

Eigenvalue equation. The equation resulting when the effect of an operator operating on a function or vector yields a constant (the eigenvalue) times the unchanged function or vector.

Eigenvector. A vector that satisfies an eigenvalue equation.

Excited state. Any state of a system having an energy greater than the ground (lowest-energy) state.

Expectation value. The average value of a property in some state. The term is usually used when the property is not a state-defining property.

Generators of a group. The simplest set of operations from which the complete group can be generated by products and powers of the operations.

Ground state. The lowest-energy (most stable) state of a system.

Group. A set of quantities having a defined law of combination (called multiplication) such that (a) the multiplication is associative, (b) the group contains an identity, (c) every element of the group possesses an inverse, (d) all products and powers of the elements are contained in the group.

Group element. Any member of the set forming a group, that is, a group operation.

Hermitian matrix. A matrix that is equal to its conjugate transpose; that is, $M_{ij} = M_{ji}^*$.

Homomorphism. A many-to-one mapping.

Identity. The element of a group that leaves the system unchanged.

Improper axis of rotation. The axis about which an improper rotation can leave a system in a configuration indistinguishable from the original configuration. The improper rotation is a single operation that combines a rotation with a reflection through a plane perpendicular to the rotation axis.

Irreducible representation. A member of the set of simplest possible matrix representations of a group.

Isodynamic operations. Operations of nonrigid molecules which take the molecule into conformations which have the same energy as the starting conformation, but which are not point-symmetry operations.

Isomorphism. A one-to-one mapping.

Kronecker delta function. A function, δ_{ij}, which equals zero if the two indices are different, or unity if they are the same.

Matrix. A system of quantities a_{ij}, with two indices, usually arranged in a rectangular array, with the index i labeling the rows and j the columns. A second-order tensor.

Matrix representation of a group. A set of matrices that transform among themselves in the same manner as the operations of the group.

Mapping. An association between the members of one set of quantities and those of another.

Normalized functions. Functions (say a) for which the integral $\int a^*a\,dv$ equals unity.

Normalized vectors. Vectors (say **a**) for which the scalar product $\mathbf{a} \cdot \mathbf{a}$ equals unity.

Orthogonal functions. Functions (say a and b) for which the integral $\int a^*b\,dv$ vanishes.

Orthogonal vectors. Vectors (say **a** and **b**) for which the scalar product $\mathbf{a} \cdot \mathbf{b}$ vanishes.

Pauli-allowed state. A state of a system in which the restrictions on the interchange of the particles are properly accounted for. Usually, an antisymmetrized function of "spin-$\frac{1}{2}$" particles is being referred to.

Pauli-forbidden state. A state of a system that cannot be achieved because the restrictions on the interchanges of the particles cannot be satisfied.

Plane of symmetry. The plane through which a reflection can leave a system in a configuration indistinguishable from the original configuration.

Point group. The group describing the symmetry of a rigid physical object.

Point of inversion. The point through which inversion can leave a system in a configuration indistinguishable from the original configuration.

Projection operator. An operator that projects out a specified component from a function, vector, and so on. Used, for example, to construct symmentry adapted linear combinations of functions.

Proper axis of rotation. The axis about which a simple rotation can leave a system in a configuration indistinguishable from the original configuration.

Quantization. The property of existing only in discrete (or quantized) states.

Representation of a group. A set of quantities that have the same multiplication properties as the operations of the group.

Scalar product (of vectors). A row–column product of two vectors, the result of which is a scalar. A "dot product."

Space groups. Symmetry groups that include transitional symmetry operations.

State. The condition of a system arising when the property that defines the system is completely determined.

Subgroup. A subset, of the set of group operations, which obeys the group requirements.

Symmetric (permutation) group (of degree n). The set of all permutations on n objects.

Symmetry element. A geometric entity (point, line, plane) about which a symmetry operation is performed.

Symmetry operation. An operation that carries a system into an orientation or configuration indistinguishable from the starting orientation or configuration.

Tensor. An indexed array of quantities $a_{ijk\ldots}$. The number of indices required to define the tensor is its *order*.

Transition dipole. The expectation value of the dipole operator between two different states of a system. The direct absorption or emission of electromagnetic radiation by a system is dependent upon the transition dipole.

Vector. A system of quantities, a_i, with one index, usually arranged in a row or a column array. A first-order tensor.

Young diagrams. Diagrams expressing the partition structure of the irreducible representations of the symmetric group as patterns of blocks.

Index